Linear and Discrete
MATHEMATICS

CUSTOM EDITION FOR THE GEORGIA INSTITUTE OF TECHNOLOGY

Excerpts taken from:

Discrete Mathematics with Graph Theory, Third Edition
by Edgar G. Goodaire and Michael M. Parmenter

Elementary Linear Algebra with Applications, Ninth Edition
by Bernard Kolman and David R. Hill

PEARSON
Custom
Publishing

PEARSON
Prentice
Hall

Cover art: Pattern 10/Data Strategies, by Angela Sciaraffa

Excerpts taken from:

Discrete Mathematics with Graph Theory, Third Edition
by Edgar G. Goodaire and Michael M. Parmenter
Copyright © 2006, 2002, 1998 Pearson Education, Inc.
Published by Prentice Hall
Upper Saddle River, New Jersey 07458

Elementary Linear Algebra with Applications, Ninth Edition
by Bernard Kolman and David R. Hill
Copyright © 2008, 2004, 2000, 1996 by Pearson Education, Inc.
Published by Prentice Hall

Printed in the United States of America

10 9 8 7 6 5 4 3 2 1

ISBN 0-536-50344-3

2007361291

EC

Please visit our web site at *www.pearsoncustom.com*

PEARSON CUSTOM PUBLISHING
501 Boylston Street, Suite 900, Boston, MA 02116
A Pearson Education Company

Contents

PART I

Taken from:

Discrete Mathematics with Graph Theory, Third Edition
by Edgar G. Goodaire and Michael M. Parmenter

5

Induction and Recursion

One of the most basic methods of proof is *mathematical induction*, which is a way to establish the truth of a statement about all the natural numbers or, sometimes, all sufficiently large integers. Mathematical induction is important in every area of mathematics. In addition to the examples presented in this section, other proofs by mathematical induction appear elsewhere in this book in a variety of different contexts. In the index (see "induction"), we draw attention to some theorems whose proofs serve as especially good models of the technique.

PROBLEM 1. A certain store sells envelopes in packages of five and packages of twelve and you want to buy n envelopes. Prove that for every $n \geq 44$ this store can sell you exactly n envelopes (assuming an unlimited supply of each type of envelope package).

Solution. If you want to purchase 44 envelopes, you can buy two packages of twelve and four packages of five. If you want to purchase 45 envelopes, you can buy nine packages of five. If you want to purchase 46 envelopes, pick up three packages of twelve and two packages of five. If you want to buy 47 envelopes, get one package of twelve and seven packages of five and, if you want 48 envelopes, purchase four packages of twelve.

The obvious difficulty with this way of attacking the problem is that it never ends. Even supposing that we continued laboriously to answer the question for n as big as 153, say, could we be sure of a solution for $n = 154$? What is needed is a general, not ad hoc, way to continue; that is, if it is possible to fill an order for exactly k envelopes at this store, we would like to be able to deduce that the store can also fill an order for $k + 1$ envelopes. Then, knowing that we can purchase exactly 44 envelopes and knowing that we can always continue, we could deduce that we can purchase exactly 45 envelopes. Knowing this and knowing that we can always continue, we would know that we can purchase exactly 46 envelopes. And so on.

Suppose—just suppose—that it is possible to buy exactly k envelopes at this store, where $k \geq 44$. If this purchase requires seven packages of five, then exchanging these for three packages of twelve fills an order of exactly $k + 1$ envelopes.

On the other hand, if k envelopes are purchased without including seven packages of five, then the order for k envelopes included at most 30 envelopes in packages of five and so, since $k \geq 44$, at least two packages of twelve must have been required. Exchanging these for five packages of five then fills exactly an order for $k + 1$ envelopes. We conclude that any order for $n \geq 44$ envelopes can be filled exactly.

This example demonstrates the key ingredients of a proof by mathematical induction. Asked to prove something about all the integers greater than or equal to a particular given integer, for instance, that any order of $n \geq 44$ envelopes can be filled with packages of five and twelve, we first establish truth for the first integer, for example, $n = 44$, and then show how the truth of the statement for $n = k$ enables us to deduce truth for $n = k + 1$.

PROBLEM 2. Chess is a game played on an 8×8 grid, that is, a board consisting of eight rows of eight small squares, like that shown in Fig. 5.1. Suppose our board is *defective* in the sense that one of its squares is missing. Given a box of L-shaped *trominos* like this, 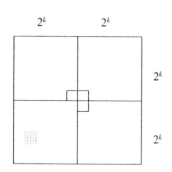, each of which covers exactly three squares of a chess board, is it possible to tile the board without overlapping or going off the board? Show, in fact, that it is possible to tile any $2^n \times 2^n$ defective board.

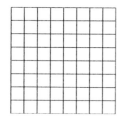

Figure 5.1 An 8×8 board.

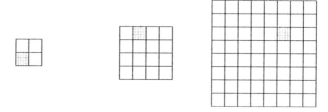

Figure 5.2 Three defective boards.

Solution. We begin our solution by thinking of some easier situations. Figure 5.2 shows defective 2×2, 4×4, and 8×8 boards (with the missing square highlighted in each case). Certainly, the 2×2 board can be tiled because its shape is exactly that of a single tromino. A little experimentation would show how to tile the 4×4 board. Rather than proceeding case by case, however, we use the idea suggested by our first example and attempt to understand how a solution for one particular board can be used to obtain a solution for the next bigger board. Suppose then that we know how to tile any $2^k \times 2^k$ defective board. How might we tile a defective board of the next size, $2^{k+1} \times 2^{k+1}$? The idea is to realize that a $2^{k+1} \times 2^{k+1}$ board can be divided into four boards, each of size $2^k \times 2^k$, as shown in Fig. 5.3.

2^k 2^k

2^k

2^k

Figure 5.3

One of these smaller boards contains the missing square and so is defective. Now place a tromino at the center so as to cover squares in each of the three remaining smaller boards. Each of the boards is now defective and so, by assumption, can be tiled with trominos. So we have tiled the larger board!

The two examples discussed so far made assertions about infinitely many consecutive integers. In each case, we adopted the following strategy.

- Verify that there is a solution for the smallest integer.
- Show how a solution for one integer leads to a solution for the next.

We now give a formal statement of the principle that has been at work, the *Principle of Mathematical Induction.*

Given a statement $\mathcal{P}$ concerning the integer n, suppose

1. $\mathcal{P}$ is true for some particular integer n_0;
2. if $k \geq n_0$ is an integer and $\mathcal{P}$ is true for k, then $\mathcal{P}$ is true for the next integer $k + 1$.

Then $\mathcal{P}$ is true for all integers $n \geq n_0$.

In Step 2, the assumption that $\mathcal{P}$ is true for some particular integer is known as the *induction hypothesis*.

In our first example, we had to prove that any order of n envelopes, $n \geq 44$, could be filled with packages of five and of twelve: n_0 was 44 and the induction hypothesis was the assumption that there was a way to purchase k envelopes with packages of five and twelve. In the second example, we had to demonstrate that any defective board of size $2^n \times 2^n$, $n \geq 1$, could be covered in a certain way; n_0 was 1 and the induction hypothesis was the assumption that we could properly cover a $2^k \times 2^k$ board.

Our next example is suggested by the following pattern. Notice that

$$\begin{aligned}
1 &= & 1 &= 1^2 \\
1 + 3 &= & 4 &= 2^2 \\
1 + 3 + 5 &= & 9 &= 3^2 \\
1 + 3 + 5 + 7 &= & 16 &= 4^2 \\
1 + 3 + 5 + 7 + 9 &= & 25 &= 5^2.
\end{aligned}$$

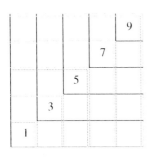

Figure 5.4 The sum of the first n odd integers is n^2.

The first odd integer is 1^2; the sum of the first two odd integers is 2^2; the sum of the first three odd integers is 3^2; and so on. It appears as if the sum of the first n odd integers might always be n^2. The picture in Fig. 5.4 adds force to this possibility.

PROBLEM 3. Prove that for any integer $n \geq 1$ the sum of the odd integers from 1 to $2n - 1$ is n^2.

Before solving this problem, we remark that the sum in question is often written

(1)
$$1 + 3 + 5 + \cdots + (2n - 1),$$

where the first three terms here, $1 + 3 + 5$, are present just to indicate that odd numbers are being added, beginning with 1, and the last term, $2n - 1$, describes the last term and gives a formula for the general term: The second odd number is $2(2) - 1$; the third odd number is $2(3) - 1$; the kth odd number is $2k - 1$. Do not infer from this expression that each of the three numbers 1, 3, 5 is always present. For example, when $n = 2$, $2n - 1 = 3$, and so the sum in (1) is, by definition, $1 + 3$.

We can also describe the sum (1) with *sigma* notation,

(2)
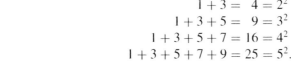
$$1 + 3 + 5 + \cdots + (2n - 1) = \sum_{i=1}^{n}(2i - 1),$$

so named because the capital Greek letter, $\sum$, used to denote summation, is pronounced "sigma." The letter i is called the *index of summation*; the $i = 1$ at the bottom and the n at the top mean that the summation starts with $i = 1$ and continues with $i = 2, 3$ and so on, until $i = n$. Thus, the first term in the sum is $2i - 1$ with $i = 1$; that is, $2(1) - 1 = 1$. The second term is $2i - 1$ with $i = 2$; that is, $2(2) - 1 = 3$. Summing continues until $i = n$: The last term is $2n - 1$.

Write $\sum_{i=1}^{4}(2i - 1)$ without using sigma notation and evaluate this sum.   ∎

Problem 3 asks us to prove that, for all integers $n \geq 1$,

(3)
$$1 + 3 + 5 + \cdots + (2n - 1) = n^2$$

or, equivalently, that

$$\sum_{i=1}^{n}(2i - 1) = n^2.$$

Solution. In this problem, $n_0 = 1$. When $n = 1$, $1 + 3 + 5 + \cdots + (2n - 1)$ means "the sum of the odd integers from 1 to $2(1) - 1 = 1$." Thus, the sum is just 1. Since 1^2 is also 1, the statement is true for $n = 1$. Now suppose that k is an integer, $k \geq 1$, and the statement is true for $n = k$; in other words, suppose

$$1 + 3 + 5 + \cdots + (2k - 1) = k^2 \qquad \textbf{induction hypothesis.}$$

We must show that the statement is true for the next integer, $n = k + 1$; that is, we must show that

$$1 + 3 + 5 + \cdots + (2(k + 1) - 1) = (k + 1)^2.$$

Since $2(k + 1) - 1 = 2k + 1$, we have to show

$$1 + 3 + 5 + \cdots + (2k + 1) = (k + 1)^2.$$

!!!!——— **WAIT A SECOND** ———!!!!

The sum on the left is the sum of the odd integers from 1 to $2k + 1$; this is the sum of the odd integers from 1 to $2k - 1$, plus the next odd integer, $2k + 1$:

$$1 + 3 + 5 + \cdots + (2k + 1) = [1 + 3 + 5 + \cdots + (2k - 1)] + (2k + 1).$$

By the induction hypothesis, we know that

$$1 + 3 + 5 + \cdots + (2k + 1)$$
$$= 1 + 3 + 5 + \cdots + (2k - 1) + (2k + 1) = k^2 + (2k + 1).$$

Since $k^2 + (2k + 1) = (k + 1)^2$, this is the result we wanted. By the Principle of Mathematical Induction, statement (3) is true for all integers $n \geq 1$.   ⧫

Why did we "wait a second" in the preceding argument? It has been the authors' experience that students sometimes confuse their statement of what is to be proved when $n = k + 1$ with the start of their actual proof. Consequently, we strongly recommend the following approach to a proof by mathematical induction:

- Verify the statement for $n = n_0$.
- Write down the induction hypothesis (the statement for $n = k$) in the form "Now suppose that … " and be explicit about what is being assumed.
- Write down what is to be proven (the statement for $n = k + 1$) in the form "We must show that … " again being very explicit about what is to be shown; and finally (after waiting a second):
- Give a convincing argument as to why the statement for $n = k + 1$ is true (and make sure this argument uses the induction hypothesis).

We continue with several examples that you should take as models for proofs by mathematical induction.

PROBLEM 4. Prove that, for any natural number $n \geq 1$,

$$1^2 + 2^2 + 3^2 + \cdots + n^2 = \frac{n(n+1)(2n+1)}{6}.$$

Solution. When $n = 1$, the sum of the integers from 1^2 to 1^2 is 1. Also

$$\frac{1(1+1)(2 \cdot 1 + 1)}{6} = 1,$$

so the statement is true for $n = 1$. Now suppose that $k \geq 1$ and the statement is true for $n = k$; that is, suppose that

$$1^2 + 2^2 + 3^2 + \cdots + k^2 = \frac{k(k+1)(2k+1)}{6}.$$

We have to show that the statement is true for $n = k + 1$; that is, we have to show that

$$1^2 + 2^2 + 3^2 + \cdots + (k+1)^2$$

$$= \frac{(k+1)[(k+1)+1][2(k+1)+1]}{6} = \frac{(k+1)(k+2)(2k+3)}{6}.$$

!!!!——— **WAIT A SECOND** ———!!!!

Observe that

$$1^2 + 2^2 + 3^2 + \cdots + (k+1)^2 = (1^2 + 2^2 + 3^2 + \cdots + k^2) + (k+1)^2$$

$$= \frac{k(k+1)(2k+1)}{6} + (k+1)^2$$

$$= \frac{k(k+1)(2k+1) + 6(k+1)^2}{6}$$

$$= \frac{(k+1)[k(2k+1) + 6(k+1)]}{6}$$

$$= \frac{(k+1)[2k^2 + 7k + 6]}{6}$$

$$= \frac{(k+1)(k+2)(2k+3)}{6}$$

which is just what we wanted. By the Principle of Mathematical Induction, the statement is true for all integers $n \geq 1$.

PROBLEM 5. Prove that for any integer $n \geq 1$, $2^{2n} - 1$ is divisible by 3.

Solution. When $n = 1$, $2^{2(1)} - 1 = 2^2 - 1 = 4 - 1 = 3$ is divisible by 3. Now suppose that $k \geq 1$ and the statement is true for $n = k$; that is, suppose that $2^{2k} - 1$ is divisible by 3. We must prove that the statement is true for $n = k + 1$; that is, we must prove that $2^{2(k+1)} - 1$ is divisible by 3. The key to what follows is the fact that we must somehow involve the induction hypothesis. Observe that $2^{2(k+1)} - 1 = 2^{2k+2} - 1 = 4(2^{2k}) - 1$. This is helpful since it introduces 2^{2k}. By the induction hypothesis, $2^{2k} - 1 = 3t$ for some integer t, so $2^{2k} = 3t + 1$. Now it's smooth sailing. We have

$$2^{2(k+1)} - 1 = 4(2^{2k}) - 1 = 4(3t + 1) - 1$$

$$= 12t + 4 - 1 = 12t + 3 = 3(4t + 1).$$

Thus, $2^{2(k+1)} - 1$ is divisible by 3, as required. By the Principle of Mathematical Induction, $2^{2n} - 1$ is divisible by 3 for all integers $n \geq 1$.

Pause 2   Prove that $3^{2n} - 1$ is divisible by 8 for every $n \geq 1$. ∎

Let n be a given positive integer. It is convenient to have some notation for the product of all the integers between 1 and n since this sort of product occurs frequently in statistical and in counting problems. (See Chapter 7.)

5.1.2 DEFINITION   Define $0! = 1$ and, for any integer $n \geq 1$, define

$$n! = n(n-1)(n-2)\cdots(3)(2)(1).$$ ❖

The symbol $n!$ is read "n factorial." The first few factorials are $0! = 1$, $1! = 1$, $2! = 2 \cdot 1 = 2$, $3! = 3(2)(1) = 6$, $4! = 4(3)(2)(1) = 24$. It is useful to notice that $4! = 4(3!)$, $5! = 5(4!)$, and so on. Thus, if we know that $8! = 40,320$, then it is easy to deduce that $9! = 9(40,320) = 362,880$. Factorials grow very quickly. James Stirling (1730) provided an important estimate for the size of $n!$ when n is large.

5.1.3 STIRLING'S APPROXIMATION $\lim\limits_{n \to \infty} \dfrac{n!}{\sqrt{2\pi n}(n/e)^n} = 1$; equivalently, $n! \sim \sqrt{2\pi n}\left(\dfrac{n}{e}\right)^n$.

In this formula, $e = 2.71828\ldots$ denotes the base of the natural logarithms. Remember from our discussion of the Prime Number Theorem (Theorem 4.3.13) that we read "is asymptotic to" at the symbol $\sim$. Thus, Stirling's formula says that $n!$ is asymptotic to $\sqrt{2\pi n}(\frac{n}{e})^n$, meaning that $n!$ is approximately equal to $\sqrt{2\pi n}(\frac{n}{e})^n$, for large n. For example, $15! \approx \sqrt{30\pi}(\frac{15}{e})^{15} \approx 1.3 \times 10^{12}$, which, by most people's standards, is indeed a large number.

Our next problem provides another indication of the size of $n!$, albeit a rather crude one. For example, it says that $15! > 2^{15} = 32,768$ and $30! > 2^{30} \approx 10^9$.

PROBLEM 6.   Prove that $n! > 2^n$ for all $n \geq 4$.

Solution. In this problem, $n_0 = 4$ and certainly $4! = 24 > 16 = 2^4$. Thus, the statement is true for n_0. Now suppose that $k \geq 4$ and the statement is true for $n = k$. Thus, we suppose that $k! > 2^k$. We must prove that the statement is true for $n = k + 1$; that is, we must prove that $(k+1)! > 2^{k+1}$. Now

$$(k+1)! = (k+1)k! > (k+1)2^k$$

using the induction hypothesis. Since $k \geq 4$, certainly $k + 1 > 2$, so $(k+1)2^k > 2 \cdot 2^k = 2^{k+1}$. We conclude that $(k+1)! > 2^{k+1}$ as desired. By the Principle of Mathematical Induction, we conclude that $n! > 2^n$ for all integers $n \geq 4$. ◢

Pause 3   What was the induction hypothesis in this problem? ∎

Pause 4   Why did the induction in this example start at $n = 4$ instead of some smaller integer? ∎

The Principle of Mathematical Induction is one of the most powerful tools of mathematics. With it, we can prove many interesting things, but if it is not applied correctly, we can also prove some interesting things that are not true!

PROBLEM 7. What is the flaw in the following argument, which purports to show that

$$2 + 4 + 6 + \cdots + 2n = (n - 1)(n + 2)$$

for all positive integers n?

"Assume that $2 + 4 + 6 + \cdots + 2k = (k - 1)(k + 2)$ for some integer k. Then

$$
\begin{aligned}
2 + 4 + 6 + \cdots + 2(k + 1) &= (2 + 4 + 6 + \cdots + 2k) + 2(k + 1) \\
&= (k - 1)(k + 2) + 2(k + 1) \\
&\qquad \text{(by the induction hypothesis)} \\
&= k^2 + k - 2 + 2k + 2 \\
&= k^2 + 3k \\
&= k(k + 3) \\
&= [(k + 1) - 1][(k + 1) + 2],
\end{aligned}
$$

which is the given statement for $n = k + 1$. It follows, by the Principle of Mathematical Induction, that the statement is true for all positive integers n."

Solution. The inductive step, as given, is correct, but we neglected to check the case $n = 1$, for which the statement is most definitely false.

There is another form of the Principle of Mathematical Induction, called the *strong form*, because, at first glance, it appears to be more powerful than the principle stated previously. The two forms are completely equivalent, however: The collection of statements that can be proved true using one form is exactly the collection that can be proved true using the other. It just so happens that in certain problems the strong form is more convenient than the other.

5.1.4 PRINCIPLE OF MATHEMATICAL INDUCTION (STRONG FORM)

Given a statement $\mathcal{P}$ concerning the integer n, suppose

1. $\mathcal{P}$ is true for some integer n_0;
2. if $k > n_0$ is any integer and $\mathcal{P}$ is true for all integers ℓ in the range $n_0 \leq \ell < k$, then it is true also for k.

Then $\mathcal{P}$ is true for all integers $n \geq n_0$.

The two forms of the Principle of Mathematical Induction differ only in the statement of the induction hypothesis (the assumption in the second step). Previously, we assumed the truth of the statement for just one particular integer, and we had to prove it true for the next largest integer. In the strong form of mathematical induction, we assume the truth of the statement for **all** integers less than some integer and prove that the statement is true for that integer. When we first encounter mathematical induction, it seems to be the weak form that is always used; problems requiring the strong form are seldom encountered. In the analysis of finite structures, however, the strong form is employed extensively. We want to acquire knowledge about structures of a certain size from knowledge about similar structures of smaller size. Recall that part of the Fundamental Theorem of Arithmetic states that every natural number greater than 1 is the product of primes. The strong form of mathematical induction affords a very straightforward proof of this result.

PROBLEM 8. Use the strong form of mathematical induction to prove that every natural number $n \geq 2$ is either prime or the product of prime numbers. (See 4.3.9, the Fundamental Theorem of Arithmetic.)

Solution. The theorem is a statement about all integers $n \geq 2$. The first such integer, $n_0 = 2$, is prime, so the assertion of the theorem is true. Now let $k > 2$ and suppose that the assertion is true for all positive integers ℓ, $2 \leq \ell < k$; in other words, suppose that every integer ℓ in the interval $2 \leq \ell < k$ is either prime or the product of primes. We must prove that k has this same property. If k is prime, there is nothing more to do. On the other hand, if k is not prime, then k can be factored $k = ab$, where a and b are integers satisfying $2 \leq a, b < k$. By the induction hypothesis, each of a and b is either prime or the product of primes. Thus, k is the product of primes, as required. By the Principle of Mathematical Induction, we conclude that every $n \geq 2$ is prime or the product of primes.

PROBLEM 9. Use the strong form of mathematical induction to give another proof of Problem 1.

Solution. Given that envelopes are available in packages of five and twelve, we wish to show that an order for n envelopes can be filled exactly, provided $n \geq 44$. As before we begin by noting that an order for 44 envelopes can be filled with two packages of twelve and four packages of five. For reasons that will become clear in a minute, we also check that orders for 45, 46, 47, and 48 can also be filled, like this.

45 nine packages of five
46 three packages of twelve, two packages of five
47 one package of twelve, seven packages of five
48 four packages of twelve

Now assume that $k > 44$ and that an order for ℓ envelopes can be filled if $44 \leq \ell < k$. We must show that an order for k envelopes can be filled exactly. Our argument will be that $k = (k - 5) + 5$. By the induction hypothesis, $k - 5$ envelopes can be purchased with packages of five and twelve so, by adding one more package of five, we can purchase k. The problem, of course, is that we can only apply the induction hypothesis if $\ell = k - 5 \geq 44$; that is, $k \geq 49$. The remaining cases, however, $k = 45, 46, 47, 48$ have been checked individually, so our proof is complete.

Our next problem demonstrates another common error in "proofs" by mathematical induction.

PROBLEM 10. Canada has a two-dollar coin known colloquially as the "toonie." What is wrong with the following argument, which purports to prove that any debt of $n > 1$ Canadian dollars can be repaid (exactly) with only toonies?

Here $n_0 = 2$. We begin by noting that any two-dollar debt can be repaid with a single toonie. Thus, the assertion is true for $n = 2$.

Now let $k \geq 2$ and suppose that the assertion is true for all ℓ, $2 \leq \ell < k$. We must prove that the assertion is true for $n = k$. For this, we apply the induction hypothesis to $k - 2$ and see that a $(k - 2)$-dollar debt can be repaid with toonies. Adding one more toonie allows us to repay k dollars with only toonies, as required. By the Principle of Mathematical Induction, any debt of $n > 1$ dollars can be repaid with toonies.

Solution. The problem here is that the latter part of the argument does not work if $k = 3$.

The induction hypothesis, that the assertion is true for all ℓ, $2 \leq \ell < k$, was applied to $\ell = k - 2$. If $k = 3$, however, then $k - 2 = 1$ and the induction hypothesis cannot be applied.

We conclude with a brief discussion about the equivalence of the two Principles of Mathematical Induction and the Well-Ordering Principle.

Mathematical Induction and Well Ordering

Recall that the Well-Ordering Principle (4.1.2) says that any nonempty set of natural numbers has a smallest element. This can be proved using the weak form of the Principle of Mathematical Induction. Here is the argument.

A set containing just one element has a smallest member, the element itself, so the Well-Ordering Principle is true for sets of size $n_0 = 1$. Now suppose it is true for sets of size k; that is, assume that any set of k natural numbers has a smallest member. Given a set S of $k + 1$ numbers, remove one element a. The remaining k numbers have a smallest element, say b, and the smaller of a and b is the smallest element of S. This proves that any finite set of natural numbers has a smallest element. We leave to the reader (Exercise 16) the extension of this result to arbitrary subsets of N.

Conversely, we may use the Well-Ordering Principle to prove the Principle of Mathematical Induction (weak form). For suppose that $\mathcal{P}$ is a statement involving the integer n that we wish to establish for all integers greater than or equal to some given integer n_0. Assume

1. $\mathcal{P}$ is true for $n = n_0$, and
2. if k is an integer, $k \geq n_0$, and $\mathcal{P}$ is true for k, then $\mathcal{P}$ is also true for $k + 1$.

How does the Well-Ordering Principle show that $\mathcal{P}$ is true for all $n \geq n_0$? For convenience we assume that $n_0 \geq 1$. (The case $n_0 < 0$ can be handled with a slight variation of the argument we present.)

If $\mathcal{P}$ is not true for all $n \geq n_0$, then the set S of natural numbers $n \geq n_0$ for which $\mathcal{P}$ is false is not empty. By the Well-Ordering Principle, S has a smallest element a. Now $a \neq n_0$ because we have established that $\mathcal{P}$ is true for $n = n_0$. Thus, $a > n_0$, so $a - 1 \geq n_0$. Also, $a - 1 < a$. By minimality of a, $\mathcal{P}$ is true for $k = a - 1$. By assumption 2, $\mathcal{P}$ is true for $k + 1 = a$, a contradiction. We are forced to conclude that our starting assumption is false: $\mathcal{P}$ must be true for all $n \geq n_0$.

The preceding paragraphs show that the principles of Well-Ordering and Mathematical Induction (weak form) are equivalent. With minor variations in the reasoning, we can prove that the principles of Well Ordering and Mathematical Induction (strong form) are equivalent. It follows, therefore, that the three principles are logically equivalent.

Answers to Pauses

1. $\sum_{i=1}^{4}(2i-1) = [2(1)-1]+[2(2)-1]+[2(3)-1]+[2(4)-1] = 1+3+5+7 = 16$.

2. When $n = 1$, $3^{2(1)} - 1 = 3^2 - 1 = 9 - 1 = 8$ is divisible by 8. Now suppose that $k \geq 1$ and the statement is true for $n = k$; that is, suppose that $3^{2k} - 1$ is divisible by 8. Thus, $3^{2k} - 1 = 8t$ for some integer t and so $3^{2k} = 8t + 1$. We have

$$3^{2(k+1)} - 1 = 3^{2k+2} - 1 = 9(3^{2k}) - 1$$
$$= 9(8t + 1) - 1 = 72t + 9 - 1 = 72t + 8 = 8(9t + 1).$$

Thus, $3^{2(k+1)} - 1$ is divisible by 8, as required. By the Principle of Mathematical Induction, $3^{2n} - 1$ is divisible by 8 for all integers $n \geq 1$.

3. The induction hypothesis was that $k! > 2^k$ for some particular integer $k \geq 4$.

4. The statement $n! > 2^n$ is not true for $n < 4$; for example, $3! = 6$, whereas $2^3 = 8$.

True/False Questions

(Answers can be found in the back of the book.)

1. The statement "$\sum_{i=1}^{n}(2i-1)=n^2$ for every $n \in \mathbb{N}$" is the type of statement that can be proved by mathematical induction.

2. The statement "$2^{3n}-1$ is divisible by 7 for every $n \in \mathbb{N}$" is the type of statement that can be proved using mathematical induction.

3. The statement "$2^x > x^2$ for every real number $x \geq 5$" is the type of statement that can be proved using mathematical induction.

4. The statement "$(1+\frac{1}{2})^n \geq 1+\frac{n}{2}$ for every integer n" is the type of statement that can be proved using one application of mathematical induction.

5. The first step in the Principle of Mathematical Induction is to check the $n=1$ case.

6. The second step in the Principle of Mathematical Induction is called the induction hypothesis.

7. Mathematical induction is not necessary if a high-speed computer can be used to check the first 100,000 cases of a statement about all $n \in \mathbb{N}$.

8. The statement "$n! > 2^n$ for all natural numbers $n \geq 3$" is true and can be proved by mathematical induction.

9. The strong form of the Principle of Mathematical Induction differs from the usual form only in the statement of the induction hypothesis.

10. The Well-Ordering Principle says that any nonempty set of integers has a smallest element.

Exercises

*The answers to exercises marked [BB] can be found in the **B**ack of the **B**ook.*

1. Write each of the following sums without using $\sum$ and evaluate.
   (a) [BB] $\sum_{i=1}^{5} i^2$
   (b) [BB] $\sum_{i=1}^{4} 2^i$
   (c) [BB] $\sum_{t=1}^{1} \sin \pi t$
   (d) $\sum_{j=0}^{2} 3^{j+2}$
   (e) $\sum_{k=-1}^{4}(2k^2-k+1)$
   (f) $\sum_{k=0}^{n}(-1)^k$

2. List the elements of each of the following sets:
   (a) [BB] $\{\sum_{i=0}^{n}(-1)^i \mid n=0,1,2,3\}$
   (b) $\{\sum_{i=1}^{n} 2^i \mid n \in \mathbb{N}, 1 \leq n \leq 5\}$

3. Prove that it is possible to fill an order for $n \geq 32$ pounds of fish given bottomless wheelbarrows full of 5-pound and 9-pound fish.

4. Use mathematical induction to prove the truth of each of the following assertions for all $n \geq 1$.
   (a) [BB] n^3+2n is divisible by 3.
   (b) $n^3+(n+1)^3+(n+2)^3$ is divisible by 9.
   (c) [BB] 5^n-1 is divisible by 4.
   (d) 8^n-3^n is divisible by 5.
   (e) $5^{2n}-2^{5n}$ is divisible by 7.
   (f) [BB] $10^{n+1}+10^n+1$ is divisible by 3.
   (g) n^3+5n is divisible by 6.
   (h) $2^n+3^n-5^n$ is divisible by 6.
   (i) $16^n+10n-1$ is divisible by 25.
   (j) [BB] $(2n)!$ is divisible by 2^n.

   (k) a^n-b^n is divisible by $a-b$ for any integers a,b with $a-b \neq 0$.

5. (a) [BB] Prove by mathematical induction that $1+2+3+\cdots+n=\frac{n(n+1)}{2}$ for any natural number n.
   (b) Prove by mathematical induction that $1^3+2^3+\cdots+n^3=\frac{n^2(n+1)^2}{4}$ for any natural number n.
   (c) Use the results of (a) and (b) to establish that $(1+2+3+\cdots+n)^2=1^3+2^3+\cdots+n^3$ for all $n \geq 1$.

6. Use mathematical induction to establish the truth of each of the following statements for all $n \geq 1$.
   (a) [BB] $1+2+2^2+2^3+\cdots+2^n=2^{n+1}-1$
   (b) [BB] $1^2-2^2+3^2-4^2+\cdots+(-1)^{n-1}n^2=(-1)^{n-1}\frac{n(n+1)}{2}$
   (c) $1^2+3^2+5^2+\cdots+(2n-1)^2=\frac{n(2n-1)(2n+1)}{3}$
   (d) $1\cdot2\cdot3+2\cdot3\cdot4+3\cdot4\cdot5+\cdots+n(n+1)(n+2)=\frac{n(n+1)(n+2)(n+3)}{4}$
   (e) $\frac{1}{1\cdot2}+\frac{1}{2\cdot3}+\frac{1}{3\cdot4}+\cdots+\frac{1}{n(n+1)}=\frac{n}{n+1}$
   (f) [BB] $\frac{2}{3}+\frac{2}{9}+\frac{2}{27}+\cdots+\frac{2}{3^n}=1-\frac{1}{3^n}$ for all integers $n \geq 1$.
   (g) [BB] $4+10+16+\cdots+(6n-2)=n(3n+1)$ for all $n \geq 1$.

(h) $\dfrac{1}{1\cdot 5} + \dfrac{1}{5\cdot 9} + \dfrac{1}{9\cdot 13} + \cdots + \dfrac{1}{(4n-3)(4n+1)} = \dfrac{n}{4n+1}$ for all $n \geq 1$.

7. [BB; (a)] Rewrite each of the sums in Exercise 6 using $\sum$ notation.

8. Use mathematical induction to establish each of the following formulas.

   (a) [BB] $\displaystyle\sum_{i=1}^{n}(i+1)2^i = n2^{n+1}$

   (b) $\displaystyle\sum_{i=1}^{n} \dfrac{i^2}{(2i-1)(2i+1)} = \dfrac{n(n+1)}{2(2n+1)}$

   (c) $\displaystyle\sum_{i=1}^{n}(2i-1)(2i) = \dfrac{n(n+1)(4n-1)}{3}$

9. Use mathematical induction to establish each of the following inequalities.

   (a) [BB] $2^n > n^2$, for $n \geq 5$.

   (b) $2^n \geq \frac{1}{8}$ for all $n \geq -3$.

   (c) [BB] $n! > n^3$ for all $n \geq 6$.

   (d) $(1+\frac{1}{2})^n \geq 1 + \frac{n}{2}$, for $n \in \mathbf{N}$.

   (e) For any $x \in \mathbf{R}$, $x > -1$, $(1+x)^n \geq 1 + nx$ for all $n \in \mathbf{N}$.

   (f) For any integer $n \geq 2$, $\frac{1}{n+1} + \frac{1}{n+2} + \frac{1}{n+3} + \cdots + \frac{1}{2n} > \frac{13}{24}$.

   (g) $\dfrac{1}{1^2} + \dfrac{1}{2^2} + \dfrac{1}{3^2} + \cdots + \dfrac{1}{n^2} < 2 - \dfrac{1}{n}$ for all $n \geq 2$.

   (h) $\displaystyle\sum_{i=1}^{n} \dfrac{1}{\sqrt{i}} > \sqrt{n}$ for $n \geq 2$.

   (i) [BB] $1(3)(5)\cdots(2n-1) \geq 2(4)(6)\cdots(2n-2)$ for every integer $n \geq 2$.

10. Suppose $c, x_1, x_2, \ldots, x_n, y_1, y_2, \ldots, y_n$ are $2n+1$ given numbers. Prove each of the following assertions by mathematical induction.

   (a) [BB] $\displaystyle\sum_{i=1}^{n}(x_i + y_i) = \sum_{i=1}^{n}x_i + \sum_{i=1}^{n}y_i$ for $n \geq 1$.

   (b) $\displaystyle\sum_{i=1}^{n}cx_i = c\sum_{i=1}^{n}x_i$ for $n \geq 1$.

   (c) $\displaystyle\sum_{i=2}^{n}(x_i - x_{i-1}) = x_n - x_1$ for $n \geq 2$.

11. [BB] Find the fault in the following "proof" that in any group of n people, everybody is the same age.

> Suppose $n = 1$. If a group consists of just one person, everybody is the same age. Suppose that in any group of k people, everyone is the same age. Let $G = \{a_1, a_2, \ldots, a_{k+1}\}$ be a group of $k+1$ people. Since each of the groups $\{a_1, a_2, \ldots, a_k\}$ and $\{a_2, a_3, \ldots, a_{k+1}\}$ consists of k people, everybody in each group has the same age, by the induction hypothesis. Since a_2 is in each group, it follows that all $k+1$ people $a_1, a_2, \ldots, a_{k+1}$ have the same age.

12. [BB] Find the fault in the following "proof" by mathematical induction that

$$1 + 2 + 3 + \cdots + n = \dfrac{(2n+1)^2}{8}$$

for all natural numbers n.

> If $1 + 2 + 3 + \cdots + k = \dfrac{(2k+1)^2}{8}$, then
>
> $1 + 2 + 3 + \cdots + (k+1)$
> $= (1 + 2 + 3 + \cdots + k) + (k+1)$
> $= \dfrac{(2k+1)^2}{8} + (k+1)$
> $= \dfrac{4k^2 + 4k + 1 + 8k + 8}{8}$
> $= \dfrac{4k^2 + 12k + 9}{8}$
> $= \dfrac{(2k+3)^2}{8} = \dfrac{[2(k+1)+1]^2}{8}$
>
> and so truth for k implies truth for $k+1$.

13. What is wrong with the following "proof" that any order for $n \geq 10$ pounds of fish can be filled with only 5-pound fish?

> We use the strong form of mathematical induction. Here $n_0 = 10$. Since an order for 10 pounds of fish can be filled with two 5-pound fish, the assertion is true for $n = 10$. Now let $k > 10$ be an integer and suppose that any order for ℓ pounds of fish, $10 \leq \ell < k$, can be filled with only 5-pound fish. We must prove that an order for k pounds can be similarly filled. But by the induction hypothesis, we can fill an order for $k - 5$ pounds of fish, so, adding one more 5-pounder, we can fill the order for k pounds. By the Principle of Mathematical Induction, we conclude that the assertion is true for all $n \geq 10$.

14. One of several differences between the Canadian and American games of football is that in Canada a team can score a single point without first having scored a touchdown. (Such a point is called a *rouge*.) So it is clear that any score is possible in the Canadian game. Is this so in the American game? Indeed this seems to be the case, even assuming (this is not true!) that in the United States points can be scored only three at a time (with a field goal) or seven at a time (with a converted touchdown). Here is an argument.

> Assume that k points can be achieved with multiples of 3 or 7. Here's how to reach $k+1$ points. If k points are achieved with at least two field goals, subtracting these and adding a touchdown gives $k+1$ points. On the other hand, if the k points are achieved with at least

two touchdowns, subtracting these and adding five field goals also gives $k + 1$ points.

Does this argument show that any score is possible in American football? Can it be used to show something about the nature of possible scores?

15. [BB] Prove that a set with n elements, $n \geq 0$, contains 2^n subsets.

16. [BB] Suppose that any nonempty finite set of natural numbers has a smallest element. Prove that **any** nonempty set of natural numbers has a smallest element.

17. (a) Prove that for any integer $n \geq 1$ any set of n positive real numbers has a smallest element.

   (b) Prove that the result of (a) is not true for infinite sets of positive real numbers in general, but that it is true for some infinite sets.

   (c) What is the name of the principle that asserts that any nonempty set of natural numbers has a smallest element?

18. [BB] Let $n \geq 1$ and let $A, B_1, B_2, \ldots, B_n$ be sets. Generalize the result of Exercise 20, Section 2.2, by proving that $A \cup \left(\bigcap_{i=1}^n B_i \right) = \bigcap_{i=1}^n (A \cup B_i)$ for all $n \geq 1$.

19. Prove that $A \cap \left(\bigcup_{i=1}^n B_i \right) = \bigcup_{i=1}^n (A \cap B_i)$ for any sets $A, B_1, B_2, \ldots, B_n$.

20. In Section 2.2, we defined the symmetric difference of two sets. More generally, the symmetric difference of $n \geq 3$ sets $A_1, \ldots, A_n$ can be defined inductively as follows:

$$A_1 \oplus \cdots \oplus A_n = (A_1 \oplus \cdots \oplus A_{n-1}) \oplus A_n.$$

Prove that for any $n \geq 2$, $A_1 \oplus A_2 \oplus \cdots \oplus A_n$ consists of those elements in an odd number of the sets $A_1, \ldots, A_n$.

21. Prove the Chinese Remainder Theorem, 4.5.1, by mathematical induction.

22. [BB] For $n \geq 3$, the *greatest common divisor* of n nonzero integers $a_1, a_2, \ldots, a_n$ can be defined inductively by

$$\gcd(a_1, \ldots, a_n) = \gcd(a_1, \gcd(a_2, \ldots, a_n)).$$

Prove that $\gcd(a_1, a_2, \ldots, a_n)$ is an integral *linear combination* of $a_1, a_2, \ldots, a_n$ for all $n \geq 2$; that is, prove that there exist integers $s_1, \ldots, s_n$ such that $\gcd(a_1, \ldots, a_n) = s_1 a_1 + s_2 a_2 + \cdots + s_n a_n$.

23. The definition of the greatest common divisor of $n \geq 3$ integers given in Exercise 22 differs from that given in the exercises to Section 4.2. Suppose $a_1, \ldots, a_n$ are nonzero integers. Show that $\gcd(a_1, \ldots, a_n)$, as defined in Exercise 22, satisfies the properties given in Definition 4.2.14.

24. Suppose n and $m_1, m_2, \ldots, m_t$ are natural numbers and that the m_i are pairwise relatively prime. Suppose each m_i divides n. Prove that the product $m_1 m_2 \cdots m_t$ divides n. [*Hint:* Induction on t and Exercise 11 of Section 4.2.]

25. Define $f : Z \to Z$ by $f(n) = \begin{cases} n - 2 & n \geq 1000 \\ f(f(n + 4)) & n < 1000. \end{cases}$

(a) Find the values of $f(1000 - n)$ for $n = 0, 1, 2, 3, 4, 5$.

(b) Guess a formula for $f(1000 - n)$ valid for $n \geq 0$ and prove your answer.

(c) Find $f(5)$ and $f(20)$.

(d) What is the range of f?

5.1.5 DEFINITION A set A of integers is called an *ideal* if and only if

   i. $0 \in A$,

   ii. if $a \in A$, then also $-a \in A$, and

   iii. if $a, b \in A$, then $a + b \in A$.   ❖

26. [BB] For any integer $n \geq 0$, recall that $nZ = \{kn \mid k \in Z\}$ denotes the set of multiples of n.

   (a) Prove that nZ is an ideal of the integers.

   (b) Let A be any ideal of Z. Prove that $A = nZ$ for some $n \geq 0$ by establishing each of the following statements.

      i. If A contains only one element, then A is of the desired form.

      Now assume that A contains more than one element.

      ii. Show that A contains a positive number.

      iii. Show that A contains a smallest positive number n.

      iv. $nZ \subseteq A$, where n is the integer found in iii.

      v. $A \subseteq nZ$. [*Hint:* 4.1.5, the Division Algorithm.]

27. [BB] Prove that for every integer $n \geq 2$ the number of lines obtained by joining n distinct points in the plane, no three of which are collinear, is $\frac{1}{2} n(n - 1)$.

28. An n-sided polygon (commonly shortened to n-gon) is a closed planar figure bounded by n straight sides no two of which intersect unless they are adjacent, in which case they intersect just at a vertex. Thus, a 3-gon is a triangle, a 4-gon is a quadrilateral, a 5-gon is a pentagon, and so on. An n-gon is *convex* if the line joining any pair of nonadjacent vertices lies entirely within the figure. A rectangle, for example, is convex. Prove that the sum of the interior angles of a convex n-gon is $(n - 2)180°$ for all $n \geq 3$.

29. Suppose a rectangle is subdivided into regions by means of straight lines each extending from one border of the rectangle to another. Prove that the regions of the "map" so obtained can be colored with just two colors in such a way that bordering "countries" have different colors.

30. (a) [BB] Given an equal arm balance capable of determining only the relative weights of two quantities and eight coins, all of equal weight except possibly one that is lighter, explain how to determine if there is a light coin and how to identify it in just two weighings.

(b) Given an equal arm balance as in (a) and $3^n - 1$ coins, $n \geq 1$, all of equal weight except possibly one that is lighter, show how to determine if there is a light coin and how to identify it in at most n weighings.

31. True or false? In each case, give a proof or provide a counterexample that disproves the given statement.

(a) [BB] $5^n + n + 1$ is divisible by 7 for all $n \geq 1$.

(b) $\sum_{k=0}^{n}(k + 1) = \frac{1}{2}n(n + 3)$ for all $n \geq 1$.

(c) If $n \geq 2$, $\gcd\left(\frac{(n + 2)!}{3}, \frac{(n + 3)!}{2}\right) = \frac{(n + 2)!}{6}$.

(d) (For students of calculus) $n^{15} \geq 2^n$ for all $n \geq 1$.

32. Let n be any integer greater than 1. Show that the following argument is valid. (See Section 1.3.)

$$
\begin{array}{c}
p_1 \rightarrow p_2 \\
p_2 \rightarrow p_3 \\
\vdots \\
\underline{p_{n-1} \rightarrow p_n} \\
p_1 \rightarrow p_n
\end{array}
$$

33. (For students who have completed a course in differential calculus) State and prove (by mathematical induction) a formula for $\frac{d}{dx}x^n$ that holds for all $n \geq 1$.

5.1.6 Notation The product of n elements $a_1, a_2, \ldots, a_n$ is denoted $\prod_{r=1}^{n} a_r$.

34. Let x be a real number, $x \neq \pm 1$. Prove that $\prod_{r=1}^{n}(1 + x^{2^r}) = \frac{1 - x^{2^{r+1}}}{1 - x^2}$ for any integer $n \geq 1$.

35. [BB] (For students of calculus) The condition $x^2 \neq 1$ is necessary in Exercise 34 since otherwise we would have a denominator of 0 on the right. However,

$$
\lim_{x \to 1}\frac{1 - x^{2^{r+1}}}{1 - x^2} \quad \text{and} \quad \lim_{x \to -1}\frac{1 - x^{2^{r+1}}}{1 - x^2}
$$

both exist. Use the result of Exercise 34 to find these limits.

36. Find an expression for $\prod_{r=2}^{n}\frac{2r - 1}{2r - 3}$ valid for $n \geq 2$ and prove by mathematical induction that your answer is correct.

37. For any $n \geq 0$, let $F_n = 2^{2^n} + 1$. (These F_n are often called *Fermat numbers*. Those that are prime are the *Fermat primes* introduced in Section 4.3.)

(a) Prove that $\prod_{r=0}^{n-1} F_r = F_n - 2$ for all $n \geq 1$.

(b) Prove that $\gcd(F_m, F_n) = 1$ for any positive integers m and n with $m \neq n$.

(c) Use the result of (b) to give another proof (different from Euclid's) that there are infinitely many primes.

38. For a given natural number n, prove that the set of all polynomials of degree at most n with integer coefficients is countable. [*Hint:* Let P_n denote the set of all polynomials of degree at most n with integer coefficients. The result for P_1 was Exercise 27b in Section 3.3.]

39. **(a)** Prove that the strong form of the Principle of Mathematical Induction implies the Well-Ordering Principle.

(b) Prove that the Well-Ordering Principle implies the strong form of the Principle of Mathematical Induction. (Assume $n_0 \geq 1$.)

40. In this section, we have studied two formulations of the Principle of Mathematical Induction.

(a) Use either of these to establish the following (peculiar?) third formulation.

Suppose $\mathcal{P}(n)$ is a statement about the natural number n such that

1. $\mathcal{P}(1)$ is true;
2. For any $k \geq 1$, $\mathcal{P}(k)$ true implies $\mathcal{P}(2k)$ true; and
3. For any $k \geq 2$, $\mathcal{P}(k)$ true implies $\mathcal{P}(k - 1)$ true.

(b) Prove that, for any two nonnegative numbers x and y, $\frac{x + y}{2} \geq \sqrt{xy}$.

(c) Use the Principle of Mathematical Induction in the form given in part (a) to generalize the result of part (b), thus establishing the *arithmetic mean–geometric mean inequality*: For any $n \geq 1$ and any n nonnegative real numbers $a_1, a_2, \ldots, a_n$,

$$
\frac{a_1 + a_2 + \cdots + a_n}{n} \geq \sqrt[n]{a_1 a_2 \cdots a_n}\,.
$$

41. Let m and n be relatively prime integers each greater than 1. Assume you have an unlimited supply of m- and n-cent stamps. Using only these stamps, show that

(a) it is not possible to purchase a selection of stamps worth precisely $mn - m - n$ cents;

(b) for any $r > mn - m - n$, it is possible to purchase a selection of stamps worth exactly r cents. [*Hint:* There exist integers a and b, with $0 < a < n$ and $0 < b < m$, such that $bn = am - 1$ and hence such that $(n - a)m = (m - b)n - 1$. See Exercise 36 of Section 4.2. Now try downward induction!]

5.2 Recursively Defined Sequences

Suppose n is a natural number. How should we define 2^n? We could write

$$2^n = \underbrace{2 \cdot 2 \cdot 2 \cdots 2}_{n \text{ 2's}}$$

or

(4) $$2^1 = 2 \quad \text{and, for } k \geq 1, \quad 2^{k+1} = 2 \cdot 2^k.$$

The latter statement is an example of a *recursive definition*. It explicitly defines 2^n when $n = 1$ and then, assuming 2^n has been defined for $n = k$, defines it for $n = k + 1$. By the Principle of Mathematical Induction, we know that 2^n has been defined for all integers $n \geq 1$.

Another expression that is most naturally defined recursively is $n!$, which was introduced in Section 5.1. If we write

$$0! = 1 \quad \text{and, for } k \geq 0, \quad (k + 1)! = (k + 1)k!,$$

then it follows by the Principle of Mathematical Induction that $n!$ has been defined for every $n \geq 0$.

Sequences of numbers are often defined recursively. A *sequence* is a function whose domain is some infinite set of integers (often N) and whose range is a set of real numbers. Since its domain is countable, we can and usually do describe a sequence by simply listing its range. The sequence that is the function $f : N \to R$ defined by $f(n) = n^2$, for instance, is generally described by the list $1, 4, 9, 16, \ldots$, the idea being to write down enough numbers from the start of the list that the rest can be inferred. The numbers in the list (the range of the function) are called the *terms* of the sequence. Sometimes we start counting at 0 (if the function has domain $N \cup \{0\}$) so that the terms are denoted $a_0, a_1, a_2, \ldots$.

The sequence $2, 4, 8, 16, \ldots$ can be defined recursively like this:

(5) $$a_1 = 2 \quad \text{and, for } k \geq 1, \quad a_{k+1} = 2a_k.$$

By this, we understand that $a_1 = 2$ and then, setting $k = 1$ in the second part of the definition, that $a_2 = 2a_1 = 2(2) = 4$. With $k = 2$, $a_3 = 2a_2 = 2(4) = 8$; with $k = 3$, $a_4 = 2a_3 = 2(8) = 16$ and so on. Evidently, (5) defines the sequence we had in mind. Again, the definition is recursive because each term in the sequence beyond the first is defined in terms of the previous term.

The equation $a_{k+1} = 2a_k$ in (5), which defines one member of the sequence in terms of a previous one, is called a *recurrence relation*. The equation $a_1 = 2$ is called an *initial condition*.

There are other possible recursive definitions that describe the same sequence as (5). For example, we could write

$$a_0 = 2 \quad \text{and, for } k \geq 0, \quad a_{k+1} = 2a_k,$$

or we could say

$$a_1 = 2 \quad \text{and, for } k \geq 2, \quad a_k = 2a_{k-1}.$$

(Verify that these definitions give the same sequence, $2, 4, 8, 16, \ldots$.)

Sometimes, after computing a few terms of a sequence that has been defined recursively, we can guess an explicit formula for a_n. In (5), for instance, $a_n = 2^n$. We say that $a_n = 2^n$ is the *solution* to the recurrence relation. Our goal in this section and the next is to gain some skill at solving recurrence relations.

PROBLEM 11. Write down the first six terms of the sequence defined by $a_1 = 1$, $a_{k+1} = 3a_k + 1$ for $k \geq 1$. Guess a formula for a_n and prove that your formula is correct.

Solution. The first six terms are

$$a_1 = 1$$
$$a_2 = 3a_1 + 1 = 3(1) + 1 = 4$$
$$a_3 = 3a_2 + 1 = 3(4) + 1 = 13$$
$$a_4 = 40$$
$$a_5 = 121$$
$$a_6 = 364.$$

Since there is multiplication by 3 at each step, we might suspect that 3^n is involved in the answer. After trial and error, we guess that $a_n = \frac{1}{2}(3^n - 1)$ and verify this by mathematical induction. (In Problem 17, we show how to get this formula without guesswork.)

When $n = 1$, the formula gives $\frac{1}{2}(3^1 - 1) = 1$, which is indeed a_1, the first term in the sequence.

Now assume that $k \geq 1$ and that $a_k = \frac{1}{2}(3^k - 1)$. We wish to prove that $a_{k+1} = \frac{1}{2}(3^{k+1} - 1)$. We have

$$a_{k+1} = 3a_k + 1 = 3[\frac{1}{2}(3^k - 1)] + 1$$

using the induction hypothesis. Hence,

$$a_{k+1} = \frac{1}{2}3^{k+1} - \frac{3}{2} + 1 = \frac{1}{2}(3^{k+1} - 1)$$

as required. By the Principle of Mathematical Induction, our guess is correct.

PROBLEM 12. A sequence is defined recursively by $a_0 = 1$, $a_1 = 4$, and $a_n = 4a_{n-1} - 4a_{n-2}$ for $n \geq 2$. Find the first six terms of this sequence. Guess a formula for a_n and establish the validity of your guess.

Solution. Here there are two initial conditions, $a_0 = 1, a_1 = 4$. Also, the recurrence relation $a_n = 4a_{n-1} - 4a_{n-2}$ defines the general term as a function of two previous terms. The first six terms of the sequence are

$$a_0 = 1$$
$$a_1 = 4$$
$$a_2 = 4a_1 - 4a_0 = 4(4) - 4(1) = 12$$
$$a_3 = 4a_2 - 4a_1 = 4(12) - 4(4) = 32$$
$$a_4 = 4a_3 - 4a_2 = 4(32) - 4(12) = 80$$
$$a_5 = 4a_4 - 4a_3 = 4(80) - 4(32) = 192.$$

Finding a general formula for a_n requires some ingenuity. Let us carefully examine some of the first six terms. We note that $a_2 = 2^2(3)$, $a_3 = 2^3(4)$, $a_4 = 2^4(5)$, and $a_5 = 2^5(6)$. We are tempted to guess that $a_n = (n + 1)2^n$ in general. To prove this, we use the strong form of mathematical induction (with $n_0 = 0$).

When $n = 0$, we have $(0 + 1)2^0 = 1(1) = 1$, in agreement with the given value for a_0. When $n = 1$, $(1 + 1)2^1 = 4 = a_1$. Now that the formula has been verified for $k = 0$ and $k = 1$, we may assume that $k > 1$ and that $a_n = (n + 1)2^n$ for all n in the interval $0 \leq n < k$. We wish to prove that the formula is valid for $n = k$; that is, we wish to prove that $a_k = (k + 1)2^k$. Since $k \geq 2$, we know that $a_k = 4a_{k-1} - 4a_{k-2}$.

Applying the induction hypothesis to $k - 1$ and to $k - 2$ (each of which is in the range $0 \leq n < k$), we have $a_{k-1} = k2^{k-1}$ and $a_{k-2} = (k - 1)2^{k-2}$. Thus,

$$a_k = 4(k2^{k-1}) - 4(k - 1)2^{k-2} = 2k2^k - k2^k + 2^k = k2^k + 2^k = (k + 1)2^k$$

as required. By the Principle of Mathematical Induction, the formula is valid for all $n \geq 0$.   ▲

In effect, our method of verifying the formula $a_n = (n + 1)2^n$ in Problem 12 amounts simply to checking that it satisfies both initial conditions and also the given recurrence relation. We prefer the more formal approach of mathematical induction since it emphasizes this important concept and avoids pitfalls associated with working on both sides of an equation at once.

As previously mentioned, there is nothing unique about a recursive definition. The sequence in the last example can also be defined by

$$a_0 = 1, a_1 = 4 \quad \text{and, for } n \geq 1, \quad a_{n+1} = 4a_n - 4a_{n-1}.$$

In this case, we again obtain $a_n = (n + 1)2^n$. We could also say

$$a_1 = 1, a_2 = 4 \quad \text{and, for } n \geq 1, \quad a_{n+2} = 4a_{n+1} - 4a_n$$

but, then, labeling the first term a_1 instead of a_0 would give $a_n = n2^{n-1}$. Other variants are also possible.

Some Special Sequences

Suppose you have $50 in an old shoe box and acquire a paper route that nets you $14 a week. Assuming all this money goes into your shoe box on a weekly basis (and you never borrow from it), after your first week delivering papers, your shoe box will contain $64; after two weeks, $78; after three weeks, $92; and so on. A sequence of numbers like $50, 64, 78, 92, \ldots$, where each term is determined by adding the same fixed number to the previous one, is called an *arithmetic sequence*. The fixed number is called the *common difference* of the sequence (because the difference of successive terms is constant throughout the sequence).

EXAMPLE 13
- $50, 64, 78, 92, \ldots$ is an arithmetic sequence with common difference 14;
- $-17, -12, -7, -2, 3, 8, \ldots$ is an arithmetic sequence with common difference 5;
- $103, 99, 95, 91, \ldots$ is an arithmetic sequence with common difference -4.   ▦

5.2.1 DEFINITION

The *arithmetic sequence* with first term a and *common difference* d is the sequence defined by

$$a_1 = a \quad \text{and, for } k \geq 1, \quad a_{k+1} = a_k + d. \qquad ❖$$

The general arithmetic sequence thus takes the form

$$a, a + d, a + 2d, a + 3d, \ldots,$$

and it is easy to see that, for $n \geq 1$, the nth term of the sequence is

$$(6) \qquad a_n = a + (n - 1)d.$$

We leave a formal proof to the exercises and also a proof of the fact that the sum of n terms of the arithmetic sequence with first term a and common difference d is

$$(7) \qquad S = \frac{n}{2}[2a + (n - 1)d].$$

EXAMPLE 14   The first 100 terms of the arithmetic sequence $-17, -12, -7, -2, 3, \ldots$ have the sum

$$S = \tfrac{100}{2}[2(-17) + 99(5)] = 50(-34 + 495) = 23{,}050.$$

The 100th term of this sequence is $a_{100} = -17 + 99(5) = 478$ by (6). The number 2038 occurs as the 412th term, as we see by solving $-17 + (n - 1)5 = 2038$. ▨

Many people with paper routes deposit their earnings in a bank account that pays interest instead of into a shoe box, which does not. Fifty dollars in a bank account that pays 1% interest per month accumulates to $50 + (.01 \times 50) = 50(1 + .01) = 50(1.01)$ dollars after one month. After another month, the original investment will have accumulated to what it was at the start of the month plus 1% of this amount; that is,

$$50(1.01) + .01(50)(1.01) = 50(1.01)(1 + .01) = 50(1.01)^2.$$

After three months, the accumulation is $50(1.01)^3$ dollars; after twelve months, it is $50(1.01)^{12}$ dollars ($\approx \$56.34$). A sequence of numbers such as

$$50, 50(1.01), 50(1.01)^2, \ldots$$

in which each term is determined by multiplying the previous term by a fixed number is called a *geometric sequence*. The fixed number is called the *common ratio*.

EXAMPLE 15
- $50, 50(1.01), 50(1.01)^2, \ldots$ is a geometric sequence with common ratio 1.01;
- $3, -6, 12, -24, \ldots$ is a geometric sequence with common ratio -2;
- $9, 3, 1, \frac{1}{3}, \ldots$ is a geometric sequence with common ratio $\frac{1}{3}$. ▨

5.2.2 DEFINITION   The *geometric sequence* with first term a and *common ratio* r is the sequence defined by

$$a_1 = a \quad \text{and, for } k \geq 1, \quad a_{k+1} = ra_k.$$ ❖

The general geometric sequence thus has the form

$$a, ar, ar^2, ar^3, ar^4, \ldots,$$

the nth term being $a_n = ar^{n-1}$. This is straightforward to prove, as is the following formula for the sum S of n terms, provided $r \neq 1$.

(8)
$$S = \frac{a(1 - r^n)}{1 - r}.$$

EXAMPLE 16   The sum of 29 terms of the geometric sequence with $a = 8^{12}$ and $r = -\frac{1}{2}$ is

$$S = 8^{12} \frac{1 - (-\frac{1}{2})^{29}}{1 - (-\frac{1}{2})} = 2^{36} \frac{1 + (\frac{1}{2})^{29}}{\frac{3}{2}} = \frac{2^{36} + 2^7}{\frac{3}{2}} = \tfrac{1}{3}(2^{37} + 2^8).$$ ▨

Pause 5   What is the 30th term of the geometric sequence just described? ▮

PROBLEM 17.   Find a formula for a_n, given $a_1 = 1$ and $a_{k+1} = 3a_k + 1$ for $k \geq 1$, without guesswork. (We guessed a formula in Problem 11.)

Solution. Since $a_n = 3a_{n-1} + 1$ and $a_{n-1} = 3a_{n-2} + 1$, we have $a_n = 3a_{n-1} + 1 = 3(3a_{n-2} + 1) + 1 = 3^2 a_{n-2} + (1 + 3)$. Then, since $a_{n-2} = 3a_{n-3} + 1$, we get $a_n = 3^2(3a_{n-3}+1)+(1+3) = 3^3 a_{n-3}+(1+3+3^2)$. The first part of this expression has the form $3^k a_{n-k}$ [note that $k + (n - k) = n$], and the second part is the sum of a geometric series, so eventually we will obtain $a_n = 3^{n-1}a_1+(1+3+3^2+\cdots+3^{n-2})$.

Since $a_1 = 1$ and $1+3+3^2 + \cdots + 3^{n-2} = \dfrac{1(1 - 3^{n-1})}{1 - 3} = \frac{1}{2}(3^{n-1} - 1)$, we obtain

$$a_n = 3^{n-1} + \tfrac{1}{2}(3^{n-1} - 1)$$

$$= \tfrac{1}{2}(2 \cdot 3^{n-1} + 3^{n-1} - 1) = \tfrac{1}{2}(3 \cdot 3^{n-1} - 1) = \frac{1}{2}(3^n - 1)$$

as in Problem 11.

Leonardo Fibonacci,[1] also known as Leonardo of Pisa, was one of the brightest mathematicians of the Middle Ages. His writings in arithmetic and algebra were standard authorities for centuries and are largely responsible for the introduction into Europe of the Arabic numerals 0, 1, ... , 9 we use today. Fibonacci was fond of problems, his most famous of which is concerned with rabbits!

Suppose that newborn rabbits start producing offspring on the last day of the second month of life and that, after this point, they produce a pair (one male, one female) at the end of every month. Assuming just one pair of rabbits initially, how many pairs of rabbits, Fibonacci asked, will be alive after one year? The sequence that gives the number of pairs at the end of successive months is the famous *Fibonacci sequence*.

After one month, there is still only one pair of rabbits in existence, but after a further month, this pair is joined by its offspring; thus, after two months, there are two pairs of rabbits. At the end of any month, the number of pairs of rabbits is the number alive at the end of the previous month plus the number of pairs alive two months ago, since each pair alive two months ago produced one pair of offspring. We obtain the sequence 1, 1, 2, 3, 5, 8, 13, ... , which is defined recursively as follows.

5.2.3 THE FIBONACCI SEQUENCE

$f_1 = 1$, $f_2 = 1$ and, for $k \geq 2$, $f_{k+1} = f_k + f_{k-1}$

Pause 6 Think of the Fibonacci sequence as a function fib: N → N. List eight elements of this function as ordered pairs. Is fib a one-to-one function? Is it onto? ∎

Pause 7
1. Starting with one pair of rabbits on January 1 and assuming the conditions of Fibonacci's problem, how many rabbits will be available for Christmas dinner?
2. What is the answer to Fibonacci's question? ∎

Although we have found an explicit formula for the nth term of most of the sequences discussed so far, there are many sequences for which such a formula is difficult or impossible to obtain. (This is one reason why recursive definitions are important.) Is there a specific formula for the nth term of the Fibonacci sequence? As a matter of fact, there is, though it is certainly not one that many people would discover by themselves. We show in the next section (see Problem 22) that the nth

[1]Fibonacci was born around the year 1180 and died in 1228. "Fibonacci" is a contraction of "Filius Bonaccii," Latin for "son of Bonaccio."

term of the Fibonacci sequence is the integer closest to the number

$$\frac{1}{\sqrt{5}}\left(\frac{1+\sqrt{5}}{2}\right)^{n}.$$

The first few values of $\frac{1}{\sqrt{5}}\left(\frac{1+\sqrt{5}}{2}\right)^{n}$ are approximately 0.72361, 1.17082, 1.89443, 3.06525, 4.95967, 8.02492, 12.98460, and 21.00952; the integers closest to these numbers are the first eight terms of the Fibonacci sequence.

We conclude this section by advising caution with sequences **apparently** defined recursively, since some recursive definitions do not define actual sequences! Consider, for example,

$$a_1 = 1 \quad \text{and, for } k > 1, \quad a_k = \begin{cases} 1 + a_{k/2} & \text{if } k \text{ is even} \\ 1 + a_{3k-1} & \text{if } k \text{ is odd.} \end{cases}$$

What happens if we try to write down the first few terms of this sequence?

$$a_1 = 1$$
$$a_2 = 1 + a_1 = 1 + 1 = 2$$
$$a_3 = 1 + a_8 = 1 + (1 + a_4) = 2 + a_4 = 2 + (1 + a_2) = 3 + a_2 = 5$$
$$a_4 = 1 + a_2 = 1 + 2 = 3,$$

but then
$$a_5 = 1 + a_{14} = 1 + (1 + a_7) = 2 + a_7$$
$$= 2 + (1 + a_{20}) = 3 + a_{20} = 3 + (1 + a_{10})$$
$$= 4 + a_{10} = 4 + (1 + a_5) = 5 + a_5$$

and, to our dismay, we have reached the absurdity $5 = 0$. Obviously, no sequence has been defined.

Compute the first six terms of the sequence "defined" as follows:

$$a_1 = 1 \quad \text{and, for } k > 1, \quad a_k = \begin{cases} 1 + a_{k/2} & \text{if } k \text{ is even} \\ 1 + a_{3k+1} & \text{if } k \text{ is odd.} \end{cases} \quad ■$$

Application: Pseudorandom Numbers

Randomly chosen numbers are in common use. For example, you might want to play a game involving the roll of a single die sitting on board an airplane with a laptop computer but no die. What you want is a random sequence of digits between 1 and 6. An approximation to such a list can be generated by an appropriate algorithm. The numbers in the list are called *pseudorandom* because they are generated by a specific procedure. One common procedure works like this. Choose an integer $n \geq 3$, an integer a in the range $2 \leq a < n$, and nonnegative integers b, $x_0 < n$. We obtain a sequence of pseudorandom numbers between 0 and $n - 1$ with the recursive definition

$$x_{k+1} = (ax_k + b) \pmod{n}.$$

For example, with $n = 7$, $a = 5$, $b = 0$, and $x_0 = 4$, we obtain

$$4, 6, 2, 3, 1, 5, \ldots.$$

After $x_5 = 5$, we get $x_6 = 5(5) = 25 \pmod 7 = 4$, so the sequence repeats because each term is determined by its predecessor.[2]

---

[2]In the 1990s, a man won over a half-million dollars at a Montreal casino by correctly choosing 19 of 20 numbers correctly. At first the casino refused to pay, but eventually this fellow's astronomical success was attributed to a random number generator that by accident was starting every game with the same number (so that the sequence generated each time was the same)!

Sometimes, a list of random numbers between 0 and 1 is desired. In this case, we might simply divide the numbers produced as above by the modulus n. For example, with $n = 97$, $a = 2$, $x_0 = 3$, and $b = 5$, the first 15 integers produced by (10) are

$$3, 11, 27, 59, 26, 57, 22, 49, 6, 17, 39, 83, 74, 56, 20$$

and dividing each by 97 gives

$$0.03, 0.11, 0.28, 0.61, 0.27, 0.59, 0.23, 0.51, 0.06, 0.18, 0.40, 0.86, 0.76, 0.58, 0.21.$$

Answers to Pauses

5. Here $n = 30$, $a = 8^{12} = (2^3)^{12} = 2^{36}$, and $r = -(2^{-1})$, so
$$a_{30} = 2^{36}[-(2^{-1})]^{29} = -2^{36}2^{-29} = -2^7 = -128.$$

6. The most obvious eight pairs are $(1, 1)$, $(2, 1)$, $(3, 2)$, $(4, 3)$, $(5, 5)$, $(6, 8)$, $(7, 13)$, and $(8, 21)$. The Fibonacci function is not one-to-one because $(1, 1) \in$ fib and $(2, 1) \in$ fib, but $1 \neq 2$. It's not onto since, for example, 4 is not in the range.

7. 1. The number of rabbits available on December 25 is the number in existence after eleven months. This is the **twelfth** term of the Fibonacci sequence, 144.

   2. The number in existence after twelve months is the **thirteenth** term of the Fibonacci sequence, 233.

8. $a_1 = 1$; $a_2 = 1 + a_1 = 1 + 1 = 2$; $a_3 = 1 + a_{10} = 1 + 1 + a_5 = 2 + 1 + a_{16} = 3 + a_{16}$. Now $a_{16} = 1 + a_8 = 1 + 1 + a_4 = 1 + 1 + 1 + a_2 = 3 + 2 = 5$, so that $a_3 = 3 + 5 = 8$. Continuing, $a_4 = 1 + a_2 = 3$; $a_5 = 1 + a_{16} = 1 + 5 = 6$; $a_6 = 1 + a_3 = 1 + 8 = 9$. The first six terms are $1, 2, 8, 3, 6, 9$.

True/False Questions

(Answers can be found in the back of the book.)

1. If $a_1 = 5$ and $a_{k+1} = 3a_k$ for $k \geq 1$, then $a_4 = 135$.
2. If $a_0 = 5$ and $a_k = 3a_{k-1}$ for $k \geq 1$, then $a_4 = 135$.
3. If $a_1 = 5$ and $a_k = 3a_{k-1}$ for $k \geq 2$, then $a_4 = 135$.
4. The fourth term of the arithmetic sequence with $a = 3$ and $d = 4$ is 19.
5. The sum of the first four terms of the arithmetic sequence with $a = 3$ and $d = 4$ is 36.
6. The formula $S = \dfrac{a(1 - r^n)}{1 - r}$ for the sum of the first n terms of a geometric sequence holds for all values of a and r.
7. The sequence $1, 1, 1, \ldots$ is both an arithmetic sequence and a geometric sequence.
8. The Fibonacci sequence arose from a problem concerning the breeding of sheep.
9. The Fibonacci sequence is defined by $f_0 = f_1 = 1$ and, for $k \geq 2$, $f_k = f_{k-1} + f_{k-2}$.
10. The Fibonacci sequence is defined by $f_1 = f_2 = 1$ and, for $k \geq 3$, $f_k = f_{k-1} + f_{k-2}$.

Exercises

*The answers to exercises marked [BB] can be found in the **B**ack of the **B**ook.*

1. Give recursive definitions of each of the following sequences:
   (a) [BB] $1, 5, 5^2, 5^3, 5^4, \ldots$
   (b) $5, 3, 1, -1, -3, \ldots$
   (c) $4, 1, 3, -2, 5, -7, 12, -19, 31, \ldots$
   (d) $1, 2, 0, 3, -1, 4, -2, \ldots$

2. (a) [BB] Find the first seven terms of the sequence $\{a_n\}$ defined by $a_1 = 16$, and for $k \geq 1$,
   $$a_{k+1} = \begin{cases} 1 & \text{if } a_k = 1 \\ \frac{1}{2}a_k & \text{if } a_k \text{ is even} \\ \frac{1}{2}(a_k - 1) & \text{if } a_k \neq 1 \text{ is odd.} \end{cases}$$
   (b) Repeat part (a) with $a_1 = 17$.
   (c) Repeat part (a) with $a_1 = 18$.
   (d) Repeat part (a) with $a_1 = 100$.

3. Let $a_1, a_2, a_3, \ldots$ be the sequence defined by $a_1 = 1$, $a_{k+1} = 3a_k$ for $k \geq 1$. Prove that $a_n = 3^{n-1}$ for all $n \geq 1$.

4. [BB] Suppose $a_1, a_2, a_3, \ldots$ is a sequence of integers such that $a_1 = 0$ and, for $n > 1$, $a_n = n^3 + a_{n-1}$. Prove that $a_n = \frac{(n-1)(n+2)(n^2+n+2)}{4}$ for every integer $n \geq 1$.

5. Define the sequence $a_1, a_2, a_3, \ldots$ by $a_1 = 0, a_2 = \frac{1}{2}$ and $a_{k+2} = \frac{1}{2}(a_k + a_{k+1})$ for $k \geq 1$. Find the first seven terms of this sequence. Prove that
   $$a_n = \frac{1}{3}\left(1 - \left(-\frac{1}{2}\right)^{n-1}\right)$$
   for every $n \geq 1$.

6. [BB] Let $a_1, a_2, a_3, \ldots$ be the sequence defined by $a_1 = 1$ and, for $n > 1, a_n = 2a_{n-1} + 1$. Write down the first six terms of this sequence. Guess a formula for a_n and prove that your guess is correct.

7. Let $a_1, a_2, a_3, \ldots$ be the sequence defined by $a_1 = \frac{3}{2}$ and $a_n = 5a_{n-1} - 1$ for $n \geq 2$. Write down the first six terms of this sequence. Guess a formula for a_n and prove that your guess is correct.

8. Suppose $a_0, a_1, a_2, \ldots$ is a sequence such that $a_0 = a_1 = 1$ and, for $n \geq 1, a_{n+1} = n(a_n + a_{n-1})$.
   (a) [BB] Find $a_2, a_3, a_4,$ and a_5.
   (b) Guess a formula for a_n, valid for $n \geq 0$, and use mathematical induction to prove that your guess is correct.

9. [BB] Consider the sequence defined by $a_1 = 1, a_{n+1} = (n + 1)^2 - a_n$ for $n \geq 1$. Find the first six terms. Guess a general formula for a_n and prove that your answer is correct.

10. Let $a_1, a_2, a_3, \ldots$ be the sequence defined by $a_1 = 1$, $a_{k+1} = (k + 1)a_k$ for $k \geq 1$. Find a formula for a_n and prove that your formula is correct.

11. [BB] Suppose $a_1, a_2, a_3, \ldots$ is a sequence of integers such that $a_1 = 0, a_2 = 1$ and, for $n > 2, a_n = 4a_{n-2}$. Guess a formula for a_n and prove that your guess is correct.

12. A sequence is defined recursively by $a_0 = 2, a_1 = 3$, and $a_n = 3a_{n-1} - 2a_{n-2}$ for $n \geq 2$.
    (a) Find the first five terms of this sequence.
    (b) Guess a formula for a_n.
    (c) Verify that your guess in (b) is correct.
    (d) Find a formula for a_n that involves only one preceding term.

13. [BB] Let $a_1, a_2, a_3, \ldots$ be the sequence defined by $a_1 = 1, a_2 = 0$ and, for $n > 2, a_n = 4a_{n-1} - 4a_{n-2}$. Prove that $a_n = 2^n(1 - \frac{n}{2})$ for all $n \geq 1$.

14. Let $a_1, a_2, a_3, \ldots$ be the sequence defined by
    $$a_1 = 1, \quad \text{and for } k \geq 1, \quad a_{k+1} = k^2 a_k.$$
    Find the first six terms of this sequence. Guess a general formula for a_n and prove your answer by mathematical induction.

15. Select two points on a circle and join them with a straight line. The circle has been divided into regions. Select three points and join each pair with a line; the circle is divided into four regions. Select four points and join each pair; the circle is divided into eight regions.

    (a) If five points are selected on a circle and each pair is joined with a line, into how many regions has the circle been divided?
    (b) What do you think happens in general with n points? Guess a formula and investigate with $n = 6$.
    [This exercise emphasizes the need for care when drawing inferences from "obvious" patterns.]

5.2.4 DEFINITION   The *powers of a function* $f : A \rightarrow A$ are defined recursively by
$$f^1 = f \quad \text{and, for } n > 1, \quad f^n = f \circ f^{n-1}. \quad ❖$$

16. Suppose $f : \mathsf{N} \rightarrow \mathsf{N}$ is defined by
    $$f(m) = \begin{cases} \frac{2m}{3} & \text{if } m \equiv 0 \pmod 3 \\ \frac{4m-1}{3} & \text{if } m \equiv 1 \pmod 3 \\ \frac{4m+1}{3} & \text{if } m \equiv 2 \pmod 3. \end{cases}$$
    (a) Prove that f is one-to-one and onto.
    (b) [BB] Find the first ten terms of the sequence $f^n(1)$.

(c) Find the sequence $f^n(2), n \geq 1$.

(d) Find the sequence $f^n(4), n \geq 1$.

(e) Find the first ten terms of the sequence $f^n(8), n \geq 1$.[3]

17. Define $g: \mathbb{N} \to \mathbb{N}$ by

$$g(m) = \begin{cases} \frac{m}{2} & \text{if } m \text{ is even} \\ \frac{3m+1}{2} & \text{if } m \text{ is odd.} \end{cases}$$

This function is known as the "$3m + 1$" function. It is suspected that for **any** starting number m the sequence $g(m), g^2(m), g^3(m), \ldots$ eventually terminates with 1. Verify this assertion for each of the five integers $m = 341$, 96, 104, 336, and 133.[4]

18. Consider the arithmetic sequence with first term 2 and common difference 3.

(a) [BB] Find the first ten terms and the 123rd term of this sequence.

(b) [BB] Does 752 belong to this sequence? If so, what is the number of the term where it appears?

(c) Repeat (b) for 1023 and 4127.

(d) [BB] Find the sum of the first 75 terms of this sequence.

19. [BB] Consider the arithmetic sequence with first term 7 and common difference $-\frac{1}{2}$.

(a) Find the 17th and 92nd terms.

(b) Find the sum of the first 38 terms.

20. An arithmetic sequence begins 116, 109, 102.

(a) Find the 300th term of this sequence.

(b) Determine whether -480 belongs to this sequence. If it does, what is its term number?

(c) Find the sum of the first 300 terms of the sequence.

21. The arithmetic sequence $4, 15, 26, 37, \ldots$ begins with a *perfect square*, that is, an integer of the form k^2, where k is also an integer. Find the next three perfect squares in this sequence.

22. Establish formulas (6) [BB] and (7) for the nth term and the sum of the first n terms of the arithmetic sequence with first term a and common difference d.

23. The sum of the first ten terms of an arithmetic sequence is twice the sum of the first six terms, and the sum of the first twenty terms is 1360. Find the sum of n terms.

24. The first four terms x, y, z, w of an arithmetic sequence satisfy $x + y + z + w = 8$ and $xw + yz = -2$. Find all possible values of x, y, z, w.

25. [BB] Consider the geometric sequence with first term 59,049 and common ratio $-\frac{1}{3}$.

(a) Find the first ten terms and the 33rd term of this sequence.

(b) Find the sum of the first 12 terms.

26. Consider the geometric sequence that begins -3072, 1536, -768.

(a) Find the 13th and 20th terms of this sequence.

(b) Find the sum of the first nine terms.

27. If the first term of a geometric sequence is 48 and the sixth term is $-\frac{3}{2}$, find the sum of the first ten terms.

28. (a) [BB] Find, to four decimal places, the 129th term of the geometric sequence that begins $-0.00001240, 0.00001364$.

(b) [BB] Find the approximate sum of the first 129 terms of the sequence in (a).

29. [BB] Verify formula (8) for the sum of n terms of a geometric sequence with first term a and common ratio $r \neq 1$.

30. Consider the sequence defined recursively by $a_1 = 1$ and, for $n > 1$, $a_n = \sum_{i=1}^{n-1} a_i$. Write down the first six terms of this sequence, guess a formula for a_n valid for $n \geq 2$, and prove your answer.

31. (a) Find the sum of 18 terms of the geometric sequence with first term $\frac{7}{1024}$ and common ratio 8.

(b) [BB] Suppose $|r| < 1$. Explain why the sum of the first n terms of the geometric sequence with first term a and common ratio r is approximately $\frac{a}{1-r}$.

(c) [BB] Approximate $\sum_{k=0}^{100} \frac{3}{2^k}$.

(d) Find the approximate sum of the first 1 million terms of the geometric sequence that begins 144, 48, 16.

32. (a) Find the 19th and 100th terms of the geometric sequence that has first term 98,415 and common ratio $\frac{1}{3}$.

(b) Find the sum of the first 15 terms of the sequence in (a).

(c) Find the approximate sum of the first 10,000 terms of the sequence in (a).

33. Given that each sum below is the sum of part of an arithmetic or geometric sequence, find each sum.

(a) [BB] $75 + 71 + 67 + 63 + \cdots + (-61)$

(b) [BB] $75 + 15 + 3 + \frac{3}{5} + \cdots + \frac{3}{5^7}$

(c) $-52 - 41 - 30 - 19 + \cdots + 949$

(d) $1 - \frac{1}{2} + \frac{1}{4} - \frac{1}{8} + \cdots + \frac{1}{2^{60}}$

(e) $2 + 6 + 18 + 54 + \cdots + 354{,}294$

34. Find each of the following sums:

(a) [BB] $1004 + 1001 + 998 + \cdots - 394 - 397$

(b) $324 - 216 + 144 - 96 + \cdots - \dfrac{131{,}072}{177{,}147}$

---

[3] It is unknown whether the terms of this sequence ever repeat.

[4] While this conjecture has been established for all integers $m < 2^{40} \approx 10^{12}$, it is unknown whether it holds for all integers! This problem has attracted the interest of many people, some of whom have offered a sizable monetary reward for its solution! We refer the interested reader to the excellent article "The $3x + 1$ Problem and Its Generalizations," by Jeffrey C. Lagarias, *American Mathematical Monthly* **92** (1985) no. 1, 1–23.

35. [BB] Is it possible for an arithmetic sequence to be also a geometric sequence? Explain your answer.

36. Given positive numbers a and b, find numbers $x_1, x_2, \ldots, x_n$ such $a, x_1, x_2, \ldots, x_n, b$ are the first terms of

(a) [BB] an arithmetic sequence;

(b) a geometric sequence.

37. Prove that the sum of n terms of the sequence $1, 1+r, 1+r+r^2, 1+r+r^2+r^3, \ldots$ is $\dfrac{1}{(1-r)^2}[n-(n+1)r+r^{n+1}]$, for $r \neq 1$.

38. (a) Using calculus, or by other means, find the sum $1 + 2x + 3x^2 + 4x^3 + \cdots + nx^{n-1}$.

(b) Assuming $|x| < 1$, find $1 + 2x + 3x^2 + 4x^3 + \cdots$.

(c) Assuming $|x| < 1$, find $1 + 3x + 5x^2 + 7x^3 + \cdots$.

(d) Assuming $|x| < 1$, find $1 + 3x + 6x^2 + 9x^3 + 12x^4 + \cdots$.

39. Find $1 + \frac{3}{4} + \frac{7}{16} + \frac{15}{64} + \frac{31}{256} + \cdots$.
[*Hint:* This is $a_1 + a_2 + a_3 + \cdots$. Find a formula for a_k.]

40. A bank account pays interest at the rate of $100i\%$ a year. Assume an initial balance of P, which accumulates to s_n after n years.

(a) Find a recursive definition for s_n.

(b) Find a formula for s_n.

41. [BB] Maurice borrows $1000 at an interest rate of 15% compounded annually.

(a) How much does Maurice owe after two years?

(b) In how many years will the debt grow to $2000?

42. On January 1, 2001, you have $50 in a savings account that pays interest at the rate of 1% per month. At the end of January and at the end of each month thereafter, you deposit $56 to this account. Assuming no withdrawals, what will be your balance on January 1, 2002?

43. On June 1, you win $1 million in a lottery and immediately acquire numerous "friends," one of whom offers you the deal of a lifetime. In return for the million, she'll pay you a cent today, two cents tomorrow, four cents the next day, eight cents the next, and so on, stopping with the last payment on June 21.

(a) Assuming you take this deal, how much money will you receive on June 21?

(b) Should you take the deal? Explain.

(c) Would you take the deal if payments continued for the entire month of June?

44. Define a sequence $\{a_n\}$ recursively as follows:

$$a_0 = 0, \quad \text{and for } n > 0, \quad a_n = a_{\lfloor n/5 \rfloor} + a_{\lfloor 3n/5 \rfloor} + n.$$

Prove that $a_n \leq 20n$ for all $n \geq 0$. (Recall that $\lfloor x \rfloor$ denotes the floor of the real number x. See paragraph 3.1.7.)

45. The number $\Phi = \dfrac{1+\sqrt{5}}{2} \approx 1.618$ is known as the *golden mean*. It has many remarkable properties. For instance, the geometric sequence $1, \Phi, \Phi^2, \ldots$ satisfies the Fibonacci recurrence relation $a_{n+1} = a_n + a_{n-1}$. Establish this fact.

46. [BB] Suppose we think of the Fibonacci sequence as going backward as well as forward. What seven terms precede $1, 1, 2, 3, 5, 8, \ldots$? How is f_{-n} related to f_n?

47. [BB] Let $\{f_n\}$ denote the Fibonacci sequence. Prove that $f_{n+1} f_n = \sum_{i=1}^{n} f_i^2$ for all $n \geq 1$.

48. Represent the Fibonacci sequence by $f_1 = f_2 = 1$, $f_n = f_{n-1} + f_{n-2}$ for $n > 2$.

(a) Verify the formula $f_1 + f_2 + f_3 + \cdots + f_n = f_{n+2} - 1$ for $n = 4, 5, 6$.

(b) Prove that the formula in (a) is valid for all $n \geq 1$.

49. Let $f_1, f_2, \ldots$ be the Fibonacci sequence as defined in 5.2.3. Use the definition of the Fibonacci sequence to prove that $f_n < 2^n$ for every $n \geq 1$. (You will need the strong form of the Principle of Mathematical Induction.)

50. Let $f_1, f_2, f_3, \ldots$ be the terms of the Fibonacci sequence as defined in 5.2.3. Prove that $f_n > (\frac{5}{4})^n$ for all $n \geq 3$. (You will need the strong form of the Principle of Mathematical Induction.)

51. [BB] What is wrong with the following argument, which purports to prove that all the Fibonacci numbers after the first two are even?

> Let f_n denote the nth term of the Fibonacci sequence. We prove that f_n is even for all $n \geq 3$ using the strong form of the Principle of Mathematical Induction. The Fibonacci sequence begins $1, 1, 2$. Certainly, $f_3 = 2$ is even and so the assertion is true for $n_0 = 3$. Now let $k > 3$ be an integer and assume that the assertion is true for all n, $3 \leq n < k$; that is, assume that f_n is even for all $n < k$. We wish to show that the assertion is true for $n = k$, that f_k is even. But $f_k = f_{k-1} + f_{k-2}$. Applying the induction hypothesis to $k - 1$ and to $k - 2$, we conclude that each of f_{k-1} and f_{k-2} is even, hence, so is the sum. By the Principle of Mathematical Induction, f_n is even for all $n \geq 3$.

52. Let $f_1 = f_2 = 1$, $f_k = f_{k-1} + f_{k-2}$ for $k > 2$ be the Fibonacci sequence. Which terms of this sequence are even? Prove your answer.

53. For $n \geq 1$, let a_n denote the number of ways to express n as the sum of natural numbers, taking order into account. For example, $3 = 1+1+1 = 2+1 = 1+2$, so $a_3 = 4$.

(a) [BB] Find the first five terms of the sequence $\{a_n\}$.

(b) Guess and then establish a formula for a_n.

54. For $n \geq 1$, let b_n denote the number of ways to express n as the sum of 1's and 2's, taking order into account. Thus, $b_4 = 5$ because $4 = 1+1+1+1 = 2+2 = 2+1+1 = 1+1+2 = 1+2+1$.

(a) Find the first five terms of the sequence $\{b_n\}$.

(b) Find a recursive definition for b_n and identify this sequence.

55. (a) [BB] Let a_n be the number of ways of forming a line of n people distinguished only by sex. For example, there are four possible lines of two people, MM, MF, FM, FF, so $a_2 = 4$. Find a recurrence relation satisfied by a_n and identify the sequence $a_1, a_2, a_3, \ldots$.

(b) Let a_n be the number of ways in which a line of n people can be formed such that no two males are standing beside each other. For example, $a_3 = 5$ because there are five ways to form lines of three people with no two males beside each other: FFF, MFF, FMF, FFM, MFM. Find a recurrence relation satisfied by a_n and identify the sequence $a_1, a_2, a_3, \ldots$.

56. Define the Fibonacci sequence by $f_1 = f_2 = 1$, $f_{n+1} = f_n + f_{n-1}$ for $n \geq 2$.

(a) Prove that $\gcd(f_{n+1}, f_n) = 1$ for all $n \geq 1$.

(b) Prove that $f_n = f_{n-m+1} f_m + f_{n-m} f_{m-1}$ for any positive integers n and m with $n > m > 1$.

(c) Prove that, for any positive integers n and m, the greatest common divisor of f_n and f_m is $f_{\gcd(n,m)}$.

57. Suppose u_n and v_n are sequences defined recursively by
$$u_1 = 0, \ v_1 = 1,$$

and, for $n \geq 1$,

$$u_{n+1} = \tfrac{1}{2}(u_n + v_n), \ v_{n+1} = \tfrac{1}{4}(u_n + 3v_n).$$

(a) Prove that $v_n - u_n = \frac{1}{4^{n-1}}$ for $n \geq 1$.

(b) Prove that u_n is an increasing sequence; that is, $u_{n+1} > u_n$ for all $n \geq 1$.

(c) Prove that v_n is a decreasing sequence; that is, $v_{n+1} < v_n$ for all $n \geq 1$.

(d) Prove that $u_n = \frac{2}{3} - \frac{1}{6}\left(\frac{1}{4^{n-2}}\right)$ for all $n \geq 1$.
(This problem is taken from a Portuguese examination designed to test the level of mathematical knowledge of graduating high school students. It was reprinted in *Focus*, the newsletter of the Mathematical Association of America **13**, no. 3, June 1993, p. 13.)

58. (For students who have had a course in linear algebra) Give a recursive definition of the "determinant" of an $n \times n$ matrix, for $n \geq 1$.

5.3 Solving Recurrence Relations; The Characteristic Polynomial

Recursively defined sequences were introduced in the previous section. Given a particular recurrence relation and certain initial conditions, you were encouraged to guess a formula for the nth term and prove that your guess was correct. Guessing is an important tool in mathematics and a skill that can be sharpened through practice, but we now confess that there is a definite procedure for solving most of the recurrence relations we have encountered so far.

In this section, we describe a procedure for solving recurrence relations of the form

$$(11) \qquad a_n = ra_{n-1} + sa_{n-2} + f(n),$$

where r and s are constants and $f(n)$ is some function of n. Such a recurrence relation is called a *second-order linear recurrence relation with constant coefficients*. If $f(n) = 0$, the relation is called *homogeneous*. *Second order* refers to the fact that the recurrence relation (11) defines a_n as a function of the two terms preceding it, *linear* to the fact that the terms a_{n-1} and a_{n-2} appear by themselves, to the first power, and with constant coefficients. You should consult more specialized books in combinatorics for a general treatment of constant coefficient recurrence relations, where a_n is a function of any number of terms of the form ca_{n-i}, $c \in \mathbf{R}$.[5]

EXAMPLE 18   Here are some second-order linear recurrence relations with constant coefficients.

- $a_n = a_{n-1} + a_{n-2}$, the recurrence relation that appears in the definition of the Fibonacci sequence. This is homogeneous with $r = s = 1$. Notice that we have modified slightly the definition $a_{n+1} = a_n + a_{n-1}$ given in paragraph 5.2.3 so that it is readily seen to be of the type we are considering here.
- $a_n = 5a_{n-1} - 6a_{n-2} + n$. Here $r = 5$, $s = -6$, $f(n) = n$.
- $a_n = 3a_{n-1}$. This is homogeneous with $r = 3$, $s = 0$.

---

[5]See, for example, Alan Tucker, *Applied Combinatorics*. New York: Wiley, 1980.

EXAMPLE 19   Consider the following two recurrence relations.

- $a_n = 5a_{n-1} - 3a_{n-3}$
- $a_n = a_{n-1}a_{n-2} + n^2$

Neither is of interest to us in this section. The first is not second order while the second is not linear (because of the product $a_{n-1}a_{n-2}$).

With the homogeneous recurrence relation $a_n = ra_{n-1} + sa_{n-2}$, which can be rewritten in the form

$$a_n - ra_{n-1} - sa_{n-2} = 0,$$

we associate the quadratic polynomial

$$x^2 - rx - s,$$

which is called the *characteristic polynomial* of the recurrence relation.[6] Its roots are called the *characteristic roots* of the recurrence relation. For example, the recurrence relation $a_n = 5a_{n-1} - 6a_{n-2}$ has characteristic polynomial $x^2 - 5x + 6$ and characteristic roots 2 and 3.

The following theorem, whose proof is left to the exercises, shows how to solve any second-order linear **homogeneous** recurrence relation with constant coefficients.

5.3.1 THEOREM   Let x_1 and x_2 be the roots of the polynomial $x^2 - rx - s$. Then the solution of the recurrence relation $a_n = ra_{n-1} + sa_{n-2}, n \geq 2$, is

$$a_n = \begin{cases} c_1 x_1^n + c_2 x_2^n & \text{if } x_1 \neq x_2 \\ c_1 x^n + c_2 n x^n & \text{if } x_1 = x_2 = x. \end{cases}$$

In each case, c_1 and c_2 are constants determined by initial conditions.

PROBLEM 20.   Solve the recurrence relation $a_n = 5a_{n-1} - 6a_{n-2}, n \geq 2$, given $a_0 = -3, a_1 = -2$.

Solution. The characteristic polynomial $x^2 - 5x + 6$ has distinct roots $x_1 = 2, x_2 = 3$. Theorem 5.3.1 tells us that the solution is $a_n = c_1(2^n) + c_2(3^n)$. Since $a_0 = -3$, we must have $c_1(2^0) + c_2(3^0) = -3$ and, since $a_1 = -2$, we have $c_1(2^1) + c_2(3^1) = -2$. Therefore,

$$\begin{aligned} c_1 + c_2 &= -3 \\ 2c_1 + 3c_2 &= -2. \end{aligned}$$

Solving, we have $c_1 = -7, c_2 = 4$, so the solution is $a_n = -7(2^n) + 4(3^n)$. (You are encouraged to verify that this formula is correct.)

PROBLEM 21.   Solve the recurrence $a_n = 4a_{n-1} - 4a_{n-2}, n \geq 2$, with initial conditions $a_0 = 1, a_1 = 4$. (We solved this by guesswork and ingenuity in Problem 12.)

Solution. The characteristic polynomial $x^2 - 4x + 4$ has the repeated root $x = 2$. Hence, the solution is $a_n = c_1(2^n) + c_2 n(2^n)$. The initial conditions yield $c_1 = 1$, $2c_1 + 2c_2 = 4$, so $c_2 = 1$. Thus, $a_n = 2^n + n(2^n) = (n+1)2^n$.

PROBLEM 22.   Find a formula for the nth term of the Fibonacci sequence.

---

[6]The term *characteristic polynomial* has its origins in linear algebra. See Remark 5.3.3-2.

Solution. To obtain the "nicest" formula, we take for initial conditions $a_0 = a_1 = 1$, rather than $a_1 = a_2 = 1$, and solve the recurrence relation $a_n = a_{n-1} + a_{n-2}, n \geq 2$. The nth term is then a_{n-1}. The characteristic polynomial $x^2 - x - 1$ has distinct roots $\frac{1 \pm \sqrt{5}}{2}$. Hence, the solution to our recurrence relation is

$$a_n = c_1 \left(\frac{1+\sqrt{5}}{2} \right)^n + c_2 \left(\frac{1-\sqrt{5}}{2} \right)^n .$$

The initial conditions give

$$c_1 + c_2 = 1$$

$$c_1 \left(\frac{1+\sqrt{5}}{2} \right) + c_2 \left(\frac{1-\sqrt{5}}{2} \right) = 1$$

yielding $c_1 = \frac{1}{\sqrt{5}} \left(\frac{1+\sqrt{5}}{2} \right)$ and $c_2 = -\frac{1}{\sqrt{5}} \left(\frac{1-\sqrt{5}}{2} \right)$. Thus, the solution is

$$\begin{aligned} a_n &= \frac{1}{\sqrt{5}} \left(\frac{1+\sqrt{5}}{2} \right) \left(\frac{1+\sqrt{5}}{2} \right)^n - \frac{1}{\sqrt{5}} \left(\frac{1-\sqrt{5}}{2} \right) \left(\frac{1-\sqrt{5}}{2} \right)^n \\ &= \frac{1}{\sqrt{5}} \left(\frac{1+\sqrt{5}}{2} \right)^{n+1} - \frac{1}{\sqrt{5}} \left(\frac{1-\sqrt{5}}{2} \right)^{n+1} . \end{aligned}$$

The nth term of the Fibonacci sequence is

$$a_{n-1} = \frac{1}{\sqrt{5}} \left(\frac{1+\sqrt{5}}{2} \right)^n - \frac{1}{\sqrt{5}} \left(\frac{1-\sqrt{5}}{2} \right)^n .$$

In Exercise 21, we ask you to use this result to obtain the simpler formula (9) on page 165.

 Pause 9   Why is the real number $\frac{1}{\sqrt{5}} \left(\frac{1+\sqrt{5}}{2} \right)^n - \frac{1}{\sqrt{5}} \left(\frac{1-\sqrt{5}}{2} \right)^n$ an integer for any $n \geq 1$? ∎

We now turn our attention to the general second-order recurrence relation $a_n = ra_{n-1} + sa_{n-2} + f(n)$ and show that the solution is closely related to the corresponding homogeneous recurrence relation.

Suppose we could find one specific solution p_n to the given recurrence relation. (Such a function p_n is called a *particular solution*.) Thus, $p_n = rp_{n-1} + sp_{n-2} + f(n)$. Suppose t_n were another solution. Then we would also have $t_n = rt_{n-1} + st_{n-1} + f(n)$ and, subtracting,

$$t_n - p_n = r(t_{n-1} - p_{n-1}) + s(t_{n-2} - p_{n-2}).$$

This equation shows that $t_n - p_n$ satisfies the homogeneous recurrence relation $a_n = ra_{n-1} + sa_{n-2}$. Setting $t_n - p_n = q_n$, we have $t_n = p_n + q_n$, where p_n is a particular solution to the given recurrence relation and q_n satisfies the associated homogeneous recurrence relation. This is the content of our next theorem.

5.3.2 THEOREM   Let p_n be any particular solution to the recurrence relation $a_n = ra_{n-1} + sa_{n-2} + f(n)$, ignoring initial conditions. Let q_n be the general solution to the homogeneous recurrence $a_n = ra_{n-1} + sa_{n-2}$ given by Theorem 5.3.1, again ignoring initial conditions. Then $a_n = p_n + q_n$ is the general solution to the recurrence relation $a_n = ra_{n-1} + sa_{n-2} + f(n)$. The initial conditions determine the constants in q_n.

As we have seen, the result of this theorem seems plausible. In the exercises, you will be invited to supply a proof. The main point of the theorem is that, once some particular solution to the recurrence has been found, the problem is reduced to the homogeneous case, which we have already considered. Finding a particular solution can be difficult. As we shall see, a useful trick is to try a formula for p_n that is of the same type as $f(n)$. For example, if $f(n)$ is a linear function, try a linear function for p_n.

PROBLEM 23. Solve the recurrence relation $a_n = -3a_{n-1} + n$, $n \geq 1$, where $a_0 = 1$.

Solution. Since $f(n) = n$ is linear, we try a linear function for p_n; that is, we set $p_n = a + bn$ and attempt to determine a and b. Putting this expression for p_n in the given recurrence relation, we obtain

$$a + bn = -3[a + b(n-1)] + n = -3a + 3b + (1 - 3b)n.$$

This equation will hold if $a = -3a + 3b$ and $b = 1 - 3b$, which is the same as $a = \frac{3}{16}$, $b = \frac{1}{4}$. We conclude that $p_n = \frac{3}{16} + \frac{1}{4}n$ is a particular solution to the recurrence, ignoring initial conditions.

   The corresponding homogeneous recurrence relation in this case is $a_n = -3a_{n-1}$, whose characteristic polynomial is $x^2 + 3x$. The characteristic roots are -3 and 0, so the solution to the homogeneous recurrence relation is

$$q_n = c_1(-3)^n + c_2(0^n) = c_1(-3)^n.$$

Thus,

$$a_n = p_n + q_n = \frac{3}{16} + \frac{1}{4}n + c_1(-3)^n.$$

Since $a_0 = 1$, $\frac{3}{16} + \frac{1}{4}(0) + c_1(-3)^0 = 1$; that is, $\frac{3}{16} + c_1 = 1$. Thus, $c_1 = \frac{13}{16}$ and the solution is $a_n = \frac{3}{16} + \frac{1}{4}n + \frac{13}{16}(-3)^n$.

PROBLEM 24. Solve $a_n = -2a_{n-1} + 3a_{n-2} + 6^n$, $n \geq 2$, given $a_0 = -1$, $a_1 = 5$.

Solution. In looking for a particular solution, it seems reasonable to try $p_n = a(6^n)$, where a is a constant to be determined. Substituting into the recurrence relation, we get $a(6^n) = -2a(6^{n-1}) + 3a(6^{n-2}) + 6^n$. Dividing by 6^{n-2} gives $36a = -12a + 3a + 36$, so $45a = 36$ and $a = \frac{36}{45} = \frac{4}{5}$. The reader should confirm that $p_n = \frac{4}{5}(6^n)$ is a particular solution.

   Next we solve the homogeneous recurrence relation $a_n = -2a_{n-1} + 3a_{n-2}$. The characteristic polynomial $x^2 + 2x - 3$ has distinct roots 1 and -3, so the solution is $q_n = c_1(1)^n + c_2(-3)^n = c_1 + c_2(-3)^n$. By Theorem 5.3.2, the given recurrence relation has the solution

$$a_n = p_n + q_n = \frac{4}{5}(6^n) + c_1 + c_2(-3)^n.$$

The initial conditions give

$$a_0 = -1 = \frac{4}{5} + c_1 + c_2$$

$$a_1 = 5 = \frac{4}{5}(6) + c_1 - 3c_2;$$

hence, $c_2 = -\frac{1}{2}$ and $c_1 = -\frac{13}{10}$. Our solution is $a_n = \frac{4}{5}(6^n) - \frac{13}{10} - \frac{1}{2}(-3)^n$.

5.3.3 REMARKS

1. The characteristic polynomials that have appeared in this section have all had real (in fact, integer) roots. Is it possible for some recurrence relations to have associated charcteristic polynomials with imaginery roots? Consider, for example, the sequence $1, 4, -1, -4, 1, 4, -1, -4, \ldots$, which can be defined by $a_0 = 1$, $a_1 = 4$ and, for $n \geq 2$, $a_n = -a_{n-2}$. The characteristic polynomial associated with the recurrence relation $a_n = -a_{n-2}$ is $x^2 + 1$ whose roots are $\pm i$. By Theorem 5.3.1, the solution to the given recurrence is $a_n = c_1 i^n + c_2(-i)^n$.

The initial conditions give $a_0 = 1 = c_1 + c_2$, $a_1 = 4 = c_1 i - c_2 i$, so $c_1 = \frac{1}{2}(1 - 4i)$, $c_2 = \frac{1}{2}(1 + 4i)$. The solution is $a_n = \frac{1}{2}(1 - 4i)i^n + \frac{1}{2}(1 + 4i)(-i)^n$. (See Exercise 19 for more instances of characteristic polynomials with nonreal roots.)

2. Students who have taken some linear algebra may wonder if our use of the term characteristic polynomial is connected to its use in the study of eigenvalues. It indeed is! The recurrence relation $a_n = ra_{n-1} + sa_{n-2}$ can be expressed in matrix form $\begin{bmatrix} a_n \\ a_{n-1} \end{bmatrix} = \begin{bmatrix} r & s \\ 1 & 0 \end{bmatrix}\begin{bmatrix} a_{n-1} \\ a_{n-2} \end{bmatrix}$, which is $v_n = Av_{n-1}$, with $v_n = \begin{bmatrix} a_n \\ a_{n-1} \end{bmatrix}$ and $A = \begin{bmatrix} r & s \\ 1 & 0 \end{bmatrix}$. The characteristic polynomial of A is $\det\begin{bmatrix} r - x & s \\ 1 & -x \end{bmatrix} = x^2 - rx - s$, which is the characteristic polynomial of the recurrence relation.

Answer to Pause

9. All the terms of the Fibonacci sequence are integers!

True/False Questions

(Answers can be found in the back of the book.)

1. The recurrence relation $a_n = 3a_{n-1} + 7a_{n-2} + n^3$ can be solved by the methods of this section.

2. The recurrence relation $a_n = 5a_{n-2} - 7a_{n-3} + 2n$ can be solved by the methods of this section.

3. The recurrence relation $a_n = 2a_{n-1} + na_{n-2}$ can be solved by the methods of this section.

4. The recurrence relation $a_n = a_{n-1}^2$ can be solved by the methods of this section.

5. The recurrence relation $a_n = 2a_{n-1} - a_{n-2} + 1$ is homogeneous.

6. A characteristic polynomial is associated with every second-order linear homogeneous recurrence relation with constant coefficients.

7. In this section, a formula is found for the nth term of the Fibonacci sequence.

8. $a_n = c_1$ is the general solution of the recurrence relation $a_n = a_{n-1}$.

9. $p_n = n$ is a particular solution of the recurrence relation $a_n = a_{n-1} + 1$.

10. $a_n = n + 1$ is the general solution of the recurrence relation $a_n = a_{n-1} + 1$, $a_0 = 1$.

Exercises

*The answers to exercises marked [BB] can be found in the **B**ack of the **B**ook.*

1. [BB] Solve the recurrence relation $a_n = a_{n-1} + 6a_{n-2}$, $n \geq 2$, given $a_0 = 1$, $a_1 = 3$.

2. Solve the recurrence relation $a_n = -6a_{n-1} + 7a_{n-2}$, $n \geq 2$, given $a_0 = 32$, $a_1 = -17$.

3. [BB] Solve the recurrence relation $a_n = 6a_{n-1} - 9a_{n-2}$, $n \geq 2$, given $a_0 = -5$, $a_1 = 3$.

4. Solve the recurrence relation $a_{n+1} = 7a_n - 10a_{n-1}$, $n \geq 2$, given $a_1 = 10$, $a_2 = 29$.

5. [BB] Solve the recurrence relation $a_n = -8a_{n-1} - a_{n-2}$, $n \geq 2$, given $a_0 = 0$, $a_1 = 1$.

6. Solve the recurrence relation $a_n = -5a_{n-1} + 6a_{n-2}$, $n \geq 2$, given $a_0 = 5$, $a_1 = 19$.

7. [BB] Solve the recurrence relation $a_{n+1} = 2a_n + 3a_{n-1}$, $n \geq 1$, given $a_0 = 0$, $a_1 = 8$.

8. Solve the recurrence relation $a_n = 2a_{n-1} - a_{n-2}$, $n \geq 2$, given $a_0 = 40$, $a_1 = 37$.

9. Solve the recurrence relation $9a_n = 6a_{n-1} - a_{n-2}$, $n \geq 2$, given $a_0 = 3$, $a_1 = -1$.

10. (a) [BB] Solve the recurrence relation $a_n = -2a_{n-1} + 15a_{n-2}$, $n \geq 2$, given $a_0 = 1$, $a_1 = -1$.

    (b) [BB] Solve the recurrence relation $a_n = -2a_{n-1} + 15a_{n-2} + 24$, $n \geq 2$, given $a_0 = 1$, $a_1 = -1$.

11. (a) Solve the recurrence relation $a_{n+1} = -8a_n - 16a_{n-1}$, $n \geq 1$, given $a_0 = 5$, $a_1 = 17$.

(b) Solve the recurrence relation $a_{n+1} = -8a_n - 16a_{n-1} + 5$, $n \geq 1$, given $a_0 = 2$, $a_1 = -1$.

12. (a) [BB] Solve the recurrence relation $a_n = 4a_{n-1}$, $n \geq 1$, given $a_0 = 1$.

(b) [BB] Solve the recurrence relation $a_n = 4a_{n-1} + 8^n$, $n \geq 1$, given $a_0 = 1$.

(c) [BB] Verify that your answer to (b) is correct.

13. (a) Solve the recurrence relation $a_n = 5a_{n-1} - 6a_{n-2}$, $n \geq 2$, given $a_0 = 2$, $a_1 = 11$.

(b) Solve the recurrence relation $a_n = 5a_{n-1} - 6a_{n-2} + 3n$, $n \geq 2$, given $a_0 = 2$, $a_1 = 14$.

(c) Verify that your answer to (b) is correct.

14. (a) Solve the recurrence relation $a_n = -6a_{n-1} - 9a_{n-2}$, $n \geq 2$, given $a_0 = 1$, $a_1 = -4$.

(b) Solve the recurrence relation $a_n = -6a_{n-1} - 9a_{n-2} + n^2 + 3n$, $n \geq 2$, given $a_0 = \frac{179}{128}$, $a_1 = -\frac{21}{128}$.

(c) Verify that your answer to (b) is correct.

15. (a) [BB] Solve the recurrence relation $a_n = 4a_{n-1} - 9$, $n \geq 1$, given $a_0 = 4$.

(b) [BB] Solve the recurrence relation $a_n = 4a_{n-1} + 3n2^n$, $n \geq 1$, given $a_0 = 4$.

16. Solve the recurrence relation $a_n = 4a_{n-1} - 4a_{n-2} + n$, $n \geq 2$, given $a_0 = 5$, $a_1 = 9$.

17. [BB] Solve the recurrence relation $a_n = 5a_{n-1} - 2a_{n-2} + 3n^2$, $n \geq 2$, given $a_0 = 0$, $a_1 = 3$.

18. Solve the recurrence relation $a_n = 2a_{n-1} + 3a_{n-2} + 5^n$, $n \geq 2$, given $a_0 = -2$, $a_1 = 1$.

19. Find the first ten terms of each of the following recursively defined sequences. Then find a general formula for a_n.

(a) [BB] $a_0 = 1$, $a_1 = 1$ and, for $n \geq 2$, $a_n = a_{n-1} - a_{n-2}$

(b) $a_0 = 1$, $a_1 = 1$ and, for $n \geq 2$, $a_n = 2a_{n-1} - 2a_{n-2}$

(c) $a_0 = -2$, $a_1 = 0$ and, for $n \geq 2$, $a_n = -2a_{n-1} - 10a_{n-2}$

20. Let $f_0, f_1, f_2, \ldots$ be the terms of the Fibonacci sequence. Compute the values of $\frac{1}{\sqrt{5}}\left(\frac{1+\sqrt{5}}{2}\right)^{n+1}$ for $n = 0, 1, \ldots, 9$ (to three decimal place accuracy) and compare with the values of $f_0, f_1, \ldots, f_9$. What do you observe?

21. [BB] Using the result of Problem 22, show that the nth term of the Fibonacci sequence is the integer closest to $\frac{1}{\sqrt{5}}\left(\frac{1+\sqrt{5}}{2}\right)^n$. This result was stated without proof in the text. [*Hint:* Show that $\left|\frac{1}{\sqrt{5}}\left(\frac{1-\sqrt{5}}{2}\right)\right| < \frac{1}{2}$.]

22. Let a_n denote the number of n-digit numbers, each of whose digits is 1, 2, 3, or 4 and in which the number of 1's is even.

(a) Find a recurrence relation for a_n.

(b) Find an explicit formula for a_n.

23. The Towers of Hanoi is a popular puzzle. It consists of three pegs and a number of discs of differing diameters, each with a hole in the center. The discs initially sit on one of the pegs in order of decreasing diameter (smallest at top, largest at bottom, as in Fig. 5.5), thus forming a triangular tower. The object is to move the tower to one of the other pegs by transferring the discs to any peg one at a time in such a way that no disc is ever placed upon a smaller one.

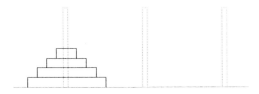

Figure 5.5 The Towers of Hanoi.

(a) Solve the puzzle when there are $n = 2$ discs and show your moves by completing a little table like that below. [The pegs are labeled A, B, C, and we have used an asterisk (∗) to denote an empty peg. The disks are numbered in order of increasing size, thus disk 1 is the smallest.]

	A	B	C
Initial position	1,2	∗	∗
Move 1	??	??	??
Move 2	??	??	??
etc.			

Also solve the puzzle, with a similar table, when $n = 3$. How many moves are required in each case?

(b) Give a recurrence relation for a_n, the number of moves required to transfer n discs from one peg to another.

(c) Find an explicit formula for a_n.

(d) Suppose we can move a disc a second. Estimate the time required to transfer the discs if $n = 8$, $n = 16$, $n = 32$, and $n = 64$.

24. Suppose we modify the traditional rules for the Towers of Hanoi as described in the preceding question by requiring that one move discs only to an **adjacent** peg. Answer all four parts of the previous question for this new version of the puzzle.

25. [BB] Let $a_n = ra_{n-1} + sa_{n-2}$, $n \geq 2$, be a second-order homogeneous recurrence relation with constant coefficients.

(a) If x is a root of the characteristic polynomial and c is any constant, show that $a_n = cx^n$ satisfies the given recurrence relation for $n \geq 2$.

(b) If p_n and q_n both satisfy the given recurrence for $n \geq 2$, show that $a_n = p_n + q_n$ also satisfies the recurrence for $n \geq 2$.

(c) Using (a) and (b), prove Theorem 5.3.1 for the case where the characteristic polynomial has distinct roots.

26. Let $a_n = ra_{n-1} + sa_{n-2}$, $n \geq 2$, be a second-order homogeneous recurrence relation with constant coefficients and assume that its characteristic polynomial has just one (repeated) nonzero root.

(a) [BB] If x is the characteristic root, show that $r = 2x$ and $s = -x^2$.

(b) Conclude from (a) that if c is any constant then $a_n = cnx^n$ is a solution of the recurrence relation.

(c) Use (b) and the previous exercise to prove Theorem 5.3.1 for this case.

27. Let $a_n = ra_{n-1} + sa_{n-2} + f(n)$, $n \geq 2$, be a second-order recurrence relation with constant coefficients.

(a) If p_n satisfies this recurrence relation for $n \geq 2$ and q_n satisfies the associated homogeneous recurrence relation $a_n = ra_{n-1} + sa_{n-2}$ for $n \geq 2$, show that $p_n + q_n$ satisfies the given relation for $n \geq 2$.

(b) Complete the proof of Theorem 5.3.2.

5.4 Solving Recurrence Relations; Generating Functions

The brief introduction to generating functions that we give in this section belies the importance of this concept in combinatorial mathematics. Our purpose is just to give an indication as to how generating functions can be used to solve recurrence relations.

Roughly speaking, a generating function is a polynomial that "goes on forever," that is, an expression of the form

$$f(x) = a_0 + a_1 x + a_2 x^2 + a_3 x^3 + \cdots + a_n x^n + \cdots .$$

Unlike the usual polynomial, in which the coefficients a_i are all zero after a certain point, a generating function usually has infinitely many nonzero terms. There is an obvious correspondence between generating functions and sequences $a_0, a_1, a_2, \ldots$; that is,

$$a_0 + a_1 x + a_2 x^2 + a_3 x^3 + \cdots \quad \longleftrightarrow \quad a_0, a_1, a_2, a_3, \ldots .$$

5.4.1 DEFINITION The *generating function* of a sequence $a_0, a_1, a_2, \ldots$ is the expression $f(x) = a_0 + a_1 x + a_2 x^2 + \cdots$. ❖

EXAMPLE 25 The generating function of the sequence $1, 2, 3, \ldots$ of natural numbers is $f(x) = 1 + 2x + 3x^2 + \cdots$, while the generating function of the arithmetic sequence $1, 4, 7, 10, \ldots$ is $f(x) = 1 + 4x + 7x^2 + 10x^3 + \cdots$. ▨

Two generating functions can be added and multiplied term by term just like polynomials. If $f(x) = a_0 + a_1 x + a_2 x^2 + \cdots$ and $g(x) = b_0 + b_1 x + b_2 x^2 + \cdots$, then

$$f(x) + g(x) = (a_0 + b_0) + (a_1 + b_1)x + (a_2 + b_2)x^2 + \cdots$$

$$f(x)g(x) = (a_0 b_0) + (a_1 b_0 + a_0 b_1)x + (a_0 b_2 + a_1 b_1 + a_2 b_0)x^2 + \cdots .$$

Note that, while generating functions have infinitely many terms, the definitions of addition and multiplication involve no infinite sums; for example, the coefficient of x^n in the product $f(x)g(x)$ is the finite sum

$$a_0 b_n + a_1 b_{n-1} + a_2 b_{n-2} + \cdots + a_n b_0 .$$

PROBLEM 26. If $f(x) = 1 + x + x^2 + \cdots + x^n + \cdots$

and $g(x) = 1 - x + x^2 - x^3 + \cdots + (-1)^n x^n + \cdots$,

find $f(x) + g(x)$ and $f(x)g(x)$.

Solution.
$$f(x) + g(x) = (1 + x + x^2 + \cdots + x^n + \cdots)$$
$$+ (1 - x + x^2 - x^3 + \cdots + (-1)^n x^n + \cdots)$$
$$= (1 + 1) + (1 - 1)x + (1 + 1)x^2$$
$$+ \cdots + (1 + (-1)^n)x^n + \cdots$$
$$= 2 + 2x^2 + 2x^4 + \cdots$$

$$f(x)g(x) = (1 + x + x^2 + \cdots + x^n + \cdots)$$
$$\cdot (1 - x + x^2 - x^3 + \cdots + (-1)^n x^n + \cdots)$$
$$= 1 + [1(-1) + 1(1)]x + [1(1) + 1(-1) + 1(1)]x^2 + \cdots$$
$$= 1 + x^2 + x^4 + x^6 + \cdots$$

Students who have studied calculus for more than one year should notice the obvious similarity between generating functions and power series and will be comfortable with the fact that generating functions often can be expressed as the quotient of polynomials. An important example is

$$\frac{1}{1 - x} = 1 + x + x^2 + x^3 + \cdots ,$$

which shows that $\dfrac{1}{1 - x}$ is the generating function of the sequence $1, 1, 1, \ldots$.

Suppose a is a real number. Show that $\dfrac{1}{1 - ax}$ is the generating function for a certain geometric sequence. ∎

In combinatorics, the fundamental distinction between power series and generating functions is that, whereas power series in calculus are **functions** R → R with radii of convergence, generating functions are purely formal objects that will never be "evaluated" at a specific real number x. Thus, we do not worry about what the infinite sum $a_0 + a_1 x + a_2 x^2 + \cdots$ means. Whereas it is a topic of interest in calculus to prove formula (12), for instance, and to discover for which real numbers this formula is valid, for us the proof is a routine application of the definition of multiplication of generating functions.

$$(1 - x)(1 + x + x^2 + \cdots + x^n + \cdots)$$
$$= 1 + [1(1) - 1(1)]x + [1(1) - 1(1)]x^2 + \cdots + [1(1) - 1(1)]x^n + \cdots$$
$$= 1 + 0x + 0x^2 + \cdots + 0x^n + \cdots$$
$$= 1$$

Another very useful formula for us is

$$\frac{1}{(1 - x)^2} = 1 + 2x + 3x^2 + 4x^3 + \cdots + (n + 1)x^n + \cdots ,$$

which says that $\dfrac{1}{(1 - x)^2}$ is the generating function of the sequence of natural numbers.

Prove formula (13). ∎

Suppose $f(x)$ is the generating function of the sequence $0, 1, 2, 3, \ldots$; that is, $f(x) = 0 + 1x + 2x^2 + 3x^3 + 4x^4 + \cdots$. Then

$$f(x) = x + 2x^2 + 3x^3 + 4x^4 + \cdots = x(1 + 2x + 3x^2 + 4x^3 + \cdots) = x\frac{1}{(1 - x)^2}$$

by (13), so $f(x)$ takes the simpler form $f(x) = \dfrac{x}{(1-x)^2}$.

We now present a few examples that show how generating functions can be used to solve recurrence relations.

PROBLEM 27. Solve the recurrence relation $a_n = 3a_{n-1}$, $n \geq 1$, given $a_0 = 1$.

Solution. Consider the generating function $f(x) = a_0 + a_1x + a_2x^2 + \cdots + a_nx^n + \cdots$ of the sequence $a_0, a_1, a_2, \ldots$. Multiplying by $3x$ and writing the product $3xf(x)$ below $f(x)$ so that terms involving x^n match, we obtain

$$
\begin{array}{llllll}
f(x) = a_0 & + & a_1x & + & a_2x^2 & + & \cdots & + & a_nx^n & + & \cdots \\
3xf(x) = & & 3a_0x & + & 3a_1x^2 & + & \cdots & + & 3a_{n-1}x^n & + & \cdots.
\end{array}
$$

Subtracting gives

$$f(x) - 3xf(x)$$
$$= a_0 + (a_1 - 3a_0)x + (a_2 - 3a_1)x^2 + \cdots + (a_n - 3a_{n-1})x^n + \cdots.$$

Since $a_0 = 1$, $a_1 = 3a_0$, and, in general, $a_n = 3a_{n-1}$, this says that $(1 - 3x)f(x) = 1$. Thus, $f(x) = \dfrac{1}{1 - 3x}$ and, using (12),

$$f(x) = 1 + 3x + (3x)^2 + \cdots + (3x)^n + \cdots = 1 + 3x + 9x^2 + \cdots + 3^nx^n + \cdots.$$

We conclude that a_n, which is the coefficient of x^n in $f(x)$, must equal 3^n. So we have $a_n = 3^n$ as the solution to our recurrence relation.

PROBLEM 28. Solve the recurrence relation $a_n = 2a_{n-1} - a_{n-2}$, $n \geq 2$, given $a_0 = 3$, $a_1 = -2$.

Solution. Letting $f(x)$ be the generating function of the sequence in question, we have

$$
\begin{array}{llllll}
f(x) = a_0 & + & a_1x & + & a_2x^2 & + & \cdots & + & a_nx^n & + & \cdots \\
2xf(x) = & & 2a_0x & + & 2a_1x^2 & + & \cdots & + & 2a_{n-1}x^n & + & \cdots \\
x^2f(x) = & & & & a_0x^2 & + & \cdots & + & a_{n-2}x^n & + & \cdots.
\end{array}
$$

Therefore,

$$f(x) - 2xf(x) + x^2f(x) = a_0 + (a_1 - 2a_0)x + (a_2 - 2a_1 + a_0)x^2 + \cdots$$
$$+ (a_n - 2a_{n-1} + a_{n-2})x^n + \cdots$$
$$= 3 - 8x$$

since $a_0 = 3$, $a_1 = -2$ and $a_n - 2a_{n-1} + a_{n-2} = 0$ for $n \geq 2$.

So $(1 - 2x + x^2)f(x) = 3 - 8x$, $(1 - x)^2 f(x) = 3 - 8x$, and

$$f(x) = \frac{1}{(1-x)^2}(3 - 8x)$$
$$= (1 + 2x + 3x^2 + \cdots + (n + 1)x^n + \cdots)(3 - 8x) \qquad \text{by (13)}$$
$$= 3 - 2x - 7x^2 - 12x^3 + \cdots + [3(n + 1) - 8n]x^n + \cdots$$
$$= 3 - 2x - 7x^2 - 12x^3 + \cdots + (-5n + 3)x^n + \cdots,$$

and $a_n = 3 - 5n$ is the desired solution. (Verify that this recurrence can also be solved by Theorem 5.3.1.)

PROBLEM 29. Solve the recurrence $a_n = -3a_{n-1} + 10a_{n-2}$, $n \geq 2$, given $a_0 = 1$, $a_1 = 4$.

Solution. Letting $f(x)$ be the generating function of the sequence in question, we have

$$
\begin{aligned}
f(x) &= a_0 + a_1 x + a_2 x^2 + \cdots + a_n x^n + \cdots \\
3xf(x) &= \qquad\;\; 3a_0 x + 3a_1 x^2 + \cdots + 3a_{n-1} x^n + \cdots \\
10x^2 f(x) &= \qquad\qquad\;\; 10a_0 x^2 + \cdots + 10a_{n-2} x^n + \cdots .
\end{aligned}
$$

Therefore,

$$
\begin{aligned}
f(x) + 3xf(x) - 10x^2 f(x) &= a_0 + (a_1 + 3a_0)x + (a_2 + 3a_1 - 10a_0)x^2 \\
&\quad + \cdots + (a_n + 3a_{n-1} - 10a_{n-2})x^n + \cdots \\
&= 1 + 7x
\end{aligned}
$$

since $a_0 = 1$, $a_1 = 4$, and $a_n + 3a_{n-1} - 10a_{n-2} = 0$ for $n \geq 2$. So

$$
(1 + 3x - 10x^2)f(x) = 1 + 7x
$$

and

$$
f(x) = \frac{1 + 7x}{1 + 3x - 10x^2} = \frac{1 + 7x}{(1 + 5x)(1 - 2x)}.
$$

At this point, it is useful to recall the method of *partial fractions*. We set

$$
\frac{1}{(1 + 5x)(1 - 2x)} = \frac{A}{1 + 5x} + \frac{B}{1 - 2x} = \frac{A(1 - 2x) + B(1 + 5x)}{(1 + 5x)(1 - 2x)}.
$$

Equating numerators, $1 = (A + B) + (-2A + 5B)x$, so $A + B = 1$, $-2A + 5B = 0$.

Solving for A and B, we get $A = \frac{5}{7}$, $B = \frac{2}{7}$. Therefore,

$$
\frac{1}{(1 + 5x)(1 - 2x)} = \frac{5}{7}\left(\frac{1}{1 + 5x}\right) + \frac{2}{7}\left(\frac{1}{1 - 2x}\right)
$$

and

$$
\begin{aligned}
f(x) &= \frac{1 + 7x}{(1 + 5x)(1 - 2x)} \\
&= \frac{5}{7}\left(\frac{1}{1 + 5x}\right)(1 + 7x) + \frac{2}{7}\left(\frac{1}{1 - 2x}\right)(1 + 7x) \\
&= \tfrac{5}{7}(1 + (-5x) + (-5x)^2 + \cdots)(1 + 7x) \\
&\quad + \tfrac{2}{7}(1 + 2x + (2x)^2 + \cdots)(1 + 7x) \\
&= \tfrac{5}{7}(1 - 5x + 25x^2 + \cdots + (-5)^n x^n + \cdots)(1 + 7x) \\
&\quad + \tfrac{2}{7}(1 + 2x + 4x^2 + \cdots + 2^n x^n + \cdots)(1 + 7x) \\
&= \tfrac{5}{7}(1 + 2x - 10x^2 + \cdots + [(-5)^n + 7(-5)^{n-1}]x^n + \cdots) \\
&\quad + \tfrac{2}{7}(1 + 9x + 18x^2 + \cdots + [2^n + 7(2^{n-1})]x^n + \cdots) \\
&= \tfrac{5}{7}(1 + 2x - 10x^2 + \cdots + 2(-5)^{n-1}x^n + \cdots) \\
&\quad + \tfrac{2}{7}(1 + 9x + 18x^2 + \cdots + 9(2^{n-1})x^n + \cdots) \\
&= 1 + 4x - 2x^2 + \cdots + (-\tfrac{2}{7}(-5)^n + \tfrac{9}{7}(2^n))x^n + \cdots ,
\end{aligned}
$$

and hence $a_n = -\frac{2}{7}(-5)^n + \frac{9}{7}(2^n)$ is the desired solution. (Again, we suggest that you verify that this recurrence can also be solved by the methods of Section 5.3.) ▲

PROBLEM 30. Solve the recurrence relation $a_n = -a_{n-1} + 2n - 3$, $n \geq 1$, given $a_0 = 1$.

Solution. Let $f(x)$ be the generating function of the sequence $a_0, a_1, a_2, \ldots$. Then

$$
\begin{aligned}
f(x) &= a_0 + a_1 x + a_2 x^2 + \cdots + a_n x^n + \cdots \\
x f(x) &= \qquad a_0 x + a_1 x^2 + \cdots + a_{n-1} x^n + \cdots.
\end{aligned}
$$

Therefore,

$$ f(x) + x f(x) = a_0 + (a_1 + a_0)x + (a_2 + a_1)x^2 + \cdots + (a_n + a_{n-1})x^n + \cdots. $$

We are given that $a_0 = 1$ and $a_n + a_{n-1} = 2n - 3$. Thus $a_1 + a_0 = 2(1) - 3 = -1$, $a_2 + a_1 = 2(2) - 3 = 1$, and so on. We obtain $(1 + x)f(x) = 1 - x + x^2 + \cdots + (2n - 3)x^n + \cdots$, and so

$$
\begin{aligned}
f(x) &= \frac{1}{1 + x}(1 - x + x^2 + \cdots + (2n - 3)x^n + \cdots) \\
&= (1 + (-x) + (-x)^2 + \cdots + (-x)^n + \cdots) \\
&\quad \cdot (1 - x + x^2 + \cdots + (2n - 3)x^n + \cdots) \\
&= (1 - x + x^2 - x^3 + \cdots + (-x)^n + \cdots) \\
&\quad \cdot (1 - x + x^2 + \cdots + (2n - 3)x^n + \cdots) \\
&= 1 - 2x + 3x^2 + \cdots \\
&\quad + [(2n - 3) - (2n - 5) + \cdots + (-1)^{n-1}(-1) + (-1)^n]x^n + \cdots.
\end{aligned}
$$

Now a_n is the coefficient of x^n, the term in brackets:

$$
\begin{aligned}
a_n &= \left\{ \sum_{k=0}^{n-1} (-1)^k [2n - (2k + 3)] \right\} + (-1)^n \\
&= (2n - 3) \sum_{k=0}^{n-1} (-1)^k - 2 \sum_{k=0}^{n-1} (-1)^k k + (-1)^n.
\end{aligned}
$$

We leave it to you to verify that

$$ \sum_{k=0}^{n-1} (-1)^k k = \begin{cases} -\frac{n}{2} & \text{if } n \text{ is even} \\ \frac{n-1}{2} & \text{if } n \text{ is odd.} \end{cases} $$

So, if n is even, $a_n = 0 - 2(-\frac{n}{2}) + 1 = n + 1$, while if n is odd, $a_n = (2n - 3) - 2(\frac{n-1}{2}) - 1 = 2n - 3 - n + 1 - 1 = n - 3$. The solution is

$$ a_n = \begin{cases} n + 1 & \text{if } n \text{ is even} \\ n - 3 & \text{if } n \text{ is odd.} \end{cases} $$

Note that this solution could also be written as $a_n = 2(-1)^n + n - 1$, which is the answer one would obtain by the methods of Section 5.3.

Answers to Pauses

10. Replacing x by ax in (12), we see that

$$ \frac{1}{1 - ax} = 1 + (ax) + (ax)^2 + (ax)^3 + \cdots = 1 + ax + a^2 x^2 + a^3 x^3 + \cdots. $$

From this, we see that $\dfrac{1}{1 - ax}$ is the generating function for the sequence $1, a, a^2, a^3, \ldots$, which is the geometric sequence with first term 1 and common ratio a.

11. $(1 - x)^2(1 + 2x + 3x^2 + \cdots + (n + 1)x^n + \cdots)$
$$= (1 - 2x + x^2)(1 + 2x + 3x^2 + \cdots + (n + 1)x^n + \cdots)$$
$$= 1 + [1(2) - 2(1)]x + [1(3) - 2(2) + 1(1)]x^2 + \cdots$$
$$+ [1(n + 1) - 2(n) + 1(n - 1)]x^n + \cdots = 1$$

since $n + 1 - 2n + n - 1 = 0$.

True/False Questions

(Answers can be found in the back of the book.)

1. The sequence associated with the generating function $(1 + 3x)^2$ is $1, 0, 9, 0, 0, 0, \ldots$.

2. If $f(x) = 1 + 3x + 9x^2 + 27x^3 + \cdots$ and $g(x) = 1 + 3x + 5x^2 + 7x^3 + \cdots$, then the coefficient of x^3 in $f(x) + g(x)$ is 34.

3. If $f(x) = 1 + 3x + 9x^2 + 27x^3 + \cdots$ and $g(x) = 1 + 3x + 5x^2 + 7x^3 + \cdots$, then the coefficient of x^3 in $f(x)g(x)$ is 76.

4. $\dfrac{1}{1 + 2x}$ is the generating function for a certain geometric sequence.

5. $\dfrac{4}{1 - x}$ is the generating function for a certain constant sequence.

6. The generating function associated with the sequence $2, 0, 2, 0, 2, 0, \ldots$ is $\dfrac{1}{2 - 2x^2}$.

7. The generating function of the geometric sequence $2, 6, 18, 54, \ldots$ is $\dfrac{2x}{1 - 3x}$.

8. The sequence associated with the generating function $\dfrac{1}{(1 - 2x)^2}$ is $1 + 4x + 12x^2 + 32x^3 + \cdots$.

9. For a generating function $a_0 + a_1x + a_2x^2 + \cdots$ to exist, we must have $\lim_{n \to \infty} a_n = 0$.

10. Partial fractions are sometimes useful when solving recurrence relations by the method of generating functions.

Exercises

The answers to exercises marked [BB] can be found in the Back of the Book.

1. What sequence is associated with each of the following generating functions?

(a) [BB] $(2 - 3x)^2$ **(b)** $\dfrac{x^4}{1 - x}$

(c) [BB] $\dfrac{1}{(1 + 3x)^2}$ **(d)** $\dfrac{1}{(1 - x^3)^2}$

(e) $\dfrac{x^2}{(1 + x)^2} + \dfrac{1}{1 + 5x}$

2. Express the generating function of each of the following sequences as a polynomial or as the quotient of polynomials.

(a) [BB] $1, 2, 5, 0, 0, \ldots$ **(b)** $0, 1, 4, 1, 0, 0, \ldots$

(c) $1, 2, 4, 8, 16, \ldots$ **(d)** $1, -1, 1, -1, \ldots$

(e) $3, 3, 3, \ldots$ **(f)** [BB] $1, 0, 1, 0, \ldots$

(g) $1, -2, 3, -4, \ldots$

3. [BB] Using the method of generating functions, solve the recurrence relation $a_n = 2a_{n-1}$, $n \geq 1$, given $a_0 = 1$.

Compare this solution to the sequence defined by (5), page 160.

4. Use the method of generating functions to solve the recurrence relation $a_n = 3a_{n-1} + 1$, $n \geq 1$, given $a_0 = 1$. Compare your solution with the sequence given in Problem 11, page 161.

5. [BB] Use the method of generating functions to solve the recurrence relation $a_n = 5a_{n-1} - 6a_{n-2}$, given $a_0 = -3$, $a_1 = -2$. Verify your answer by comparing with Problem 20, page 171.

6. Use the method of generating functions to solve the recurrence relation $a_n = 4a_{n-1} - 4a_{n-2}$, $n \geq 2$, given $a_0 = 1$, $a_1 = 4$. Compare your solution with the sequence given in Problem 21, page 171.

7. [BB] Use generating functions to find a formula for a_n given $a_0 = 5$ and $a_n = a_{n-1} + 2^n$ for $n \geq 1$.

8. **(a)** Use the method of the characteristic polynomial (as in Section 5.3) to solve the recurrence relation $a_n = 4a_{n-1} - 4a_{n-2} + 4^n$, $n \geq 2$, with the initial conditions $a_0 = 2$, $a_1 = 8$.

   (b) Solve the recurrence in (a) by means of generating functions.

   Which of the preceding methods do you prefer in this case?

9. Solve each of the following using generating functions. In each case, use the methods of Section 5.3 to verify your answer.

   (a) [BB] $a_n = -5a_{n-1}$, $n \geq 1$, given $a_0 = 2$.

   (b) $a_n = -5a_{n-1} + 3$, $n \geq 1$, given $a_0 = 2$.

10. Solve each of the following using generating functions. Verify your answer by the method of Section 5.3.

    (a) $a_n = 4a_{n-1} - 3a_{n-2}$, $n \geq 2$, given $a_0 = 2$, $a_1 = 5$.

    (b) $a_n = -10a_{n-1} - 25a_{n-2}$, $n \geq 2$, given $a_0 = 1$, $a_1 = 25$.

11. [BB] Using generating functions, solve the recurrence relation $a_n = 2a_{n-1} + a_{n-2} - 2a_{n-3}$, $n \geq 3$, given $a_0 = 1$, $a_1 = 3$, $a_2 = 6$. (Note that this recurrence is not second order and so cannot be solved by the methods of Section 5.3.)

12. [BB] Use the method of generating functions to solve the recurrence relation $a_n = a_{n-1} + a_{n-2} - a_{n-3}$, $n \geq 3$, given $a_0 = 2$, $a_1 = -1$, $a_2 = 3$.

    [*Hint*: $\dfrac{1}{(ax + b)^2(cx + d)} = \dfrac{Ax + B}{(ax + b)^2} + \dfrac{C}{cx + d}$.]

13. The Pell sequence is defined by $p_0 = 1$, $p_1 = 2$, and $p_n = 2p_{n-1} + p_{n-2}$ for $n \geq 2$.

    (a) Use the characteristic polynomial to solve this recurrence relation.

    (b) Show that p_n is the integer closest to $\left(\frac{2+\sqrt{2}}{4}\right)(1 + \sqrt{2})^n$.

    (c) Find the generating function of the Pell sequence, finding explicitly its first four terms.

    Remarkably, there exist closed form solutions for p_n. For example,

    $$p_n = \sum_{\substack{i,j,k \geq 0 \\ i+j+2k=n}} \frac{(i + j + k)!}{i!\,j!\,k!}.$$

    See the *American Mathematical Monthly* **107** (2000), no. 4, p. 370, for three verifications of this formula.

14. This question concerns the Fibonacci sequence defined by the recurrence relation $a_n = a_{n-1} + a_{n-2}$, where $a_0 = a_1 = 1$.

    (a) Suppose $f(x)$ is the generating function of the Fibonacci sequence. Show that $f(x) = \dfrac{1}{1 - x - x^2}$.

    (b) Find α and β such that $1 - x - x^2 = (1 - \alpha x)(1 - \beta x)$.

    (c) Find A and B, in terms of α and β, such that $\dfrac{1}{1 - x - x^2} = \dfrac{A}{1 - \alpha x} + \dfrac{B}{1 - \beta x}$.

    (d) Use the results of the previous parts to obtain a formula for a_n and compare your answer with that found in Problem 22, page 171. Which method for finding a_n do you prefer?

Key Terms & Ideas

Here are some technical words and phrases that were used in this chapter. Do you know the meaning of each? If you're not sure, check the glossary or index at the back of the book.

arithmetic sequence

common difference

common ratio

factorial

Fibonacci sequence

generating function

geometric sequence

ideal

Principle of Mathematical Induction

sequence

symmetric difference

term (of a sequence)

Review Exercises for Chapter 5

1. Use mathematical induction to show that $\sum_{i=1}^{n} i(i!) = (n + 1)! - 1$.

2. Using mathematical induction, show that

   $$\sum_{i=1}^{n} 3^{i-1} = \frac{3^n - 1}{2} \quad \text{for all } n \geq 1.$$

3. Using mathematical induction, show that

   $$\left(1 - \frac{1}{2}\right)^n \geq 1 - \frac{n}{2} \quad \text{for all } n \geq 1.$$

4. Prove that $\sum_{i=1}^{n} \frac{1}{\sqrt{i}} > 2(\sqrt{n + 1} - 1)$ for all integers $n \geq 1$.

5. Use mathematical induction to prove that $10^{n+2} + 10^n + 1$ is divisible by 3 for all $n \geq 1$.

6. Prove that $8^n \mid (4n - 2)!$ for all $n \geq 5$.

7. For $n \geq 2$, prove that the number of 2-element subsets of a set of n elements is $\frac{1}{2}n(n - 1)$.

8. (a) Give an example of a function f with domain A a subset of R with the property that $f(ab) = f(a) + f(b)$ for all $a, b \in A$.

 (b) Suppose f is a function as in part (a). Prove that $f(x_1x_2 \cdots x_n) = f(x_1) + f(x_2) + \cdots + f(x_n)$ for any $n \geq 1$ and any $x_1, x_2, \ldots, x_n \in A$.

9. Give a recursive definition of each of the following sequences:

 (a) $1, 5, 29, 173, 1037, \ldots$

 (b) $3, 5, 13, 85, 3613, \ldots$

 (c) $1, 9, 36, 100, 225, \ldots$

10. Guess a simple formula for each of the following products and prove that your guess is correct for all integers $n \geq 2$.

 (a) $(1 - \frac{1}{2})(1 - \frac{1}{3})(1 - \frac{1}{4}) \cdots (1 - \frac{1}{n})$

 (b) $(1 - \frac{1}{4})(1 - \frac{1}{9})(1 - \frac{1}{16}) \cdots (1 - \frac{1}{n^2})$

11. Consider the sequence defined by $a_1 = 47$ and $a_n = a_{n-1} - 6$ for $n \geq 2$. What is $a_1 + a_2 + a_3 + \cdots + a_{100}$?

12. Find the sum $529 + 525 + 521 + 517 + \cdots + (-459)$.

13. Let a_n be defined recursively by $a_1 = 0$, $a_2 = \frac{1}{3}$, and, for $k \geq 1$, $a_{k+2} = \frac{1}{2}(a_k + a_{k+1})$. Prove that $a_n = \frac{2}{9}(1 - (-\frac{1}{2})^{n-1})$ for all integers $n \geq 1$.

14. Define $f : \mathsf{Z} \to \mathsf{Z}$ by $f(a) = 3 - 4a$, and for $t \in \mathsf{Z}$ define a sequence $a_1, a_2, a_3, \ldots$ by $a_1 = f(t)$ and, for $k \geq 1$, $a_{k+1} = f(a_k)$.

 (a) Given $t = 1$, find a_1, a_2, a_3, a_4, a_5.

 (b) Find a number t such that the sequence defined is constant.

 (c) Does there exist t such that $a_1 < a_2 < a_3 < \cdots$?

15. Consider the arithmetic sequence that begins $5, 9, 13$.

 (a) Find the 32nd and 100th terms of this sequence.

 (b) Does 125 belong to the sequence? If so, where does it occur?

 (c) Repeat (b) for the numbers 429 and 1000.

 (d) Find the sum of the first 18 terms.

16. The first two terms of a sequence are 6 and 2.

 (a) If the sequence is arithmetic, find the 27th term and the sum of the first 30 terms.

 (b) If the sequence is geometric, find an expression for the 27th term and the sum of the first 30 terms.

17. Let a_1, a_2, a_3, a_4 be the first four terms of an arithmetic sequence. Show that $a_1a_4 + 3a_2a_3 = 2(a_1a_3 + a_2a_4)$ and use this fact to factor the polynomial $f(x) = 3x^2 - 2(a_1a_3 + a_2a_4)x + a_1a_2a_3a_4$. [Students of calculus should recognize $f(x)$ as the derivative of $g(x) = x^3 - (a_1a_3 + $

$a_2a_4)x^2 + a_1a_2a_3a_4x = x(x - a_1a_3)(x - a_2a_4)$. Finding classes of polynomials that, together with their derivative and second derivative, factor over the rationals is a very hard problem.]

18. Explain why the sum of 500 terms of the series $(\frac{3}{2})^{742} - (\frac{3}{2})^{740} + (\frac{3}{2})^{738} - \cdots$ is $\frac{9}{13}[(\frac{3}{2})^{742} - (\frac{2}{3})^{258}]$.

19. (a) Define the Fibonacci sequence.

 (b) Is it possible for three successive terms in the Fibonacci sequence to be odd?

 (c) Is it possible for two successive terms in the Fibonacci sequence to be even?
 Justify your answers.

20. Show that, for $n \geq 2$, the nth term of the Fibonacci sequence is less than $(\frac{7}{4})^{n-1}$. [Use the definition of the Fibonacci sequence, not the approximation to f_n given in equation (9).]

21. Let $f_1, f_2, \ldots$ be the Fibonacci sequence as defined in 5.2.3. Prove that $f_2 + f_4 + f_6 + \cdots + f_{2n} = f_{2n+1} - 1$ for every $n \geq 1$.

22. Suppose you walk up a flight of stairs one or two steps at a time. In how many ways can you reach stair n (starting from the floor in front of stair 1)?

23. Solve the recurrence relation $a_n = 5a_{n-1} - 4a_{n-2}$, $n \geq 2$, given that $a_0 = -3$ and $a_1 = 6$. Use the characteristic polynomial as described in Section 5.3.

24. Solve Exercise 23 using the method of generating functions described in Section 5.4.

25. Find a formula for a_n, given $a_0 = a_1 = 1$ and $a_n = 3a_{n-1} - 2a_{n-2} + 5$ for $n \geq 2$.

26. Let a_n be the sequence defined by $a_0 = -2$, $a_1 = 1$, and $a_n = -6a_{n-1} - 9a_{n-2}$ for $n \geq 2$.

 (a) Find the first five terms of this sequence.

 (b) Find a formula for a_n.

27. Solve $a_n = 4a_{n-1} + 5a_{n-2} + 3^n$, $n \geq 2$, given $a_0 = 4$, $a_1 = -1$.

28. Let $\tau = \frac{1+\sqrt{5}}{2}$ denote the golden mean and $\lfloor \ \rfloor : \mathsf{R} \to \mathsf{Z}$ the usual floor function. Let $n \geq 1$ be an integer.

 (a) Show that $n\tau^2 - n\tau$ is an integer.

 (b) Show that $\lfloor n\tau^2 \rfloor - \lfloor n\tau \rfloor = n$.

29. (For students of calculus) Let a and b be any positive integers and define the sequence $a_1, a_2, a_3, \ldots$ recursively by $a_1 = a$, $a_2 = b$ and $a_{n+1} = a_n + a_{n-1}$ for $n \geq 2$. Assume that the sequence $\frac{a_2}{a_1}, \frac{a_3}{a_2}, \frac{a_4}{a_3}, \ldots$ has a limit k. What is k?

30. (For students of calculus) Let $f_1, f_2, f_3, \ldots$ denote the Fibonacci sequence as defined in 5.2.3. Evaluate $\sum_{1}^{\infty} \frac{f_k}{100^k}$ exactly. Then approximate this sum to 19 decimal places and admire its beauty. What do you notice?

6

Principles of Counting

6.1   The Principle of Inclusion-Exclusion

Glenys is thinking about registering for a course in data analysis. Of the 100 people who have registered so far, she discovers that 80 people have own personal digital assistants (PDAs) and three-quarters of the group are men.

(a) Estimate the number of women in the course who do not have PDAs. How large might this number be? How small?

(b) How many of the men registered in this course could conceivably own PDAs?

The object of this chapter is to illustrate some basic principles of counting. We consider first the number of elements in various combinations of finite sets such as union, intersection, and difference. As in Section 3.3, the number of elements in a finite set S will be denoted $|S|$.

To analyze Glenys's questions, we introduce the sets U of all registrants, M of male registrants, and P of those registrants who own a PDA. We are given that $|U| = 100$, $|M| = 75$, and $|P| = 80$. The set of women who do not have a PDA is $M^c \cap P^c$ and it is the size of this set with which part (a) is concerned. By one of the laws of De Morgan,

$$M^c \cap P^c = (M \cup P)^c,$$

and so

$$|M^c \cap P^c| = |(M \cup P)^c| = 100 - |M \cup P|.$$

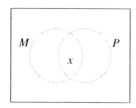

Figure 6.1 $|M \cup P| = |M| + |P| - |M \cap P|$ because Region x gets counted twice in the sum $|M| + |P|$.

How big is $M \cup P$? Adding the number of men and the number of registrants who have PDAs counts twice the men with PDAs (see Fig. 6.1), so

$$|M \cup P| = |M| + |P| - |M \cap P| = 75 + 80 - |M \cap P| = 155 - |M \cap P|.$$

Therefore,

$$|M^c \cap P^c| = 100 - (155 - |M \cap P|) = |M \cap P| - 55,$$

which is a formula for the number of women without PDAs. Since $M \cap P$ is a subset of M, a set of 75 people, $|M \cap P| \leq |M| = 75$, and so $|M^c \cap P^c| \leq 75 - 55 = 20$. Conceivably, $|M^c \cap P^c|$ could be 0 (if $|M \cap P| = 55$). So the number of women without PDAs is between 0 and 20 (inclusive).

Part (b) asks about $M \cap P$. Observing that $|M \cap P| - 55 \geq 0$ (because it is the number of women without PDAs), we see that $|M \cap P| \geq 55$; that is, at least 55 men must own PDAs. As noted previously, the upper bound for $|M \cap P|$ is 75 and it is possible for this number to be realized.

Suppose, in fact, that $|M \cap P| = 72$. Then

$$|M \cup P| = |M| + |P| - |M \cap P| = 75 + 80 - 72 = 83.$$

There are 83 people in the class who are either men or own a PDA.

How many men registered in the class would not have PDAs? Surely, $75 - 72 = 3$:

$$|M \setminus P| = |M| - |M \cap P| = 75 - 72 = 3.$$

How many of the owners of PDAs are women? Surely, $80 - 72 = 8$:

$$|P \setminus M| = |P| - |P \cap M| = 80 - 72 = 8.$$

How many of those registered are either men without PDAs or women with PDAs? This question, which asks for $|M \oplus P|$, can be answered in several ways. It is the number of men without PDAs plus the number of women with a PDA; that is,

$$|M \oplus P| = |M \setminus P| + |P \setminus M| = 3 + 8 = 11.$$

It is also the number of people who are men or owners of a PDA but not both:

$$|M \oplus P| = |M \cup P| - |M \cap P| = 83 - 72 = 11.$$

We could also legitimately argue that this number is

$$|M \oplus P| = |M| + |P| - 2|M \cap P| = 75 + 80 - 2(72) = 155 - 144 = 11$$

because adding the number of men and the number of people with PDAs counts twice the "unwanted" individuals, the men with PDAs.

We summarize the basic principles of counting, most of which we have just illustrated.

6.1.1 PROPOSITION   Let A and B be subsets of a finite universal set U. Then

    (a) $|A \cup B| = |A| + |B| - |A \cap B|$
    (b) $|A \cap B| \leq \min\{|A|, |B|\}$, the minimum of $|A|$ and $|B|$
    (c) $|A \setminus B| = |A| - |A \cap B| \geq |A| - |B|$
    (d) $|A^c| = |U| - |A|$
    (e) $|A \oplus B| = |A \cup B| - |A \cap B| = |A| + |B| - 2|A \cap B| = |A \setminus B| + |B \setminus A|$
    (f) $|A \times B| = |A| \times |B|$

Proof   **(a)** If $A = \emptyset$, then $A \cap B = \emptyset$, and $|A| = |A \cap B| = 0$, so the result holds because each side of (a) equals $|B|$. Similarly, the result holds if $B = \emptyset$, so we assume henceforth that neither A nor B is empty.

Suppose $A \cap B = \emptyset$. Let $A = \{a_1, a_2, \ldots, a_r\}$ and $B = \{b_1, b_2, \ldots, b_s\}$. Then

$$A \cup B = \{a_1, a_2, \ldots, a_r, b_1, b_2, \ldots, b_s\}$$

and, since there is no repetition among the elements listed here,

$$|A \cup B| = r + s = |A| + |B| = |A| + |B| - |A \cap B|$$

and the desired formula is true.

On the other hand, if $A \cap B \neq \emptyset$ and we let

$$A \setminus B = \{a_1, a_2, \ldots, a_r\}$$
$$B \setminus A = \{b_1, b_2, \ldots, b_s\}$$
$$A \cap B = \{x_1, x_2, \ldots, x_t\}$$

then

$$A = \{a_1, a_2, \ldots, a_r, x_1, x_2, \ldots, x_t\}$$

and

$$B = \{b_1, b_2, \ldots, b_s, x_1, x_2, \ldots, x_t\},$$

so

$$A \cup B = \{a_1, \ldots, a_r, b_1, \ldots, b_s, x_1, \ldots, x_t\}$$

with no repetition among the elements listed in any of these sets. Thus,

$$|A| + |B| - |A \cap B| = (r + t) + (s + t) - t = r + s + t = |A \cup B|$$

and the formula holds in this case as well.

We omit the proofs of (b)–(e) since, as with the proof of part (a), these follow in a straightforward way from the definitions of $\cup, \cap, \setminus, \oplus$, and set complement. The proof of (f) is left to the exercises.

The formula for the number of elements in the union of two sets—part (a) of Proposition 6.1.1—is the simplest case of the *Principle of Inclusion–Exclusion*, which gives the general formula for the number of elements in the union of any finite collection of finite sets.

Suppose, for instance, we have three finite sets A, B, and C. Then

$$|A \cup B \cup C| = |A \cup (B \cup C)|$$
$$= |A| + |B \cup C| - |A \cap (B \cup C)|$$
$$= |A| + |B \cup C| - |(A \cap B) \cup (A \cap C)|$$
$$= |A| + \big[|B| + |C| - |B \cap C|\big]$$
$$\quad - \big[|A \cap B| + |A \cap C| - |(A \cap B) \cap (A \cap C)|\big]$$
$$= |A| + |B| + |C| - |B \cap C| - |A \cap B| - |A \cap C| + |A \cap B \cap C|,$$

where, at the spots marked with single arrows, we used the fact that $|X \cup Y| = |X| + |Y| - |X \cap Y|$ and, at the last step, that $(A \cap B) \cap (A \cap C) = A \cap B \cap C$.

 **Pause 1**   What happened at the double arrow?   ∎

Here is the formula for the cardinality of the union of four finite sets:

$$|A \cup B \cup C \cup D|$$
$$= |A| + |B| + |C| + |D|$$
$$\quad - |A \cap B| - |A \cap C| - |A \cap D| - |B \cap C| - |B \cap D| - |C \cap D|$$
$$\quad + |A \cap B \cap C| + |A \cap B \cap D| + |A \cap C \cap D| + |B \cap C \cap D|$$
$$\quad - |A \cap B \cap C \cap D|.$$

The general pattern should be evident. Add the cardinalities of each, subtract the cardinalities of the intersections of all pairs of sets, add the cardinalities of all intersections of the sets taken three at a time, subtract the cardinalities of all intersections of the sets taken four at a time, and so on.

6.1.2 PRINCIPLE OF INCLUSION–EXCLUSION Given a finite number of finite sets, $A_1, A_2, \ldots, A_n$, the number of elements in the union $A_1 \cup A_2 \cup \cdots \cup A_n$ is

$$|A_1 \cup A_2 \cup \cdots \cup A_n| = \sum_i |A_i| - \sum_{i<j} |A_i \cap A_j| + \sum_{i<j<k} |A_i \cap A_j \cap A_k|$$
$$- \cdots + (-1)^{n+1}|A_1 \cap A_2 \cap \cdots \cap A_n|,$$

where the first sum is over all i, the second sum is over all pairs i, j with $i < j$, the third sum is over all triples i, j, k with $i < j < k$, and so forth.

PROBLEM 1. Of 30 personal computers (PCs) owned by faculty members in a certain university department, 20 do not have A drives, eight have 19-inch monitors, 25 are running Windows XP, 20 have at least two of these properties, and six have all three.

    (a) How many PCs have at least one of these properties?
    (b) How many have none of these properties?
    (c) How many have exactly one property?

Solution. Let A be the set of PCs without A drives, let M be the set of PCs with 19-inch monitors, and let X be the set of PCs running under Windows XP. We are given that $|A| = 20$, $|M| = 8$, $|X| = 25$, $|(A \cap M) \cup (A \cap X) \cup (M \cap X)| = 20$, and $|A \cap M \cap X| = 6$. Using the Principle of Inclusion–Exclusion,

$$20 = |(A \cap M) \cup (A \cap X) \cup (M \cap X)|$$
$$= |A \cap M| + |A \cap X| + |M \cap X| - |(A \cap M) \cap (A \cap X)|$$
$$- |(A \cap M) \cap (M \cap X)| - |(A \cap X) \cap (M \cap X)|$$
$$+ |(A \cap M) \cap (A \cap X) \cap (M \cap X)|.$$

Since each of the last four terms here is $|A \cap M \cap X|$, we obtain

$$20 = |A \cap M| + |A \cap X| + |M \cap X| - 2|A \cap M \cap X|;$$

therefore, $|A \cap M| + |A \cap X| + |M \cap X| = 20 + 2(6) = 32$.

    (a) The number of PCs with at least one property is

$$|A \cup M \cup X| = |A| + |M| + |X|$$
$$- |A \cap M| - |A \cap X| - |M \cap X| + |A \cap M \cap X|$$
$$= 20 + 8 + 25 - \big(|A \cap M| + |A \cap X| + |M \cap X|\big) + 6$$
$$= 59 - 32 = 27.$$

    (b) It follows that $30 - 27 = 3$ PCs have none of the specified properties.
    (c) Since the number of computers with exactly one property is the number with at least one of the properties less the number with at least two, the number with exactly one is $27 - 20 = 7$.

Pause 2 Continuing the preceding problem, how many faculty have computers with exactly two of the three features described?

Some readers may notice that the problems discussed so far could also have been solved by Venn diagrams, which are an acceptable approach wherever possible. When more than three sets are involved, however, Venn diagrams can no longer be used. Thus, our solutions, which avoid Venn diagrams, illustrate techniques that can be applied in general.

PROBLEM 2. Suppose 18 of the 30 personal computers in Problem 1 have Pentium III processors, including 10 of those running Windows, all of those with 19-inch monitors, and 15 of those with CD-ROM drives. Suppose also that every computer has at least one of the four features now specified. How many have at least three features?

Solution. Let P be the set of PCs with Pentium III processors. Then, with W, M, and C as before, the question asks for the number

$$
\begin{aligned}
n &= |(W \cap M \cap C) \cup (W \cap M \cap P) \cup (W \cap C \cap P) \cup (M \cap C \cap P)| \\
&= |W \cap M \cap C| + |W \cap M \cap P| + |W \cap C \cap P| + |M \cap C \cap P| \\
&\quad - 6|W \cap M \cap C \cap P| + 4|W \cap M \cap C \cap P| - |W \cap M \cap C \cap P| \\
&= |W \cap M \cap C| + |W \cap M \cap P| + |W \cap C \cap P| + |M \cap C \cap P| \\
&\quad - 3|W \cap M \cap C \cap P|.
\end{aligned}
$$

We are given that

$$
\begin{aligned}
30 &= |W \cup M \cup C \cup P| \\
&= |W| + |M| + |C| + |P| \\
&\quad - |W \cap M| - |W \cap C| - |W \cap P| - |M \cap C| - |M \cap P| - |C \cap P| \\
&\quad + |W \cap M \cap C| + |W \cap M \cap P| + |W \cap C \cap P| + |M \cap C \cap P| \\
&\quad - |W \cap M \cap C \cap P| \\
&= |W| + |M| + |C| + |P| \\
&\quad - |W \cap M| - |W \cap C| - |W \cap P| - |M \cap C| - |M \cap P| - |C \cap P| \\
&\quad + n + 2|W \cap M \cap C \cap P|
\end{aligned}
$$

because

$$
\begin{aligned}
|W \cap M \cap C| + |W \cap M \cap P| + |W \cap C \cap P| + |M \cap C \cap P| \\
= n + 3|W \cap M \cap C \cap P|.
\end{aligned}
$$

In Problem 1, we learned that $|W \cap C| + |W \cap M| + |M \cap C| = 32$ and were told that $|W \cap M \cap C| = 6$. Here, since $M \subseteq P$, we have $W \cap M \cap C \cap P = W \cap M \cap C$, and so $|W \cap M \cap C \cap P| = 6$. Therefore,

$$
30 = 20 + 8 + 25 + 18 - 32 - 10 - 8 - 15 + n + 2(6),
$$

so $n = 30 - 71 + 65 - 12 = 12$.

PROBLEM 3. How many integers between 1 and 300 (inclusive) are

(a) divisible by at least one of 3, 5, 7?

(b) divisible by 3 and by 5 but not by 7?

(c) divisible by 5 but by neither 3 nor 7?

(d) relatively prime to 105?

Solution. Let A, B, and C be the sets of those integers between 1 and 300 that are divisible by 3, by 5, and by 7, respectively; thus,

$$A = \{n \mid 1 \leq n \leq 300, 3 \mid n\}$$
$$B = \{n \mid 1 \leq n \leq 300, 5 \mid n\}$$
$$C = \{n \mid 1 \leq n \leq 300, 7 \mid n\}.$$

(a) To be divisible by either 3 or 5 or 7 is to be in at least one of the sets A, B, or C. Thus, part (a) asks us to find $|A \cup B \cup C|$. To determine this number, we need $|A|, |B|, |C|, |A \cap B|, |A \cap C|, |B \cap C|$ and $|A \cap B \cap C|$. The elements of A are $3, 6, 9, 12, \ldots, 300$, so $|A| = 100$. Note that this number is $\lfloor \frac{300}{3} \rfloor$, where, as in paragraph 3.1.7, $\lfloor x \rfloor$ denotes the floor of the real number x.

In general, for natural numbers a and b, the number of positive integers less than or equal to a and divisible by b is $\lfloor \frac{a}{b} \rfloor$. (See Exercise 18.) Thus, we also have

$$|B| = \left\lfloor \frac{300}{5} \right\rfloor = 60 \quad \text{and} \quad |C| = \left\lfloor \frac{300}{7} \right\rfloor = 42.$$

Next we have to find $A \cap B$, the set of integers between 1 and 300 that are divisible by both 3 and 5. Since 3 and 5 are relatively prime numbers, any number divisible by each of them must be divisible by their product. (See Exercise 11 of Section 4.2.) Therefore, $A \cap B$ is just the set of integers between 1 and 300 that are divisible by 15 and, similarly, $A \cap C$, $B \cap C$, and $A \cap B \cap C$ are the sets of integers between 1 and 300 that are divisible by 21, 35, and 105, respectively. So we have

$$|A \cap B| = \left\lfloor \frac{300}{15} \right\rfloor = 20, \qquad |A \cap C| = \left\lfloor \frac{300}{21} \right\rfloor = 14,$$
$$|B \cap C| = \left\lfloor \frac{300}{35} \right\rfloor = 8, \quad |A \cap B \cap C| = \left\lfloor \frac{300}{105} \right\rfloor = 2$$

and hence $|A \cup B \cup C| = 100 + 60 + 42 - 20 - 14 - 8 + 2 = 162$.

(b) The numbers divisible by 3 and by 5, but not by 7, are precisely those numbers in $(A \cap B) \setminus C$, a set of cardinality $|A \cap B| - |A \cap B \cap C| = 20 - 2 = 18$.

(c) The numbers divisible by 5 but by neither 3 nor 7 are those in $B \setminus (A \cup C)$, a set of cardinality $|B| - |B \cap (A \cup C)|$. Since

$$B \cap (A \cup C) = (B \cap A) \cup (B \cap C),$$

the Principle of Inclusion–Exclusion gives

$$\begin{aligned} |B \cap (A \cup C)| &= |B \cap A| + |B \cap C| - |(B \cap A) \cap (B \cap C)| \\ &= |B \cap A| + |B \cap C| - |B \cap A \cap C| \end{aligned}$$

because $(B \cap A) \cap (B \cap C) = B \cap A \cap C$. Therefore, $|B \cap (A \cup C)| = 20 + 8 - 2 = 26$ and the number we seek is $|B| - 26 = 60 - 26 = 34$.

(d) Since $105 = 3(5)(7)$, an integer is relatively prime to 105 if and only if it is **not** divisible by 3, by 5, or by 7. Since 162 integers n in the range $1 \leq n \leq 300$ are divisible by at least one of these numbers, $300 - 162 = 138$ are not.

In Problem 3, we characterized the set of integers divisible by both 3 and 5 as those divisible by 15. In general, for any natural numbers a and b, how can we characterize the set of natural numbers divisible by both a and b? ∎

Pause 4 Suppose the Sieve of Eratosthenes (4.3.5) is used to enumerate all primes between 1 and 100. How many integers will remain after the first five steps of the procedure?

■

Answers to Pauses

1. See equation (3) on p. 44.
2. The number of computers with exactly two of the properties is the number with at least two less the number with exactly three; that is, $20 - 6 = 14$.
3. This set is just the set of integers divisible by the *least common multiple* of a and b since $a \mid n, b \mid n$ if and only if $\text{lcm}(a, b) \mid n$. (See Section 4.2.)
4. The integers that have been crossed out after five steps are those that are divisible by, but not equal to, at least one of 2, 3, 5, 7, 11. Letting A, B, C, D, and E be the sets of integers between 2 and 100 that are divisible by 2, by 3, by 5, by 7, and by 11, respectively, the set of numbers divisible by at least one of these has cardinality

$$|A \cup B \cup C \cup D \cup E| = (50 + 33 + 20 + 14 + 9)$$
$$- (16 + 10 + 7 + 4 + 6 + 4 + 3 + 2 + 1 + 1)$$
$$+ (3 + 2 + 1 + 1) = 79.$$

(There are no terms arising from intersections of four or five sets, since these intersections are empty.) These 79 numbers, with the exception of 2, 3, 5, 7, 11, are those that have been crossed out after five steps. So 25 numbers remain. (Remember that the list of numbers used with the Sieve of Eratosthenes starts with 2.)

True/False Questions

(Answers can be found in the back of the book.)

1. If A and B are finite sets, then $|A \cup B| \leq \max\{|A|, |B|\}$.
2. If A and B are finite sets, then $|A \oplus B| = |A \cap B^c| + |A^c \cap B|$.
3. If A and B are finite sets, then $|A \cap B| = |A| + |B| - |A \cup B|$.
4. If A and B are finite sets, then $|A \setminus B| \leq |A| - |B|$.
5. If A and B are finite sets, then $|A \times B| = |B \times A|$.
6. If A and B are finite sets and $|A \cup B| = |A| + |B|$, then $A \cap B = \emptyset$.
7. The exact statement of the Principle of Inclusion–Exclusion is $|A \cup B \cup C| = |A| + |B| + |C| - |A \cap B| - |A \cap C| - |B \cap C| + |A \cap B \cap C|$.
8. When expanding $|A_1 \cup A_2 \cup \cdots \cup A_n|$ using the Principle of Inclusion–Exclusion, there are $2^n - 1$ terms.
9. When three sets are involved, Venn diagram arguments work just as well as the Principle of Inclusion–Exclusion.
10. The Principle of Inclusion–Exclusion can be proved using mathematical induction.

Exercises

*The answers to exercises marked [BB] can be found in the **B**ack of the **B**ook.*

1. [BB] In a group of 15 pizza experts, ten like Canadian bacon, seven like anchovies, and six like both.
   (a) How many people like at least one of these toppings?
   (b) How many like Canadian bacon but not anchovies?
   (c) How many like exactly one of the two toppings?
   (d) How many like neither?

2. Multiple personality disorder (MPD) is a condition in which different personalities exist within one person and

at various times control that person's behavior. In a recent survey of people with MPD, it was reported that "98% had been emotionally abused, 89% had been physically abused, and **most** had experienced both types of abuse." Make this statement more precise.

3. Among the 30 students registered for a course in discrete mathematics, 15 people know the JAVA programming language, 12 know HTML, and 5 know both of these languages.

   (a) How many students know at least one of JAVA or HTML?

   (b) How many students know only JAVA?

   (c) How many know only HTML?

   (d) How many know exactly one of the languages JAVA and HTML?

   (e) How many students know neither JAVA nor HTML?

4. [BB] In a recent survey of college graduates, it was found that 200 had undergraduate degrees in arts, 95 had undergraduate degrees in science, and 120 had graduate degrees. Fifty-five of those with undergraduate arts degrees had also a graduate degree, 40 of those with science degrees had a graduate degree, 25 people had undergraduate degrees in both arts and science, and 5 people had undergraduate degrees in arts and science and also a graduate degree.

   (a) How many people had at least one of the types of degrees mentioned?

   (b) How many people had an undergraduate degree in science but no other degree?

5. The owner of a corner store stocks popsicles, gum, and candy bars. After school one day, he is swamped by an influx of 15 schoolchildren. They are in and out of his store in minutes. Later, the clerk reports that ten children purchased popsicles, seven purchased gum, twelve purchased candy bars, five purchased popsicles and gum, six purchased popsicles and candy bars, and two purchased gum and candy bars. The owner is very upset. Why?

6. (a) In a group of 82 students, 59 are taking English, 46 are taking mathematics, and 12 are taking neither of these subjects. How many are taking both English and math?

   (b) In a group of 97 students, the number taking English is twice the number taking math. Fifty-three students take exactly one of these subjects and 15 are taking neither course. How many students are taking math? How many are taking English?

7. [BB] Of the 2300 delegates at a political convention, 1542 voted in favor of a motion to decrease the deficit, 569 voted in favor of a motion dealing with environmental issues, and 1197 voted in favor of a motion not to increase taxes. Of those voting in favor of the motion concerning environmental issues, 327 also voted to decrease the deficit, and 92 voted not to increase taxes. Eight hundred and thirty-nine people voted to decrease the deficit while also voting against increasing taxes, but of these

839, only 50 also voted in favor of the motion dealing with the environment.

   (a) How many delegates did not vote in favor of any of the three motions?

   (b) How many of those who voted against increasing taxes voted in favor of neither of the other two motions?

8. Seven members of a group of nineteen people dislike the New Democratic Party (NDP), ten dislike the Liberals, eleven dislike the Conservatives, and six dislike the Green Party. Five of the group dislike both the Liberals and the New Democratic Party, five dislike both the NDP and the Conservatives, six dislike the Liberals and Conservatives, three dislike the New Democratic and Green parties, four dislike the Liberals and the Greens, and five dislike the Conservatives and the Greens. Three people dislike the Conservatives, Liberals, and the NDP, while two dislike the Liberals, NDP, and Green Party; three dislike the Conservatives, New Democrats, and Greens; and four dislike the Conservatives, Liberals, and Greens. Two people dislike all four parties. How many members of the group like all four parties?

9. The owner of a convenience store reports that of 890 people who bought bottled fruit juice in a recent week,
   - 750 bought orange juice.
   - 400 bought apple juice.
   - 100 bought grapefruit juice.
   - 50 bought citrus punch.
   - 328 bought orange juice and apple juice.
   - 25 bought orange juice and grapefruit juice.
   - 12 bought orange juice and citrus punch.
   - 35 bought apple juice and grapefruit juice.
   - 8 bought apple juice and citrus punch.
   - 33 bought grapefruit juice and citrus punch.
   - 4 bought orange juice, apple juice, and citrus punch.
   - 17 bought orange juice, apple juice, and grapefruit juice.
   - 2 bought citrus punch, apple juice, and grapefruit juice.
   - 9 bought orange juice, grapefruit juice and citrus punch.

   Determine the numbers of people who bought

   (a) [BB] all four kinds of juice.

   (b) grapefruit juice, but nothing else.

   (c) exactly two kinds of juice.

   (d) more than two kinds of juice.

10. Suppose U is a set containing 75 elements and A_1, A_2, A_3, A_4 are subsets of U with the following properties:
    - Each subset contains 28 elements.
    - The intersection of any two of the subsets contains 12 elements.
    - The intersection of any three of the subsets contains 5 elements.
    - The intersection of all four subsets contains 1 element.

(a) [BB] How many elements belong to none of the four subsets?

(b) How many elements belong to exactly two of the four subsets?

11. [BB] How many integers between 1 and 500 are
(a) divisible by 3 or 5?
(b) divisible by 3 but not by 5 or 6?

12. (a) How many integers less than 500 are relatively prime to 500?

(b) How many integers less than 9975 are relatively prime to 9975?

13. [BB] How many integers between 1 and 250 are divisible by at least one of the three integers 4, 6, and 15?

14. (a) [BB] How many integers between 1 and 1000 (inclusive) are not divisible by 2, 3, 5, or 7?

(b) How many integers between 1 and 1000 (exclusive) are not divisible by 2, 3, 5, or 7?

15. Find the number of integers between 1 and 10,000 inclusive that are
(a) divisible by at least one of 3, 5, 7, 11.
(b) divisible by 3 and 5, but not by either 7 or 11.
(c) divisible by exactly three of 3, 5, 7, 11.

(d) divisible by at most three of 3, 5, 7, 11.

16. How many integers between 1 and 10^6 (inclusive) are neither perfect squares nor perfect cubes? (See Exercise 31, Section 4.3.)

17. [BB] How many primes are less than 200? Explain your answer.

18. [BB] Let a and b be natural numbers. Show that the number of positive integers less than or equal to a and divisible by b is $\lfloor \frac{a}{b} \rfloor$.

19. Suppose A and B are finite sets with $|A \cup B| < |A| + |B|$. Show that A and B have an element in common.

20. [BB] Suppose A and B are finite sets. Prove that $|A \times B| = |A| \times |B|$.

21. Suppose A and B are subsets of a universal set U. Find a formula for $|A \cup B^c|$ and prove that it is correct.

22. Let A, B, and C be sets. Prove that
(a) [BB] $|(A \oplus B) \cap C| = |A \cap C| + |B \cap C| - 2|A \cap B \cap C|$
(b) $|A \oplus B \oplus C| = |A| + |B| + |C| - 2|A \cap B| - 2|A \cap C| - 2|B \cap C| + 4|A \cap B \cap C|$

23. Prove the Principle of Inclusion–Exclusion by mathematical induction. (For this, the result of Exercise 19, Section 5.1 will be helpful.)

6.2 The Addition and Multiplication Rules

The Principle of Inclusion–Exclusion gives a formula for the number of elements in the union of a finite number of finite sets. If the sets are pairwise disjoint (that is, if the intersection of any pair of sets is empty), then the formula takes a particularly simple form.

6.2.1 PRINCIPLE OF INCLUSION–EXCLUSION (DISJOINT SETS)

Given n pairwise disjoint finite sets, $A_1, A_2, \ldots, A_n$, then

$$|A_1 \cup A_2 \cup \cdots \cup A_n| = \sum_{i=1}^{n} |A_i|.$$

In this section, we use the general term *event* to mean the result of any process or experiment, for example, the courses a student selects to complete his or her degree. Events are *mutually exclusive* if no two of them can occur together; for example, if a student needs one course to complete his or her degree, then Mathematics 2320 and Statistics 2500 are mutually exclusive.

If n sets $A_1, A_2, \ldots, A_n$ correspond to events with the elements of A_i representing the ways in which the corresponding event can occur, then the events are mutually exclusive if and only if the A_i are pairwise disjoint. Thus, the Principle of Inclusion–Exclusion for disjoint sets translates into the following basic principle of counting.

6.2.2 ADDITION RULE

The number of ways in which precisely one of a collection of mutually exclusive events can occur is the sum of the numbers of ways in which each event can occur.

For example, a student who needs one course to complete her degree decides to take either computer science or statistics and makes lists of the courses for which she is eligible. The computer science courses might comprise the set $A_1 =$ {CS2602, CS2700, CS2721, CS2800, CS2500} and the statistics courses the set $A_2 =$ {S2510, S2511, S3500}. There are $5 + 3 = 8$ ways in which this student can register for a course because the two sets here are disjoint: The events "register for CS" and "register for Statistics" are mutually exclusive.

It is Friday night and Ursula has been invited to two parties but feels more inclined to go to a movie; there are six new movies in town. Assuming she is not permitted two engagements in the same evening (that is, assuming that the events "party" and "movie" are mutually exclusive), there are $2 + 6 = 8$ possible ways to spend her evening.

In the two examples just given, the individual events A_i were clearly specified. By contrast, the addition rule is probably most often applied in situations where this is not the case. A problem asking for the number of ways in which a certain event can occur can sometimes be analyzed by partitioning the event into mutually exclusive subevents (cases), precisely one of which must occur, and then applying the addition rule. It is for the problem solver to find a convenient set of subevents.

PROBLEM 4.   In how many ways can you get a total of six when rolling two dice?

Solution.   The event "get a six" is the union of the mutually exclusive subevents.

- A_1: "two 3's"
- A_2: "a 2 and a 4"
- A_3: "a 1 and a 5"

Event A_1 can occur in one way, A_2 can occur in two ways (depending on which die lands 4), and A_3 can occur in two ways, so the number of ways to get a six is $1 + 2 + 2 = 5$.

In Section 6.1, we observed that if A and B are finite sets, then the Cartesian product $A \times B$ contains $|A| \times |B|$ elements. More generally, if $A_1, A_2, \ldots, A_n$ are finite sets,

$$|A_1 \times A_2 \times \cdots \times A_n| = \prod_{i=1}^{n} |A_i|.$$

As before, thinking of A_i as the set of ways a certain event can occur, we are led to another basic principle of counting.

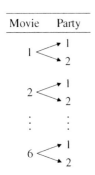

Movie   Party

Figure 6.2   There are $6 \times 2 = 12$ ways to choose one of six movies and then one of two parties.

6.2.3 MULTIPLICATION RULE

The number of ways in which a sequence of events can occur is the product of the numbers of ways in which each individual event can occur.

If Ursula's parents had a change of mind and permitted her to go to a party after the show, there would be $6 \times 2 = 12$ ways in which she could spend her Friday night, as shown in Fig. 6.2. The figure also illustrates why this number is the cardinality of the Cartesian product Movie $\times$ Party, where Movie $= \{1, 2, 3, 4, 5, 6\}$ and Party $= \{1, 2\}$.

Suppose that there are five computer science courses and three statistics courses in which a student is eligible to enroll and that this student wishes to take a course in each subject. There are $5 \times 3 = 15$ ways in which the choice can be made.

If Jack, Maurice, and Tom each roll two dice, then the number of ways in which Jack can get a total of six, Maurice a total of four, and Tom a total of three is $5 \times 3 \times 2 = 30$, since there are five ways to get a total of six, as shown before, three ways to get a total of four (two 2's, a 1 and a 3, or a 3 and a 1), and two ways to get a total of three.

There are several ways to prove that a set of n elements has 2^n subsets. We present one here that illustrates the multiplication rule.

6.2.4 PROPOSITION

A set of cardinality n contains 2^n subsets (including the empty set and the entire set itself).

Proof

Given n objects $a_1, a_2, \ldots, a_n$, each subset corresponds to a sequence of choices. Is a_1 in the subset? Is a_2 in the subset? Finally, is a_n in the subset? There are two answers to the first question, two for the second, and so on. In all, there are

$$\underbrace{2 \times 2 \times \cdots \times 2}_{n \text{ factors}} = 2^n$$

ways in which all n choices can be made. Thus, there are 2^n subsets.

We continue with a series of problems that show how the addition and multiplication rules are useful in answering questions that ask "How many?"

PROBLEM 5. How many numbers in the range 1000–9999 do not have any repeated digits?

Solution. Imagine enumerating all numbers of the desired type in the spirit of Fig. 6.2. There are nine choices for the first digit (any of 1–9). Once this has been chosen, there remain still nine choices for the second (the chosen first digit cannot be repeated but now 0 can be used). There are now eight choices for the third digit and seven for the fourth. Altogether, there are $9 \times 9 \times 8 \times 7 = 4536$ possible numbers.

PROBLEM 6. License plates in the Canadian province of Ontario consist of four letters followed by three of the digits 0–9 (not necessarily distinct). How many different license plates can be made in Ontario?

Solution. There are 26 ways in which the first letter can be chosen, 26 ways in which the second can be chosen, and similarly for the third and fourth. By the multiplication rule, the number of ways in which the three letters can be chosen is $26 \times 26 \times 26 \times 26 = 26^4$. By the same reasoning there are 10^3 ways in which the final three digits of an Ontario license plate can be selected and, all in all, $26^4 \times 10^3 = 456,976,000$ different license plates that can be manufactured by the government of Ontario under its current system.

 Pause 5

How many different license plates can be made by a government that permits four letters followed by three digits or three digits followed by four letters?

PROBLEM 7. Darlene wishes to fly from Portland, Maine, to Portland, Oregon. There are two possible routes she can take; Portland–Detroit–Portland and Portland–Chicago–Portland. Two flights from Portland to Detroit each connect with three flights from Detroit to Portland, while two flights from Portland to Chicago each connect with four flights from Chicago to Portland.

    (a) Find the total number of different flight sequences from Portland, Maine, to Portland, Oregon, via Detroit.

    (b) Repeat (a) if "via Detroit" is omitted.

Solution.   **(a)** The multiplication rule applies. There are $2 \times 3 = 6$ possibilities.

(b) By (a), there are six routes via Detroit. Also, there are $2 \times 4 = 8$ routes via Chicago. Using the addition rule, the number of routes via Detroit or Chicago is $6 + 8 = 14$.

To determine the number of ways in which some event can occur, it is often helpful to break the event into mutually exclusive subevents or cases, one of which must occur. By counting the number of ways in which each case can occur and adding these numbers, the addition rule gives the total number of ways in which the entire event can occur. Such a subtle use of the addition rule is probably its most important virtue.

PROBLEM 8. How many **even** numbers in the range 1000–9999 have no repeated digits?

Solution. The question is equivalent to asking for the number of ways in which one can write down an even number in the range 1000–9999 without using any of the ten digits 0–9 more than once. This event can be partitioned into two mutually exclusive cases.

Case 1: The number ends in 0.
In this case, there are nine choices for the first digit (1–9), then eight for the second digit (since 0 and the first digit must be excluded), and then seven for the third. So there are $9 \times 8 \times 7 = 504$ numbers of this type.

Case 2: The number does not end in 0.
Now there are four choices for the final digit (2, 4, 6, and 8), then eight choices for the first digit (0 and the last digit are excluded), eight choices for the second digit (the first and last digits are excluded), and seven choices for the third. There are $4 \times 8 \times 8 \times 7 = 1792$ numbers of this type.

By the addition rule, there are $504 + 1792 = 2296$ even numbers in the range 1000–9999 with no repeated digits.

In Case 2 of Problem 8, suppose we choose the last digit, then the second, then the first, and finally the third digit. By considering two subcases,

    2a: the second digit is 0
    2b: the second digit is not 0

show again that there are 1792 even numbers in the range 1000–9999 with no repeated digits and last digit different from 0. ∎

Answer Problem 8 again by considering these four cases:

    1. First two digits are even
    2. First two digits are odd
    3. First digit even, second digit odd
    4. First digit odd, second digit even ∎

These last two PAUSEs illustrate an important point. There are usually several ways to approach a combinatorial problem!

PROBLEM 9. A typesetter (long ago) has before him 26 trays, one for each letter of the alphabet. Each tray contains ten copies of the same letter. In how many ways can he form a three letter "word" that requires at most two different letters? By "word," we mean any sequence of three letters, xpt, for example, not necessarily a real word from a dictionary. Two "ways" are different unless they use the identical pieces of type.

Solution. The event "at most two different letters" is comprised of two mutually exclusive cases:

Case 1: The first two letters are the same.
Here, the third letter can be arbitrary; that is, any of the 258 letters that remain after the first two have been selected can be used. So the number of ways in which this case can occur is $260 \times 9 \times (260 - 2) = 603,720$.

Case 2: The first two letters are different.
In this case, the third letter must match one of the first two, so it must be one of the 18 letters remaining in the two trays used for the first two letters. The number of ways in which this case occurs is $260 \times 250 \times 18 = 1,170,000$.

By the addition rule, the number of ways to form a word using at most two different letters is $603,720 + 1,170,000 = 1,773,720$.

With many counting problems, there are several different ways of arriving at the same answer. Another approach to the previous problem is to count the total number of ways of forming words and to subtract from this the number of cases in which all three letters are different. (Recall that $|A^c| = |U| - |A|$.) There are $260 \times 259 \times 258 = 17,373,720$ possible words of which $260 \times 250 \times 240 = 15,600,000$ consist of three different letters. So the number of ways of forming words in which at most two different letters are used is $17,373,720 - 15,600,000 = 1,773,720$ as before.

PROBLEM 10. Continuing Problem 9, determine the number of ways of forming words which use **exactly** two different letters.

Solution. We subtract from the 1,773,720 cases requiring at most two different letters the number of ways of forming words that use just one letter. So the answer is $1,773,720 - (260 \times 9 \times 8) = 1,755,000$.

It is instructive to observe that this number could also be obtained by consideration of three mutually exclusive cases:

Case 1. The first two letters are the same, but the third is different.

Case 2. The first and third letters are the same, but the second is different.

Case 3. The second and third letters are the same, but different from the first.

By this method, we obtain $(260 \times 9 \times 250) + (260 \times 250 \times 9) + (250 \times 260 \times 9) = 3(260 \times 250 \times 9) = 1,755,000$, as before.

In Problems 9 and 10, we counted the number of ways of forming certain three-letter words, not the number of different words that can be formed. How many different "words" can be formed in each of these problems? ∎

Answers to Pauses

5. As in Problem 6, the number of different plates with the letters first is $26^4 \times 10^3 = 456,976,000$. Similarly, the number of different plates with the digits first is also $10^3 \times 26^4 = 456,976,000$. By the addition rule, the number of plates altogether is $456,976,000 + 456,976,000 = 913,952,000$.

6. **Case 2a:** The second digit is 0.
Here, there are four choices for the last digit, one choice for the second digit, eight choices for the first digit (which can be any of 1–9 except that chosen for the last digit), and seven choices for the third digit (which can be any of 0–9

except those three digits already chosen). There are $4 \times 1 \times 8 \times 7 = 224$ possible numbers in Case 2a.

Case 2b: The second digit is not 0.
In this case, there are again four choices for the last digit, but now eight choices for the second (which can be neither 0 nor the last digit). This leaves seven choices for the first digit (which can be any of 1–9 except those two digits already chosen) and seven choices for the third digit, as before. There are $4 \times 8 \times 7 \times 7 = 1568$ numbers in Case 2b.

As before, there are $224 + 1568 = 1792$ even numbers in Case 2.

7. *Case 1.* The first digit can be chosen in four ways (2, 4, 6, or 8), then the second digit in four ways (avoid repeating the first), the last digit in three ways (avoid repeating either of the first two) and the third digit in seven ways (avoid repeating any of the first three digits). There are $4 \times 4 \times 3 \times 7 = 336$ ways for Case 1 to occur.

Case 2. The first digit can be chosen in five ways, the second in four, the last in five, and the third in seven. There are $5 \times 4 \times 5 \times 7 = 700$ ways for Case 2 to occur.

Case 3. There are four choices for the first digit, five for the second, four for the last (avoid repeating the first), and seven for the third. There are $4 \times 5 \times 4 \times 7 = 560$ ways for Case 3 to occur.

Case 4. There are five choices for the first digit, five choices for the second, four for the last (avoid repeating the second), and seven for the third. There are $5 \times 5 \times 4 \times 7 = 700$ ways for Case 4 to occur.

By the addition rule, the number we seek is $336 + 700 + 560 + 700 = 2296$, as before.

8. In Problem 9, there are 26^2 different words that have the same first two letters and $(26)(25)(2)$ that have the first two letters different. So the answer is $26^2 + (26)(25)(2) = 1976$.

In Problem 10, there are $1976 - 26 = 1950$ words that use exactly two different letters.

True/False Questions

(Answers can be found in the back of the book.)

1. If A_1, A_2, and A_3 are pairwise disjoint sets with $|A_1| = 6$, $|A_2| = 8$, and $|A_3| = 5$, then $|A_1 \cup A_2 \cup A_3| = 6 \times 8 \times 5 = 240$.

2. Events are mutually exclusive if no two of them can occur together.

3. There are eight ways of choosing one of five chocolate bars and then one of three soft drinks.

4. There are eight ways of choosing a chairperson for a committee consisting of five men and three women.

5. There is usually only one way to solve a combinatorial problem.

6. It is often a good idea to solve a combinatorial problem by breaking it up into mutually exclusive cases.

7. The rule $|A^c| = |U| - |A|$ is sometimes helpful in solving combinatorial problems.

8. A set of cardinality five contains 31 nonempty subsets.

9. There are $26 \times 26 = 676$ different three-letter palindromes. (See Exercise 6 below.)

10. The number of different ways of answering these 10 true/false questions is 2^{10}.

Exercises

*The answers to exercises marked [BB] can be found in the **B**ack of the **B**ook.*

1. [BB] **(a)** Roberta needs two courses to complete her university degree. Three sections of the first course that meet in the morning and four sections of the second course meet in the afternoon. In how many different ways can she select the two courses she needs?

   (b) Suppose Roberta needs just one course to complete her degree. In how many ways can she select this course?

2. A building supplies store carries metal, wood, and plastic moldings. Metal and wood molding comes in two different colors. Plastic molding comes in six different colors.

   (a) How many choices of molding does this store offer?

   (b) If each kind and each color of molding comes in four different lengths, how many choices does the consumer have in the purchase of one piece of molding?

3. [BB] In how many of the three-digit numbers 000–999 are all the digits different?

4. **(a)** How many numbers in the range 100–999 have no repeated digits?

   (b) How many **odd** numbers in the range 100–999 have no repeated digits?

   (c) How many **even** numbers in the range 100–999 have no repeated digits? Answer in two different ways.

5. [BB] **(a)** Some license plates in California consist of one of the digits 1–9, followed by three (not necessarily distinct) letters and then three of the digits 0–9 (not necessarily distinct). How many possible license plates can be produced by this method?

   (b) Other California license plates consist of one of the digits 1–9 followed by one letter, and then five of the digits 0–9 (not necessarily distinct). (The same digit or letter can be used more than once.) How many license plates of this type can be made?

   (c) What is the maximum number of license plates in California that can be made assuming plates have one of the two types described in (a) and in (b)?

6. In Mark Salas, the 1991 Detroit Tigers had probably the only *palindromic* player in major league baseball (certainly, the only palindromic catcher). A *palindrome* is a word that reads the same forward and backward, like SALAS.

   (a) How many five-letter palindromes (not necessarily real words) can be made from the letters of the English alphabet?

   (b) How many eight-letter palindromes are possible?

   (c) How many "words" not exceeding eight letters in length are palindromes?

   (d) One of the most famous palindromes of all time is one that might have been uttered by Napoleon (had his native tongue been English): ABLE WAS I ERE I SAW ELBA. How many palindromes (not necessarily real words) are of this length?

7. [BB] From a group of 13 men, 6 women, 2 boys, and 4 girls,

   (a) In how many ways can a man, a woman, a boy, and a girl be selected?

   (b) In how many ways can a man or a girl be selected?

   (c) In how many ways can one person be selected?

8. From a standard deck of 52 playing cards, in how many ways can you draw

   (a) a heart or a spade?   **(b)** an ace or a king?

   (c) a card numbered 2 through 10?

   (d) a card numbered 2 through 10 or a king?

9. [BB] Using only the digits 1, 3, 4, and 7,

   (a) how many two-digit numbers can be formed?

   (b) how many three-digit numbers can be formed?

   (c) how many two- or three-digit numbers can be formed?

10. How many possible telephone numbers consist of seven digits, the first two in the range 2–9 (inclusive), the third in the range 1–9 (inclusive), and each of the last four in the range 0–9 (inclusive)?

11. [BB] A company produces combination locks, the combinations consisting of three different numbers in the range 0–59 (inclusive) that must be dialed in order. How many different combinations are possible?

12. In how many ways can two adjacent squares be selected from an 8 × 8 chess board?

13. [BB] New parents wish to give their baby one, two, or three different names. In how many ways can the baby be named if the parents will choose from a book containing 500 names?

14. There are three different roads from Cupids to Harbour Grace and five different roads from Harbour Grace to Heart's Desire.

    (a) How many different routes are there from Cupids to Heart's Desire via Harbour Grace?

    (b) How many different round trips are there from Cupids to Heart's Desire and back, passing through Harbour Grace each way?

    (c) Repeat (b) if you don't want to drive on any road more than once.

15. How many three-digit numbers contain the digits 2 and 5 but none of the digits 0, 3, 7?

16. You are dealt four cards from a standard deck of 52 playing cards. In how many ways can you get

    (a) [BB] four of a kind (four 2's, or four kings, etc.)?

(b) two (different) pairs?

(c) four of a kind or two (different) pairs?

(d) three, but not four, of a kind?

(e) at least one pair?

17. Two dice are rolled.

   (a) In how many ways can a total of eight arise?

   (b) In how many ways can a total of seven arise?

   (c) In how many ways can a total of eight or seven arise?

   (d) In how many ways can you get "doubles" (the dice land with the same side up)?

18. [BB] Make a table that shows all the possible totals when two dice are rolled and the number of ways in which each total can occur.

19. **(a)** In how many ways can two dice land?

   (b) In how many ways can five dice land?

   (c) In how many ways can n dice land?

   (d) If n dice are rolled, in how many ways can they land not all showing the same number?

20. A coin is tossed four times.

   (a) [BB] Make a list of all the possible outcomes. For example, the sequence HHTH, representing head, head, tail, head, is one possibility. How many possibilities are there altogether?

   (b) In how many ways can you get

      i. exactly one head?   **ii.** exactly two heads?
      iii. exactly three heads?   **iv.** at least one head?

21. **(a)** How many five-digit numbers can be formed using the digits 0–9 inclusive if repetitions are allowed? (Leading 0's are not allowed: 07392, for example, should not be considered a five-digit number.)

   (b) How many five-digit numbers can be formed if repetition is not allowed?

   (c) How many five-digit numbers have one or more repeated digits?

22. How many possible license plates can be manufactured if a license plate consists of three letters followed by three digits and

   (a) [BB] the digits must be distinct; the letters can be arbitrary?

   (b) the letters must be distinct; the digits can be arbitrary?

   (c) the digits and the letters must be distinct?

23. The complete menu from a local gourmet restaurant is shown in Table 6.3.

(a) In how many ways can John plan a four-course meal, one course from each group?

(b) Suppose Mary wants two appetizers and one course from each other group. How many meals are possible?

(c) Mike wants a two-course meal. How many choices does he have?

(d) Suppose Rod wants at most one course from each group and at least one course from some group. How many meals are possible?

Table 6.3

Appetizers	Beverages
cod au gratin	house wine
squid ribs	imported wine
snail's tails	soft drink
smoked seaweed	coffee
	tea
	milk

Entrée	Vegetables
flipper pie	spinach
cod tongues	fiddleheads
caplin fillets	cabbage
	turnip
	potatoes

24. Suppose $n = p_1^{\alpha_1} p_2^{\alpha_2} \cdots p_r^{\alpha_r}$ is the decomposition of n into the product of powers of distinct primes $p_1, p_2, \ldots, p_r$. How many (unordered) pairs $\{s, t\}$ of positive integers satisfy both $st = n$ and $\gcd(s, t) = 1$?

25. [BB] Let $A = \{a_1, a_2, \ldots, a_n\}$ be a set of n elements and $B = \{0, 1\}$.

   (a) Show that there are 2^n functions from A to B.

   (b) Show that there are $2^n - 2$ onto functions from A to B.

26. Let $A = \{a_1, a_2, \ldots, a_n\}$ be a set of n elements, $n \geq 1$, and $B = \{1, 2, 3\}$.

   (a) Prove that there are 3^n functions $A \to B$.

   (b) How many functions $A \to B$ are **not** onto?

   (c) How many onto functions are there $A \to B$? Justify your answer.

6.3 The Pigeonhole Principle

This section deals with a deceptively simple restatement of a certain fact about functions between finite sets: if A and B are finite sets with $|A| > |B|$, no function $f : A \to B$ can be one-to-one. For example, no function $\{1, 2, 3\} \to \{x, y\}$ can be one-to-one.

Think of B as a set of birdhouses, A as a set of pigeons, and f as a function that assigns a birdhouse to each pigeon. The statement that f is not one-to-one is just the observation that at least two pigeons live in the same house. Thus, we obtain the *Pigeonhole Principle*.

6.3.1 THE PIGEONHOLE PRINCIPLE

If n objects are put into m boxes and $n > m$, then at least one box contains two or more of the objects.

We said that this principle is "deceptively" simple. The deception often lies in recognizing that the principle can be applied. For example, within any group of 13 people, there must be two who have their birthdays in the same month. (The people are the objects and the months of the year are the boxes.)

PROBLEM 11. Given five points inside a square whose sides have length 2, prove that two are within $\sqrt{2}$ of each other.

Solution. Subdivide the square into four squares with sides of length 1, as shown. By the Pigeonhole Principle, at least two of the five chosen points must lie in, or on the boundary of, the same smaller square. But these points are at most $\sqrt{2}$ apart (the length of the diagonal of a smaller square). ⬛

We continue with some subtler applications of the Pigeonhole Principle.

PROBLEM 12. Show that among $n + 1$ arbitrarily chosen integers, there must exist two whose difference is divisible by n.

Solution. Denote the integers $a_1, a_2, \dots, a_{n+1}$. As we know, the n congruence classes $\overline{0}, \overline{1}, \dots, \overline{n-1}$ of integers mod n partition the integers into disjoint sets whose union is **Z**. (See Proposition 4.4.5.) Put each integer a_i into its own congruence class. By the Pigeonhole Principle, two integers, a_i and a_j will go to the same class $\overline{k}$. Since $a_i \in \overline{k}$, $\overline{a_i} = \overline{k}$ (Proposition 4.4.3) and, similarly, $\overline{a_j} = \overline{k}$. Thus, $\overline{a_i} = \overline{a_j}$, so $a_i \equiv a_j \pmod{n}$; that is, $n \mid (a_i - a_j)$, as desired. ⬛

The solution to Problem 12 involves a property of the integers that is often used in Pigeonhole problems: If two numbers lie in the same congruence class of integers mod n, then their difference is divisible by n.

PROBLEM 13. Prove that in any list of 10 natural numbers, $a_1, a_2, \dots, a_{10}$, there is a string of consecutive items of the list $a_\ell, a_{\ell+1}, a_{\ell+2}, \dots$ whose sum is divisible by 10. (We include the possibility that the "string" consists of just one number.)

Solution. Consider the ten numbers

$$a_1, a_1 + a_2, a_1 + a_2 + a_3, \dots, a_1 + a_2 + \cdots + a_{10}.$$

If any of these is divisible by 10, we have the desired conclusion; otherwise, each number lies in one of the nine congruence classes $\overline{1}, \overline{2}, \dots, \overline{9}$ of integers mod 10. By the Pigeonhole Principle, two of them must lie in the same class and hence have a difference divisible by 10. Again we reach the desired conclusion because, if $s > t$, $(a_1 + a_2 + \cdots + a_s) - (a_1 + a_2 + \cdots + a_t) = a_{t+1} + a_{t+2} + \cdots + a_s$. ⬛

PROBLEM 14. Martina has three weeks to prepare for a tennis tournament. She decides to play at least one set every day, but not more than 41 sets in all. Show that there is a period of consecutive days during which she will play exactly 21 sets.

Solution. Suppose Martina plays a_1 sets on day 1, a_2 sets on day 2, and so on, and eventually a_{21} sets on the last day of her preparation period. Consider the 21 natural numbers $a_1, a_1 + a_2, \ldots, a_1 + a_2 + \cdots + a_{21}$. Since each $a_i \geq 1$ and since the sum $a_1 + a_2 + \cdots + a_{21}$ is the total number of sets Martina will play, we have

$$1 \leq a_1 < a_1 + a_2 < \cdots < a_1 + a_2 + \cdots + a_{21} \leq 41.$$

Now the only natural number between 1 and 41 that is divisible by 21 is 21 itself. Therefore, each of these sums is either 21 or it belongs to one of the 20 nonzero congruence classes of integers mod 21. In the first case, we have $a_1 + a_2 + \cdots + a_i = 21$ for some i; so Martina would play precisely 21 sets on days 1 through i, giving the desired result. In the second case, by the Pigeonhole Principle, two sums lie in the same congruence class and hence have a difference divisible by 21. As in Problem 13, we obtain $a_{t+1} + a_{t+2} + \cdots + a_s$ divisible by 21 for some s and t. Since this is a number between 1 and 41, it must equal 21, and we conclude that Martina plays 21 games on days $t + 1$ through s. ▲

PROBLEM 15. Suppose Martina has 11 weeks to prepare for her tournament and that she intends to play at least one set a day and at most 132 practice sets in all. Draw again the conclusion that during some period of consecutive days Martina will play precisely 21 sets.

Solution. The approach used before doesn't work this time (see Exercise 10), so we find a slightly different solution. We let b_i be the number of sets Martina plays on days 1 through i inclusive ($b_i = a_1 + a_2 + \cdots + a_i$ in the notation of Problem 14) and consider the 154 numbers

$$b_1, b_2, \ldots, b_{77}, b_1 + 21, b_2 + 21, \ldots, b_{77} + 21.$$

The largest number here, $b_{77} + 21$, is at most $132 + 21 = 153$. By the Pigeonhole Principle, we conclude that two are the same. Since $b_i > b_j$ if $i > j$, the only way for two to be equal is for $b_i = b_j + 21$ for some i and j with $i > j$. Therefore, $b_i - b_j = 21$ and Martina plays 21 sets on days $j + 1$ through i. ▲

We noted earlier that in any group of 13 people at least two must have birthdays in the same month. The same must hold in any larger group, but surely something stronger is also true. If at most two people in a group of 30 had birthdays in the same month, we would account for at most 24 people. Thus, in any group of 30, there must be at least **three** with birthdays in the same month.

Recall the definition of the *ceiling function* given in 3.1.7. For any real number x, $\lceil x \rceil$ means the least integer that is greater than or equal to x. For example, $\lceil 3.5 \rceil = 4$, $\lceil 0.24 \rceil = 1$, $\lceil -2.9 \rceil = -2$, and $\lceil \frac{30}{12} \rceil = 3$.

6.3.2 PIGEONHOLE PRINCIPLE (STRONG FORM)

If n objects are put into m boxes and $n > m$, then some box must contain at least $\lceil \frac{n}{m} \rceil$ objects.

EXAMPLE 16   If there are 44 chairs positioned around five tables in a room, some table must have at least $\lceil \frac{44}{5} \rceil = 9$ chairs around it. ▨

To prove the strong form of the Pigeonhole Principle, we establish the truth of its contrapositive. Note that

$$\left\lceil \frac{n}{m} \right\rceil < \frac{n}{m} + 1 \quad \text{and hence} \quad \left\lceil \frac{n}{m} \right\rceil - 1 < \frac{n}{m}$$

because, for any real number x,

$$x \leq \lceil x \rceil < x + 1.$$

Thus, if a box contains fewer than $\lceil \frac{n}{m} \rceil$ objects, then it contains at most $\lceil \frac{n}{m} \rceil - 1$ and so fewer than $\frac{n}{m}$ objects. If all m boxes are like this, we account for fewer than $m \times \frac{n}{m} = n$ objects.

PROBLEM 17. In any group of six people, at least three must be mutual friends or at least three must be mutual strangers.

Solution. Pretend you are one of the six people and put the other $n = 5$ people into $m = 2$ "boxes" labeled "my friends" and "strangers to me." Since $\lceil \frac{n}{m} \rceil = \lceil \frac{5}{2} \rceil = 3$, by the strong form of the Pigeonhole Principle, at least one of these boxes must contain three people. Suppose three people are your friends. If any two of these three are friends, then, together with you, we have a set of three mutual friends. If no two of these three are friends, then these three people are mutual strangers. In either case, we have one of the desired conclusions. The remaining possibility, that three of the five people are strangers to you, leads again to the desired conclusion with an argument, which we omit, similar to the one already presented. ▲

Provide the details of this omitted argument. ∎

Answer to Pause

9. Either the three people in this group are mutual friends or there are two who are strangers. Since each of these two is a stranger to you, we have a set of three mutual strangers.

True/False Questions

(Answers can be found in the back of the book.)

1. If A and B are finite sets with $|A| > |B|$, then no function $f : A \rightarrow B$ can be one-to-one.
2. The Pigeonhole Principle is named after the famous Canadian combinatorist Fred Pigeon.
3. In a group of 15 people, there must be 2 who have their birthdays in the same month.
4. In a group of 366 people, there must be 2 who have their birthdays on the same day.
5. If two integers lie in the same congruence class of integers mod n, then their difference is divisible by n.
6. If n objects are put into m boxes and $n < m$, then at least one box contains two or more of the objects.
7. It is not always easy to see how to apply the Pigeonhole Principle.
8. In a group of 49 people, there must be 6 who have their birthdays in the same month.
9. In n objects are put into m boxes and $n > m$, then some box must contain at least $\lceil \frac{n}{m} \rceil$ objects.
10. In any group of three people, either all three are mutual friends or all three are mutual strangers.

Exercises

*The answers to exercises marked [BB] can be found in the **B**ack of the **B**ook.*

1. [BB] Show that in any group of eight people at least two have birthdays that fall on the same day of the week in any given year.

2. Write down any six natural numbers. Verify that there is a string of consecutive numbers in your list (possibly a string of just one number) whose sum is divisible by 6. Prove that this must always be the case.

3. In any list of n natural numbers, prove that there must always exist a string of consecutive numbers (possibly just one number in the string) whose sum is divisible by n.

4. [BB] In a group of 100 people, several will have their birthdays in the same month. At least how many must have birthdays in the same month? Why?

5. You are given 102 points inside a square of side 2.
   (a) You can be assured that at least how many points are within $\sqrt{2}$ of each other?
   (b) You can be assured that at least two points are how close to each other?

6. A standard deck of playing cards contains 52 cards divided into four suits (club, diamond, heart, spade) of 13 denominations (Ace, 2, 3, . . . , 10, Jack, Queen, King). How many cards of a single suit must be present in any set of n cards? How many cards of the same denomination? Explain.

7. (a) [BB] If 20 processors are interconnected and every processor is connected to at least one other, show that at least two processors are directly connected to the same number of processors.
   (b) [BB] Is the result of (a) still true without the assumption that every processor is connected to at least one other? Explain.

8. Thirty buses are to be used to transport 2000 refugees from Gander to St. John's, Newfoundland. Each bus has 80 seats. Assume one seat per passenger.
   (a) Prove that one of the buses will carry at least 67 passengers.
   (b) Prove that one of the buses will have at least 14 empty seats.

9. In a gathering of 30 people, there are 104 different pairs of people who know each other.
   (a) Show that some person must have at least seven acquaintances.
   (b) Show that some person must have fewer than seven acquaintances.

10. [BB] Try to solve Problem 15 with the method used to solve Problem 14. What goes wrong?

11. [BB] Brad has five weeks to prepare for his driver's test. His mother volunteers to drive with him for either 15 minutes or a half-hour every day until the test, but not for more than 15 hours in all. Show that during some period of consecutive days Brad and his mother will drive for exactly eight and three quarter-hours.

12. Linda has six weeks to prepare for an examination and at most 50 hours available to study. She plans to study at least an hour a day and a whole number of hours each day. Show that no matter how she schedules her study time there is a period of consecutive days during which she will have studied exactly 33 hours.

13. George has promised to increase his vocabulary by learning the meanings of 90 new words during his summer holidays. Suppose he has 53 days in which to accomplish this task and he will learn at least one new word a day. Show that during some span of consecutive days George will learn precisely 15 new words.

14. [BB] In a 12-day period, a small business mailed 195 bills to customers. Show that during some period of three consecutive days at least 49 bills were mailed.

15. The circumference of a roulette wheel is divided into 36 sectors to which the numbers 1, 2, 3, . . . , 36 are assigned in some arbitrary manner. Show that there must be three consecutive sectors whose assigned numbers add to at least 56.

16. What is the smallest number of seats in a large auditorium that must be occupied in order to be certain that at least three people in attendance have the same first and last initials?

17. [BB] Of any 26 points within a rectangle measuring 20 cm by 15 cm, show that at least two are within 5 cm of each other.

18. Of any five points chosen within an equilateral triangle whose sides have length 1, show that two are within a distance of $\frac{1}{2}$ of each other.

19. A cake is in the shape of a regular hexagon with each of its sides exactly 30 cm long. Seven flowers of icing adorn the top. Show that at least two flowers are not more than 30 cm apart.

20. Let $S = \{2, 3, 5, 7, 11, 13, 17, 19\}$ be the set of prime numbers less than 20. If A is a subset of S, we can form the sum and product of the elements of A. For example, if $A = \{7, 11, 13\}$, then the associated sum is $7 + 11 + 13 = 31$ and the associated product is $7(11)(13) = 1001$.
   (a) Use the Pigeonhole Principle to show that there are four nonempty subsets of S with the same sum.
   (b) Are there two nonempty subsets of S with the same product? Explain.

21. [BB] Given any positive integer n, show that some multiple of n is an integer whose representation in base 10 requires just 3's and 0's. [*Hint*: Let $M_1 = 3$, $M_2 = 33$, $M_3 = 333, \ldots$. Then think about the remainders when each of these numbers is divided by n.]

22. Show that some multiple of 2002 consists of a string of 1's followed by a string of 0's.

23. [BB] Show that the decimal expansion of a rational number must, after some point, become periodic or stop. [*Hint*: Think about the remainders in the process of long division.]

24. One hundred and one numbers are chosen from the set $\{1, 2, 3, \ldots, 200\}$. Show that one must be a multiple of another. [*Hint*: Any natural number can be written in the form $2^k a$ with $k \geq 0$ and a odd.]

25. In a room where there are more than 50 people with ages between 1 and 100, show the following:
   (a) [BB] Either two people have the same age or there are two people whose ages are consecutive integers.

(b) Either two people have the same age or one person's age is a multiple of another's.

(c) Some of the people shake hands. Show that at least two shook the same number of hands. ("No hands" is a possibility.)

(d) Some people shake hands. Show that among those who shook at least one hand, two people shook the same number of hands.

26. (a) Let A be a set of seven (distinct) natural numbers none of which exceeds 21. Prove that the sums of the elements in all the nonempty subsets of A are not distinct.

(b) Improve the result of (a) by showing that the result holds under the assumption that the integers of A do not exceed 23.

(c) Assume none of the elements of A exceeds 12. At least how many subsets of A must have the same sum?

27. (a) [BB] Show that in any group of 10 people there is either a set of three mutual strangers or a set of four mutual friends.

(b) Show that in any group of 20 people there is either a set of four mutual strangers or a set of four mutual friends.

28. Suppose $a_1, a_2, \ldots, a_{10}$ are 10 integers between 1 and 100 (inclusive).

(a) [BB] Prove that there exist two subsets $\{a_{i_1}, a_{i_2}, \ldots, a_{i_r}\}$ and $\{a_{j_1}, a_{j_2}, \ldots, a_{j_s}\}$ with equal sums.

(b) Prove that there exist two **disjoint** subsets $\{a_{i_1}, a_{i_2}, \ldots, a_{i_r}\}$ and $\{a_{j_1}, a_{j_2}, \ldots, a_{j_s}\}$ with equal sums.

29. Prove the (first form of the) Pigeonhole Principle by mathematical induction on m, the number of boxes.

30. Given any 52 integers, show that there exist two whose sum or difference is divisible by 100. [*Hint*: $x_1 \pm x_i$.]

Review Exercises for Chapter 6

1. Suppose A and B are nonempty finite sets and $|A \cup B| < |A| + |B|$. Show that $A \cap B \neq \emptyset$.

2. Using the Principle of Inclusion–Exclusion, find the number of integers between 1 and 2000 (inclusive) that are divisible by at least one of 2, 3, 5, 7.

3. John Sununu was once the governor of New Hampshire, and his name reminds one of the authors of a palindrome.

(a) What is a *palindrome* and what made the author think of this?

(b) How many seven-letter palindromes (not necessarily real words) begin with the letter S and contain at most three different letters?

(c) How many seven-letter palindromes (not necessarily real words) are there in all?

(d) How many seven-letter palindromes contain at most three different letters one of which is S?

(e) Name a palindromic rock band of the late 1970s that is still popular today.

4. Two Math 2320 students are arguing about the number of palindromes with nine and ten letters. One claims there are more with ten letters than with nine; the other says there are the same number in each case. Who is right? Explain.

5. Four sets A_1, A_2, A_3, A_4 have the property that $A_i \cap A_j \cap A_k = \emptyset$ whenever i, j, k are distinct. In addition, $|A_i \cap A_j| = 1$ whenever $i \neq j$ and $|A_i| = 5$ for all i. Find the number of elements that belong to at least one of the sets.

6. Seventy cars sit on a parking lot. Thirty have stereo systems, 30 have air conditioners and 40 have sun roofs. Thirty of the cars have at least two of these three options and 10 have all three. How many cars on the lot have at least one of these three options? How many have exactly one?

7. State the **strong form** of the Pigeonhole Principle.

8. Show that among 18 arbitrarily chosen integers there must exist two whose difference is divisible by 17.

9. Use the Pigeonhole Principle and the definition of *infinite set* to prove that Z is infinite.

10. Show that, of any ten points chosen within an equilateral triangle whose sides have length 1, there are two whose distance apart is at most $\frac{1}{3}$.

11. Five hermits live on a rectangular island 6 kilometers wide and 8 kilometers long. Show that two of them live at most 5 kilometres apart.

12. (a) Suppose the positive integer $n > 1$ is written $n = p_1^{a_1} p_2^{a_2} \cdots p_s^{a_s}$ as the product of powers of primes $p_1, p_2, \ldots, p_s$. How many factors does n have?

(b) Let $n > 1$ be an integer. Prove that n is a perfect square if and only if n has an odd number of factors.

(c) You and a buddy decide to paint a picket fence in which the pickets are numbered $1, 2, 3, \ldots, n$ in a rather strange way. First, you paint the fence white. Then your buddy paints pickets 2, 4, 6, 8, ... black. You grab some black paint as well as your white, and change the colors of pickets 3, 6, 9, 12, ... Infuriated, your buddy grabs some white paint (as well as his black) and changes the colors of pickets 4, 8, 12, 16, ... Then you change the colors of all pickets numbered a multiple of 5 white, and so on. This continues until eventually, one of you changes the color of last picket. At this point, which pickets are painted white? Experiment with fences that contain only a few pickets. Then make a guess about an n-picket fence and prove that your guess is right.

7

Permutations and Combinations

7.1 Permutations

The registrar of a school must schedule six examinations in an eight-day period and has promised the students not to schedule more than one examination per day. How many different schedules can be made? The answer to this question involves a straightforward application of the multiplication rule. The first exam can be given on any of the eight days, but once this day has been settled, the second exam can be given on only one of the remaining seven days. There are $8 \times 7 = 56$ pairs of days on which the first two examinations can be scheduled. Once the first two exams have been scheduled, there remain six days on which to schedule the third exam. Continuing to reason this way, we see that there are $8 \times 7 \times 6 \times 5 \times 4 \times 3 = 20,160$ possible schedules.

In how many ways can a blue, a white, and a red marble be put into 10 numbered boxes? If there is no limit on the number of marbles that can be put into a box, there are 10 possible boxes into which the blue marble can be placed and then 10 choices for the white one and 10 choices for the red one, giving $10^3 = 1000$ possibilities altogether. Suppose, on the other hand, we are not allowed to put more than one marble into a box. As before, there are 10 possible boxes for the blue marble, but now there are just 9 possible boxes for the white one, and 8 for the red. Altogether, there are $10 \times 9 \times 8 = 720$ possibilities.

The solution to a counting problem often involves the product of consecutive integers. Remember that $n!$ denotes the product of all the natural numbers from 1 to n (inclusive):

$$n! = n(n-1)(n-2)\cdots(3)(2)(1)$$

(see Definition 5.1.2). The notation $P(n, r)$ denotes the product of the first r factors of $n!$.

7.1.1 DEFINITION   For integers n and r, $n \geq 1, 0 \leq r \leq n$, the symbol $P(n, r)$ is defined by $P(n, 0) = 1$ and, for $r > 0$,

$$P(n, r) = \underbrace{n(n-1)(n-2)\cdots(n-r+1)}_{r \text{ factors}}. \qquad \diamond$$

For example, $P(6, 2) = 6 \cdot 5 = 30$ (the first two factors of 6!), $P(7, 3) = 7 \cdot 6 \cdot 5 = 210$ (the first three factors of 7!), $P(8, 5) = 8 \cdot 7 \cdot 6 \cdot 5 \cdot 4 = 6720$, $P(12, 0) = 1$, and so on.

Find $P(5, 3)$, $P(4, 4)$, and $P(7, 2)$. ∎

Among the combinatorial problems to which $P(n, r)$ is the answer is the following, which we have already illustrated.

7.1.2 PROPOSITION

Given natural numbers r and n with $r \leq n$, the number of ways to place r marbles of different colors into n numbered boxes, at most one marble to a box, is $P(n, r)$.

Notice that

$$\underbrace{n(n-1)(n-2)\cdots(n-r+1)}_{P(n,r)}\underbrace{(n-r)(n-r-1)\cdots(3)(2)(1)}_{(n-r)!} = n!.$$

Thus,

$$P(n, r) = \frac{n!}{(n-r)!}$$

a formula that holds also for $r = 0$ and $r = n$ because $P(n, 0) = 1$ and $0! = 1$.

Some people have been known to protest that this formula is difficult to use because, for example, they are unable to evaluate numbers like $P(25, 1) = \frac{25!}{24!}$ with their calculator, 25! being too large to compute. It is good for us all to notice that

$$\frac{25!}{24!} = \frac{25 \cdot \cancel{24} \cdot \cancel{23} \cdots \cancel{3} \cdot \cancel{2}}{\cancel{24} \cdot \cancel{23} \cdots \cancel{3} \cdot \cancel{2}} = 25.$$

Find $\frac{20!}{17!}$, $\frac{100!}{98!}$, and $P(7, 0)$. ∎

For us, the symbol $P(n, r)$ is primarily a notational device that makes it easy to write down the answers to certain combinatorial problems. We caution against trying to fit a problem involving a straightforward application of the multiplication rule into the context of marbles and boxes.

PROBLEM 1. How many pairs of dance partners can be selected from a group of 12 women and 20 men?

Solution. The first woman can be paired with any of 20 men, the second woman with any of the remaining 19 men, the third with any of the remaining 18, and so on. There are $20 \cdot 19 \cdot 18 \cdots 9 = P(20, 12)$ possible couples. ▲

There is a second question, having to do with *permutations*, to which $P(n, r)$ is the answer and that explains the "P" in "$P(n, r)$."

7.1.3 DEFINITION

A *permutation* of a set of distinct symbols is an arrangement of them in a line in some order. ❖

EXAMPLE 2

ab and *ba* are permutations of the symbols *a* and *b*; 1642, 4126, and 6241 are permutations of the symbols 1, 2, 4, and 6. ▨

The permutations 1642, 4126, and 6241 are also examples of 4-*permutations* of the symbols 1, 2, 3, 4, 5, 6, that is, permutations of the symbols 1, 2, 3, 4, 5, 6 *taken four at a time*. Here are some 3-permutations of the 26 letters of the alphabet: *zxy*, *aqr*, *cat*, *how*.

7.1.4 DEFINITION   For natural numbers r and n, $r \leq n$, an *r-permutation* of n symbols is a permutation of r of them, that is, an arrangement of r of the symbols in a line in some order. ❖

As a direct consequence of the multiplication rule, we have the following.

7.1.5 PROPOSITION   The number of permutations of n symbols is $n!$. The number of r-permutations of n symbols is $P(n, r)$.

For example, there are $3! = 6$ permutations of a, b, c, that is, abc, acb, bac, bca, cab, and cba. (There are three choices for the first symbol and then two for the second and one for the third.) There are $6 \cdot 5 \cdot 4 \cdot 3 = 360 = P(6, 4)$ ways in which four of the six creatures—man, woman, boy, girl, dog, cat—can walk in a line down a road, one after the other.

PROBLEM 3.   There are $7! = 5040$ ways in which seven people can form a line. In how many ways can seven people form a circle?

Solution. A circle is determined by the order of the people to the right of any one of the individuals, say Eric. There are six possibilities for the person on Eric's right, then five possibilities for the next person, four for the next, and so on. The number of possible circles is $6! = 720$.

Another way to obtain $6!$ is to relate the two problems, line and circle. Each circle determines seven lines, determined by asking the people to join hands and then breaking the circle at one of the seven people.

$$\text{No. of circles} \times 7 = \text{no. of lines} = 7!$$

$$\text{Therefore, no. of circles} = \frac{7!}{7} = 6!$$

PROBLEM 4.   A man, woman, boy, girl, dog, and cat are walking down a long and winding road one after the other.

- **(a)** In how many ways can this happen?
- **(b)** In how many ways can this happen if the dog comes first?
- **(c)** In how many ways can this happen if the dog immediately follows the boy?
- **(d)** In how many ways can this happen if the dog (and only the dog) is between the man and the boy?
- **(e)** In how many ways can this happen if the dog is between the man and the boy?

Solution.   **(a)** There are $6! = 720$ ways for six creatures to form a line.
- **(b)** If the dog comes first, the others can form $5! = 120$ lines behind.
- **(c)** If the dog immediately follows the boy, then the dog–boy pair should be thought of as a single object to be put into a line with four others. There are $5!$ such lines.
- **(d)** If the man, dog, and boy appear in this order, then thinking of man–dog–boy as a single object to be put into a line with three others, we see that there

are 4! possible lines. Similarly, there are 4! lines in which the boy, dog, and man appear in this order. So, by the addition rule, there are $4! + 4! = 48$ lines in which the dog (and only the dog) is between the man and the boy.

(e) **Solution 1.** There are $2 \times 4! = 48$ lines with the dog and only the dog between the man and the boy. There are $3 \times 2 \times 2 \times 3! = 72$ lines with the dog and one other creature between the man and the boy. There are $3 \times 3! \times 2 \times 2$ lines with the dog and two other creatures between the man and the boy, and there are $4! \times 2$ lines with four creatures between the man and the boy. In all, the number of lines of the sought after type is $48 + 72 + 72 + 48 = 240$.

Solution 2. There are 6! lines altogether. In each of these lines, the man, dog, and boy appear in some order. There are $3! = 6$ possible orders, and in 2 of these the dog is between the man and the boy. So the number of lines with the dog between the man and the boy is $\frac{2}{6} \times 6! = 240$. ▲

PROBLEM 5. In how many ways can ten adults and five children stand in a line so that no two children are next to each other?

Solution. Imagine a line of ten adults named $A, B, \ldots, J$,

$$\times D \times J \times H \times C \times I \times E \times B \times A \times G \times F \times ,$$

the $\times$'s representing the 11 possible locations for the children. For each such line, the first child can be positioned in any of the 11 spots, the second child in any of the remaining 10, and so on. Hence, the children can be positioned in $11 \cdot 10 \cdot 9 \cdot 8 \cdot 7 = P(11, 5)$ ways. For each such positioning, there are 10! ways of ordering the adults $A, \ldots, J$, so, by the multiplication rule, the number of lines of adults and children is $10! P(11, 5)$. ▲

 In how many ways can ten adults and five children stand in a circle so that no two children are next to each other? ∎

PROBLEM 6. In how many ways can the letters of the English alphabet be arranged so that there are exactly ten letters between a and z?

Solution. There are $P(24, 10)$ arrangements of the letters of the alphabet (excluding a and z) taken ten at a time, and hence $2 \cdot P(24, 10)$ strings of 12 letters, each beginning and ending with an a and a z (either letter coming first in a string). For each of these strings, there are 15! ways to arrange the 14 remaining letters and the string. So there are altogether $2 \cdot P(24, 10) \cdot 15!$ arrangements of the desired type. ▲

 The answer to Problem 6 is also $30(24!)$. Why? ∎

Answers to Pauses

1. $P(5, 3) = 5 \cdot 4 \cdot 3 = 60$; $P(4, 4) = 4 \cdot 3 \cdot 2 \cdot 1 = 24$; $P(7, 2) = 7 \cdot 6 = 42$.
2. $\frac{20!}{17!} = 20 \cdot 19 \cdot 18 = 6840$; $\frac{100!}{98!} = 100 \cdot 99 = 9900$; $P(7, 0) = \frac{7!}{7!} = 1$.
3. Arrange the adults into a circle in one of 9! ways. There are then 10 locations for the first child, 9 for the second, 8 for the third, 7 for the fourth, and 6 for the fifth. The answer is $9!(10 \cdot 9 \cdot 8 \cdot 7 \cdot 6) = 9! \cdot P(10, 5)$.
4. First we count the number of arrangements of the prescribed type in which a precedes z. For each of the 24! permutations of the letters b through y, there are 15 locations for a after which the position of z is fixed. Thus, there are 15(24!)

arrangements with a preceding z. Similarly, there are $15(24!)$ arrangements with z preceding a giving, altogether, $2(15)(24!)$ arrangements.

(Answers can be found in the back of the book.)

1. $5! = 120$
2. $0! = 0$
3. If n is any natural number, then $P(n, 1) = n$.
4. If r and n are natural numbers with $r \le n$, then $P(n, r) = P(n, n - r)$.
5. The number of ways of placing seven marbles of different colors into 11 numbered boxes, at most one marble to a box, is $P(11, 7)$.
6. A permutation of a set of distinct symbols is an arrangement of them in a line in some order.
7. An r-permutation of n symbols is a permutation of $n - r$ of them.
8. There are 20 3-permutations of five symbols.
9. There are $4! = 24$ ways in which five people can form a line.
10. There are $4! = 24$ ways in which five people can form a circle.

Exercises

*The answers to exercises marked [BB] can be found in the **Back** of the **Book**.*

1. [BB] How many ways are there to distribute eight different books among thirteen people if no person is to receive more than one book?

2. Eight horses are entered in a race in which a first, second, and third prize will be awarded. Assuming no ties, how many different outcomes are possible?

3. [BB] A club has ten members. In how many ways can they choose a slate of four officers consisting of a president, vice-president, secretary, and treasurer?

4. There are 30 people in a class learning about permutations. One after another, eight people gradually slip out the back door. In how many ways can this exodus occur?

5. [BB] Find the number of ways in which six children can ride a toboggan if one of the three girls must steer (and therefore sit at the back).

6. Four cats and five mice enter a race. In how many ways can they finish with a mouse placing first, second, and third?

7. (a) In how many ways can ten boys and four girls sit in a row?

   (b) [BB] In how many ways can they sit in a row if the boys are to sit together and the girls are to sit together?

   (c) In how many ways can they sit in a row if the girls are to sit together?

   (d) In how many ways can they sit in a row if **just** the girls are to sit together?

8. Answer all parts of Exercise 7 with "circle" instead of "row." (In every circle, people sit facing inward.)

9. [BB] In how many ways is it possible to sit seven knights at a round table if

   (a) Friday, Saturday, and Sunday insist on sitting together?

   (b) Wednesday refuses to sit next to Saturday or Sunday?

10. [BB] Let X and Y be sets with $|X| = m$ and $|Y| = n$.

    (a) How many bijective functions are there $X \to X$?

    (b) How many injective functions are there $X \to Y$?

11. How many permutations of the letters a, b, c, d, e, f, g contain neither the string bge nor the string eaf?

12. [BB] In how many ways can two couples, the Noseworthys and the Abbotts, form a line so that

    (a) the Noseworthys are beside each other?

    (b) the Noseworthys are not beside each other?

    (c) each couple is together?

    (d) the Noseworthys are beside each other but the Abbotts are not?

    (e) at least one couple is together?

    (f) exactly one couple is together?

13. Repeat Exercise 12, assuming, in each part, that a dog also forms part of the line.

14. Three couples, the Smiths, Joneses, and Murphys, are going to form a line.

(a) [BB] In how many such lines will Mr. and Mrs. Jones be next to each other?

(b) In how many such lines will Mr. and Mrs. Jones be next to each other and Mr. and Mrs. Murphy be next to each other?

(c) In how many such lines will at least one couple be next to each other?

15. How many permutations of the letters a, b, c, d, e, f, g have either two or three letters between a and b?

16. (a) [BB] How many seven-digit numbers have no repeated digits?

(b) How many seven-digit numbers with no repeated digits contain a 3 but not a 6?
(Leading zeros are not permitted in either part of this question.)

17. (a) In how many numbers with seven distinct digits do only the digits 1–9 appear?

(b) [BB] How many of the numbers in (a) contain a 3 and a 6?

(c) In how many of the numbers in (a) do 3 and 6 occur consecutively (in either order)?

(d) [BB] How many of the numbers in (a) contain neither a 3 nor a 6?

(e) How many of the numbers in (a) contain a 3 but not a 6?

(f) In how many of the numbers in (a) do exactly one of the numbers 3, 6 appear?

(g) In how many of the numbers in (a) do neither of the consecutive pairs 36 and 63 appear?

18. Let X and Y be finite nonempty sets, $|X| = m$, $|Y| = n \le m$. Let $f(n, m)$ denote the number of partitions of X into n subsets. Prove that the number of surjective functions $X \to Y$ is $n! f(n, m)$.

7.2 Combinations

There are 12 different kinds of drinks for sale in a store and a customer wants to buy two different kinds. How many choices does this person have? There are 12 women and 20 men in a club, five of whom will be chosen to organize a Christmas party. In how many ways can these five people be chosen? If a coin is tossed eight times, in how many ways can exactly five heads turn up? These are the sorts of questions that we answer in this section.

In the last section, we found that the number of ways to place three different colored marbles into ten numbered boxes, at most one to a box, is $P(10, 3) = 720$. Suppose the marbles have the same color. Are there still 720 possibilities? In fact, the number is much smaller. When there are red, blue, and green marbles, for each choice of boxes, there are $3! = 6$ different ways of assigning the marbles to them corresponding to the six permutations of red, blue, green. Figure 7.1 illustrates the six ways the marbles can be assigned to boxes 3, 4, and 8, for instance. When the marbles have the same color, these six assignments are all the same.

BOX 1	BOX 2	BOX 3	BOX 4	⋯	BOX 8	⋯
rbg		red	blue		green	
rgb		red	green		blue	
brg		blue	red		green	
bgr		blue	green		red	
grb		green	red		blue	
gbr		green	blue		red	

Figure 7.1 There are $3! = 6$ ways to assign three different colored marbles to three boxes.

It is useful to notice that when the marbles have the same color each configuration of marbles in boxes simply amounts to a choice of three boxes. Thus, the number of ways to put three identical marbles into ten boxes is just the number of ways to select three boxes out of ten. Furthermore, for a given three boxes, there are $3 \times 2 \times 1 = 3! = 6$ ways in which three marbles of different colors can be assigned to these boxes. By the multiplication rule, the number of ways of putting three marbles of different colors into ten boxes (at most one to a box) is the product of the number of ways of selecting three boxes and the number of ways then to assign the marbles to these boxes.

$$P(10, 3) = (\text{number of ways to select 3 boxes from 10}) \times 3!$$

To summarize,

Number of ways to select three boxes from ten

= number of ways to put three identical marbles into ten boxes

$$= \frac{P(10, 3)}{3!} = \frac{10!}{7!3!} = 120.$$

7.2.1 DEFINITION

For integers r and n, $n \geq 0$ and $0 \leq r \leq n$, the *binomial coefficient* $\binom{n}{r}$ (read "n choose r") is defined by

$$\binom{n}{r} = \frac{n!}{r!(n-r)!}.$$

❖

The reason for the name *binomial coefficient* will become clear in Section 7.7. The reason for saying "n choose r" is given in the following proposition.

7.2.2 PROPOSITION

Let n and r be integers with $n \geq 0$ and $0 \leq r \leq n$. The number of ways to choose r objects from n is $\binom{n}{r}$.

Proof

If $r = 0$, the result is true because there is just one way to choose 0 objects (do nothing!), while $\binom{n}{0} = \frac{n!}{0!(n-0)!} = 1$ because $0! = 1$. Thus, we may assume that $r \geq 1$ and hence $n \geq 1$. Let N be the number we are seeking; that is, there are N ways to choose r objects from the n given objects. Notice that for each way of choosing r objects there are $r!$ ways to order them. By the multiplication rule, the number of r-permutations of n objects [which we know is $P(n, r)$] is the number of ways to choose r objects multiplied by $r!$, the number of ways to order the r objects.

$$P(n, r) = N \times r!$$

Therefore,

$$N = \frac{P(n, r)}{r!} = \frac{n!}{r!(n-r)!} = \binom{n}{r},$$

which is what we wanted to show.

Pause 5

Explain why $\binom{n}{r} = \binom{n}{n-r}$.

∎

PROBLEM 7.   Wanda is going to toss a coin eight times. In how many ways can she get five heads and three tails?

Solution. Wanda might get a string of five heads followed by three tails (denote this possibility HHHHHTTT); or a string of three tails followed by five heads, TTTHHHHH; or the sequence HTHHTHTH; and so on. The number of such sequences is the number of ways of selecting five occasions (from the eight) on which the heads should arise or, equivalently, the number of ways of selecting the three occasions on which tails should come up. The answer is $\binom{8}{5} = \binom{8}{3} = 56$.

As is so often the case in mathematics, in Proposition 7.2.2, we solved one problem (in how many ways r objects can be selected from n?) by relating it to another problem for which we knew the answer (how many r-permutations of n objects are there?). This is an extremely useful and important idea.

7.2.3 DEFINITION

A *combination* of a set of objects is a subset of them. A subset of r objects is called an *r-combination* or a combination of the objects *taken r at a time*. ❖

7.2.4 COROLLARY

The number of r-combinations of n objects is $\dbinom{n}{r}$.

EXAMPLE 8

- The number of 2-combinations of the digits $0, 1, \ldots, 9$ is

$$\binom{10}{2} = \frac{10!}{2!8!} = \frac{10 \cdot 9}{2} = 45.$$

- The number of combinations of letters of the alphabet taken six at a time is

$$\binom{26}{6} = \frac{26!}{6!20!} = \frac{26 \cdot 25 \cdot 24 \cdot 23 \cdot 22 \cdot 21}{6 \cdot 5 \cdot 4 \cdot 3 \cdot 2 \cdot 1} = 230230.$$

- The number of ways to put three identical marbles into ten boxes is the number of ways of selecting three of ten boxes:

$$\binom{10}{3} = \frac{10!}{3!7!} = \frac{10 \cdot 9 \cdot 8}{3 \cdot 2} = 120.$$

- The number of ways to choose two kinds of drinks from a dozen different kinds is

$$\binom{12}{2} = \frac{12!}{2!10!} = \frac{12 \cdot 11}{2} = 66.$$

- The number of ways to choose five people from a group of 32 is

$$\binom{32}{5} = \frac{32!}{5!27!} = \frac{32 \cdot 31 \cdot 30 \cdot 29 \cdot 28}{5 \cdot 4 \cdot 3 \cdot 2 \cdot 1} = 201376.$$

The distinction between permutation and combination is the distinction between order and selection. Box 1, box 2, box 4 is one combination of boxes; box 2, box 1, box 4 is the same combination, but a different permutation. A permutation takes order into account; a combination involves only selection.

There are $\binom{32}{5} = 201,376$ ways to choose five people from 32, but $5! \times 201376 = P(32, 5)$ lines of five people that can be formed from a group of 32, a much larger number, because order is important in a line. The line Charles, Oana, Serpil, Clayton, Nabil is different from the line Nabil, Clayton, Serpil, Charles, Oana, although these two selections of people are the same.

Mr. Hiscock has ten children, but his car holds only five people (including driver). When he goes to the circus, in how many ways can he select four children to accompany him? ∎

PROBLEM 9.   In how many ways can 20 students out of a class of 32 be chosen to attend class on a late Thursday afternoon (and take notes for the others) if

(a) Paul refuses to go to class?

(b) Michelle insists on going?

(c) Jim and Michelle insist on going?

(d) either Jim or Michelle (or both) go to class?

(e) just one of Jim and Michelle attend?

(f) Paul and Michelle refuse to attend class together?

Solution.   (a) The answer is $\binom{31}{20} = 84{,}672{,}315$ since, in effect, it is necessary to select 20 students from the 31 students excluding Paul.

(b) Now the number of possibilities is $\binom{31}{19} = 141{,}120{,}525$ since 19 students must be chosen from 31.

(c) The answer is $\binom{30}{18} = 86{,}493{,}225$, it being necessary to choose the remaining 18 students from a group of 30.

(d) Let J be the set of classes of 20 that contain Jim and M the set of classes of 20 that contain Michelle. The question asks for $|J \cup M|$. Using the Principle of Inclusion–Exclusion, we obtain $|J \cup M| = |J| + |M| - |J \cap M| = \binom{31}{19} + \binom{31}{19} - \binom{30}{18} = 195{,}747{,}825$.

An alternative method of obtaining this answer would be to count separately the cases—Jim (but not Michelle) goes to class, Michelle (but not Jim) goes to class, both Jim and Michelle go to class—and add the results. (This follows because $|J \cup M| = |J \setminus M| + |M \setminus J| + |J \cap M|$.) We obtain $\binom{30}{19} + \binom{30}{19} + \binom{30}{18} = 2(54{,}627{,}300) + 86{,}493{,}225 = 195{,}747{,}825$, as before.

Yet another method would be to subtract from the total number of possible classes of 20 the number containing neither Jim nor Michelle. This gives $\binom{32}{20} - \binom{30}{20} = 225{,}792{,}840 - 30{,}045{,}015 = 195{,}747{,}825$.

(e) Using the formula $|J \oplus M| = |J| + |M| - 2|J \cap M|$, we obtain $\binom{31}{19} + \binom{31}{19} - 2\binom{30}{18} = 109{,}254{,}600$.

(f) The number of classes containing Paul and Michelle is $\binom{30}{18}$ by part (c), so the number that does not contain both is $\binom{32}{20} - \binom{30}{18} = 139{,}299{,}615$.

Alternatively, observe that this part asks for $|(P \cap M)^c| = |P^c \cup M^c|$ (by one of the laws of De Morgan). So the answer is $|P^c| + |M^c| - |P^c \cap M^c| = \binom{31}{20} + \binom{31}{20} - \binom{30}{20} = 139{,}299{,}615$.

PROBLEM 10.   How many committees of five people can be chosen from 12 men and 20 women

(a) if exactly three women must be on each committee?

(b) if at least three women must be on each committee?

Solution.   (a) We must choose three women from 20 and then two men from 12. The answer is $\binom{20}{3}\binom{12}{2} = 1140(66) = 75{,}240$.

(b) By the addition rule, this is the number of committees with exactly three women, plus the number with exactly four women, plus the number with exactly five women. The answer is $\binom{20}{3}\binom{12}{2} + \binom{20}{4}\binom{12}{1} + \binom{20}{5}\binom{12}{0}75{,}240 + 4845(12) + 15{,}504 = 148{,}884$.

The combinatorial symbols we have presented in Sections 7.1 and 7.2 are summarized, together with their interpretations, in Table 7.2.

Table 7.2 Some combinatorial symbols and their uses.

$n!$	• number of permutations of n distinct symbols
$P(n, r) = \dfrac{n!}{(n - r)!}$	• number of ways to put r different colored marbles into n numbered boxes, at most one to a box • number of permutations of n distinct symbols used r at a time
$\dbinom{n}{r} = \dfrac{n!}{r!(n - r)!}$	• number of ways to put r identical marbles into n boxes, at most one to a box • number of combinations of n distinct symbols used r at a time • number of ways to choose r objects from n

Answers to Pauses

5. Suppose we have n white marbles and we wish to paint r of them black. Choosing the r marbles is equivalent to choosing the $n - r$ marbles that are to remain white. Thus, each choice of r marbles from n corresponds to a choice of the remaining $n - r$, so the numbers of choices are the same. By Proposition 7.2.2, these are $\binom{n}{r}$ and $\binom{n}{n-r}$, respectively.

6. The question involves choosing, not order. There are $\binom{10}{4} = \frac{10!}{4!6!} = 210$ different ways.

True/False Questions

(Answers can be found in the back of the book.)

1. $\binom{6}{4} = 30$

2. $\binom{0}{0} = 1$

3. If n is any natural number, then $\binom{n}{1} = n$.

4. If r and n are nonnegative integers with $r \leq n$, then $\binom{n}{r} = \binom{n}{n-r}$.

5. The number of ways of placing seven marbles of the same color into 11 numbered boxes, at most one marble to a box, is $\binom{11}{7}$.

6. A combination of a set of objects is a subset of them.

7. A subset of r objects is called an r-combination.

8. There are 21 5-combinations of a set of seven elements.

9. The number of r-combinations of a set of n objects is greater than the number of r-permutations of the set.

*The answers to exercises marked [BB] can be found in the **B**ack of the **B**ook.*

1. [BB] A group of people is comprised of six from Nebraska, seven from Idaho, and eight from Louisiana.
   (a) In how many ways can a committee of six be formed with two people from each state?
   (b) In how many ways can a committee of seven be formed with at least two people from each state?

2. (a) In how many ways can 12 players be divided into two teams of six for a game of street hockey, one team to be called the Good Guys and the other, the Bad Guys?
   (b) Repeat part (a) if the teams are not given names.

3. [BB] How many 12-digit 0–1 strings contain precisely five 1's?

4. How many different signals, each consisting of seven flags arranged in a column, can be formed from three identical red flags and four identical blue flags?

5. [BB] In how many ways can Tom, Billie, and Peter share 15 salmon of different sizes
   (a) if each takes five?
   (b) if the youngest boy takes seven salmon and the others each take four?
   (c) if one boy takes seven salmon and the others each take four?

6. [BB] How many subsets from a basket of ten apples contain at most three apples?

7. In a popular lottery known as Lotto 6/49, a player marks a card with six different numbers from the integers 1–49 and wins if his or her numbers match six randomly selected such numbers.
   (a) In how many ways can a player complete a game card?
   (b) How many cards should you complete to have at least one chance in a million of winning?
   (c) In how many ways can a player complete a game card so that
      • no number matches any of the six selected?
      • exactly one number matches one of the six selected?
      • exactly two numbers match two of the six selected?
      • exactly three numbers match three of those selected?
      • exactly four numbers match four of those selected?
      • exactly five numbers match five of those selected?
      • all six numbers match?
   (d) Without further calculation, what is the sum of the answers to part (c)?

   (e) In how many ways can a player complete a game card so that at least one number matches one of the six selected?
   (f) In how many ways can a player complete a game card so that at least two numbers match the six numbers selected?

8. (a) [BB] How many five-card hands dealt from a standard deck of 52 playing cards are all of the same suit?
   (b) How many five-card hands contain exactly two aces?

9. A newcomers' club of 30 people wants to choose an executive board consisting of president, secretary, treasurer, and two other officers. In how many ways can this be accomplished?

10. [BB] A coin is tossed ten times and the sequence of heads and tails is observed.
    (a) How many different sequences are possible?
    (b) In how many of these sequences are there exactly four heads?

11. [BB] An urn contains 15 red numbered balls and ten white numbered balls. A sample of five balls is selected.
    (a) How many different samples are possible?
    (b) How many samples contain all red balls?
    (c) How many samples contain three red balls and two white balls?

12. A group of eight scientists is composed of five mathematicians and three geologists.
    (a) In how many ways can five people be chosen to visit an oil rig?
    (b) Suppose the five people chosen to visit the rig must be comprised of three mathematicians and two geologists. Now in how many ways can the group be chosen?

13. [BB] From 100 used cars sitting on a lot, 20 are to be selected for a test designed to check certain safety requirements. These cars will then be put back onto the lot and, again, 20 will be selected for a test designed to check antipollution standards.
    (a) In how many ways can the first selection be made?
    (b) In how many ways can the second selection be made?
    (c) In how many ways can both selections be made?
    (d) In how many ways can both selections be made if exactly five cars are to undergo both tests?

14. In how many ways can a team of six be chosen from 20 players so as to
    (a) include both the strongest and the weakest player?
    (b) include the strongest but exclude the weakest player?
    (c) exclude both the strongest and weakest player?

15. A woman has nine close friends.

   (a) In how many ways can she invite six of these to dinner?

   (b) Repeat (a) if two of her friends are divorced (from each other) and will not attend together.

   (c) Repeat (a) if the friends consist of three single people and three married couples and, if a husband or wife is invited, the spouse must be invited too.

16. The head of the Department of Mathematical Sciences at a certain university has 12 mathematicians, seven computer scientists, and three statisticians in his employ. He wishes to appoint some committees from among these 22 people.

   (a) How many five-member committees can he appoint?

   (b) How many five-member committees, each containing at least one statistician, can he appoint?

   (c) A certain professor of mathematics, Dr. G, and a certain colleague, Dr. P, refuse to serve together on the same committee. How many five-member committees can be formed so as not to contain both Dr. G and Dr. P?

   (d) How many five-member committees can be formed so that the number of mathematicians is greater than the number of computer scientists and the number of computer scientists is greater than the number of statisticians?

17. A student must answer exactly eight questions out of ten on a final examination.

   (a) [BB] In how many ways can she choose the questions to answer?

   (b) Repeat (a) if she must answer the first three questions.

   (c) [BB] Repeat (a) if she must answer at least three of the last five questions and at most four of the first five.

   (d) Repeat (a) if she must answer at least three of the last five questions.

18. Suppose U is a set of 52 elements with five subsets A_1, A_2, A_3, A_4, A_5 having the following properties:

- Each subset contains 23 elements.
- The intersection of any two of the subsets contains ten elements.
- The intersection of any three of the subsets contains four elements.

- The intersection of any four of the subsets contains one element.
- The intersection of all the subsets is empty.

How many elements belong to none of the five subsets?

19. Ten points in the plane, no three collinear, are given.

   (a) [BB] How many different line segments are formed by joining pairs of these points?

   (b) How many different triangles are formed by the line segments in (a)?

   (c) If A is one of the ten points, how many of the triangles in (b) have A as a vertex?

20. **(a)** [BB] How many triangles are determined by the vertices of a regular 12-sided polygon?

   (b) Repeat (a) if the sides of the polygon are not to be the sides of any triangle.

21. A *diagonal* of a polygon is a line joining two nonadjacent vertices.

   (a) [BB] How many diagonals does an octagon have?

   (b) *Loonie* is the colloquial name for the Canadian one dollar coin. It has the shape of a regular 11-sided polygon. How many diagonals does a loonie have?

22. **(a)** How many diagonals does a regular n-sided polygon have?

   (b) Which regular n-sided polygon has three times as many diagonals as sides?

23. [BB] Prove that the product of any n consecutive natural numbers is divisible by $n!$.

24. [BB] **(a)** Use Definition 7.2.1 to prove that $\binom{n}{k}\binom{n-k}{\ell} = \binom{n}{\ell}\binom{n-\ell}{k}$, where n, k, and ℓ are natural numbers with $k + \ell \leq n$.

   (b) Establish the identity in part (a) without appealing to Definition 7.2.1. [*Hint:* In how many ways can one choose two teams, one of size k and the other of size ℓ, from a group of n people?]

25. **(a)** Let k and n be natural numbers with $k < n$. Use the definition of $\binom{n}{r}$ given in 7.2.1 to prove that $\binom{n}{k} = \binom{n-1}{k-1} + \binom{n-1}{k}$.

   (b) Establish the identity in (a) without appealing to any definition.

26. **(a)** Use Definition 7.2.1 to prove that $\binom{2n}{2} = 2\binom{n}{2} + n^2$ for any natural number n.

   (b) Establish the identity in (a) without using the definition.

7.3 Elementary Probability

Most people have an intuitive idea of how to calculate probabilities, and more often than not this intuitive notion gives the correct answer. Without learning any preliminary theory, many readers will be happy with the following calculations.

EXAMPLE 11   The probability that a 5 appears when a fair die is rolled once is $\frac{1}{6}$. The probability that an odd number appears when a fair die is rolled is $\frac{3}{6} = \frac{1}{2}$.

EXAMPLE 12   When a pair of fair dice is rolled, $6 \times 6 = 36$ outcomes are possible. The probability that a pair of 5's appears is $\frac{1}{36}$. Because there are two ways the event can occur, the probability that a 2 and a 3 appear is $\frac{2}{36} = \frac{1}{18}$. The probability that the sum of the numbers that appear is 6 is $\frac{5}{36}$ (5 of the 36 outcomes add to 6).

EXAMPLE 13   The probability that a head appears when a fair coin is tossed once is $\frac{1}{2}$.

EXAMPLE 14   If a fair coin is tossed eight times, the number of possible outcomes is $2^8 = 256$. The probability of getting 8 heads is $\frac{1}{256}$. In Problem 7 of Section 7.2, we saw that the number of ways of getting five heads and three tails is $\binom{8}{5} = \binom{8}{3} = 56$, so the probability of this occurring is $\frac{56}{256} = \frac{7}{32}$.

These examples all have several things in common. First, they are indirectly related to gambling. This is no surprise! Historically, probability theory began with the study of games of chance by Blaise Pascal and Pierre Laplace[1] in the 17th and 18th centuries. Second, they all represent situations where the possible outcomes are equally likely. In this section this will always be the case; in Section 7.4, we discuss more general situations.

It is time now to be a bit more formal. The word *experiment* is often used for a procedure with a set of possible outcomes, and this set of outcomes is called the *sample space* of the experiment. The word *event* is used for a subset A of the sample space, and we will be interested in $P(A)$, the probability that event A occurs. In this section, we always assume that the sample space is finite.

7.3.1 DEFINITION   If all outcomes in a finite sample space S are equally likely and A is a subset of S, then $P(A) = \frac{|A|}{|S|}$. ❖

In Example 11, the sample space S is $\{1, 2, 3, 4, 5, 6\}$. In the first part, about getting a 5, the set $A = \{5\}$ and $P(A) = \frac{|A|}{|S|} = \frac{1}{6}$.

Pause 7   What is A in the second part of Example 11, about odd numbers? ∎

In Example 12, the sample space S is the set of 36 ordered pairs (x, y), where x and y are both in $\{1, 2, 3, 4, 5, 6\}$ (think of one die as the first coordinate and the other as the second coordinate). In the first part, $A = \{(5, 5)\}$ and $P(A) = \frac{1}{36}$, as seen. In the second part, $A = \{(2, 3), (3, 2)\}$ and so $P(A) = \frac{2}{36} = \frac{1}{18}$.

Pause 8   What is A in the third part of Example 12? ∎

In Example 13, $S = \{H, T\}$ and $A = \{H\}$, so $P(A) = \frac{1}{2}$. In Example 14, the sample space is the set of $2^8 = 256$ different sequences of length 8 consisting of H and T (see Problem 7 in Section 7.2). In the first part, $A = \{HHHHHHHH\}$ and $P(A) = \frac{1}{256}$. In the second part, A consists of the $\binom{8}{5} = 56$ sequences that contain five H's and three T's, and $P(A) = \frac{56}{256}$.

Although the study of probability arose with games of chance, it can be applied much more widely.

PROBLEM 15.   A basket contains three red balls, four green balls, and nine yellow balls.

---

[1] 1749–1827, a French astronomer and mathematician

1. If one ball is drawn from the basket, find the probability that it is yellow.
2. If one ball is drawn, find the probability that it is not red.
3. Assume two balls are drawn one after the other. After the first ball is drawn, it is put back in the basket before the second ball is drawn. Find the probability that both balls are the same color.
4. Do part 3 assuming that the first ball is **not** put back before the second is drawn.

Solution.

1. There are 16 balls in total, nine of which are yellow. So the answer is $\frac{9}{16}$.
2. Since 13 balls are not red, the answer is $\frac{13}{16}$.
3. The sample space consists of the $16 \times 16 = 256$ different sequences of balls. There are $(3 \times 3) + (4 \times 4) + (9 \times 9) = 106$ cases where the colors are the same. Hence the answer is $\frac{106}{256} = \frac{53}{128}$.
4. Now the sample space has size $16 \times 15 = 240$, while the number of cases where the balls have the same color is $(3 \times 2) + (4 \times 3) + (9 \times 8) = 90$. The answer is $\frac{90}{240} = \frac{3}{8}$.

Note that the answer to part 4 would be the same if the two balls were drawn simultaneously from the basket; in this case, the sample space would have size $\binom{16}{2}$, the number of cases in the event would be $\binom{3}{2} + \binom{4}{2} + \binom{9}{2}$, and, since these numbers are half those in 4, the ratio is the same.

The reader might initially think that an appropriate sample space in 1 could be $\{R, G, Y\}$, the three possible colors. The difficulty, however, is that these outcomes are no longer equally likely. In fact, $P(\{Y\}) = \frac{9}{16}$, as we saw in 1, while $P(\{R\}) = \frac{3}{16}$. The reader should be aware of more subtle occurrences of this potential error.

Pause 9

In the third part of Example 12, the part concerning the probability of getting a total of 6 when two dice are rolled, Frank suggests that the sample space should be $\{2, 3, 4, 5, 6, 7, 8, 9, 10, 11, 12\}$, the set of possible totals. Is this correct? ∎

PROBLEM 16. A committee of five people is chosen randomly from four men and six women. Find the probability that

1. exactly four women are on the committee;
2. at least four women are on the committee;
3. at most four women are on the committee.

Solution.

1. The number of possible committees is $\binom{10}{5} = 252$, while the number containing exactly four women is $\binom{6}{4}\binom{4}{1} = 60$. So the answer is $\frac{60}{252} = \frac{5}{21}$.
2. Using counting techniques from Section 7.2 (for example, see Problem 10), the answer is $\dfrac{\binom{6}{4}\binom{4}{1} + \binom{6}{5}\binom{4}{0}}{\binom{10}{5}} = \dfrac{11}{42}$.
3. The answer is $\dfrac{252 - \binom{6}{5}\binom{4}{0}}{252} = \dfrac{41}{42}$.

PROBLEM 17. (See Exercise 12, Section 7.1) Two couples, the Noseworthys and the Abbotts, are arranged randomly in a straight line. Find the probability that

1. the Noseworthys are beside each other;
2. the Noseworthys are not beside each other;

3. each couple is together.

Solution. The sample space for this experiment has $4! = 24$ elements, since 24 different straight lines are possible.

1. As noted in the answer to Exercise 12, Section 7.1, this event can happen in $2 \times 3! = 12$ ways. The answer is $\frac{12}{24} = \frac{1}{2}$.

2. Referring again to the answer to Exercise 12, we get $\frac{24-12}{24} = \dfrac{1}{2}$.

3. We get $\frac{8}{24} = \frac{1}{3}$.

The previous problems have demonstrated that the concepts of permutation and combination (Sections 7.1 and 7.2) are crucial to calculating probabilities. In addition, the counting techniques seen in Chapter 6 are also indispensable.

In Problem 17, suppose we wanted to find the probability that at least one of the two couples is together. As in the solution to Exercise 12(c) of Section 7.1, this is just $\frac{|N \cup A|}{24}$, where N and A have the same meanings as before. We obtain

$$\frac{|N \cup A|}{24} = \frac{|N| + |A| - |N \cap A|}{24} = \frac{12 + 12 - 8}{24} = \frac{2}{3}.$$

 **Pause 10**

In Problem 17, find the probability that

1. exactly one couple is together;

2. at most one couple is together.   ∎

PROBLEM 18. (See Problem 3 of Section 6.1.) A box contains 300 tickets, each labeled with an integer between 1 and 300 (inclusive). No two tickets bear the same integer. Find the probability that a ticket drawn randomly from the box bears a number that is

1. divisible by at least one of 3, 5, 7;
2. divisible by 3 and by 5, but not by 7;
3. divisible by 3, but by neither 5 nor 7;
4. divisible by at most two of 3, 5, 7.

Solution. In Section 6.1, the number of integers satisfying 1 was seen to be 162. So the answer to 1 is $\frac{162}{300} = \frac{27}{50}$. Similarly, the answer to 2 is $\frac{18}{300} = \frac{3}{50}$. To answer 3, we employ the method illustrated in Problem 3 of Section 6.1. Using the notation introduced there, the answer is $\frac{|A \setminus (B \cup C)|}{300}$. Now

$$\begin{aligned}
|A \setminus (B \cup C)| &= |A| - |A \cap (B \cup C)| \\
&= |A| - |(A \cap B) \cup (A \cap C)| \\
&= |A| - (|A \cap B| + |A \cap C| - |A \cap B \cap C|) \\
&= 100 - (20 + 14 - 2) = 68.
\end{aligned}$$

So the answer to 3 is $\frac{68}{300} = \frac{17}{75}$. Since only $3 \times 5 \times 7 = 105$ and 210 are divisible by all three of 3, 5, 7, the answer to 4 is $\frac{300-2}{300} = \frac{149}{150}$.

Counting formulas developed earlier in the text can easily be restated as results about probability.

Let S be the sample space of some experiment.

1. If A is any event, then $0 \le P(A) \le 1$. Also $P(\emptyset) = 0$, $P(S) = 1$.

2. If A is any event and A^c is the complement of A in S (that is, $A^c = S \setminus A$), then $P(A^c) = 1 - P(A)$.
3. If A and B are events, $P(A \cup B) = P(A) + P(B) - P(A \cap B)$.

Proof   The proofs given are based on the underlying assumptions of this section, that S is finite and all outcomes in S are equally likely. Nevertheless, the results stated are true more generally. (See Section 7.4.)

1. Since $A \subseteq S$, $0 \leq |A| \leq |S|$. Dividing by $|S|$ gives the first result. Also, $P(\emptyset) = \frac{|\emptyset|}{|S|} = \frac{0}{|S|} = 0$ and $P(S) = \frac{|S|}{|S|} = 1$.

2. $P(A^c) = \frac{|A^c|}{|S|} = \frac{|S|-|A|}{|S|} = 1 - P(A)$.

3. $P(A \cup B) = \dfrac{|A \cup B|}{|S|}$

   $= \dfrac{|A| + |B| - |A \cap B|}{|S|} = P(A) + P(B) - P(A \cap B)$.

More generally, the Principle of Inclusion–Exclusion (Section 6.1) gives the following result.

7.3.3 THEOREM   Let S be the sample space of some experiment and let $A_1, A_2, \ldots, A_n$ be events. Then

$$P(A_1 \cup A_2 \cup \cdots \cup A_n) = \sum_i P(A_i) - \sum_{i<j} P(A_i \cap A_j) + \sum_{i<j<k} P(A_i \cap A_j \cap A_k)$$

$$+ \cdots + (-1)^{n+1} P(A_1 \cap A_2 \cap \cdots \cap A_n).$$

Pause 11   Prove Theorem 7.3.3.   ∎

An important special case is reflected in the following definition, which we met informally at the start of Section 6.2.

7.3.4 DEFINITION   Two events A and B are *mutually exclusive* if $A \cap B = \emptyset$. Events $A_1, A_2, \ldots, A_n$ are pairwise mutually exclusive if A_i and A_j are mutually exclusive whenever $i \neq j$.   ❖

7.3.5 COROLLARY   Let S be the sample space of some experiment and let $A_1, A_2, \ldots, A_n$ be pairwise mutually exclusive events. Then

$$P(A_1 \cup A_2 \cup \cdots \cup A_n) = P(A_1) + P(A_2) + \cdots + P(A_n).$$

Proof   Since $A_i \cap A_j = \emptyset$ whenever $i \neq j$, for all $s \geq 2$ and all increasing lists of subscripts $i_1 < i_2 < \cdots < i_s$, we have $P(A_{i_1} \cap A_{i_2} \cap \cdots \cap A_{i_s}) = 0$. The result follows.

Corollary 7.3.5 gives us a very efficient way to compute probabilities in certain cases.

PROBLEM 19.   A pair of fair dice is thrown. Find the probability that the sum of the numbers that appear is a perfect square or a multiple of 7.

Solution. There are two possible perfect squares that could appear, 4 and 9. If A is the event that the sum is 4, then $P(A) = \frac{3}{36}$. If B is the event that the sum is 9, then $P(B) = \frac{4}{36}$. The only multiple of 7 that could occur is 7 itself. Letting C denote the probability of this event, we have $P(C) = \frac{6}{36}$. Since A, B, and C are pairwise mutually exclusive, the probability we want is $P(A) + P(B) + P(C) = \frac{13}{36}$.

There is nothing very deep about this particular problem. All we are doing is breaking the requested event into disjoint cases and adding the probabilities of these cases.

Answers to Pauses

7. $A = \{1, 3, 5\}$

8. $A = \{(1, 5), (2, 4), (3, 3), (4, 2), (5, 1)\}$

9. This is not correct. The outcomes in this sample space are not equally likely. For instance, we saw that $P(6) = \frac{5}{36}$ in Example 11, while $P(2) = \frac{1}{36}$.

10. (a) As seen in the text, there are 16 cases where at least one couple is together and 8 cases where both are together. So the answer is $\frac{16-8}{24} = \frac{1}{3}$.

    (b) There are 8 cases where both couples are together, so the answer is $\frac{24-8}{24} = \frac{2}{3}$.

11. $P(A_1 \cup A_2 \cup \cdots \cup A_n) = \dfrac{|A_1 \cup A_2 \cup \cdots \cup A_n|}{|S|}$

$$= \frac{1}{|S|}\left[\sum_i |A_i| - \sum_{i<j} |A_i \cap A_j| + \sum_{i<j<k} |A_i \cap A_j \cap A_k| \right.$$
$$\left. + \cdots + (-1)^{n+1} |A_1 \cap A_2 \cap \cdots \cap A_n| \right]$$
$$= \sum_i \frac{|A_i|}{|S|} - \sum_{i<j} \frac{|A_i \cap A_j|}{|S|} + \sum_{i<j<k} \frac{|A_i \cap A_j \cap A_k|}{|S|}$$
$$+ \cdots + (-1)^{n+1} \frac{|A_1 \cap A_2 \cap \cdots \cap A_n|}{|S|}$$
$$= \sum_i P(A_i) - \sum_{i<j} P(A_i \cap A_j) + \sum_{i<j<k} P(A_i \cap A_j \cap A_k)$$
$$+ \cdots + (-1)^{n+1} P(A_1 \cap A_2 \cap \cdots \cap A_n).$$

True/False Questions

(Answers can be found in the back of the book.)

1. If a pair of fair dice is rolled, the probability that a 4 and a 6 will appear is $\frac{1}{36}$.

2. If A and B are subsets of a sample space in which all outcomes are equally likely and if $P(A) = x$, $P(B) = y$, then the probability that A or B occurs is always $x \times y$.

3. If two balls are drawn one after the other without replacement from a basket containing five red balls and seven blue balls, then the probability the balls are of different color is $\frac{9 \times 7}{12 \times 11}$.

4. If two balls are drawn one after the other without replacement from a basket containing five red balls and seven blue balls, then the probability the balls are of the same color is $1 - \frac{2(5 \times 7)}{12 \times 11}$.

5. If the two balls in Question 4 are drawn at the same time, the answer would remain the same.

6. If a committee of six people is chosen randomly from five men and eight women, the probability that exactly four men would be on the committee is $\dfrac{\binom{5}{4}}{\binom{13}{6}}$.

7. If A is any event, $P(A) = 1 - P(A^c)$.

8. If A and B are any events, $P(A \cap B) = P(A \cup B) - P(A) - P(B)$.

9. If $P(A) = \frac{1}{2}$, $P(B) = \frac{2}{3}$, and $P(A \cap B) = \frac{1}{6}$, then $P(A \cup B) = 1$.

10. If A and B are mutually exclusive events, then $P(A \cup B^c) = P(B^c)$.

Exercises

*The answers to exercises marked [BB] can be found in the **B**ack of the **B**ook.*

1. [BB] Two fair dice are rolled. Find the probability that the numbers that appear
   (a) are both 4;
   (b) add to 4;
   (c) differ by 1;
   (d) are of different parity.

2. One fair die is rolled. Find the probability that the number that appears is
   (a) 4;
   (b) at most 2;
   (c) not greater than 5;
   (d) a prime number;
   (e) divisible by 3, but not by 2.

3. Two fair dice are rolled. Find the probability that the numbers that appear
   (a) are both 2;
   (b) have a total that is at most 10;
   (c) are both factors of 70 whose product divides 70;
   (d) add to a number that is divisible by 5.

4. Three dice are rolled. Find the probability that the numbers that appear
   (a) are all multiples of 5;
   (b) have a total that is at most 16;
   (c) are three different primes;
   (d) are all different.

5. [BB] A fair coin is tossed six times. Find the probability of obtaining
   (a) no heads;
   (b) exactly two heads;
   (c) at most two heads;
   (d) at most five heads;
   (e) an odd number of heads.

6. A fair coin is tossed seven times. Find the probability of obtaining
   (a) seven heads;
   (b) exactly five heads;
   (c) at most five heads;
   (d) at most one head;
   (e) an odd number of heads.

The next two exercises refer to Lotto 6/49, a lottery described in Exercise 7 of Section 7.2. In all cases, give an exact answer involving binomial coefficients first, then give an estimate correct to three decimal places.

7. [BB] In Lotto 6/49, find the probability of having
   (a) exactly three of your numbers matching the selected numbers;
   (b) at least three of your numbers matching the selected numbers;
   (c) at most five of your numbers matching the selected numbers.

8. In Lotto 6/49, find the probability of having
   (a) exactly four of your numbers matching the selected numbers;
   (b) at most four of your numbers matching the selected numbers;
   (c) at most one of your numbers matching the selected numbers.

9. [BB] A basket contains five red balls, four white balls, and three blue balls. Two balls are drawn, one after the other, with the first ball replaced before the second is drawn. Find the probability of drawing
   (a) two white balls;
   (b) at most one white ball;
   (c) at least one white ball;
   (d) a red ball and a white ball;
   (e) either at least one white ball or exactly one red ball.

10. Continuing Exercise 9, find the probability of drawing
   (a) two blue balls;
   (b) at most one blue ball;
   (c) at least one blue ball;
   (d) a blue ball and a white ball;
   (e) either at least one blue ball or at least one white ball.

11. [BB] Repeat Exercise 9 assuming the first ball drawn is not replaced before the second draw.

12. Repeat Exercise 10 assuming the two balls are drawn at the same time.

13. [BB] A committee consisting of six members to oversee trade between Canada and the United States is chosen randomly from seven Americans and five Canadians. Find the probability that
   (a) the committee has exactly four Canadians;
   (b) a majority on the committee are Americans;
   (c) the committee is not equally split;
   (d) the committee has either a majority of Americans or exactly four Canadians.

14. A committee consisting of five members to oversee North American missile defense is chosen randomly from six Canadians and five Americans. Find the probability that
   (a) the committee has exactly three Americans;
   (b) Canadians have a majority on the committee;
   (c) the committee has at most three Canadians;
   (d) the committee has either exactly three Americans or at most three Canadians.

15. [BB] In Exercise 1 of Section 6.1, find the probability that a person selected at random likes
    (a) at least one of the two toppings;
    (b) Canadian bacon but not anchovies;
    (c) exactly one of the two toppings;
    (d) neither topping;
    (e) at most one of the two toppings.

16. [BB] (See Exercise 11 of Section 6.1.) Find the probability that an integer selected at random between 1 and 500 (inclusive) is divisible by
    (a) 3 or 5;   (b) 3, but not by 5 or 6;
    (c) 3 and 5, but not by 6.

17. Find the probability that an integer selected at random between 1 and 5000 (inclusive) is divisible by at least one of 3, 5, 7, but is not divisible by all of these numbers.

18. (See Exercise 15 of Section 6.1.) Find the probability that an integer selected at random between 1 and 10000 (inclusive) is divisible by
    (a) at least one of 3, 5, 7, 11;
    (b) all four of 3, 5, 7, 11;
    (c) at least three of 3, 5, 7, 11.

19. [BB] (See Exercise 3 of Section 6.2.) Find the probability that a three-digit number selected at random from 000 to 999 (inclusive) has all digits different.

20. Repeat Exercise 19 if the three-digit number is selected at random from the range 100 to 999 (inclusive).

21. In Exercise 14 of Section 6.2, assume that exactly one of the roads from Cupids to Harbour Grace is unpaved and that exactly one of the roads from Harbour Grace to Heart's Desire is unpaved. If a traveller chooses a route at random from Cupids to Heart's Desire via Harbour Grace, find the probability that he will encounter at least one unpaved road.

22. In Exercise 23(a) of Section 6.2, find the probability that John's meal (if chosen randomly) will include cod tongues but not fiddleheads.

23. [BB] In Exercise 3 of Section 7.1, find the probability that a slate chosen randomly has Abigail as president and does not have Frank as treasurer.

24. In Exercise 6 of Section 7.1, find the probability that a mouse places first, second, and third.

25. (See Exercise 11 of Section 7.1.) Find the probability that a permutation of the letters a, b, c, d, e, f, g
    (a) contains the string ab;
    (b) does not contain the string bgc;
    (c) contains neither the string ab nor the string bgc.

26. [BB] In Exercise 13 of Section 7.2, find the probability that
    (a) exactly five cars are selected for both tests;
    (b) no car is selected for both tests.
    (It is not necessary to simplify your answers.)

27. (See Exercise 14 of Section 7.2.) Find the probability that a team of six chosen randomly from 20 players
    (a) includes both the strongest and weakest players;
    (b) includes the strongest player but excludes the weakest player;
    (c) excludes both the strongest and weakest players.

28. In Exercise 3, let A, B, C, D denote the events described in parts (a), (b), (c), (d), respectively. Determine whether each pair of these events is mutually exclusive. ([BB] for $\{A, B\}$ and $\{A, C\}$)

29. If A and B are events, prove that $P(A) = P(A \cap B) + P(A \cap B^c)$.

30. (a) [BB] Assume that $B_1, B_2, \ldots, B_n$ are pairwise mutually exclusive events and that $S = B_1 \cup B_2 \cdots \cup B_n$. Let A be any event. Generalize the result stated in Exercise 29 to a result about $A, B_1, B_2, \ldots, B_n$.
    (b) Prove the result of part (a).

31. Assuming that the sample space S is finite and that all outcomes are equally likely, prove each of the following:
    (a) [BB] $P(A \setminus B) = P(A) - P(A \cap B)$;
    (b) $P(A \setminus B) = P(A \cup B) - P(B)$;
    (c) $P(A \oplus B) = P(A) + P(B) - 2P(A \cap B)$;
    (d) [BB] $P(A \oplus B) = 2P(A \cup B) - P(A) - P(B)$;
    (e) [BB] $P(A \cap (B \cup C)) = P(A \cap B) + P(A \cap C) - P(A \cap B \cap C)$;
    (f) $P(A \cap (B \cup C)) = 2P(A) + P(B) + P(C) - P(A \cup B) - P(A \cup C) - P(A \cap B \cap C)$;
    (g) $P(A \cup (B \cap C)) = P(A \cup B) + P(A \cup C) - P(A \cup B \cup C)$;
    (h) $P(A \cup (B \cap C)) = 2P(A) + P(B) + P(C) - P(A \cap B) - P(A \cap C) - P(A \cup B \cup C)$;
    (i) [BB] (See Exercise 22(a) of Section 6.1.) $P((A \oplus B) \cap C) = P(A \cap C) + P(B \cap C) - 2P(A \cap B \cap C)$;
    (j) (See Exercise 22(b) of Section 6.1.) $P(A \oplus B \oplus C) = P(A) + P(B) + P(C) - 2P(A \cap B) - 2P(A \cap C) - 2P(B \cap C) + 4P(A \cap B \cap C)$.

32. A fair coin is tossed n times, n odd. Prove that the probability that the number of heads is greater than the number of tails is $\frac{1}{2}$.

7.4 Probability Theory

In Section 7.3, a crucial underlying assumption was that all outcomes in the sample space were equally likely. It was remarked, however, and we emphasize this here, that Theorems 7.3.2 and 7.3.3 still hold without that condition—in fact, they become much more important because simply counting the number of elements in an event is no longer sufficient. This is illustrated by the following problem.

PROBLEM 20. Assume that a biased die has $P(1) = \frac{1}{3}$, $P(2) = P(3) = \frac{1}{12}$, and $P(4) = P(5) = P(6) = \frac{1}{6}$. [Here, we write $P(x)$ for the strictly correct $P(\{x\})$.] If the die is tossed once, find the probability that

(a) an odd number appears;

(b) the number that appears is greater than 1.

Solution. (a) We add the probabilities of the pairwise mutually exclusive events $\{1\}, \{3\}, \{5\}$, obtaining $P(1) + P(3) + P(5) = \frac{1}{3} + \frac{1}{12} + \frac{1}{6} = \frac{7}{12}$.

(b) It is easiest to use Theorem 7.3.2(2), obtaining $1 - P(1) = 1 - \frac{1}{3} = \frac{2}{3}$. ▲

In general, assigning probabilities to events in a sample space S is just a function with domain the power set of S. Not all such functions will yield possible probabilities. To see what the restrictions are, let us look again at the results of Section 7.3.

We continue to assume that S is finite, so $S = \{x_1, x_2, \ldots, x_n\}$. Let A be a subset of S; thus, $A = \{x_{j_1}, x_{j_2}, \ldots, x_{j_t}\}$. Observe that the singleton sets $\{x_{j_1}\}, \{x_{j_2}\}, \ldots, \{x_{j_t}\}$ are pairwise mutually exclusive and have union A, so Corollary 7.3.5 says that $P(A) = \sum_{i=1}^{t} P(x_{j_i})$.

It follows that once P is defined on the outcomes $x_1, x_2, \ldots, x_n$ of an experiment, it is automatically defined on all events. On the outcomes, P must satisfy the two properties

(i) $0 \leq P(x_i) \leq 1$ for $1 \leq i \leq n$;

(ii) $\sum_{i=1}^{n} P(x_i) = 1$.

The above observations actually give the formal definition of $P(A)$, for any event A.

7.4.1 DEFINITION   If $P: S \to R$ is a real-valued function on the sample space S satisfying conditions (i) and (ii), the *probability* $P(A)$ of any event A is the sum of the values of P on all outcomes of A.   ❖

Pause 12   Use the definition of probability to give new proofs of the identities

(a) $P(A \cup B) = P(A) + P(B) - P(A \cap B)$;

(b) $P(A^c) = 1 - P(A)$.   ∎

In some of the examples studied in Section 7.3, we talked about rolling a die several times or tossing a coin several times. Intuitively, we understand that these tosses or rolls are *independent* in the sense that the result of one toss (or roll) does not affect the result of any other.

In Section 6.2, we learned the multiplication rule, which stated that the number of ways in which a sequence of events can occur is the product of the number of ways in which each individual event can occur. Analogously, we have

> The probability that a sequence of independent events occurs is the product of the probabilities that each event occurs.

Several of the problems studied in Section 7.3 could have been solved using this rule. For example, the probability that a pair of 5's appears when two fair dice are rolled is $\frac{1}{6}(\frac{1}{6}) = \frac{1}{36}$ since $P(5) = \frac{1}{6}$. Note, however, that to find the probability that a 2 and a 3 appear, we must consider the two cases $(2, 3)$ and $(3, 2)$, so the answer is $2(\frac{1}{36}) = \frac{1}{18}$.

 Show how the coin toss problem (Example 14) can be solved using the multiplication rule. ∎

The multiplication rule is more important when outcomes in the sample space are not equally likely.

PROBLEM 21. If the die in Problem 20 is tossed twice in succession, find the probability that the sum of the numbers that appear is odd.

Solution. This problem is most efficiently handled by observing first that, for the sum to be odd, exactly one of the integers appearing must be odd. Next, observe that the probability that an odd number appears is $\frac{7}{12}$ (see Problem 20), so the probability an even number appears is $\frac{5}{12}$. Finally, we apply the multiplication rule. Since the odd number could be either first or second, our answer is $2(\frac{7}{12})(\frac{5}{12}) = \frac{35}{72}$.

 Assume a coin has $P(H) = \frac{1}{3}$ and $P(T) = \frac{2}{3}$. If the coin is tossed eight times in succession, find the probability that five heads occur. ∎

We now want to discuss the notion of independent events a bit more formally. First, we introduce the important concept of conditional probability.

In Problem 21, we saw that if the die in Problem 20 is tossed twice in succession and B is the event that the sum of the numbers appearing is odd, then $P(B) = \frac{35}{72}$.

Suppose we have the additional knowledge that the number appearing on the first die is odd (call this event A). Does this change the probability of B occurring? Well, the sum will then be odd if and only if the second toss is even, and this has probability $\frac{5}{12} \neq \frac{35}{72}$. We have just calculated a *conditional* probability, $P(B \mid A)$, the probability that B occurs given that A has occurred.

Here is the proper definition.

7.4.2 DEFINITION Let A and B be events with $P(A) > 0$. The *conditional probability* of B given A, denoted $P(B \mid A)$, is $P(B \mid A) = \dfrac{P(B \cap A)}{P(A)}$. ❖

Consider, for example, the problem just discussed. Here $P(A) = \frac{7}{12}$, as calculated in Problem 20, while $B \cap A$ is the event that the first toss is odd and the second even. We have $P(B \cap A) = \frac{7}{12}(\frac{5}{12})$ and $P(B \mid A) = \dfrac{\frac{7}{12}(\frac{5}{12})}{\frac{7}{12}} = \frac{5}{12}$, as noted.

We could also calculate $P(A \mid B) = \dfrac{P(A \cap B)}{P(B)} = \dfrac{\frac{7}{12}(\frac{5}{12})}{\frac{35}{72}} = \frac{1}{2}$. Note that $P(A \mid B)$ is the probability that the number appearing on the first die is odd, given that the total of the tosses is odd. This makes sense because if we know the sum is odd, then the two tosses must have opposite parity. Since the same die is used both times, the probability is $\frac{1}{2}$ that the first die is odd.

Pause 15   With A and B as above and C the event that the second die is even, calculate $P(C \mid A)$, $P(A \mid C)$, $P(C \mid B)$, and $P(B \mid C)$. ∎

PROBLEM 22. A fair coin is tossed five times. Find the probability of obtaining at most one head, given that at least one head appears.

Solution. We want $P(B \mid A)$, where A is the event of obtaining at least one head and B is the event of obtaining at most one head. Note that $B \cap A$ is the event of obtaining exactly one head. We have $P(B \cap A) = \dfrac{\binom{5}{1}}{2^5} = \frac{5}{32}$, and $P(A) = 1 - \frac{1}{32} = \frac{31}{32}$. So

$$P(B \mid A) = \frac{P(B \cap A)}{P(A)} = \frac{5}{31}.$$

As we have noted, to say that two events A and B are *independent* means that they have no effect on each other. In other words, the probability of B occurring does not depend on whether A occurs. In terms of conditional probability, $P(B \mid A) = P(B)$.

Substituting this in the formula for $P(B \mid A)$, we obtain a workable definition of independence.

7.4.3 DEFINITION   Events A and B are *independent* if $P(A \cap B) = P(A)P(B)$. ❖

EXAMPLE 23
1. Consider two successive throws of a fair die. If A is the event of getting a 5 on the first throw and B is the event of getting a 5 on the second throw, then A and B are independent. We noted this informally earlier, but following the definition and using the fact that $A \cap B$ is the event of getting two 5s, we see that $P(A) = \frac{1}{6}$, $P(B) = \frac{1}{6}$, and $P(A \cap B) = \frac{1}{36} = P(A)P(B)$.
2. Most pairs of events we have considered have not been independent. For instance, in Problem 22, $P(A) = \frac{31}{32}$ and $P(B) = \frac{1}{32} + \frac{5}{32} = \frac{6}{32}$, while $P(A \cap B) = \frac{5}{32} \neq P(A)P(B)$.

PROBLEM 24. The probability that a student will pass math is .85, while the probability the student will pass English is .92. The probability that she will fail both courses is .004. Show that the events "pass math" and "pass English" are not independent.

Solution. Let M denote the event "pass math" and let E denote the event "pass English." We are given that $P(M) = .85$, $P(E) = .92$, and $P(M^c \cap E^c) = .004$. So $P((M \cup E)^c) = .004$ and $P(M \cup E) = 1 - .004 = .996$. By Theorem 7.3.2, the third part, $P(M \cap E) = P(M) + P(E) - P(M \cup E) = .85 + .92 - .996 = .774$. But $P(M)P(E) = .85(.92) = .782 \neq P(M \cap E)$. So M and E are not independent. ▲

It is a little tricky and beyond the scope of this book to formalize the notion of independence for events $A_1, A_2, \ldots, A_n$ when $n > 2$. It turns out that we must stipulate

$$P(A_{i_1} \cap A_{i_2} \cap \cdots \cap A_{i_t}) = P(A_{i_1})P(A_{i_2}) \cdots P(A_{i_t}),$$

for all integers $i_1, i_2, \ldots, i_t$ with $1 \leq i_1 < i_2 < \cdots < i_t \leq n$.

For our purposes, it is sufficient to remark that this condition does hold in many familiar situations where we would naturally consider events to be independent; for example, a head appearing on the ith toss of a coin.

Pause 16   Verify that if $P(B \mid A) = P(B)$ and $P(B) > 0$ then $P(A \mid B) = P(A)$.   ∎

When events A and B are independent, we have $P(A \cap B) = P(A)P(B)$. Whether independent or not, we can always cross-multiply the conditional probability formula and obtain

$$P(A \cap B) = P(A)P(B \mid A) = P(B)P(A \mid B).$$

These formulas can be useful.

PROBLEM 25. Buymore Supermarket orders light bulbs from two suppliers, AA Electronics and AAA Electronics. Buymore purchases 30% of its light bulbs from AA and 70% from AAA. Two percent of the light bulbs purchased from AA are defective, while 3% of the light bulbs purchased from AAA are defective. Find the probability that a randomly selected light bulb

   (a) was purchased from AA and is defective;

   (b) was purchased from AAA and is not defective;

   (c) is defective.

Solution. Let A be the event "the light bulb was purchased from AA," let B be the event "the light bulb was purchased from AAA," and let C be the event "the light bulb is defective." We are given $P(A) = .3$, $P(B) = .7$, $P(C \mid A) = .02$, and $P(C \mid B) = .03$.

   (a) This is $P(A \cap C) = P(A)P(C \mid A) = .3(.02) = .006$.

   (b) This is $P(B \cap C^c) = P(B) - P(B \cap C) = P(B) - P(B)P(C \mid B) = .7 - .7(.03) = .679$.

   (c) Since $B = A^c$, we have $C = (C \cap A) \cup (C \cap B)$. (See Exercise 29 of Section 7.3.) Since $C \cap A$ and $C \cap B$ are mutually exclusive,

$$P(C) = P(C \cap A) + P(C \cap B)$$
$$= P(A)P(C \mid A) + P(B)P(C \mid B) = .3(.02) + .7(.03) = .027. \ \triangle$$

The calculation in part (c) of Problem 25 illustrates a useful basic fact. If a collection of pairwise mutually exclusive events $A_1, A_2, \ldots, A_n$ cover the entire sample space, each $P(A)_i > 0$, and if X is any event, then

$$(1) \quad P(X) = P(A_1)P(X \mid A_1) + P(A_2)P(X \mid A_2) + \cdots + P(A_n)P(X \mid A_n).$$

Pause 17   Prove formula (1) using Exercise 30 of Section 7.3.   ∎

PROBLEM 26. Verify the identity

$$(2) \qquad P(B \mid A) = \frac{P(B)P(A \mid B)}{P(A)}.$$

Solution. $P(B \mid A) = \dfrac{P(A \cap B)}{P(A)} = \dfrac{P(B)P(A \mid B)}{P(A)}.$

Identity (2) turns conditional probabilities around and sometimes gives answers that may not be obvious otherwise. For example, in Problem 25, say we wanted to find the probability that a randomly selected defective light bulb was purchased from AAA Electronics. This is just $P(B \mid C)$, and (2) says

$$P(B \mid C) = \frac{P(B)P(C \mid B)}{P(C)} = \frac{.7(.03)}{.027} = .078$$

using part (c) of Problem 25.

Pause 18

In Problem 25, a bulb selected at random works fine. Find the probability this bulb was purchased from AA electronics. ∎

We have actually derived, and seen how to apply, a classical result in probability theory.

7.4.4 BAYES'S FORMULA

Suppose events $A_1, A_2, \ldots, A_n$ are pairwise mutually exclusive and $A_1 \cup A_2 \cup \cdots \cup A_n = S$. Assume that $P(A_i) > 0$ for each i. If X is any event with $P(X) > 0$, then, for each j,

$$P(A_j \mid X) = \frac{P(A_j)P(X \mid A_j)}{P(X)},$$

where $P(X) = \sum_{i=1}^{n} P(A_i)P(X \mid A_i)$.

Answers to Pauses

12. **(a)** Label the elements in A, B, and $A \cap B$ as follows:

$$A \cap B = \{x_1, \ldots, x_n\},$$

$$A = \{x_1, \ldots, x_n, y_1, \ldots, y_s\}, \qquad B = \{x_1, \ldots, x_n, z_1, \ldots, z_t\},$$

where we assume that the sets of xs, ys, and zs are pairwise disjoint. Then $A \cup B = \{x_1, \ldots, x_n, y_1, \ldots, y_s, z_1, \ldots, z_t\}$, so

$$P(A \cup B) = \sum_{i=1}^{n} P(x_i) + \sum_{i=1}^{s} P(y_i) + \sum_{i=1}^{t} P(z_i)$$

while $P(A) + P(B) - P(A \cap B)$

$$= \sum_{i=1}^{n} P(x_i) + \sum_{i=1}^{s} P(y_i) + \sum_{i=1}^{n} P(x_i) + \sum_{i=1}^{t} P(z_i) - \sum_{i=1}^{n} P(x_i)$$

$$= \sum_{i=1}^{n} P(x_i) + \sum_{i=1}^{s} P(y_i) + \sum_{i=1}^{t} P(z_i) = P(A \cup B)$$

as required.

(b) Let $A = \{x_1, \ldots, x_n\}$ and suppose $S = \{x_1, \ldots, x_n, y_1, \ldots, y_m\}$. Then $A^c = \{y_1, \ldots, y_m\}$, so

$$P(A^c) = \sum_{i=1}^{m} P(y_i) = \left[\sum_{i=1}^{n} P(x_i) + \sum_{i=1}^{m} P(y_i)\right] - \sum_{i=1}^{n} P(x_i)$$

$$= 1 - \sum_{i=1}^{n} P(x_i) = 1 - P(A).$$

13. $P(H) = \frac{1}{2}$, so the probability of obtaining eight consecutive heads is $(\frac{1}{2})^8 = \frac{1}{256}$. There are $\binom{8}{5}$ ways of choosing a sequence with five heads. Each sequence has probability $(\frac{1}{2})^8$, so the answer is $\binom{8}{5}(\frac{1}{2})^8 = \frac{56}{256} = \frac{7}{32}$.

14. As in PAUSE 13, there are $\binom{8}{5}$ sequences satisfying this, and each has probability $(\frac{1}{3})^5(\frac{2}{3})^3$. So the answer is $\binom{8}{5}\frac{2^3}{3^8} = \frac{448}{6561}$.

15. $P(C \mid A) = \dfrac{P(C \cap A)}{P(A)} = \dfrac{\frac{7}{12}(\frac{5}{12})}{\frac{7}{12}} = \frac{5}{12}$.

$P(A \mid C) = \dfrac{P(A \cap C)}{P(C)} = \dfrac{\frac{7}{12}(\frac{5}{12})}{\frac{5}{12}} = \frac{7}{12}$.

$P(C \mid B) = \dfrac{P(C \cap B)}{P(B)} = \dfrac{\frac{7}{12}(\frac{5}{12})}{\frac{35}{72}} = \frac{1}{2}$.

$P(B \mid C) = \dfrac{P(B \cap C)}{P(C)} = \dfrac{\frac{7}{12}(\frac{5}{12})}{\frac{5}{12}} = \frac{7}{12}$.

16. We are given that $P(B \mid A) = P(B)$, which implies $P(B \cap A) = P(A)P(B)$. So $P(A \mid B) = \dfrac{P(A \cap B)}{P(B)} = \dfrac{P(A)P(B)}{P(B)} = P(A)$.

17. Since $P(X \mid A_i) = \dfrac{P(X \cap A_i)}{P(A_i)}$ for each i, the given formula is the same as that in Exercise 30.

18. We want $P(A \mid C^c)$. Now

$$P(A \mid C^c) = \frac{P(A)P(C^c \mid A)}{P(C^c)}$$
$$= \frac{P(A)(1 - P(C \mid A))}{P(C^c)} = \frac{.3(1 - .02)}{.973} = .302.$$

[A PAUSE within a PAUSE!] Prove the formula $P(C^c \mid A) = 1 - P(C \mid A)$ used in the solution to PAUSE 18. ∎

19. $P(C^c \mid A)$
$= \dfrac{P(C^c \cap A)}{P(A)} = \dfrac{P(A) - P(C \cap A)}{P(A)} = 1 - \dfrac{P(C \cap A)}{P(A)} = 1 - P(C \mid A)$.

True/False Questions

(Answers can be found in the back of the book.)

1. If a biased coin with $P(H) = \frac{3}{4}$ and $P(T) = \frac{1}{4}$ is thrown twice, the probability of getting two heads is $2(\frac{3}{4}) = \frac{3}{2}$.

2. If the biased coin in Question 1 is thrown twice, the probability of getting at least one head is $\frac{15}{16}$.

3. If $A^c = \emptyset$, then $P(A) = 1$.

4. If A is an event such that $P(A) = 1$, then $A^c = \emptyset$.

5. It is possible to have $P(A) = \frac{1}{4}$, $P(B) = \frac{1}{3}$, and $P(A \cup B) = \frac{2}{3}$.

6. Given $P(A) > 0$, $P(A \mid B) = \frac{P(B \cap A)}{P(A)}$.

7. Events A and B are independent if $P(A \cap B) = P(A)P(B)$.

8. $P(A \mid B) = P(B \mid A)$ if and only if $P(A) = P(B) > 0$.

9. $P(A \mid B) = \frac{P(A)}{P(B)} P(B \mid A)$, assuming $P(A) > 0$, $P(B) > 0$.

10. If $A_1, A_2, \ldots, A_n$ cover the entire sample space, each $P(A_i) > 0$, and $A_1 \cap A_2 \cap \cdots \cap A_n = \emptyset$, then it is always the case that $P(X) = P(A_1)P(X \mid A_1) + P(A_2)P(X \mid A_2) + \cdots + P(A_n)P(X \mid A_n)$.

Exercises

*The answers to exercises marked [BB] can be found in the **B**ack of the **B**ook.*

1. [BB] Assume that a biased die has $P(1) = \frac{1}{4}$, $P(2) = \frac{1}{8}$, $P(3) = P(4) = \frac{1}{6}$, $P(5) = \frac{1}{12}$, $P(6) = \frac{5}{24}$. If the die is tossed once, find the probability that
   (a) an even number appears;
   (b) the number that appears is at least 5.

2. If the die in Exercise 1 is tossed twice, find the probability that
   (a) [BB] the sum of the numbers appearing is 8;
   (b) the sum of the numbers appearing is at least 11;
   (c) the sum of the numbers appearing is even;
   (d) [BB] the numbers that appear differ by 4;
   (e) the numbers that appear differ by at least 4.

3. [BB] If heads is four times as likely as tails when a biased coin is flipped, what values should be given to $P(H)$ and $P(T)$?

4. If the events "two tails" and "one head, one tail" are equally likely when a biased coin is flipped, what values should be given to $P(H)$ and $P(T)$. (Find all answers.)

5. [BB] Mike tosses a five-sided "die" with faces labeled $1, 2, 3, 4, 5$ and $P(i) = iP(1)$ for $i = 1, 2, 3, 4, 5$. Find $P(i)$ for each i.

6. Louis tosses a five-sided "die" with faces labeled $1, 2, 3, 4, 5$ and $P(i) = 2^{i-1}P(1)$ for $i = 1, 2, 3, 4, 5$. Find $P(i)$ for each i.

7. [BB] A coin has $P(H) = \frac{1}{4}$. If it is tossed six times in succession, find the probability of getting
   (a) exactly four heads;   (b) at least five heads;
   (c) at most five heads.

8. A coin has $P(T) = \frac{2}{5}$. If it is tossed five times in succession, find the probability of getting
   (a) exactly two heads;   (b) at most one head;
   (c) at least one head.

9. [BB] A fair coin is tossed five times in succession. Let A be the event "at least three heads appear," B the event "at most four heads appear," and C the event "exactly two heads appear." Find
   (a) $P(A \mid B)$;   (b) $P(B \mid A)$;
   (c) $P(A \mid C)$;   (d) $P(C \mid A)$;
   (e) $P(B \mid C)$;   (f) $P(C \mid B)$.

10. A fair die is tossed twice. Let A be the event "the total is at least eight," B the event "the total is at most nine," and C the event "the total is odd." Find
    (a) $P(A \mid B)$;   (b) $P(B \mid A)$;

(c) $P(A \mid C)$;   (d) $P(C \mid A)$;
(e) $P(B \mid C)$;   (f) $P(C \mid B)$.

11. [BB] In Exercise 1, let A and B be the events described in parts (a) and (b), respectively. Find $P(A \mid B)$ and $P(B \mid A)$. Are A and B independent? Are A and B mutually exclusive?

12. In Exercise 2, let A and B be the events described in parts (b) and (e), respectively. Find $P(A \mid B)$ and $P(B \mid A)$. Are A and B independent? Are A and B mutually exclusive?

13. [BB] In the experiment of throwing two dice, give an example of a pair of events A and B that are independent but not mutually exclusive.

14. Is it possible for events A and B to be both independent and mutually exclusive? Explain.

15. A fair coin is tossed n times. Let A be the event "at least $n - 1$ heads appear" and let B be the event "at most $n - 1$ heads and at most $n - 1$ tails appear."
    (a) [BB] Show that A and B are not independent if $n = 2$.
    (b) [BB] Show that A and B are independent if $n = 3$.
    (c) Prove that, for all $n > 3$, A and B are not independent.

16. Show that A and B are independent if $P(A) = .8$, $P(B) = .6$, and $P(A \cup B) = .92$.

17. [BB] If A and B are independent events, prove that A^c and B^c are also independent.

18. If A and B are independent events, prove that A and B^c are independent. [*Hint:* Exercise 29 of Section 7.3]

19. The probability that Brian will pass Math 2320 is .93, while the probability that Jennifer will pass is .95. The probability that Brian will pass and Jennifer will fail is .04. Is Brian's performance in Math 2320 independent of Jennifer's?

20. [BB] Given $n \geq 1$ events $A_1, A_2, \ldots, A_n$, prove that $P(A_1 \cup A_2 \cup \cdots \cup A_n) \leq P(A_1) + P(A_2) + \cdots + P(A_n)$.

21. Given $n \geq 1$ events $A_1, A_2, \ldots, A_n$, prove that $P(A_1 \cap A_2 \cap \cdots \cap A_n) \geq P(A_1) + P(A_2) + \cdots + P(A_n) - (n-1)$.

22. (a) Find the probability that everyone in a group of $n \leq 365$ people has a different birthday. (Ignore birthdays on February 29 and assume that all 365 days of the year are equally likely birthdays.)
    (b) Find the value of n such that the probability in (a) is as close as possible to $\frac{1}{2}$.

In the next five exercises, we use the notation $_nP_x$ for the probability that a person who has just turned age x will survive for the next n years. For example, $_5P_{30}$ is the probability of a 30-year old surviving to age 35. The identity in Exercise 23 will be needed in Exercises 24–27.

23. A standard identity concerning the symbol $_nP_x$ is
$_{n+m}P_x = (_nP_x)(_mP_{x+n})$. What is being asserted and assumed here?

24. [BB] Given $_{30}P_{20} = .8$, $_{20}P_{50} = .7$, and $_{10}P_{40} = .9$, find
(a) $_{50}P_{20}$;   (b) $_{30}P_{40}$;   (c) $_{20}P_{20}$.

25. Given $_{70}P_{20} = .3$, $_{40}P_{50} = .5$, and $_{10}P_{40} = .9$, find
(a) $_{50}P_{40}$;   (b) $_{30}P_{20}$;   (c) $_{20}P_{20}$.

26. [BB] The probability that two persons aged 20 and 30 will both live for 10 years is .9. The probability that a person aged 20 will live for 15 years is .94. The probability that a person aged 20 will live for 60 years is .55. Find the probability that a 35-year-old will die between ages 40 and 80. (Assume that survival of different lives is independent.)

27. The probability that a person aged 20 will survive to age 60 is .95. Eighty per cent of the deaths between age 20 and age 80 occur after age 60. The probability that two people aged 60 and 75 will both survive for 15 years is .3. Find $_{10}P_{80}$.

28. Given $n > 1$ events $A_1, A_2, \dots, A_n$, prove that
$$P(A_1 \cap A_2 \cap \dots \cap A_n)$$
$$= P(A_1)P(A_2 \mid A_1)P(A_3 \mid (A_1 \cap A_2)) \cdots$$
$$P(A_n \mid (A_1 \cap A_2 \cap \dots \cap A_{n-1})).$$

29. [BB] Consumers in the town of Trout River have their choice of three restaurants. The table lists the fraction of customers each restaurant serves per week and, for each restaurant, the fraction of customers who are satisfied.

Restaurant	Fraction of Customers	Fraction Satisfied
Leonce's Seafood Emporium	0.4	0.85
Harold's Steak Shack	0.35	0.9
Vegan Delights	0.25	0.95

For example, 25% of all customers eat at Vegan Delights and 95% of these are satisfied. Find the probability that
(a) a randomly selected customer eats at Vegan Delights and is satisfied;
(b) a randomly selected customer eats at Harold's and is dissatisfied;
(c) a randomly selected customer is satisfied;
(d) a satisfied customer has eaten at Leonce's;
(e) a customer who has not eaten at Vegan Delights is dissatisfied.

30. In Exercise 29, a customer selected at random from among those who ate at one of the three restaurants in the past week states he was satisfied. At which of the restaurants is he most likely to have eaten?

31. A new three-screen cinema has just opened in the town of Quirpoon. The table summarizes the fraction of customers attending each of the three movies showing on a given night and, for each film, the fraction who purchase popcorn.

Movie	Rarer Birds	Codroy Vampire Project	La Vie d'un Elan
Fraction Attending	0.5	0.3	0.2
Fraction Purchasing Popcorn	0.7	0.9	0.4

Find the probability that
(a) a randomly selected patron attends *La Vie d'un Elan* and purchases popcorn;
(b) a randomly selected patron attends *Rarer Birds* and does not purchase popcorn;
(c) a randomly selected patron purchases popcorn;
(d) a customer attending *Rarer Birds* or *Codroy Vampire Project* does not purchase popcorn;
(e) a customer who attends *La Vie d'un Elan* purchases popcorn.

7.5 Repetitions

In the first two sections we counted the number of ways to put r marbles into n boxes with at most one marble to a box in two situations: The marbles have different colors and the marbles are all the same color. Suppose we allow any number of marbles in a box. If the marbles are all colored differently, then there are n choices for the first marble, n for the second, and so forth. There are, altogether, $n \times n \times \dots \times n = n^r$ possibilities. When the marbles are all the same colour, however, we expect far fewer possibilities.

Suppose we want to place three white marbles into ten boxes and we are allowed to put as many marbles into a box as we like. There are three mutually exclusive ways in which this can be accomplished: Each marble goes into a different box [in one of $\binom{10}{3} = 120$ ways]; two marbles go into the same box, but the third goes into its own box (in one of $10 \times 9 = 90$ ways), or all the marbles go into the same box (in one of 10 ways). By the addition rule, the number of ways in all is $120 + 90 + 10 = 220$. We note in passing that $220 = \binom{10+3-1}{3}$.

In how many ways can ten marbles, all of the same color, be put into three boxes? While this problem is obviously similar to the previous, it becomes quickly apparent that a case by case examination of the possibilities is very difficult this time. There are three ways in which the marbles all go into the same box, but in how many ways can they be placed into exactly two boxes or into exactly three? The question seems quite complicated, so we consider it from a new perspective.

One way to put the marbles into the boxes is to put three marbles into box 1, five into box 2, and two into box 3. This situation can be represented by the 12-digit string 000100000100, which has strings of three, five, and two 0's separated by two 1's. There is a one-to-one correspondence between ways of putting the marbles into the boxes and 12-digit strings consisting of two 1's and ten 0's. The string 001000000100 would represent the situation of two marbles in box 1, six in box 2, and two in box 3. The string 100000010000 would indicate that there are no marbles in box 1, six in box 2, and four in box 3. To count the number of ways of putting ten marbles in three boxes is, therefore, just to count the number of 12-digit 0–1 strings that contain precisely two 1's. This latter number is easy to find! There are $\binom{12}{2}$ such numbers corresponding to the number of ways of selecting two positions for the 1's from 12 positions. Therefore, the number of ways to put ten identical marbles into three boxes, any number to a box, is $\binom{12}{2} = 66 = \binom{3+10-1}{10}$. We have seen two instances of the next proposition.

The number of ways to put r identical marbles into n boxes is $\binom{n+r-1}{r}$.

PROBLEM 27. Doughnuts come in 30 different varieties and Catherine wants to buy a dozen. How many choices does she have?

Solution. Imagine that the 30 varieties are in $n = 30$ boxes labeled chocolate white, Boston creme, peanut crunch, and so on. Catherine can indicate her choice by dropping $r = 12$ (identical) marbles into the boxes. So there are $\binom{30+12-1}{12} = 7,898,654,920$ possibilities. ▵

Pause 20 David wants to buy 30 doughnuts and finds just 12 varieties available. In how many ways can he make his selection? ∎

The basic facts about marbles and boxes that we have discussed so far are summarized in Table 7.3.

In Section 7.1, we counted the number of ways to put three marbles of different colors into ten boxes, at most one marble to a box; and, in Section 7.2, we considered the same problem for identical marbles. What about the intermediate possibility that two marbles have the same color, say red, and the third is a different color, perhaps blue? In how many ways can these three marbles be put into ten boxes, at most one to a box? There are $\binom{10}{2}$ ways in which to pick boxes for the red marbles and then $\binom{8}{1}$ ways to choose the box for the blue marble. By the multiplication rule, the number of ways to put two reds and one blue marble into ten boxes, at most one to

Table 7.3 The number of ways to put r marbles into n numbered boxes.

	Same	All Different Colors
At most one to a box	$\dbinom{n+r-1}{r}$	$P(n, r)$
Any number in a box	$\dbinom{n+r-1}{r}$	n^r

a box, is

$$\binom{10}{2} \times \binom{8}{1} = \frac{10!}{2!8!} \times \frac{8!}{7!1!} = \frac{10!}{2!1!7!} = 360.$$

The number of ways to put two red, four blue, and three green marbles into ten boxes, at most one to a box, is $\binom{10}{2}$ (choose boxes for the reds) $\times \binom{8}{4}$ (choose boxes for the blues) $\times \binom{4}{3}$ (choose boxes for the greens); that is,

$$\frac{10!}{2!8!} \times \frac{8!}{4!4!} \times \frac{4!}{3!1!} = \frac{10!}{2!4!3!1!}.$$

PROBLEM 28. Suppose ten players are to be assigned to three teams, the Xtreme, the Maniax, and the Enforcers. The Xtreme and the Maniax are to receive four players each, and the Enforcers are to receive two. In how many ways can this be done?

Solution. The assignment of players is accomplished by choosing four players from ten for the Xtreme, then choosing four players from the remaining six for the Maniax, and assigning the remaining two players to the Enforcers. The number of possible teams is

$$\binom{10}{4} \times \binom{6}{4} = 210(15) = 3150.$$

 In how many ways can 14 men be divided into six named teams, two with three players and four with two? In how many ways can 14 men be divided into two unnamed teams of three and four teams of two? ∎

In how many ways can the letters of the word *easy* be rearranged? The question just asks for the number of permutations of four different letters: The answer is $4! = 24$. In how many ways can the letters of the word *ease* be rearranged? This is a slightly different problem because of the repeated e: When the first and last letters of *easy* are interchanged, we get two different arrangements of the four letters, but when the first and last letters of *ease* are interchanged we get the same word. To see how to count the ways in which the four letters of *ease* can be arranged, we imagine the list of all these arrangements.

$$s\ e\ a\ e$$
$$a\ e\ e\ s$$
$$e\ e\ s\ a$$
$$\vdots$$

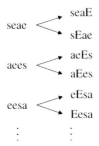

seae $\begin{cases} \text{seaE} \\ \text{sEae} \end{cases}$

aees $\begin{cases} \text{aeEs} \\ \text{aEes} \end{cases}$

eesa $\begin{cases} \text{eEsa} \\ \text{Eesa} \end{cases}$

$\vdots \qquad \vdots$

Figure 7.4

Pretending for a moment that the two e's are different (say one is a capital E), then each "word" in this list will produce two different arrangements of the letters e a s E. (See Fig. 7.4.)

The list on the right contains the $4! = 24$ arrangements of the four letters e a s E, so the list on the left contains half as many. There are $\frac{4!}{2!} = 12$ ways in which the letters of *ease* can be arranged.

PROBLEM 29. In how many ways can the letters of the word *attention* be rearranged?

Solution. The word *attention* has nine letters, three of one kind, two of another, and four other different letters. The number of rearrangements of this word is $\frac{9!}{3!2!} = 30{,}240$.

This answer is obtained, as before, by imagining the list of arrangements and imagining how many arrangements could be formed if the letters were all different. If the two n's were different, each rearrangement would produce two more, giving a second list twice as long. If the three t's were different, each word in this second list would yield $3! = 6$ more. For instance, replacing the three t's by t, T, and τ, then *tanetoeti* yields

taneToeτi, taneτoeTi, Tanetoeτi, Taneτoeti, τanetoiTi, τaneToiti

corresponding to the 3! permutations of t, T, τ.

We would obtain a third list 3! times as long as the second and $3! \times 2$ times as long as the first. Since this third list consists of all the permutations of the nine symbols a, t, T, e, n, τ, i, o, N, it contains 9! words, so the original list contained $\frac{9!}{3!2!}$ words.

Pause 22

In how many ways can the letters of the word *rearrange* be rearranged? ∎

Answers to Pauses

20. As in Problem 27, we imagine the 12 varieties in boxes. Each of David's possible decisions can be indicated by dropping 30 identical marbles into these boxes. There are $\binom{12+30-1}{30} = 3{,}159{,}461{,}968$ possibilities ($r = 30, n = 12$).

21. If the teams are named, the answer is

$$\binom{14}{3} \times \binom{11}{3} \times \binom{8}{2} \times \binom{6}{2} \times \binom{4}{2} = 364(165)(28)(15)(6) = 151{,}351{,}200.$$

This number is $2!4! = 48$ times the number of divisions into unnamed teams of sizes 3, 3, 2, 2, 2, and 2 because, for each division into unnamed teams, there are two ways to name the teams of three and 4! ways to name the teams of two. The answer in the case of unnamed teams is $\frac{151{,}351{,}200}{48} = 3{,}153{,}150$.

22. There are $\frac{9!}{3!2!2!} = 15{,}120$ rearrangements of the letters of the word *rearrange*.

True/False Questions

(Answers can be found in the back of the book.)

1. The number of ways of putting eight marbles, all of the same color, into 11 numbered boxes is $\binom{18}{8}$.

2. The number of ways of putting eight marbles, all of the same color, into 11 numbered boxes is $\binom{18}{10}$.

3. The number of ways of putting eight marbles, all of the same color, into 11 numbered boxes, at most one to a box, is $\binom{11}{8}$.

4. The number of ways of putting eight marbles, all different colors, into 11 numbered boxes is $P(11, 8)$.

5. The number of ways of purchasing a box of five doughnuts if 12 varieties are available is $\binom{16}{12}$.

6. The number of ways of purchasing a box of 12 doughnuts if five varieties are available is $\binom{16}{12}$.

7. The number of ways of purchasing a box of five doughnuts of different varieties if 12 varieties are available is $\binom{12}{5}$.

8. The number of ways of purchasing a box of five doughnuts of different varieties and then distributing them among five children (one per child) if 12 varietites are available is 12^5.

9. The number of ways of putting r marbles, all of the same color, into n numbered boxes is the same as the number of ways of putting the same r marbles into $n + r - 1$ boxes, at most one to a box.

10. There are $\dfrac{11!}{2!2!2!}$ ways of rearranging the letters of the word *arrangement*.

Exercises

*The answers to exercises marked [BB] can be found in the **B**ack of the **B**ook.*

1. [BB] In how many ways can 30 identical dolls be placed on seven different shelves?

2. There are 15 questions on a multiple-choice exam and five possible answers to each question.
   (a) In how many ways can the exam be answered?
   (b) In how many ways can the exam be answered with exactly eight answers correct?

3. [BB] How many different outcomes are possible when five dice are rolled? (Two 6's, two 5's, and a 1 is one outcome.)

4. [BB] How many different collections of ten coins can be made from pennies, nickels, dimes, and quarters?

5. A florist sells roses in five different colors.
   (a) How many bunches of a half-dozen roses can be formed?
   (b) How many bunches of a half-dozen can be formed if each bunch must contain at least one rose of each color?

6. Twenty varieties of chocolates are available and Linda wants to buy eight chocolates.
   (a) [BB] How many choices does she have?
   (b) How many choices does she have if her boyfriend insists that at least one chocolate should have a cherry center?
   (c) How many choices does she have if there remain only two chocolates with caramel centers? (At least 20 chocolates of all other varieties are available.)

7. (a) In how many ways can five different mathematics books, three different physics books, and four different chemistry books be arranged on a shelf?
   (b) Repeat (a) if all books of the same subject are to be together.
   (c) [BB] Repeat (a) if three of the five mathematics books are the same.
   (d) Repeat (c) if, in addition, all the physics books are the same.

8. In how many ways can 18 different books be given to Tara, Danny, Shannon, and Mike so that one person has six books, one has two books, and the other two people have five books each?

9. (a) Twenty basketball players are going to be drafted by the professional basketball teams in Philadelphia, Boston, Miami, and Toronto such that each team drafts five players. In how many ways can this be accomplished?
   (b) In how many ways can 20 players be divided into four unnamed teams of five players each?

10. Suppose 12 baseball players are to be drafted by San Diego, Houston, and Toronto. If San Diego is to get six players, Houston four players, and Toronto two, in how many ways can this be accomplished?

11. (a) [BB] In how many ways can ten red balls, ten white balls, and ten blue balls be placed in 60 different boxes, at most one ball to a box?
    (b) In how many ways can ten red balls, ten white balls, and ten blue balls be placed in 60 different boxes?

12. In how many ways can two white rooks, two black bishops, eight black pawns, and eight white pawns be placed on a prescribed 20 squares of a chess board?

13. [BB] A committee wishes to award one scholarship of $10,000, two scholarships of $5000, and five scholarships of $1000. The list of potential award winners has been narrowed to 13 possibilities. In how many ways can the scholarships be awarded?

14. Find the number of arrangements of the letters of each of the following words:
    (a) [BB] SCIENTIFIC   (b) SASKATOON
    (c) PICCININI   (d) CINCINNATI

15. [BB] A department store in downtown Victoria, British Columbia, has 30 flags to hang along its roof line to celebrate Queen Victoria's birthday. If there are ten red flags, five white flags, seven yellow flags, and eight blue flags, how many ways can the flags be displayed in a row?

16. In a university residence there are five single rooms, five doubles, and five rooms that hold three students each. In how many ways can 30 students be assigned to the 15 rooms? (All rooms are numbered.)

17. (a) Show that there is a one-to-one correspondence between the number of ways to put ten identical marbles into three boxes and the number of ordered triples (x, y, z) of nonnegative integers that satisfy $x + y + z = 10$.

    (b) How many triples (x, y, z) of nonnegative integers satisfy $x + y + z = 10$?

    (c) How many 5-tuples (x, y, z, u, v) of nonnegative integers satisfy $x + y + z + u + v = 19$?

18. (a) [BB] Show that there is a one-to-one correspondence between the solutions to

    $$(+) \qquad x_1 + x_2 + x_3 + x_4 = 21$$

    with x_1, x_2, x_3, x_4 nonnegative integers, $x_1 \geq 8$, and solutions to

    $$(++) \qquad x_1 + x_2 + x_3 + x_4 = 13$$

with x_1, x_2, x_3, x_4 nonnegative integers. How many solutions are there?

(b) Show that there is a one-to-one correspondence between the solutions to (*) with $x_1 \geq 8$, $x_2 \geq 8$, and solutions to

$$(*\,*\,*) \qquad x_1 + x_2 + x_3 + x_4 = 5$$

with x_1, x_2, x_3, x_4 nonnegative integers. How many solutions are there?

(c) How many solutions are there to (*) with all variables nonnegative integers not exceeding 7? [Hint: Let A_i be the set of solutions to (*) with $x_i \geq 8$.]

(d) How many solutions (x_1, x_2, x_3, x_4) are there to the equation

$$x_1 + x_2 + x_3 + x_4 = 35$$

with all x_i integers, $0 \leq x_i \leq 10$?

19. How many integer solutions are there to the equation $x + y + z + w = 20$ subject to $x \geq 1$, $y \geq 2$, $z \geq 3$, and $w \geq 4$?

7.6 Derangements

There are four houses on a street. A mischievous postman arrives with one letter addressed to each house. In how many ways can he deliver the letters, one to each house, so that no letter arrives at the correct house? The person in charge of coats at the arts center loses all claim checks and returns coats randomly to the patrons. What are the chances that nobody gets his or her own coat?

7.6.1 DEFINITION

A *derangement* of n distinct symbols that have some natural order is a permutation in which no symbol is in its correct position. The number of derangements of n symbols is denoted D_n.   ❖

EXAMPLE 30

- There is just one derangement, 21, of the symbols 1, 2, so $D_2 = 1$.
- There are two derangements of 1, 2, 3 (312 and 231), so $D_3 = 2$.
- There are nine derangements of 1, 2, 3, 4,

$$\begin{array}{ccc} 2341 & 2413 & 2143 \\ 3142 & 3412 & 3421 \\ 4123 & 4312 & 4321 \end{array}$$

so $D_4 = 9$. There are nine ways our mischievous postman can deliver four letters, each to the wrong address.

Finding a general formula for D_n involves a nice application of the Principle of Inclusion–Exclusion, binomial coefficients, and a famous irrational number. We consider again D_4, the number of derangements of 1, 2, 3, 4.

Let A_1 be the set of permutations of 1, 2, 3, 4 in which the number 1 is in the first position. Let A_2 be the set of permutations of 1, 2, 3, 4 in which the number 2 is in the second position. Define A_3 and A_4 similarly. The set of permutations in which at least one of the four numbers is left in its natural position is then $A_1 \cup A_2 \cup A_3 \cup A_4$, and the complement of this set consists precisely of the derangements of 1, 2, 3, 4.

Since there are $4! = 24$ permutations altogether, the number of derangements of four symbols is

$$D_4 = 4! - |A_1 \cup A_2 \cup A_3 \cup A_4|.$$

How many elements are in the union $A_1 \cup A_2 \cup A_3 \cup A_4$? By the Inclusion–Exclusion Principle,

$$|A_1 \cup A_2 \cup A_3 \cup A_4| = \sum_i |A_i| - \sum_{i<j} |A_i \cap A_j| + \sum_{i<j<k} |A_i \cap A_j \cap A_k|$$
$$- |A_1 \cap A_2 \cap A_3 \cap A_4|.$$

Now $|A_1| = 3!$ (1 is in the first position, numbers 2, 3, and 4 go to any of the next three positions). Similarly, $|A_i| = 3!$ for any i.

The set $A_1 \cap A_2$ contains those permutations of 1, 2, 3, 4 in which 1 and 2 are in the correct positions. There are just two such permutations, 1234 and 1243. Thus, $|A_i \cap A_j| = 2!$ for each of the $6 = \binom{4}{2}$ terms in the second sum on the right of equation (3).

Similar reasoning shows that each of the $4 = \binom{4}{3}$ terms $|A_i \cap A_j \cap A_k|$ equals 1, as does the last term. Therefore,

$$|A_1 \cup A_2 \cup A_3 \cup A_4| = 4(3!) - \binom{4}{2}(2!) + \binom{4}{3}(1!) - 1$$

and hence

$$D_4 = 4! - \left(4(3!) - \binom{4}{2}2! + \binom{4}{3}1! - 1\right)$$

$$= 4! - 4! + \frac{4!}{2!2!}2! - \frac{4!}{3!} + 1$$

$$= 4! - 4! + \frac{4!}{2!} - \frac{4!}{3!} + \frac{4!}{4!}$$

$$= 4!\left(1 - \frac{1}{1!} + \frac{1}{2!} - \frac{1}{3!} + \frac{1}{4!}\right)$$

$$= 24\left(1 - 1 + \frac{1}{2} - \frac{1}{6} + \frac{1}{24}\right)$$

$$= 24 - 24 + 12 - 4 + 1 = 9.$$

To find a general formula for D_n, for general n, we mimic this calculation of D_4.

7.6.2 PROPOSITION   The number of derangements of $n \geq 1$ ordered symbols is

$$D_n = n!\left(1 - \frac{1}{1!} + \frac{1}{2!} - \frac{1}{3!} + \cdots + (-1)^n\frac{1}{n!}\right).$$

For example,

$$D_5 = 5!\left(1 - \frac{1}{1!} + \frac{1}{2!} - \frac{1}{3!} + \frac{1}{4!} - \frac{1}{5!}\right)$$

$$= 5! - 5! + 5 \cdot 4 \cdot 3 - 5 \cdot 4 + 5 - 1 = 60 - 20 + 5 - 1 = 44.$$

Some readers may have encountered the number e, the base of the natural logarithm, in a calculus course. The *Taylor expansion* for e^x is the formula

$$e^x = 1 + \frac{x}{1!} + \frac{x^2}{2!} + \frac{x^3}{3!} + \cdots ,$$

(4)

which, among its uses, allows us to approximate various powers of e. To approximate e itself, for instance, we evaluate the first several terms of the Taylor expansion for e^x with $x = 1$:

$$e = e^1 \approx 1 + \frac{1}{1!} + \frac{1^2}{2!} + \frac{1^3}{3!} + \frac{1^4}{4!} = 1 + 1 + \frac{1}{2} + \frac{1}{6} + \frac{1}{24} \approx 2.708.$$

Better approximations can be obtained by including more terms of the Taylor expansion. To approximate $\sqrt{e}$, we have

$$\sqrt{e} = e^{1/2} = e^{.5} \approx 1 + \frac{.5}{1!} + \frac{(.5)^2}{2!} + \frac{(.5)^3}{3!}$$

$$= 1 + .5 + .125 + .0208\dot{3} \approx 1.646.$$

With $x = -1$, we have

$$\frac{1}{e} = e^{-1} \approx 1 - \frac{1}{1!} + \frac{1}{2!} - \frac{1}{3!} + \cdots + (-1)^n \frac{1}{n!}$$

for any $n \geq 1$.

Comparison with the formula for D_n given in Proposition 7.6.2 shows that $D_n \approx n!e^{-1} = \frac{n!}{e}$.[2] Equivalently, $\frac{D_n}{n!} \approx \frac{1}{e} \approx 0.368$, an observation that shows that the derangements of n symbols comprise about 36.8% of all the permutations of n symbols. This percentage can also be viewed as the probability that a randomly selected permutation of n symbols will be a derangement. It is curious that for any $n > 5$ this probability is 36.8% to one decimal place. The chance that a postman, delivering letters randomly, will deliver six letters to six incorrect addresses is just about the same as the chance that he will deliver 50 letters to incorrect addresses.

 Pause 23

Express $\frac{D_4}{4!}$ as a decimal and compare with $\frac{1}{e}$. Do the same for D_5. ∎

Answers to Pauses

23. $\frac{D_4}{4!} = \frac{9}{24} = 0.375$. Even for $n = 4$, $\frac{D_n}{n!}$ is remarkably close to $\frac{1}{e}$.
$\frac{D_5}{5!} = \frac{44}{120} = .3\dot{6}$. In fact, for $n > 5$, $\frac{D_n}{n!} = 0.368\ldots$ agrees with $\frac{1}{e}$ to three decimal places.

True/False Questions

(Answers can be found in the back of the book.)

1. 34125 is a derangement of 1, 2, 3, 4, 5.
2. 341265 is a derangement of 1, 2, 3, 4, 5, 6.
3. $D_3 = 3$.
4. If n is a natural number, $D_n = n! - |A_1 \cup A_2 \cdots \cup A_n|$ for certain suitable sets $A_1, A_2, \ldots, A_n$.
5. If n is a natural number, $D_n = n!\left(1 - \frac{1}{2!} + \frac{1}{3!} - \cdots + (-1)^n \frac{1}{n!}\right)$.
6. $e^3 = 1 + \frac{3}{1!} + \frac{3^2}{2!} + \frac{3^3}{3!} + \cdots$

---

[2]Students who have studied Taylor polynomials may see why the error in approximating D_n by $\frac{n!}{e}$ is less than $\frac{1}{n+1}$.

7. $e = 2.708$.

8. $D_n \approx \dfrac{n!}{e}$.

9. $D_{10} \equiv 1 \pmod{10}$. [See Exercise 10(a).]

10. D_{20} is even. [See Exercise 10(b).]

Exercises

*The answers to exercises marked [BB] can be found in the **B**ack of the **B**ook.*

1. [BB] Find D_6, D_7, and D_8.

2. A simple code is made by permuting the letters of the alphabet such that every letter is replaced by a different letter. How many different codes can be made in this way?

3. [BB] Eleven books are arranged on a shelf in alphabetical order by author name. In how many ways can your little sister rearrange these books so that no book is in its original position?

4. Fifty students take an exam. For the purposes of grading, the teacher asks the students to exchange papers so that no one marks his or her own paper. In how many ways can this be accomplished?

5. Your letter carrier has a drinking problem. When she delivers letters to the seven houses in your block, she delivers completely at random. Suppose she has seven letters, one addressed to each house, and she delivers one letter to each house. In how many ways can this be accomplished if

    (a) no letter arrives at the right house?

    (b) [BB] at least one letter arrives at the right house?

    (c) all letters arrive at the right house?

6. Twenty people check their hats at a theater. In how many ways can their hats be returned so that

    (a) no one receives his or her own hat?

    (b) at least one person receives his or her own hat?

    (c) [BB] exactly one person receives his or her own hat?

    (d) at least two people receive their own hats?

    (e) at most two people receive their own hats?

7. (a) [BB] In how many ways can the integers 1 through 9 be permuted such that no odd integer will be in its natural position?

    (b) In how many ways can the integers 1 through 9 be permuted such that no even integer is in its natural position?

    (c) In how many ways can the integers 1 through 9 be permuted such that exactly four of the nine integers are in their natural positions?

8. Without any calculation, prove that

$$n! = D_n + \binom{n}{1}D_{n-1} + \binom{n}{2}D_{n-2} + \cdots + \binom{n}{n-1}D_1 + 1.$$

9. Prove Proposition 7.6.2.

10. (a) [BB] Prove that $D_n \equiv (-1)^n \pmod{n}$.

    (b) [BB] Prove that D_n is even if and only if n is odd.

11. (a) [BB] Prove that $D_n = (n-1)(D_{n-1} + D_{n-2})$ for all $n \geq 3$.

    (b) Prove that $D_n = nD_{n-1} + (-1)^n$ for all $n \geq 2$.

    (c) Use (b) to find D_n and $\dfrac{D_n}{n!}$ to six decimal places for $n = 1, 2, 3, \ldots, 10$. Use your answers to approximate $\dfrac{1}{e}$ to six decimal places.

12. While the concept of a derangement of zero objects is rather dubious, the formula for D_n given by Proposition 7.6.2 does make sense for $n = 0$ and gives $D_0 = 1$. Taking $D_0 = 1$, show that the generating function for the sequence $\dfrac{D_0}{0!}, \dfrac{D_1}{1!}, \dfrac{D_2}{2!}, \ldots$ is $\dfrac{e^{-x}}{1-x}$.

7.7 The Binomial Theorem

The arrangement of integers in Fig. 7.5 is named after Blaise Pascal (1623–1662) because of the many applications in combinatorics and probability that Pascal found for it.[3] Each row begins and ends with a 1; each other number in a row is the sum of the two numbers to the right and left in the row above it. For example, $10 = 4 + 6$, $6 = 1 + 5$ and $21 = 15 + 6$, as shown in the figure.

This famous triangle has many fascinating properties. For example, if we number the rows starting at 0 and interpret each row as the "digits" of a single number written in base 10,[4] then row k of the triangle is 11^k. For example, row 0 is $1 = 11^0$,

---

[3] The triangle itself was known in India as early as the third century B.C.
[4] In this context, by the "digits" of a number, we mean the coefficients required to write the number as a linear combination of powers of 10.

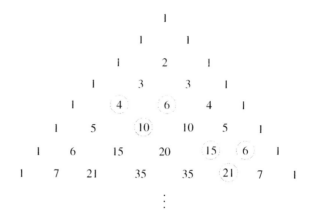

Figure 7.5 Pascal's triangle.

row 1 is $11 = 11^1$, row 2 is $121 = 11^2$, row 3 is $1331 = 11^3$, and row 5 is

$$1(10^5) + 5(10^4) + 10(10^3) + 10(10^2) + 5(10^1) + 1(10^0) = 11^5,$$

and so on.

If, beginning at each initial 1, we follow the diagonal pattern suggested by the figure to the right, adding alternate numbers along the way (at the positions marked with a bullet, •), we discover the terms of the Fibonacci sequence. For example, after two 1's, we obtain the sums $1 + 1 = 2$, $1 + 2 = 3$, $1 + 3 + 1 = 5$ (see Fig. 7.6), $1 + 4 + 3 = 8$, $1 + 5 + 6 + 1 = 13$, and so on.

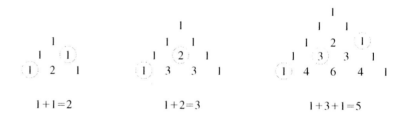

Figure 7.6 The Fibonacci sequence, hidden within Pascal's triangle.

Our major interest in Pascal's triangle concerns its connection with the expansion of $(x + y)^n$, for the numbers in row n of the triangle give the coefficients. (See Fig. 7.7.) As shown in the following equations, which we number starting with 0, the coefficients needed to expand $(x + y)^0$ are in row 0. In row 1, we see the coefficients needed to expand $(x + y)^1$; in row 2, the coefficients needed to expand $(x + y)^2$; and so forth.

$$(x + y)^0 = \underline{1}$$

$$(x + y)^1 = x + y = \underline{1}x + \underline{1}y$$

$$(x + y)^2 = x^2 + 2xy + y^2 = \underline{1}x^2 + \underline{2}xy + \underline{1}y^2$$

$$(x + y)^3 = x^3 + 3x^2y + 3xy^2 + y^3 = \underline{1}x^3 + \underline{3}x^2y + \underline{3}xy^2 + \underline{1}y^3$$

$$(x + y)^4 = x^4 + 4x^3y + 6x^2y^2 + 4xy^3 + y^4$$
$$= \underline{1}x^4 + \underline{4}x^3y + \underline{6}x^2y^2 + \underline{4}xy^3 + \underline{1}y^4$$

$$1$$

$$
\begin{array}{ccc}
1 & & 1 \\
x & + & y
\end{array}
$$

$$
\begin{array}{ccccc}
1 & & 2 & & 1 \\
x^2 & + & 2xy & + & y^2
\end{array}
$$

$$
\begin{array}{ccccccc}
1 & & 3 & & 3 & & 1 \\
x^3 & + & 3x^2y & + & 3xy^2 & + & y^3
\end{array}
$$

$$
\begin{array}{ccccccccc}
1 & & 4 & & 6 & & 4 & & 1 \\
x^4 & + & 4x^3y & + & 6x^2y^2 & + & 4xy^3 & + & x^4
\end{array}
$$

$$\vdots$$

Figure 7.7 The rows of Pascal's triangle give the co-efficients required to expand $(x + y^n$.

How might we obtain the expansion of $(x + y)^{11}$? We could continue to build Pascal's triangle as far as row 11, but it would be better to observe that the numbers in Pascal's triangle are just the values of the binomial coefficients $\binom{n}{k}$. Figure 7.8 shows Pascal's triangle again, but in terms of these combinatorial symbols.

$$\binom{0}{0}$$

$$\binom{1}{0} \quad \binom{1}{1}$$

$$\binom{2}{0} \quad \binom{2}{1} \quad \binom{2}{2}$$

$$\binom{3}{0} \quad \binom{3}{1} \quad \binom{3}{2} \quad \binom{3}{3}$$

$$\binom{4}{0} \quad \binom{4}{1} \quad \binom{4}{2} \quad \binom{4}{3} \quad \binom{4}{4}$$

$$\binom{5}{0} \quad \binom{5}{1} \quad \binom{5}{2} \quad \binom{5}{3} \quad \binom{5}{4} \quad \binom{5}{5}$$

$$\binom{6}{0} \quad \binom{6}{1} \quad \binom{6}{2} \quad \binom{6}{3} \quad \binom{6}{4} \quad \binom{6}{5} \quad \binom{6}{6}$$

$$\binom{7}{0} \quad \binom{7}{1} \quad \binom{7}{2} \quad \binom{7}{3} \quad \binom{7}{4} \quad \binom{7}{5} \quad \binom{7}{6} \quad \binom{7}{7}$$

$$\vdots$$

Figure 7.8 A useful presentation of Pascal's triangle.

Note that $\binom{n}{0} = \binom{n}{n} = \frac{n!}{n!0!} = 1$ because $0! = 1$, so each row begins and ends with a 1 as it should. The reader is encouraged to evaluate all the symbols in this second presentation of Pascal's triangle to verify that they do indeed agree with the numbers in Fig. 7.5. A proof that this correspondence extends to further rows of the triangle depends on the identity

$$\binom{n}{k} = \binom{n-1}{k-1} + \binom{n-1}{k}$$

(the proof of which was Exercise 25, Section 7.2) and is left to the exercises. The advantage in identifying the entries of the triangle as the symbols $\binom{n}{r}$ should be apparent: Any particular row can be obtained without first constructing all the rows above it. Row 11, for instance, which gives the coefficients needed to expand $(x + y)^{11}$, is

$$\binom{11}{0}, \quad \binom{11}{1}, \quad \binom{11}{2}, \quad \binom{11}{3}, \quad \cdots, \quad \binom{11}{10}, \quad \binom{11}{11}$$

and these numbers are, respectively, the coefficients of the terms

$$x^{11}, \quad x^{10}y, \quad x^9y^2, \quad x^8y^3, \quad \cdots, \quad xy^{10}, \quad y^{11}.$$

Notice that each of these terms is of the form $x^i y^j$, that the sum $i + j$ of the exponents is always 11, and that the exponent of x decreases one at a time from 11 to 0 as the exponent of y increases from 0 to 11.

7.7.1 THE BINOMIAL THEOREM

For any x and y and any natural number n,

$$(x + y)^n = \sum_{k=0}^{n} \binom{n}{k} x^{n-k} y^k$$

$$= x^n + \binom{n}{1} x^{n-1} y + \binom{n}{2} x^{n-2} y^2 + \cdots + \binom{n}{n-1} xy^{n-1} + y^n.$$

It is, of course, from this theorem that binomial coefficients take their name.

While the Binomial Theorem can be proved by mathematical induction, a different argument explains why the binomial coefficients $\binom{n}{k}$ are involved. Computing $(x + y)^2$ from first principles, we obtain

$$(x + y)^2 = (x + y)(x + y)$$
$$= x(x + y) + y(x + y)$$
$$= xx + xy + yx + yy = x^2 + 2xy + y^2.$$

Computing $(x + y)^3$ the same way, we have

$$(x + y)^3 = (x + y)(x + y)(x + y)$$
$$= (x + y)(xx + xy + yx + yy)$$
$$= xxx + xxy + xyx + xyy + yxx + yxy + yyx + yyy$$
$$= x^3 + 3x^2y + 3xy^2 + y^3.$$

In the third line of this expansion, each of the $8 = 2^3$ terms xxx, xxy, and so on, corresponds to the selection of an x or a y from each of the original three factors $x + y$. Since xxx arises only when an x is selected from each factor, there is just one x^3 term in the final expansion. The coefficient of x^2y in the final expansion is 3 because there are three terms involving two x's and one y: xxy, xyx, and yxx. The reason why there are three terms is that there are three ways to select one y (and hence two x's) from the three factors $x + y$.

In the full expansion of $(x + y)^n$, before any simplification and before like terms are collected, there are 2^n terms. Each such term is a string of x's and y's, n symbols in all, and corresponds to a selection of x or y from each of the n factors $x + y$. Any term containing k y's (and hence $n - k$ x's) simplifies to $x^{n-k}y^k$. The eventual coefficient of $x^{n-k}y^k$ is the number of terms that simplify to $x^{n-k}y^k$. This number is $\binom{n}{k}$ because there are $\binom{n}{k}$ ways to select k factors for the y's.

We conclude this section with a sampling of problems that can be solved using the Binomial Theorem.

PROBLEM 31. Using the Binomial Theorem, expand $(3x^2 + 2y)^5$ and simplify.

Solution.

$$
(3x^2 + 2y)^5 = (3x^2)^5 + \binom{5}{1}(3x^2)^4(2y) + \binom{5}{2}(3x^2)^3(2y)^2
$$

$$
+ \binom{5}{3}(3x^2)^2(2y)^3 + \binom{5}{4}(3x^2)(2y)^4 + (2y)^5
$$

$$
= 243x^{10} + 5(81x^8)(2y) + 10(27x^6)(4y^2) + 10(9x^4)(8y^3)
$$

$$
+ 5(3x^2)(16y^4) + 32y^5
$$

$$
= 243x^{10} + 810x^8 y + 1080x^6 y^2 + 720x^4 y^3 + 240x^2 y^4 + 32y^5
$$

PROBLEM 32. Using the Binomial Theorem, expand $\left(x - \dfrac{4}{x}\right)^6$ and simplify.

Solution.

$$
\left(x - \frac{4}{x}\right)^6 = x^6 + \binom{6}{1}x^5\left(-\frac{4}{x}\right) + \binom{6}{2}x^4\left(-\frac{4}{x}\right)^2 + \binom{6}{3}x^3\left(-\frac{4}{x}\right)^3
$$

$$
+ \binom{6}{4}x^2\left(-\frac{4}{x}\right)^4 + \binom{6}{5}x\left(-\frac{4}{x}\right)^5 + \left(-\frac{4}{x}\right)^6
$$

$$
= x^6 + 6x^5\left(-\frac{4}{x}\right) + 15x^4\left(\frac{16}{x^2}\right) + 20x^3\left(-\frac{64}{x^3}\right) + 15x^2\left(\frac{256}{x^4}\right)
$$

$$
+ 6x\left(-\frac{1024}{x^5}\right) + \frac{4096}{x^6}
$$

$$
= x^6 - 24x^4 + 240x^2 - 1280 + \frac{3840}{x^2} - \frac{6144}{x^4} + \frac{4096}{x^6}
$$

PROBLEM 33. Find the coefficient of x^{16} in the expansion of $\left(2x^2 - \dfrac{x}{2}\right)^{12}$.

Solution. The general term in the expansion of this expression by the Binomial Theorem is

$$
\binom{12}{k}(2x^2)^{12-k}\left(-\frac{x}{2}\right)^k = \binom{12}{k}2^{12-k}\left(-\frac{1}{2}\right)^k x^{24-k}.
$$

We want $24 - k = 16$; thus, $k = 8$. The coefficient is $\binom{12}{8}2^4\left(-\frac{1}{2}\right)^8 = \frac{1}{16}\binom{12}{8} = \frac{495}{16}$.

PROBLEM 34. Prove that $\binom{n}{0} + \binom{n}{1} + \binom{n}{2} + \cdots + \binom{n}{n} = 2^n$ for all natural numbers n.

Solution. Consider $(x + y)^n = \sum_{k=0}^{n}\binom{n}{k}x^{n-k}y^k$. Setting $x = y = 1$, we obtain

$$
(1 + 1)^n = \sum_{k=0}^{n}\binom{n}{k}1^{n-k}1^k; \text{ that is, } 2^n = \sum_{k=0}^{n}\binom{n}{k}, \text{ as desired.}
$$

Pause 24   Use the result of Problem 34 to show that a set with n elements has 2^n subsets. ∎

Answer to Pause

24. There are $\binom{n}{0}$ subsets with no elements, $\binom{n}{1}$ subsets with 1 element, $\binom{n}{2}$ subsets with two elements, and so on. The number of subsets in all is $\binom{n}{0} + \binom{n}{1} +$

$$\binom{n}{2} + \cdots + \binom{n}{n} = 2^n.$$

True/False Questions

(Answers can be found in the back of the book.)

1. Pascal's Triangle is named after the French mathematician Blaise Pascal.

2. $\binom{n}{n} = n$ for all natural numbers n.

3. If k and n are natural numbers, $k \le n$, then $\binom{n}{k} = \binom{n}{n-k}$.

4. If k and n are natural numbers with $k > n$, then $\binom{n}{k} = \binom{n-1}{k-1} + \binom{n-1}{k}$.

5. The eighth row of Pascal's Triangle starts with $\binom{8}{0}$.

6. The fifteenth row of Pascal's Triangle has one number that does not repeat.

7. If n is any natural number, $(x + y)^n = \sum_{k=0}^{n} \binom{n}{k} x^{n-k} y^k$.

8. If n is any natural number, $(x + y)^n = \sum_{k=0}^{n} \binom{n}{k} x^k y^{n-k}$.

9. The expansion of $\left(3x - \dfrac{5}{x}\right)^8$ has a constant term.

10. The expansion of $\left(3x^2 - \dfrac{5}{x}\right)^8$ has a constant term.

Exercises

*The answers to exercises marked [BB] can be found in the **B**ack of the **B**ook.*

1. [BB] For each of the following, expand using the Binomial Theorem and simplify.
   (a) $(x + y)^6$ (b) $(2x + 3y)^6$

2. Use the Binomial Theorem to expand $(a + 4b)^5$. Simplify your answer.

3. For each of the following, expand using the Binomial Theorem and simplify.
   (a) $(2x^3 - y^2)^8$ (b) [BB] $(2x^3 - x^2)^8$
   (c) $\left(2x^3 - \dfrac{1}{x^2}\right)^8$

4. [BB] Find the fourth term in the binomial expansion of $(x^3 - 2y^2)^{12}$.

5. Consider the binomial expansion of $(x + y)^{20}$.
   (a) What are the first three terms?
   (b) What are the last three terms?
   (c) [BB] What is the seventh term? the fifteenth term?
   (d) What is the coefficient of $x^{13} y^7$?

6. [BB] Consider the binomial expansion of $(2x - y)^{16}$.
   (a) How many terms are there altogether?
   (b) Is there a middle term or are there two middle terms? Find and explain.

7. Consider the binomial expansion of $(x + 3y)^{17}$.
   (a) How many terms are there altogether?
   (b) Is there a middle term or are there two middle terms? Find and explain.

8. [BB] Find the coefficient of $x^3 y^7$ in the binomial expansion of $(4x + 5y)^{10}$.

9. [BB] Find the coefficient of the term containing y^8 in the binomial expansion of $(x + 3y^2)^{17}$.

10. What is the coefficient of x^5 in the binomial expansion of $(x - 2x^{-2})^{20}$?

11. [BB] What is the coefficient of x^{27} in the binomial expansion of $\left(\dfrac{3}{x} + x^2\right)^{18}$?

12. Find the coefficient of x^{25} in the binomial expansion of $\left(2x - \dfrac{3}{x^2}\right)^{58}$.

13. Prove that $4^n > n^4$ for all integers $n \ge 5$.

14. Sequences of integers, $\{x_n\}, \{y_n\}, n \ge 0$, are defined by $(1 + \sqrt{2})^n = x_n + y_n \sqrt{2}$.
   (a) [BB] Find the first three terms and the sixth term of each sequence.
   (b) Find formulas for x_n and y_n.

(c) Without using the result of (b), establish the recursion formulas

$$x_{n+1} = x_n + 2y_n$$
$$y_{n+1} = x_n + y_n$$

for $n \geq 0$.

15. (For students who have studied calculus) In Problem 8 on p. 14, we proved that $\sqrt{2}$ is irrational, that is, not the quotient of integers. In this exercise, we give an alternative proof using the binomial theorem.

   (a) If n is an integer, show that there exist integers x_n and y_n, depending on n, such that $(\sqrt{2} - 1)^n = x_n + y_n\sqrt{2}$.

   (b) Explain why $\lim_{n\to\infty}(\sqrt{2} - 1)^n = 0$.

   (c) Suppose that $\sqrt{2}$ is rational and show that (a) and (b) lead to a contradiction.

16. [BB] At the beginning of this section, we said that the numbers in row n of Pascal's triangle, interpreted as the "digits" of a single number in base 10, give the integer 11^n. Prove this.

17. Suppose that we construct Pascal's triangle as described at the beginning of this section. Prove that the entries of row n are $\binom{n}{0}$, $\binom{n}{1}$, $\binom{n}{2}$, ..., $\binom{n}{n}$. [*Hint*: Identity (5).]

18. Prove the Binomial Theorem by mathematical induction. [*Hint*: Identity (5) will be useful.]

19. (a) Show that $\sum_{k=2}^{6}\binom{k}{2} = \binom{7}{3}$ and interpret this result with reference to Pascal's triangle.

   (b) Show that $\sum_{k=r}^{n}\binom{k}{r} = \binom{n+1}{r+1}$ for any r and n, $1 \leq r \leq n$, and interpret with reference to Pascal's triangle.

20. [BB] Show that $\binom{n}{0} - \binom{n}{1} + \binom{n}{2} - \cdots + (-1)^n\binom{n}{n} = 0$ for all natural numbers n.

21. (a) By direct calculation, show that $3^4 = 1 + 2\binom{4}{1} + 4\binom{4}{2} + 8\binom{4}{3} + 16$.

   (b) Find a simple expression for $\binom{n}{0} + 2\binom{n}{1} + 4\binom{n}{2} + \cdots + 2^n\binom{n}{n}$ valid for all natural numbers n and prove your answer.

22. (a) [BB] Find a simple expression for $\sum_{k=1}^{n}k\binom{n}{k}$ and prove your answer.

   (b) Find a simple expression for $\sum_{k=1}^{n}k^2\binom{n}{k}$ and prove your answer.
   [*Hint*: In both of these questions, to begin, it may prove helpful to evaluate the sum for small values of n.]

23. Consider the Fibonacci sequence $a_0, a_1, a_2, \ldots$, where $a_0 = a_1 = 1$ and, for $n \geq 1$, $a_{n+1} = a_n + a_{n-1}$. Express a_n for $n \geq 1$ as the sum of certain binomial coefficients and prove your answer. [*Hint*: See remarks at the beginning of this section.]

24. There are n books in a line on a shelf and we want to choose k of them in such a way that no two adjacent books are selected. Denote this number $\left[\begin{smallmatrix}n\\k\end{smallmatrix}\right]$.

   (a) Explain why $\left[\begin{smallmatrix}n\\0\end{smallmatrix}\right] = 1$ whenever $n \geq 1$.

   (b) Show that $\left[\begin{smallmatrix}n\\k\end{smallmatrix}\right] = 0$ whenever $k \geq \frac{n}{2} + 1$.

   (c) Use mathematical induction on n to show that $\left[\begin{smallmatrix}n\\k\end{smallmatrix}\right] = \binom{n-k+1}{k}$ for $n \geq 1$ whenever $0 \leq k < \frac{n}{2} + 1$.

25. Construct a Pascal-type triangle for the symbol $\left[\begin{smallmatrix}n\\k\end{smallmatrix}\right]$ defined in Exercise 24. Investigate properties of this triangle and relate them to results proved in Exercise 24. [As with binomial coefficients, define $\left[\begin{smallmatrix}0\\0\end{smallmatrix}\right] = 1$, agreeing with the formula derived in Exercise 24(c).]

Key Terms & Ideas

Here are some technical words and phrases that were used in this chapter. Do you know the meaning of each? If you're not sure, check the glossary or index at the back of the book.

combination

derangement

permutation

r-combination

r-permutation

Review Exercises for Chapter 7

1. Prove that $2^n \mid P(2n, n)$ for all integers $n \geq 1$.

2. In how many ways can seven boys and six girls stand in a row if the girls are to stand together, but the boys must not stand together?

3. Do Exercise 2 again with circle instead of row.

4. How many permutations of the letters a, b, c, d, e, f contain at least one of the patterns aeb and bcf?

5. (a) In how many permutations of the 26 letters a–z will you find either *wendy*, *patrick*, or *josh*?

   (b) In how many permutations of the 26 letters a–z will you find either *wendy*, *patrick*, or *john*?

6. Find an expression for the number of five-card poker hands that contain exactly three kings.

7. A committee of seven is to be chosen from eight men and nine women.

   (a) How many such committees contain at least six women?

(b) How many such committees contain either Bob or Alice, but not both?

8. In how many ways can 12 people form four groups of three if
(a) the groups have names?
(b) the groups are unnamed?

9. A car manufacturer is forced to admit that the latest model of its best selling recreational vehicle has problems with the exhaust system. Twenty of your (wealthy) friends have just bought this particular vehicle.
(a) In how many ways can seven vehicles be recalled for an inspection?
(b) In how many ways can four of seven vehicles selected for inspection be found faulty?

10. Ten students find themselves in an exceptionally tough course and decide immediately to form three study groups. Each group must have at least two people in it. How many different groups can be formed?

11. For Christmas, Gail wants to buy each of her five boyfriends books about sports. She finds twelve different suitable books for sale in her local superstore. In how many ways can she purchase eight books and distribute them as gifts so that each of her boyfriends gets at least one book?

12. A Middle East peace conference will be attended by five Arab countries, four Western countries, and Israel. Each delegation will sit together at a round table subject only to the requirement that no Arab delegation be seated next to the Israeli delegation. How many seating arrangements are possible?

13. **(a)** How many paths are there from A to B along vertical and horizontal lines?

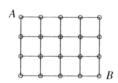

(b) Generalize the result of part (a) to an $m \times n$ grid pattern.

14. Frank wants to buy 12 muffins and finds seven different types available. In how many ways can he make his selection?

15. Twelve ships enter the St. John's harbor one after the other. Three ships are Canadian, three are Portuguese, two each are from Iceland and Greenland. There is one ship from the Bahamas and one from the United States. In how many ways can the ships enter the harbour if
(a) there is no restriction on how the ships enter the harbor?
(b) the Canadian ships must be kept together and the Icelandic ships must be kept together?

(c) the Canadian and Icelandic ships must be kept together (as a group)?
(d) the U.S. ship and that from the Bahamas must not enter one after the other?

16. A candy merchant carries bubble gum balls in seven different colors. In how many ways can you
(a) buy ten bubble gum balls?
(b) buy ten bubble gum balls, with exactly three red ones?
(c) buy ten bubble gum balls including at least one of each color?
(d) buy ten bubble gum balls of at most six different colors?

17. In how many ways can the letters of the word NUNAVUT be rearranged?

18. In how many ways can five rings be put onto the four fingers of one hand (no thumb) if
(a) the rings are all different;
(b) the rings are identical.

19. Find the coefficient of x^5 in the binomial expansion of $(x - 2x^{-2})^{20}$. Do not simplify.

20. Find the coefficient of x^{-6} in $\left(16x^2 - \dfrac{1}{2x}\right)^{12}$. Simplify your answer.

21. Prove that $1^3 + 2^3 + 3^3 + \cdots + (n-1)^3 < \dfrac{n^4}{4} < 1^3 + 2^3 + 3^3 + \cdots + n^3$ for any $n \geq 1$.

22. **(a)** Give a verbal argument for the truth of the identity $\binom{n}{k} = \binom{n-1}{k-1} + \binom{n-1}{k}$.
(b) If $n \geq k+2$ and $k \geq 2$, show that $\binom{n}{k} - \binom{n-2}{k} - \binom{n-2}{k-2}$ is even.

23. Find a simple expression for $3^n - \binom{n}{1}3^{n-1} + \cdots + (-1)^k\binom{n}{k}3^{n-k} + \cdots + (-1)^n$.

24. Show that $\binom{2n}{n}$ is even for all $n \geq 1$.

25. On the day before midterm break, 20 of the 32 students enrolled in a psychology course decide to skip class. Asked in how many ways can this be accomplished if Tim and Nicole refuse to skip together, students X and Y come up with apparently different answers.
X argues this way. There are $\binom{30}{19}$ ways in which Tim skips, but not Nicole, and another $\binom{30}{19}$ in which Nicole skips, but not Tim. Adding the $\binom{30}{20}$ ways in which neither skips gives $2\binom{30}{19} + \binom{30}{20}$.
Y says that there are $\binom{30}{18}$ ways in which both Tim and Nicole skip, so the answer is the total number of possibilities less this number, that is, $\binom{32}{20} - \binom{30}{18}$.
Who is right?

26. A fair coin is tossed n times. Prove that the probability of getting an odd number of heads is $\frac{1}{2}$.

8

Algorithms

8.1 What Is an Algorithm?

Computers! Computers! Computers! Are they the bane of our existence or the most important invention since the discovery of the wheel? Certainly, there is no denying that computers have changed almost every aspect of our lives. They are used by stockbrokers to track the performance of stocks and to provide guidance as to which should be bought and sold. Much of the blame for the October 1987 North American stock market crash was attributed to computers all giving the same "sell" advice at the same time. Nowadays, virtually every company puts personal computers on the desks of their employees, in the belief that computers increase productivity and cut revenue losses. Upon discovery of a potential flaw in some part, a car manufacturer is able almost instantly to produce a list of the names and addresses of all the people across North America who have purchased a car containing that particular part. The list of computer applications is literally endless. But what is a computer?

Fundamentally, a computer is just a box containing tiny electrical circuits on small boards cleverly put together so that the machine can follow instructions given to it. This box and peripheral items, such as monitor, keyboard, mouse, and printer, are called *hardware*; the instructions fed to the machine are called *software*. Computer programming involves writing software that allows a machine to perform various tasks that, by hand, would be tedious or so time consuming as to be essentially impossible. Machines work incredibly quickly, never get tired, and are excellent at following orders; however, they will only perform as well as the instructions presented to them. One of the oldest adages in the computer business is "Garbage in–garbage out!"

There are two parts to a computer program. There is the process or sequence of steps that is necessary to complete the given task and the translation of this process into a language that the computer can understand. In this chapter, we explore the first of these ideas, asking the reader to think about the process or *algorithm* by which familiar tasks are accomplished.

The word *algorithm* evolved from the older word *algorism* which is a corruption of the surname of a ninth-century Persian, Abu Ja'far Muḥammad ibn Mûsâ al-Khwârizmî, who wrote an important book setting forth rules for performing arithmetic with the arabic numerals $1, 2, 3 \ldots$ we use today.[1] While the older term algorism referred primarily to arithmetical rules, *algorithm* today is used in a more general sense as a virtual synonym for *procedure*. Its ingredients are an input, an output, and a sequence of precise steps for converting the input to the output. In Chapter 4, we studied the Euclidean algorithm, which, upon input of positive integers a and b, outputs the greatest common divisor of a and b through a precise series of steps.

As children, after learning the addition rules for single-digit numbers, we were taught a procedure for adding numbers with any number of digits; upon input of two arbitrary integers, the procedure outputs their sum.

$$
\begin{array}{cccc}
1 & 2 & 3 & 4 \\
5 & 6_1 & 7_1 & 8 \\
\hline
6 & 9 & 1 & 2
\end{array}
$$

We memorized multiplication tables for single-digit numbers and then were taught a procedure that, upon input of two arbitrary numbers, outputs their product.

Folklore has it that Russian peasants have an instinctive and flawless ability to multiply and divide by the number 2 and are able to use this successfully to multiply any two numbers. For example, they would compute 211×453 by the scheme shown in Fig. 8.1. Each number on the left is the quotient when the number above it is divided by two[2]; the numbers on the right are the product of 2 and the number above. After reaching 1 in the left column, the rows containing even numbers on the left are crossed out. The desired product is then the sum of the numbers that remain uncrossed on the right!

Before the days of pocket calculators, schoolchildren were taught a procedure for finding the square root of a number. To find the square root of 2, for instance, a student was taught to produce the pattern shown in Fig. 8.2. First, we find the largest integer whose square is less than 2 and write this number, 1, in the two places shown. The product of 1 and 1 is 1 and $2 - 1 = 1$. Write down 1 followed by two 0's. Next, we double the number on top, giving 2, and search for the largest digit x such that the product of x and the number $2x$ (by which we mean one of $20, 21, 22, \ldots, 29$) does not exceed 100. We have $x = 4$, $4 \times 24 = 96$, and $100 - 96 = 4$, as shown.

$$
\begin{array}{rr}
211 & \times \qquad 453 \\
105 & 906 \\
\cancel{52} & \cancel{1,812} \\
\cancel{26} & \cancel{3,624} \\
13 & 7,248 \\
\cancel{6} & \cancel{14,496} \\
3 & 28,992 \\
1 & 57,984 \\
\hline
& 95,583
\end{array}
$$

Figure 8.1 The Russian peasant method of multiplication.

Figure 8.2 The start of an algorithm for determining $\sqrt{2}$.

---

[1] The word *algebra* derives from the Latin title of this book, *Ludus algebrae et almucgrabalaeque*.
[2] Remember that when a natural number a is divided by another natural number b the *quotient* is the integer part of the fraction $\frac{a}{b}$. See Section 4.1.

Follow this 4 by another two 0's, double the number on top, giving 28, and search for the largest single digit x such that $x \times 28x$ does not exceed 400. We have $x = 1$, $1 \times 281 = 281$, and $400 - 281 = 119$, and so forth. Whether you understand this scheme is much less important today than it was formerly. We mention it here not just as a historical curiosity, but as another example of an arithmetic algorithm, one that allows the computation of square roots to any degree of accuracy.

In a course on Euclidean geometry, we learn a vast number of geometric algorithms usually called *constructions*. To bisect an angle with vertex A, for instance, we draw an arc with center A. If B and C are the points where this arc meets the arms of the angle, we then draw arcs with center s B and C and some suitably large radius (for example, the length of AB). If these arcs meet at the point P, then AP is the bisector of the angle at A. (See Fig. 8.3.)

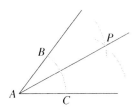

Figure 8.3 Bisection of the angle at A.

In high school and college, students learn algorithms for multiplying polynomials, multiplying matrices, solving systems of linear equations, and differentiating polynomials; the list goes on. In the rest of this chapter, we discuss important algorithms the reader may not have seen before and their relative strengths and weaknesses. Since this is not a text in computer programming, our description of algorithms is mostly in ordinary English, subject only to the requirements of clarity and precision: It should always be clear to a programmer how to implement any of our algorithms in his or her favorite language.

PROBLEM 1. Describe an algorithm whose input is a list $a_1, a_2, \ldots, a_n$ of integers and whose output is their sum.

Solution. This question requires us to confront what an expression like $5 + 17 + 3 + 6 + 4$ really means. How do the basic rules for addition of two numbers extend to permit the addition of several numbers? Most people would calculate $5 + 17 + 3 + 6 + 4$ by adding from the left, like this:

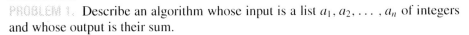

$$\{[(5 + 17) + 3] + 6\} + 4 = [(22 + 3) + 6] + 4 = (25 + 6) + 4 = 31 + 4 = 35.$$

This approach is the idea behind our algorithm.

To find the sum of n integers $a_1, a_2, \ldots, a_n$,

Step 1. set $S = 0$;

Step 2. for $i = 1$ to n, replace S by $S + a_i$;

Step 3. output S.

The value of S output at Step 3 is the desired sum.

Step 2 calls for a *loop*, a feature of every programming language. Whenever we write "for $i = 1$ to n" as part of an algorithm, we mean

- set $i = 1$ and execute the indicated statement (or statements);
- increase the value of i by 1 and, if $i \leq n$, execute the indicated statement(s);
- continue to increase the value of i by 1 and, as long as $i \leq n$, execute the indicated statement(s);
- if the stage $i > n$ is reached, skip to the next step.

The variable i used in this process is called a *counter*. For example, with a_1, a_2, a_3, a_4, a_5, respectively equal to $5, 17, 3, 6, 4$, the preceding algorithm begins by setting $S = 0$. At Step 2, the counter i is set equal to 1 and S is replaced by $S + a_1 = 0 + 5 = 5$. Then i is set equal to 2 and S is replaced by $S + a_2 = 5 + 17 = 22$. Continuing, S is replaced by $S + a_3 = 22 + 3 = 25$, then by $S + a_4 = 25 + 6 = 31$

and, finally, by $S + a_5 = 31 + 4 = 35$. Then i is set equal to 6, at which point the algorithm skips to Step 3 and outputs $S = 35$, the sum of $a_1, \ldots, a_5$.

PROBLEM 2. **(Polynomial evaluation)** Describe an algorithm that, upon input of $n+1$ integers $a_0, a_1, a_2, \ldots, a_n$ and an integer x, outputs the integer $a_0 + a_1x + a_2x^2 + \cdots + a_nx^n$.

Solution. Perhaps the most obvious approach to this problem is first to compute the powers of x from x to x^n and then to evaluate the expression $a_0 + a_1x + a_2x^2 + \cdots + a_nx^n$ term by term.

Given integers $a_0, a_1, \ldots, a_n$ and an integer x, to compute the number $a_0 + a_1x + a_2x^2 + \cdots + a_nx^n$,

Step 1. set $P = 1$;

Step 2. for $i = 1$ to n, replace P by Px, call this element x_i and store (note that $x_i = x^i$);

Step 3. set $S = a_0$;

Step 4. for $i = 1$ to n, replace S by $S + a_ix_i$;

Step 5. output S.

The value of S output at Step 5 is the desired integer $a_0 + a_1x + a_2x^2 + \cdots + a_nx^n$.

EXAMPLE 3

To evaluate the polynomial $f(x) = -1 + 2x + 4x^2 - 3x^3$ at $x = 5$, the algorithm takes as input $a_0 = -1$, $a_1 = 2$, $a_2 = 4$, $a_3 = -3$, and $x = 5$ and proceeds as follows.

Step 1. $P = 1$;

Step 2. $i = 1$: replace P by $Px = 1(5) = 5$ (P is now 5) and let $x_1 = 5$;
$\quad i = 2$: replace P by $Px = 5(5) = 25$ (now $P = 25$) and let $x_2 = 25$;
$\quad i = 3$: replace P by $Px = 25(5) = 125$ (now $P = 125$) and let $x_3 = 125$.
Since $i = n = 3$, Step 2 is complete.

Step 3. $S = a_0 = -1$;

Step 4. $i = 1$: replace S by $S + a_1x_1 = -1 + 2(5) = 9$ (now $S = 9$);
$\quad i = 2$: replace S by $S + a_2x_2 = 9 + 4(25) = 109$ (now $S = 109$);
$\quad i = 3$: replace S by $S + a_3x_3 = 109 - 3(125) = -266$ (now $S = -266$).
Since $i = n = 3$, Step 4 is complete.

Step 5. Output $S = -266$.

There is a much more efficient way to evaluate a polynomial, more efficient in the sense that it requires fewer arithmetical operations and fewer storage requirements. It is based on the observation, due to William Horner, an eighteenth-century English school headmaster, that

$$a_0 + a_1x + a_2x^2 + \cdots + a_nx^n = a_0 + (a_1 + a_2x + a_3x^2 + \cdots + a_nx^{n-1})x$$

$$= a_0 + (a_1 + (a_2 + a_3x + \cdots + a_nx^{n-2})x)x$$

$$\vdots$$

$$= a_0 + (a_1 + (a_2 + \cdots + (a_{n-1} + a_nx)x) \cdots)x.$$

8.1.1 HORNER'S ALGORITHM

Given integers $a_0, a_1, \ldots, a_n$ and an integer x, to evaluate the expression $a_0 + a_1x + a_2x^2 + \cdots + a_nx^n$,

Step 1. set $S = a_n$;

Step 2. for $i = 1$ to n, replace S by $a_{n-i} + Sx$;

Step 3. output S.

The final value of S is the desired number $a_0 + a_1x + a_2x^2 + \cdots + a_nx^n$.

EXAMPLE 4

We apply Horner's method to the same polynomial considered in Example 3, $f(x) = -1 + 2x + 4x^2 - 3x^3$, and again with $x = 5$.

Step 1. set $S = a_3 = -3$.

Step 2. $i = 1$: replace S by $a_2 + Sx = 4 - 3(5) = -11$ (now $S = -11$);
$i = 2$: replace S by $a_1 + Sx = 2 - 11(5) = -53$ (now $S = -53$);
$i = 3$: replace S by $a_0 + Sx = -1 - 53(5) = -266$ (now $S = -266$).
Since $i = n = 3$, Step 2 is complete.

Step 3. output $S = -266$.

Pause 1

Show the successive values of S when Horner's method is used to evaluate the polynomial $f(x) = 4x^3 - 2x + 1$ at $x = -2$. ∎

Many of the uses to which modern-day computers are put do not involve arithmetical calculations but take advantage of a machine's ability to perform certain logical operations. Of these, the most fundamental is its ability to compare, to decide if two elements are equal. The last two sections of this chapter are devoted to such important nonarithmetical procedures as searching, sorting, and enumerating permutations. We conclude this section with one example of an algorithm in which comparison is the basic operation.

PROBLEM 5. Given a "small" list, it is easy for a person to note the distinct items it contains. The distinct items in abc, dbc, abc, xbc, dbc are, of course, abc, dbc, and xbc. To record the distinct items in a list of a thousand or more items would be an almost intolerable task for most people, but it is a simple matter for a computer. Describe an algorithm that, upon input of a list $a_1, a_2, \ldots, a_n$, outputs the distinct items in this list.

Solution. The idea is straightforward. We compare each element in the list with those preceding it and, if it is different from all its predecessors, output it.

Step 1. output a_1;

Step 2. if $n = 1$, stop;
else for $i = 2$ to n,
if a_i does not equal any of $a_1, a_2, \ldots, a_{i-1}$, output a_i.

The algorithm outputs the distinct items among $a_1, a_2, \ldots, a_n$. ▲

Answer to Pause

1. We have $n = 3$, $a_0 = 1$, $a_1 = -2$, $a_2 = 0$ and $a_3 = 4$. The first value of S is $S = 4$. Then $S = 0 + 4(-2) = -8$, $S = -2 - 8(-2) = 14$, and, finally, $S = 1 + 14(-2) = -27$.

True/False Questions

(Answers can be found in the back of the book.)

1. The word *algorithm*, like so many mathematical terms, has its origins in the Greek language.

2. The word *algorithm* is used today as a synonym for *procedure*.

3. Many well-known geometric constructions are examples of algorithms.

4. If the Russian peasant method is used to multiply x and y, where $x > y$, it is more efficient to start by writing the product as $y \times x$.

5. If the Russian peasant method is used to multiply 2^n by 2^m, all rows except the bottom one will be crossed out.

6. It is unusual for a loop to appear in a programming language.

7. Often the variable i used inside a loop is called a counter.

8. Horner's Algorithm is a procedure for multiplying numbers together that is more efficient than the Russian peasant method.

9. An algorithm that outputs the distinct elements in a list would output a list of two elements if given the input $3.1416, \frac{22}{7}, \pi, e, 2.71828$.

10. The average of integers 9, 10, 15 is $\frac{9+10+15}{2} = 17$.

Exercises

*The answers to exercises marked [BB] can be found in the **B**ack of the **B**ook.*

In the first three exercises, ruler *means an unmarked straight edge and* compass *means an instrument that allows the describing of circles or arcs thereof.*

1. [BB] Describe a procedure for finding the midpoint of a line segment, with only ruler and compass, and explain why your procedure works.

2. Given a line ℓ in the plane and a point P not on ℓ, describe a ruler and compass procedure for constructing the line through P parallel to ℓ, and explain why your procedure works.

3. Given a point P and a line ℓ, describe a ruler and compass procedure for constructing the line through P perpendicular to ℓ in each of the following cases. In each case, explain why your procedure works.
   (a) [BB] P is not on ℓ.   (b) P is on ℓ.

4. Find each of the following products by the Russian peasant method.
   (a) [BB] 168×413 (b) 973×461
   (c) 141×141

5. [BB] Explain why the Russian peasant method works.

6. (a) Let n be a positive integer and let k be the integer that satisfies $2^{k-1} \leq n < 2^k$. Show that the Russian peasant method applied to the product $n \times m$ can be completed with at most k steps (that is, $k + 1$ lines in all). [*Hint*: Induction on k.]

   (b) Use the Russian peasant method to show that every positive integer can be expressed as the sum of at most $1 + \log_2 n$ powers of 2.

7. Find the square roots of 3 [BB], 12, and 153, to four decimal places of accuracy, by the method used to compute $\sqrt{2}$ in the text and illustrated in Fig. 8.2.

8. [BB] Describe an algorithm that, upon input of n real numbers, outputs their average.

9. [BB] Describe an algorithm that, upon input of n real numbers, outputs the maximum of these numbers.

10. Describe an algorithm that, upon input of n real numbers, $a_1, a_2, \ldots, a_n$, and another number, x, determines how many a_i are equal to x.

11. Describe an algorithm that, given n real numbers, $a_1, a_2, \ldots, a_n$, outputs the number of a_i that lie in the range 85–90, inclusive.

12. [BB] Given an ordered list $a_1 \leq a_2 \leq \cdots \leq a_n$ of real numbers and a real number x, describe an algorithm that inserts x into its correct position in the list and outputs the ordered list of $n + 1$ numbers.

13. Describe an algorithm that, upon input of integers a and b and a natural number n, outputs all solutions of $ax \equiv b \pmod{n}$ in the range $0 \leq x < n$, if there are solutions, and otherwise outputs the words *no solution*.

14. [BB] Let n be a given natural number. Find an algorithm for writing an integer a in the form $a = a_n n! + a_{n-1}(n-1)! + \cdots + a_2 2! + a_1$ with $0 \leq a_i \leq i$ for $i = 1, 2, \ldots, n-1$. [*Hint*: Modify the procedure for converting from base 10 to base b described in Section 4.1.]

15. Describe an algorithm that, upon input of a number n given in base 10, outputs the digits of n (from right to left).

16. [BB] Describe an algorithm that, upon input of n distinct symbols $a_1, a_2, \ldots, a_n$, outputs all the subsets of $\{a_1, a_2, \ldots, a_n\}$. [*Hint*: One way to do this is to recognize that the subsets of $\{a_1, a_2, \ldots, a_n\}$ are in one-to-one correspondence with the binary representations of the numbers between 0 and $2^n - 1$.]

17. For each polynomial $f(x)$ and each value of x, list in order the successive values S that occur in the calculation of $f(x)$ by
    i. the algorithm described in Problem 2;
    ii. Horner's Algorithm.
    Show your calculations.

    (a) [BB] $f(x) = 2x^2 - 3x + 1; x = 2$
    (b) $f(x) = 3x^2 + 1; x = 5$
    (c) $f(x) = -4x^3 + 6x^2 + 5x - 4; x = -1$
    (d) $f(x) = 17x^5 - 40x^3 + 16x - 7; x = 3$

18. [BB] Explain why Horner's Algorithm works.

19. Describe an algorithm that upon input of a natural number n, outputs the set of primes in the range 1–n. [*Hint*: Use the Sieve of Eratosthenes and take advantage of Lemma 4.3.4.]

20. Cite examples of five algorithms not mentioned in this text that you learned **after** leaving high school.

8.2 Complexity

Suppose that two mathematicians working in the research department of a large corporation are asked to work on a certain problem. Each of these people has a solid background in discrete mathematics and so has no difficulty in finding an algorithm, but the two algorithms obtained are very different. When implemented on a computer, one of the algorithms took far less time to produce an answer than the other. The head of the research department is pleased that an efficient algorithm was discovered, but also concerned because of the huge amount of computer time wasted running the inefficient algorithm. Is it possible to estimate the amount of time an algorithm will require before actually implementing it? The answer is yes, and we shall begin to see why in this section.

Just like a person, a computer requires a certain amount of time to carry out an arithmetical operation, a multiplication or an addition, for instance. So we can estimate the time an algorithm requires by calculating the number of arithmetical operations it involves. This is at best only approximate, of course, because different operations may well require different amounts of time.

EXAMPLE 6   To determine the distance between two points $(x_1, x_2, \ldots, x_n)$ and $(y_1, y_2, \ldots, y_n)$ in n-dimensional Euclidean space, we must calculate the number

$$\sqrt{(x_1 - y_1)^2 + (x_2 - y_2)^2 + \cdots + (x_n - y_n)^2}.$$

If $n = 2$, this requires two subtractions, two squarings, one addition, and one square root, six operations in all. (While we might expect multiplication and especially the square root operation to be more time consuming than addition and subtraction, we ignore this potential complication for now.) If $n = 3$, nine operations are required; if $n = 4$, 12 operations are required, and so on. In general, the number of operations in the n-dimensional case is $3n$. As is typical, the number of operations depends on the size of the input, in this case, the $2n$ numbers $x_1, \ldots, x_n, y_1, \ldots, y_n$.

There are other measures of the efficiency of algorithms in addition to time. For instance, different algorithms require different amounts of space to hold numbers in memory for later use; the less space required, the better. We shall, however, concentrate entirely on time estimates of efficiency, as measured by operation counts.

Often, and particularly in the graph theoretical algorithms that we will study in later chapters, it is uncertain exactly how many operations will be needed. Our approach will be to seek upper-bound, or *worst-case*, estimates of the number of operations that we know will never be exceeded.

In general, for a given algorithm, we try to find the *complexity function* $f : \mathbb{N} \to \mathbb{N}$, where, for some measure n of the size of the input, $f(n)$ is an upper bound for the number of operations required to carry out the algorithm. In the distance algorithm described in Example 6, it is logical to let n be the dimension of the Euclidean space; then $f(n) = 3n$. As we shall see, it is unusual to have such an exact count for the number of operations.

We have noted that estimating the running time of an algorithm by estimating the number of operations required is an inherently inexact process because it cannot be expected that all operations—addition, multiplication, square root—require equal amounts of time. There is yet another difficulty. The time required to perform the basic operations of arithmetic depends on the size of the integers involved. Clearly it takes more time to add or multiply two 50-digit numbers than it does to add or multiply two 3-digit numbers. The following problem indicates that it is possible to account for this additional complication.

PROBLEM 7. Find the complexity function for adding two n-digit integers if the basic operation is addition of single-digit integers.

Solution. Suppose the integers to be added are $a = (a_{n-1}a_{n-2}\ldots a_1a_0)_{10}$ and $b = (b_{n-1}b_{n-2}\ldots b_1b_0)_{10}$, expressed in base 10 using the notation of Section 4.1. The units digit of a is a_0 and the units digit of b is b_0; the tens digit of a is a_1 and the tens digit of b is b_1, and so forth. The units digit of $a + b$ is obtained by adding a_0 and b_0, a single operation. To obtain the tens digit, we add a_1 and b_1; then, perhaps, we add 1, depending on whether there is a carry from the previous step. Hence, at most two single-digit additions (two operations) are required for the tens digit of $a + b$. Similarly, at most two operations are required for each digit of $a + b$ after the units digit. An upper bound for the number of operations is $f(n) = 1 + 2(n-1) = 2n - 1$.

In this problem, and typical of most complexity problems, we were unable to obtain an exact count for the number of single-digit additions required. Remember that for us complexity is measured in worst-case terms. The addition of two n-digit numbers requires at most $2n - 1$ single-digit additions.

Because of the approximate nature of operation counts, it is useful to have some notation by which we can easily indicate the size of a function.

8.2.1 DEFINITION Let f and g be functions $\mathsf{N} \to \mathsf{R}$. We say that f is *Big Oh* of g and write $f = \mathcal{O}(g)$ if there is an integer n_0 and a positive real number c such that $|f(n)| \leq c|g(n)|$ for all $n \geq n_0$. ❖

8.2.2 REMARKS
1. Instead of saying "There exists an integer n_0 such that $|f(n)| \leq c|g(n)|$ for all $n \geq n_0$," we often say simply "$|f(n)| \leq c|g(n)|$ for all *sufficiently large n*."
2. If $f, g: \mathsf{N} \to \mathsf{R}$ are functions that count operations or, more generally, as long as $f(n)$ and $g(n)$ are positive for all sufficiently large n, then the absolute value symbols around $f(n)$ and $g(n)$ in Definition 8.2.1 are not necessary. Whenever we apply this definition without absolute value symbols, it will be because the functions in question are positive for all sufficiently large n. ❖

EXAMPLE 8   Let $f(n) = 15n^3$ and $g(n) = n^3$. With $n_0 = 1$ and $c = 15$, we see that $f = \mathcal{O}(g)$.

   It is also true that $g = \mathcal{O}(f)$. Why? ∎

EXAMPLE 9   Let $f(n) = n + 1$ and $g(n) = n^2$. If $n \geq 1$, $f(n) \leq n + n = 2n \leq 2n^2$. Taking $n_0 = 1$ and $c = 2$, we see that $f = \mathcal{O}(g)$. On the other hand, $g \neq \mathcal{O}(f)$, for

suppose that $n^2 \leq c(n + 1)$ for n greater than or equal to some positive integer n_0. Dividing by n, we have $n \leq c(1 + \frac{1}{n}) \leq 2c$ for all $n \geq n_0$. This, however, is impossible because $2c$ is a constant.

Two fundamental properties of Big Oh are summarized in the next proposition.

8.2.3 PROPOSITION

Let f, g, f_1, g_1 be functions $N \rightarrow R$.

(a) If $f = \mathcal{O}(g)$, then $f + g = \mathcal{O}(g)$.
(b) If $f = \mathcal{O}(f_1)$ and $g = \mathcal{O}(g_1)$, then $fg = \mathcal{O}(f_1 g_1)$.

Proof

We prove each part directly from the definition and, in part (a), use the *triangle inequality*, which states that $|a + b| \leq |a| + |b|$ for any real numbers a and b. (See Exercise 27.)

(a) There exists a positive constant c and an integer n_0 such that $|f(n)| \leq c|g(n)|$ for all $n \geq n_0$. So, for all $n \geq n_0$, $|f(n)+g(n)| \leq |f(n)|+|g(n)| \leq c|g(n)| + |g(n)| = (c + 1)|g(n)|$. With n_0 and $c + 1$ in Definition 8.2.1, we see that $f + g = \mathcal{O}(g)$.
(b) There exists a constant c and positive integer n_0 such that $|f(n)| \leq c|f_1(n)|$ for all $n \geq n_0$. There exists a constant d and positive integer n_1 such that $|g(n)| \leq d|g_1(n)|$ for all $n \geq n_1$. Let $N = \max\{n_0, n_1\}$. Then, if $n \geq N$, $|f(n)g(n)| = |f(n)||g(n)| \leq c|f_1(n)|d|g_1(n)| = cd|f_1(n)g_1(n)|$. Replacing the constants n_0 and c in Definition 8.2.1 with N and cd, respectively, we see that $fg = \mathcal{O}(f_1 g_1)$.

EXAMPLE 10

We showed in Example 9 that $n + 1 = \mathcal{O}(n^2)$. Thus, by part (a) of Proposition 8.2.3, we know also that $n^2 + n + 1 = \mathcal{O}(n^2)$. Since $n + 1 = \mathcal{O}(n)$, part (b) tells us that $(n + 1)(n^2 + n + 1) = \mathcal{O}(n^3)$.

Big Oh gives us a way to compare the relative sizes of functions.

8.2.4 DEFINITIONS

If f and g are functions $N \rightarrow R$, we say that f has *smaller order* than g and write $f \prec g$ if and only if $f = \mathcal{O}(g)$, but $g \neq \mathcal{O}(f)$. If $f = \mathcal{O}(g)$ and $g = \mathcal{O}(f)$, then we say that f and g have the *same order* and write $f \asymp g$. ❖

EXAMPLE 11

- Example 9 shows that $n + 1 \prec n^2$; thus, $n + 1$ has smaller order than n^2.
- Example 8 and PAUSE 2 show that $15n^3 \asymp n^3$: $15n^3$ and n^3 have the same order.

PROBLEM 12. Show that $n!$ has smaller order than n^n, that is, $n! \prec n^n$.

Solution. First note that $n! = n(n - 1)(n - 2) \cdots (3)(2) \leq n \cdot n \cdot n \cdots n \cdot n = n^n$ so, with $n_0 = c = 1$ in Definition 8.2.1, it follows that $n! = \mathcal{O}(n^n)$. On the other hand, $n^n \neq \mathcal{O}(n!)$, which we establish by contradiction. If $n^n = \mathcal{O}(n!)$, then, for some constant c, $n^n \leq cn!$, so $\frac{n^n}{n!} \leq c$ for all sufficiently large n. This is impossible because

$$\frac{n^n}{n!} = \frac{n}{n}\frac{n}{n - 1} \cdots \frac{n}{1} > n$$

for $n > 1$.

Students familiar with limits should appreciate the next remark and proposition, whose proof is left to the exercises.

8.2.5 REMARK

Suppose $f, g : \mathsf{N} \to \mathsf{R}$ are functions and that $\lim_{n \to \infty} f(n)$ and $\lim_{n \to \infty} g(n)$ both exist and are positive. If $f = \mathcal{O}(g)$, then $\frac{f(n)}{g(n)} \leq c$ for all sufficiently large n, and so $\lim_{n \to \infty} \frac{f(n)}{g(n)} \leq c$. It follows that if $\lim_{n \to \infty} \frac{f(n)}{g(n)} = \infty$ then $f \neq \mathcal{O}(g)$.

8.2.6 PROPOSITION

Let f and g be functions $\mathsf{N} \to \mathsf{R}$.

(a) If $\lim\limits_{n \to \infty} \dfrac{f(n)}{g(n)} = 0$, then $f \prec g$.

(b) If $\lim\limits_{n \to \infty} \dfrac{f(n)}{g(n)} = \infty$, then $g \prec f$.

(c) If $\lim\limits_{n \to \infty} \dfrac{f(n)}{g(n)} = L$ for some number $L \neq 0$, then $f \asymp g$.

EXAMPLE 13

- Since $\lim\limits_{n \to \infty} \dfrac{n+1}{n^2} = 0$, $n + 1 \prec n^2$, as earlier noted.

- Since $\lim\limits_{n \to \infty} \dfrac{2n^2 - 3n + 6}{n^2} = 2$, $2n^2 - 3n + 6 \asymp n^2$.

We have seen that $15n^3 \asymp n^3$ and $2n^2 - 3n + 6 \asymp n^2$. These examples illustrate a general principle whose proof we first describe in a specific case.

PROBLEM 14. Let $f(n) = 5n^2 - 6n + 3$ and $g(n) = n^2$. Show that f and g have the same order.

Solution. For $n \geq 1$, we have $5n^2 - 6n + 3 \leq 5n^2 + 6n + 3 \leq 5n^2 + 6n^2 + 3n^2 = 14n^2$, so, with $c = 14$ and $n_0 = 1$ in Definition 8.2.1, we see that $f = \mathcal{O}(g)$. On the other hand,

$$f(n) = 5n^2 - 6n + 3 = n^2 \left(5 - \frac{6}{n} + \frac{3}{n^2} \right) \geq n^2 \left(5 - \frac{6}{n} - \frac{3}{n^2} \right).$$

Since

$$\lim_{n \to \infty} \frac{6}{n} = \lim_{n \to \infty} \frac{3}{n^2} = 0,$$

there exists an integer n_0 such that both

$$\frac{6}{n} < \frac{5}{4} \quad \text{and} \quad \frac{3}{n^2} < \frac{5}{4}$$

for all $n \geq n_0$. (Evidently, $n_0 = 5$ will suffice.) It follows that

$$-\frac{6}{n} > -\frac{5}{4} \quad \text{and} \quad -\frac{3}{n^2} > -\frac{5}{4},$$

so

$$f(n) = 5n^2 - 6n + 3 \geq n^2 (5 - \frac{5}{4} - \frac{5}{4}) = n^2 (5 - \frac{5}{2}) = \frac{5}{2} n^2.$$

Thus $g(n) = n^2 \leq \frac{2}{5} f(n)$ so, with $c = \frac{2}{5}$ in Definition 8.2.1, we see that $g = \mathcal{O}(f)$. Thus, $f \asymp g$.

Here is the general result.

8.2.7 PROPOSITION

A polynomial has the same order as its highest power; that is, if $f(n) = a_t n^t + a_{t-1} n^{t-1} + \cdots + a_0$ is a polynomial of degree t, then $f(n) \asymp n^t$.

Proof This follows immediately from part (c) of Proposition 8.2.6, but we provide here a direct proof that does not require any knowledge of calculus. Our proof mimics the solution to Problem 14.

For any natural number n, the triangle inequality gives

$$|f(n)| \le |a_t n^t| + |a_{t-1} n^{t-1}| + \cdots + |a_1 n| + |a_0|$$
$$= |a_t| n^t + |a_{t-1}| n^{t-1} + \cdots + |a_1| n + |a_0|$$
$$\le |a_t| n^t + |a_{t-1}| n^t + \cdots + |a_1| n^t + |a_0| n^t$$
$$= (|a_t| + |a_{t-1}| + \cdots + |a_1| + |a_0|) n^t.$$

Thus, $|f(n)| \le c n^t$ for any $n \ge n_0 = 1$ with $c = |a_t| + |a_{t-1}| + \cdots + |a_1| + |a_0|$. By Definition 8.2.1, we see that $f(n) = \mathcal{O}(n^t)$. Now we prove that $n^t = \mathcal{O}(f(n))$.

Since $f \asymp -f$ for any $f \colon \mathsf{N} \to \mathsf{R}$ (see Exercise 15), we may assume that $a_t > 0$. We have

$$f(n) = n^t \left(a_t + \frac{a_{t-1}}{n} + \frac{a_{t-2}}{n^2} + \cdots + \frac{a_0}{n^t} \right)$$
$$\ge n^t \left(a_t - \frac{|a_{t-1}|}{n} - \frac{|a_{t-2}|}{n^2} \cdots - \frac{|a_0|}{n^t} \right).$$

As n gets large, the numbers

$$\frac{|a_{t-1}|}{n}, \quad \frac{|a_{t-2}|}{n^2}, \quad \ldots, \quad \frac{|a_0|}{n^t}$$

approach 0, so all of them are eventually smaller than the positive number $\dfrac{a_t}{2t}$. Thus, there is an n_0 such that, for any $n \ge n_0$,

$$\frac{|a_{t-1}|}{n} < \frac{a_t}{2t}, \quad \frac{|a_{t-2}|}{n^2} < \frac{a_t}{2t}, \quad \ldots, \quad \frac{|a_0|}{n^t} < \frac{a_t}{2t}.$$

Therefore,

$$-\frac{|a_{t-1}|}{n} > -\frac{a_t}{2t}, \quad -\frac{|a_{t-2}|}{n^2} > -\frac{a_t}{2t}, \quad \ldots, \quad -\frac{|a_0|}{n^t} > -\frac{a_t}{2t}$$

and

$$f(n) \ge n^t \left(a_t - \frac{a_t}{2t} - \frac{a_t}{2t} - \cdots - \frac{a_t}{2t} \right) = n^t \left(a_t - t\frac{a_t}{2t} \right) = n^t \left(\frac{a_t}{2} \right).$$

Thus, $n^t \le \dfrac{2}{a_t} f(n)$ for all $n \ge n_0$ and, with $c = \dfrac{2}{a_t}$ in Definition 8.2.1, we obtain $n^t = \mathcal{O}(f(n))$, as required.

In the exercises, you are asked to verify that the relation *same order* defines an equivalence relation on the class of functions $\mathsf{N} \to \mathsf{R}$; that is, the relation is

reflexive: $f \asymp f$ for all f;
symmetric: if $f \asymp g$, then $g \asymp f$; and
transitive: if $f \asymp g$ and $g \asymp h$, then $f \asymp h$.

(See Section 2.4.)

EXAMPLE 15 Since $5n^2 - 6n + 3 \asymp n^2$ and $2n^2 - 3n + 6 \asymp n^2$, it follows that $5n^2 - 6n + 3$ and $2n^2 - 3n + 6$ have the same order, something that is, perhaps, not so easy to see directly from the definition of Big Oh. In fact, transitivity and Proposition 8.2.7 imply that any two polynomials of the same degree have the same order.

There are also some natural connections between the binary relations $\asymp$ and $\prec$. For example, if $f \prec g$ and $g \asymp h$, then $f \prec h$. We have seen that $n + 1 \prec n^2$ and $n^2 \asymp 5n^2 + 6n + 3$, so we may conclude that $n + 1 \prec 5n^2 + 6n + 3$.

Proposition 8.2.7 says that any polynomial has the same order as its highest power. The next proposition shows that different powers of n never have the same order.

8.2.8 PROPOSITION

Suppose a and b are real numbers and $a < b$. Then $n^a \prec n^b$.

Proof

Take $n_0 = 1$ and $c = 1$ in Definition 8.2.1 to obtain $n^a = \mathcal{O}(n^b)$. To see that the reverse is not true, suppose $n^b < cn^a$ for some constant c and all sufficiently large n. Dividing by n^a, we have $n^{b-a} < c$. The left-hand side is a positive power of n, and hence, for large n, it is bigger than c. Thus, n^b is not $\mathcal{O}(n^a)$.

Students of calculus should note that Proposition 8.2.8 follows directly from part (b) of Proposition 8.2.6 because, if $b > a$,

$$\lim_{n \to \infty} \frac{n^b}{n^a} = \infty.$$

As a particular case of Proposition 8.2.8, we see that $1 \prec n^a$ for any positive power n^a of n. Thus, we begin to see that the idea of order permits the definition of a hierarchy among functions. For instance, we now know that

$$1 \prec \sqrt{n} \prec n \prec n\sqrt{n} \prec n^2 \prec n^{2.01} \prec \cdots .$$

A straightforward induction argument shows that $n^2 < 2^n$ for $n \geq 5$ (see Exercise 9 of Section 5.1). It follows that $2^n \neq \mathcal{O}(n)$; otherwise, we would have $2^n < cn$ and, hence, $n^2 < 2^n < cn$ for some constant c and all sufficiently large n. This implies $n < c$, which, for large n, is not true. Thus, $2^n \neq \mathcal{O}(n)$. Since $n = \mathcal{O}(2^n)$, we conclude that $n \prec 2^n$.

In a similar fashion, we can prove that $n^3 < 2^n$ for $n \geq 10$ and, hence, that $n^2 \prec 2^n$. (See Exercise 14.) In fact,

$$n^a \prec b^n$$

for any real numbers a and b with $b > 1$. This follows directly from Proposition 8.2.6 since

$$\lim_{n \to \infty} \frac{b^n}{n^a} = \infty$$

for any real constants a, b with $b > 1$. (For students familiar with l'Hôpital's Rule, this result will be elementary.)

Our examination of the relative orders of common functions continues.

8.2.9 PROPOSITION

$\log_b n \prec n$ for any real number b, $b > 1$.

Proof

We apply $\log_b$ to the inequality $n < b^n$, which is true for all sufficiently large n, obtaining $\log_b n < n$. With $c = 1$ in Definition 8.2.1, we see that $\log_b n = \mathcal{O}(n)$. Now $n \neq \mathcal{O}(\log_b n)$ since $n \leq c \log_b n$ implies $b^n \leq n^c$ (applying the function $x \mapsto b^x$), which, for large n, is not true. Thus, $\log_b n \prec n$.

In the Exercises, you are asked to show that any two logarithm functions (with bases larger than 1) have the same order; that is,

$$\log_a n \asymp \log_b n$$

for any $a, b > 1$. For this reason, we now frequently omit mention of the base of a logarithm, because most assertions about order that involve logarithms are true for any base $b > 1$.

Propositions 8.2.8 and 8.2.9, together with the facts that

$$n! \prec n^n$$

(Problem 12) and

$$b^n \prec n!$$

(Exercise 13), allow our hierarchy of functions to be extended considerably. For $a, b > 1$, we have

$$1 \prec \log n \prec n \prec n^a \prec b^n \prec n! \prec n^n.$$

Figure 8.4 shows the graphs of the natural logarithm and of the functions defined by $f(x) = x$, $f(x) = x^2$, and $f(x) = 3^x$ and provides dramatic evidence of the relative orders and rates of growth of these functions. In particular, note the very slow growth of the logarithm and the very rapid growth of the exponential.

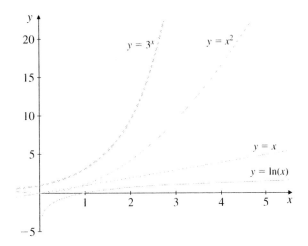

Figure 8.4   Some common complexity functions.

How does all of this relate to the efficiency of algorithms? Suppose $\mathcal{A}$ and $\mathcal{B}$ are algorithms that accomplish the same task. If the problem to which these algorithms is applied is "small," they may work so quickly on even a microcomputer that differences in performance are not noticeable. Few of us can detect the difference in a running time of 10^{-6} seconds and one that is 100 times as fast! As the problem grows in size, however, differences in running time become very significant. Suppose $\mathcal{A}$ has complexity $\mathcal{O}(n)$, while $\mathcal{B}$ is $\mathcal{O}(n^3)$. With $n = 5000$ and a computer that performs 1 million operations per second, algorithm $\mathcal{A}$ requires on the order of $5000 \times 10^{-6} = 0.005$ seconds while $\mathcal{B}$ requires about $5000^3 \times 10^{-6} = 125000$ seconds, or about a day and a half! Some algorithms may involve so many operations that they are simply impractical to implement. We become very concerned, therefore, with the relative sizes of complexity functions when n is large. This is precisely what the concept of order is designed to measure.

If complexity functions f and g, which correspond respectively to algorithms $\mathcal{A}$ and $\mathcal{B}$, have the same order ($f \asymp g$), then $\mathcal{A}$ and $\mathcal{B}$ are considered to be very similar with respect to efficiency, whereas, if f has smaller order than g, then $\mathcal{A}$ is more efficient than $\mathcal{B}$. An algorithm whose complexity function has the same order as n is said to be *linear* or to run in *linear time*. An algorithm with complexity function of order n^2 is called *quadratic*. More generally, algorithms with complexity functions of order n^a for some positive real number a are *polynomial* or said to run in *polynomial time*. Algorithms with complexity functions of order $\log n$ are *logarithmic*, and algorithms with complexity of order a^n for some $a > 0$ are *exponential*.

We have seen that an algorithm that runs in logarithmic time is more efficient than a linear algorithm, which, in turn, is more efficient than a quadratic algorithm. Any polynomial algorithm is more efficient than one that is exponential.

Here a word of caution is in order. Saying that an exponential algorithm $\mathcal{A}$ is less efficient than a polynomial algorithm $\mathcal{B}$ that runs in polynomial time means only that, when n is **sufficiently large**, algorithm $\mathcal{A}$ takes more time. For small values of n, the differences may be inconsequential; indeed, $\mathcal{A}$ may even be faster! For example, if $f(n) = 100n^3$ and $g(n) = 2^n$, then $f \prec g$, but we must have $n \geq 20$ for the polynomial algorithm to be faster. Similarly, $f(n) = n^2$ is "better" than $g(n) = \frac{n^3}{100}$ because, once n becomes sufficiently large, an algorithm with the complexity function f will take less time. This is clearly not the case for small values of n, however.

These remarks are illustrated in Table 8.5, which compares a number of complexity functions $f(n)$. The entries, which are only approximate, show the time required to run an algorithm with $f(n)$ operations on a machine performing 1 million operations each second (like a snail). The functions are ordered in decreasing order of efficiency (for sufficiently large n) (except for n^2 and $2n^2 + 5n + 100$, which have the same order). From this table, we see that an algorithm with $f(n) = 25$ operations runs much more quickly than an algorithm with $f(n) = n$ or $f(n) = \frac{n^3}{100}$, once n is big enough. While, for n as large as 100, an algorithm with $f(n) = \frac{n^3}{100}$ runs more quickly than one with $f(n) = 2n^2 + 5n + 100$, it is apparent that once $n = 5000$, the situation is reversed. Note how quickly an algorithm with $\log_2 n$ operations runs and, conversely, how slowly one with 2^n operations runs (for large n). (When viewing the numbers in the last line of the table, it is interesting to bear in mind that the universe has been around for about 7×10^9 years!) Algorithms with complexity functions that are $\mathcal{O}(\log_2 n)$ are highly efficient, whereas exponential

Table 8.5 Approximate time required to run an algorithm requiring $f(n)$ operations assuming a machine speed of 1 million operations per second.

$f(n)$ \\ n	10	100	5000
25	25×10^{-6} s	25×10^{-6} s	25×10^{-6} s
$\log_2 n$	3.3×10^{-6} s	6.6×10^{-6} s	1.2×10^{-5} s
n	10^{-5} s	10^{-4} s	5×10^{-3} s
$n \log_2 n$	3.3×10^{-5} s	6.6×10^{-6} s	6.1×10^{-2} s
n^2	10^{-4} s	.01 s	25 s
$2n^2 + 5n + 100$	3.5×10^{-4} s	.021 s	50 s
$n^3/100$	10^{-5} s	.01 s	21 min
2^n	10^{-3} s	4.0×10^{16} yr	4.5×10^{1491} yr

algorithms are so slow as to be useless from a practical point of view, once n is any reasonable size at all.

In recent years, following the initiative of Stephen Cook of the University of Toronto, computer scientists have identified a collection of problems for which no polynomial-time algorithm is currently known. These problems, which are equivalent in the sense that the existence of a polynomial-time algorithm for one of them would imply polynomial-time algorithms for them all, are called *NP-complete*. The *NP* stands for nondeterministic polynomial time. Some of the most interesting NP-complete problems are related to graphs and will be identified in later chapters. (See, for instance, the Traveling Salesman's Problem in Chapter 10 or the problem of coloring the vertices of a graph, which is discussed in Chapter 13.)

We conclude this section with a discussion of the complexity of some algorithms that will already be familiar to the reader.

PROBLEM 16. Show that the number of single-digit additions required in the addition of m n-digit numbers does not exceed $m(2n+m)$. Conclude that the complexity of such addition is $\mathcal{O}(n^2)$ if $m \le n$ and $\mathcal{O}(m^2)$ otherwise.

Solution. This addition problem has the following form.

$$\left.\begin{array}{rcl} r &=& (r_{n-1}r_{n-2}\ldots r_1 r_0)_{10} \\ &\vdots& \\ c &=& (c_{n-1}c_{n-2}\ldots c_1 c_0)_{10} \\ b &=& (b_{n-1}b_{n-2}\ldots b_1 b_0)_{10} \\ a &=& (a_{n-1}a_{n-2}\ldots a_1 a_0)_{10} \end{array}\right\} m \text{ numbers}$$

We use repeatedly the result of Problem 7 that the addition of two n-digit numbers requires at most $2n - 1$ single-digit additions. Thus, the addition of a and b requires at most $2n - 1$ additions. The sum is a number with at most $n + 1$ digits. The addition of this number and c (which we think of as an $n+1$-digit number beginning with 0) requires another $2(n + 1) - 1 = 2n + 1$ operations, at most, and gives a number with at most $n + 2$ digits. Adding the next number requires at most $2(n + 2) - 1 = 2n + 3$ operations. Continuing this way, the final addition with r requires at most $2[n + (m - 2)] - 1 = 2n + 2m - 5$ operations. Altogether, the addition requires at most

$$(2n - 1) + (2n + 1) + (2n + 3) + \cdots + (2n + 2m - 5)$$

operations. This is the sum of an arithmetic sequence with $m - 1$ terms, first term $a = 2n - 1$, and common difference $d = 2$, so it equals

$$\begin{aligned} \tfrac{m-1}{2}[2(2n - 1) + (m - 2)2] &= (m - 1)(2n - 1) + (m - 2)(m - 1) \\ &= (m - 1)(2n + m - 3) \\ &\le m(2n + m). \end{aligned}$$

[See formula (7) on p. 162.] If $m \le n$, the number of operations is at most $n(2n + n) = n(3n) = 3n^2$, so the addition has complexity $\mathcal{O}(n^2)$. If $n \le m$, $m(2n + m) \le m(2m + m) = 3m^2$, so the complexity is $\mathcal{O}(m^2)$.

PROBLEM 17. Show that the usual method of multiplying two n-digit numbers has complexity $\mathcal{O}(n^2)$. Count as equivalent operations the addition and multiplication of two single-digit numbers.[3]

---

[3] There are faster methods of multiplying. In 1962, Anatolii Karatsuba found a method that is $\mathcal{O}(n^{1.58})$.

Solution. In the multiplication of two n-digit numbers by the usual method, there are n multiplications of an n-digit number by single-digit numbers. Each such multiplication requires at most $3n - 2$ operations. (See Exercise 2.) Then it is necessary to add n numbers, each of length at most $2n$. Using the result of Problem 16, this requires at most an additional $n[2(2n) + n] = n(5n)$ operations for a total not exceeding

$$n(3n - 2) + n(5n) \asymp n^2,$$

by Proposition 8.2.7.

PROBLEM 18. Given a real number x and an integer $n \geq 1$, one straightforward way to compute x^n is to compute $x(x) = x^2$, then $x(x^2) = x^3$, then $x(x^3) = x^4$, and so forth, stopping with x^n.

   (a) Find the complexity of this algorithm in terms of the number of multiplications.

   (b) Find an algorithm that is more efficient than the one described and indicate why your algorithm is more efficient.

Solution.   **(a)** This algorithm requires $n - 1$ multiplications.

   (b) A seemingly more efficient way to compute x^n is to compute the powers $x, x^2, (x^2)^2 = x^4, (x^4)^2 = x^8$, and so on, stopping upon calculation of x^{2^k}, where $2^k \leq n < 2^{k+1}$. This requires k multiplications. Now consider how the Russian peasant method computes the product $n = n \times 1$.[4] On the left, n is divided by 2 a total of k times, while on the right, 1 is multiplied by 2 a total of k times. The product n is determined as the sum of certain numbers on the right, that is, as the sum of at most k powers of 2. Then x^n is the product of the corresponding powers of x. For example,

$$37 = 1 + 2^2 + 2^5, \text{ so } x^{37} = x^1 x^{2^2} x^{2^5}$$

and, generally,

$$n = \sum 2^{k_i}, \quad \text{so } x^n = x^{\sum 2^{k_i}} = x^{2^{k_1}} x^{2^{k_2}} \cdots,$$

for which at most a further k multiplications are required. Thus, after at most $3k$ multiplications and divisions, we can compute x^n. Applying $\log_2$ to the inequality $2^k < n$, we have $k < \log_2 n$. Thus, the number of multiplications required this time is $\mathcal{O}(\log n)$. Since $\log n \prec n$, the proposed algorithm is more efficient than the one described in (a).

PROBLEM 19. Find a Big Oh estimate of the complexity of the Euclidean algorithm in terms of the number of divisions. (Given integers a and b, $b < a$, a "division" of a by b means the determination of q and r, $0 \leq r < b$, such that $a = bq + r$.)

Solution. Given positive integers a and b with $b < a$, recall that the Euclidean algorithm finds the greatest common divisor of a and b by the following sequence

---

By December 1988, the fastest known method was $\mathcal{O}(n(\log n)(\log \log n))$. No algorithm better than $\mathcal{O}(n)$ is possible. We refer the interested reader to "Ramanujan, Modular Equations, and Approximations to Pi or How to Compute One Billion Digits of Pi," by J. M. Borwein, P. B. Borwein, and D. H. Bailey, *American Mathematical Monthly* **96** (1989), 201–219, and to the bibliography of this article.
[4]The Russian peasant method can be useful!

of divisions,

$$a = q_1 b + r_1, \qquad r_1 < b,$$
$$b = q_2 r_1 + r_2, \qquad r_2 < r_1,$$
$$r_1 = q_3 r_2 + r_3, \qquad r_3 < r_2,$$
$$\vdots$$
$$r_{k-2} = q_k r_{k-1} + r_k, \quad r_k < r_{k-1},$$
$$r_{k-1} = q_{k+1} r_k,$$

the process terminating with the first zero remainder r_{k+1}. The gcd is then r_k, the last nonzero remainder. (See Section 4.2.) The number of divisions and, hence, the number of basic operations is $k + 1$. How big is k? Note that $q_{k+1} > 1$ because $r_k < r_{k-1}$ and, since the other quotients q_i are positive integers, we have $q_i \geq 1$ for $1 \leq i \leq k$. Therefore,

$$r_k \geq 1$$
$$r_{k-1} \geq 2 r_k \geq 2$$
$$r_{k-2} \geq r_{k-1} + r_k \geq 3$$
$$r_{k-3} \geq r_{k-2} + r_{k-1} \geq 3 + 2 = 5$$
$$\vdots$$
$$r_1 \geq r_2 + r_3$$
$$b \geq r_1 + r_2.$$

Consider the two sequences

$$1, \quad r_k, \quad r_{k-1}, \quad r_{k-2}, \quad r_{k-3}, \quad \dots, \quad r_1, \quad b$$
$$1, \quad 1, \quad 2, \quad 3, \quad 5, \quad \dots.$$

Each term in the first sequence is at least as big as the corresponding term in the second sequence. In particular, b is at least as large as the $(k + 2)$th term in the second sequence. The second sequence, however, is the Fibonacci sequence, whose kth term is the nearest integer to $\frac{1}{\sqrt{5}}\left(\frac{1+\sqrt{5}}{2}\right)^k$. (See Section 5.3.) Thus,

$$b \geq \frac{1}{\sqrt{5}}\left(\frac{1+\sqrt{5}}{2}\right)^{k+2} - 1 = \frac{1}{\sqrt{5}}\left(\frac{1+\sqrt{5}}{2}\right)^2 \left(\frac{1+\sqrt{5}}{2}\right)^k - 1,$$

from which it follows that $\left(\frac{1+\sqrt{5}}{2}\right)^k \leq Ab + B$, where A and B are positive constants independent of b. Since $\frac{1+\sqrt{5}}{2} = C$ is also a constant and $C^k \leq Ab + B$, an application of the logarithm (to any base) gives $k \log C \leq \log(Ab + B)$. Since $\log(An + B) \asymp \log n$ for $A, B > 0$ (see Exercise 22), it follows that the number of operations required is $\mathcal{O}(\log b)$. The Euclidean algorithm is very efficient.

2. Take $n_0 = 1$ and $c = 1$.

True/False Questions

(Answers can be found in the back of the book.)

1. Two 3-digit integers can always be added together using at most four basic operations.

2. If f and g are functions $\mathsf{N} \to \mathsf{R}$, we say that $f = \mathcal{O}(g)$ if there is an integer n_0 such that $|f(n)| \leq c|g(n)|$ for all positive real numbers c and for all $n \geq n_0$.

3. If $f = \mathcal{O}(g)$, then $g = \mathcal{O}(f)$.

4. If $f = \mathcal{O}(g)$, then $g + f = \mathcal{O}(g)$.

5. If $f = \mathcal{O}(g)$ and $h = \mathcal{O}(g)$, then $fg = \mathcal{O}(g)$.

6. If $f(n) = 2n^2 + 3n - 1$ and $g(n) = 5n^2 - 2n + 7$, then $f = \mathcal{O}(g)$.

7. If $f(n) = 2n^2 + 3n - 1$ and $g(n) = 5n^2 - 2n + 7$, then $g = \mathcal{O}(f)$.

8. The relation *same order* defines an equivalence relation on the class of functions $\mathsf{N} \to \mathsf{R}$.

9. $\log_a n$ and $\log_b n$ have the same order for any positive real numbers a and b.

10. $3^n \prec n^3$.

Exercises

*The answers to exercises marked [BB] can be found in the **B**ack of the **B**ook.*

1. [BB] Consider the distance algorithm described in Example 6. Assume that addition and subtraction require the same amount of time, that addition is twice as fast as multiplication, and that multiplication is ten times as fast as the square root operation. Find the complexity function.

2. Show that the number of operations required to multiply an n-digit number by a single-digit number does not exceed $3n - 2$. Count the addition and the multiplication of two single-digit numbers as equivalent operations.

3. [BB] Show that the number of operations required to divide an n-digit number by a single-digit number does not exceed $3n$. Count as equivalent the following operations:
   - Multiplication of two single-digit numbers
   - Division of a single-digit number or a 2-digit number by a single-digit number provided the quotient has only a single digit (e.g., $37 \div 9$, but not $37 \div 3$)
   - Subtraction of two 2-digit numbers provided the difference has only a single digit (e.g., $37 - 32$, but not $37 - 22$)

4. Find an algorithm for finding the smallest number in a set of n real numbers. What is the complexity function of your algorithm? (Take *comparison* in the form "$x < y$?" as the basic operation.)

5. [BB] Let x be a real number and n a positive integer. Consider the following two algorithms for calculating x^{2^n}.

Algorithm A

Step 1. Set $a = 1$.
Step 2. For $i = 1$ to 2^n, replace a by xa.
Step 3. Output a.

Algorithm B

Step 1. Set $a = x$.
Step 2. For $i = 1$ to n, replace a by a^2.
Step 3. Output a.

Find complexity functions for each of these algorithms and explain why $\mathcal{B}$ is more efficient. Assume that multiplication is the basic operation.

6. (a) [BB] Justify the statement made in Section 8.1 that Horner's method of polynomial evaluation requires fewer arithmetic operations than the more obvious method described in Problem 2. Assume that powers of x cannot be stored.

   (b) Repeat part (a) assuming it is possible to store powers of x.

7. Use Definition 8.2.1 to show that $f = \mathcal{O}(g)$ in each of the following cases of functions $f, g \colon \mathsf{N} \to \mathsf{R}$.
   (a) [BB] $f(n) = 5n$, $g(n) = n^3$
   (b) $f(n) = 17n^4 + 8n^3 + 5n^2 + 6n + 1$, $g(n) = n^4$
   (c) [BB] $f(n) = 8n^3 + 4n^2 + 5n + 1$, $g(n) = 3n^4 + 6n^2 + 8n + 2$
   (d) $f(n) = 2^n$, $g(n) = 3^n$
   (e) $f(n) = 2n^2 + 3n + 1$, $g(n) = n^2 + 1$
   (f) $f(n) = 2n^2 - 3n + 5$, $g(n) = n^2 - 7n$
   (g) $f(n) = \log_2 n^5$, $g(n) = n$

8. [BB; (a), (c)] For each part of Exercise 7 decide whether $f \prec g$ or $f \asymp g$. Use Propositions 8.2.7 and 8.2.8, if appropriate.

9. If $f, g, h \colon \mathsf{N} \to \mathsf{R}$, $f = \mathcal{O}(h)$ and $g = \mathcal{O}(h)$, show that $f + g = \mathcal{O}(h)$.

10. (a) Show that $\mathcal{O}$ defines a transitive operation on the class of functions $\mathsf{N} \to \mathsf{R}$.
    (b) Suppose $f, g, h \colon \mathsf{N} \to \mathsf{R}$ are functions with $f = \mathcal{O}(g)$ and $g \asymp h$. Show that $f = \mathcal{O}(h)$.
    (c) [BB] Prove that $\prec$ defines a transitive relation on the class of functions $\mathsf{N} \to \mathsf{R}$.

11. [BB] Let f, g, and h be functions $\mathsf{N} \to \mathsf{R}$ and suppose that $f \asymp g$ and $g \prec h$. Prove that $f \prec h$.

12. [BB] Show that $a^n \prec b^n$ if $0 < a < b$.

13. (a) [BB] Show that $2^n \prec n!$.
    (b) Show that $b^n \prec n!$ for any $b > 1$.

14. (a) Prove that $n^3 < 2^n$ for all $n \geq 10$.
    (b) Use the result of part (a) to show that $n^2 \prec 2^n$.

15. [BB] Let $f \colon \mathsf{N} \to \mathsf{R}$ be a function and $0 \neq k \in \mathsf{R}$. Show that $kf \asymp f$.

16. Let A be the set of all functions $\mathsf{N} \to \mathsf{R}$ and, for $f, g \in A$, define $f \prec g$ as in Definitions 8.2.4.
    (a) Does $\prec$ define a partial order on A?

(b) For $f, g \in A$, define $f \preceq g$ if $f \prec g$ or $f = g$. Is $(A, \preceq)$ a partially ordered set?

17. [BB] Show that $\asymp$, as defined in Definitions 8.2.4, defines an equivalence relation on the class of functions $\mathsf{N} \to \mathsf{R}$.

18. [BB] Use any of the results of this section to show that $n \log_2 n \prec n^2$.

19. Find a function in the list

$$n^2, 1, n^3, n \log n, \log n, n^4, 2^n, n^n, n!, n, \pi^n, n^5$$

that has the same order as

(a) $f(n) = 3n^4 + 6n^2 - 8n - 5$

(b) [BB] $f(n) = n \log n + n^2$

(c) $f(n) = 5$ **(d)** $f(n) = 2^n + 4n^n$

(e) [BB] $f(n) = 3n! - 17n^4$

(f) $f(n) = n + \log n$

Justify your answers appealing to any of the results in this section that prove helpful.

20. Repeat Exercise 19 for each of the following functions:

(a) [BB] $f(n) = 48n^5 - 7n^4 + 6n^3 + 5n^2 - 2n - 7$

(b) $f(n) = 2^n + 375n^{1990}$

(c) $f(n) = \pi^n + n^\pi$

(d) $f(n) = 3n + 5n \log n + 7n^2$

(e) [BB] $f(n) = 2 + 4 + 6 + \cdots + 2n$

(f) $f(n) = 2 + 4 + 8 + \cdots + 2^n$

(g) $f(n) = \dfrac{(5n+7)(n^2 \log_2 n)}{n^2 + 4n}$

21. [BB] Show that $\log_a n \asymp \log_b n$ for any real numbers $a, b > 1$.

22. Suppose A and B are positive real numbers. Show that $\log(An + B)$ and $\log n$ have the same order. (Use $\log_2$, for instance.)

23. Use the Euclidean algorithm to describe an algorithm for determining whether an integer $n > 1$ is prime. You should be able to find an algorithm that requires $\mathcal{O}(\sqrt{n} \ln n)$ divisions.

24. [BB] Show that $\log n! = \mathcal{O}(n \log n)$.

25. (a) Find a Big Oh estimate of the complexity of the algorithm for writing an integer a in base 2 in terms of the number of divisions. (See Section 4.1.) As in Problem 19, by a division, we mean the determination of q and r such that a given integer $b = 2q + r$.

(b) Suppose a division counts as three basic operations. How does this affect your answer to (a)?

26. The Russian peasant method is used to multiply two n-digit numbers.

(a) Find a reasonable upper bound for the number of rows (below the first) required by this process, that is, for the number of multiplications and divisions by 2.

(b) Find a reasonable upper bound for the number of basic operations required in the multiplying and dividing by 2.

(c) Find a reasonable upper bound for the number of basic operations required by the final addition.

(d) Show that the number of basic operations in all is $\mathcal{O}(n^2)$. (Thus, the Russian peasant method is no better and no worse than the traditional method. See Problem 17.)

Count as basic operations

- the addition of two single-digit numbers,
- the multiplication of two single-digit numbers, and
- the division of a 2-digit number by a single digit number.

27. (a) Establish the *triangle inequality*: $|a + b| \leq |a| + |b|$ for any real numbers a and b. [*Hint*: For a real number x, what is $\sqrt{x^2}$?]

(b) Show that $|x_1 + x_2 + \cdots + x_n| \leq |x_1| + |x_2| + \cdots + |x_n|$ for any $n \geq 1$ and any n real numbers $x_1, x_2, \ldots, x_n$.

28. (For students of calculus) Prove Proposition 8.2.6.

8.3 Searching and Sorting

Perhaps the two most important tasks required of modern computers are the searching and sorting of lists. Since they are required by so many other processes and often must be repeated many times, efficient algorithms to search and sort lists are of supreme importance.

A car manufacturer, realizing that a certain part is a potential safety hazard, needs to search the records of all cars sold in recent years for those that contain this part. A university wishes to implement a system whereby, each semester, students will register in order of decreasing grade-point average (those with the highest grade-point average register first). To determine the numbers of students with grade-point averages in various ranges, student records will have to be searched.

How often is it required to sort alphabetically? Surely this is a key step in many tasks, from the creation of telephone directories to dictionaries to class lists. Although computers can work very quickly, given a large input and an inefficient algorithm, they can be slowed to a crawl easily.

In this section, we discuss several algorithms for searching and sorting and discuss the complexity of each. Our approach to complexity will again always be worst case. While we would hope that a sorting algorithm would not take long to alphabetize a list of names input already in alphabetical order, our concern is the length of time such an algorithm could take when the input is as disorganized as possible.

We begin with an algorithm that searches a list for one particular entry.

8.3.1 A LINEAR SEARCH ALGORITHM

To search a list $a_1, a_2, \ldots, a_n$ for the element x,

> for $i = 1$ to n
>   if $x = a_i$, output "true" and set $i = 2n$;
> if $i \neq 2n$, output "false."

The algorithm proceeds in an obvious way. Setting $i = 2n$ is a little trick that stops the loop as soon as x has been found and, if x is not in the list, ensures that "false" is output at the end.

EXAMPLE 20   For $x = -2$ and an input list

$$\begin{array}{cccc} 6 & 0 & -2 & 1 \\ a_1 & a_2 & a_3 & a_4 \end{array}$$

the algorithm sets $i = 1$, determines that $x \neq a_1 = 6$, and sets $i = 2$. Since $x \neq a_2 = 0$, it sets $i = 3$. Since $x = a_3 = -2$, it outputs "true" and sets $i = 2n = 8$. Since i is no longer in the range from 1 to n, the loop stops. Since $i = 2n$, the algorithm knows that x was found and does not output "false".

On the other hand, for $x = 2$ and the same input the algorithm determines that $x \neq a_1 = 6$, $x \neq a_2 = 0$, $x \neq a_3 = -2$, and $x \neq a_4 = 1$. At the final step, $i = 4 \neq 2n$, so the algorithm outputs "false."

In the worst of circumstances, when the element x is not in the list $a_1, a_2, \ldots, a_n$, the loop is executed n times and the algorithm requires $n + 1$ comparisons. In many searching and sorting algorithms, there are few arithmetic calculations. The best basic operation with which to measure efficiency is a *comparison*, that is, a statement of the form $x = a$, $x \leq a$, $x < a$, $x \geq a$, or $x > a$. This Linear Search Algorithm requires at most $n + 1$ comparisons, so it is $\mathcal{O}(n)$.

8.3.2 REMARK

Big Oh notation is sufficiently imprecise that we can be relatively careless when determining the complexity of an algorithm. A more thoughtful approach to the Linear Search Algorithm might have led us to count two comparisons for each value of i, for, after checking if $x = a_i$, the algorithm must also check to see if the end of the list has been reached, that is, if $i = n$. Such analysis would lead us to complexity $2n$ rather than n, but, as we know, $n \asymp 2n$, so the Big Oh estimate of complexity remains $\mathcal{O}(n)$.

It is often the case that a list to be searched is in some natural order. When searching a dictionary for the meaning of *obfuscate*, for instance, it is helpful to know which way to turn if the dictionary is open at *trisect*. When a list is already in order, it stands to reason that there should be a procedure for searching that is more efficient than a linear search. One commonly used such procedure is called *binary search*. The Binary Search Algorithm determines which half of an ordered list would have to contain the sought after element, then which half of that half, and so on. At each stage, the list to be searched is one-half the length of the previous list.

8.3.3 A BINARY SEARCH ALGORITHM

To search for an element x in an ordered list $a_1 \le a_2 \le \cdots \le a_n$, proceed as follows.

> while $n > 0$
>> if $n = 1$ then
>>> if $x = a_1$ output "true" and set $n = 0$;
>>> else output "false" and set $n = 0$;
>> else
>>> set $m = \lfloor \frac{n}{2} \rfloor$;
>>> if $x \le a_m$ replace the current list with $a_1, \ldots, a_m$ and set $n = m$;
>>> else replace the current list with $a_{m+1}, \ldots, a_n$ and replace n by $n - m$.
> end while

This is the first time we have encountered the "while/end while" construct, which works pretty much as we would imagine. In this particular case, as long as there is a list to examine ("while $n > 0$"), the algorithm decides in which half of the list the sought for element may reside and replaces the current list with this half.

EXAMPLE 21 With $x = 12$ and the input

$$\begin{array}{cccccccccc} 5 & 6 & 7 & 10 & 11 & 12 & 15 & 17 & 19 & 20 \\ a_1 & a_2 & a_3 & a_4 & a_5 & a_6 & a_7 & a_8 & a_9 & a_{10} \end{array}$$

of length $n = 10 > 0$, the algorithm sets $m = \lfloor \frac{10}{2} \rfloor = 5$. Since $x \le a_m$ is false, the algorithm replaces n by $n - m = 5$ and the original list with

$$\begin{array}{ccccc} 12 & 15 & 17 & 19 & 20 \\ a_1 & a_2 & a_3 & a_4 & a_5. \end{array}$$

The integer n is still positive, so the algorithm executes the statements inside the "while $\ldots$ end while" again. Since $n \ne 1$, it sets $m = \lfloor \frac{5}{2} \rfloor = 2$ and, because $x \le a_2 = 15$, it sets $n = 2$ and replaces the current list with

$$\begin{array}{cc} 12 & 15 \\ a_1 & a_2. \end{array}$$

Now n is still positive, so the algorithm executes the statements between "while" and "end while" again. Since $n \ne 1$, the algorithm sets $m = \lfloor \frac{2}{2} \rfloor = 1$. Since $x \le a_1 = 12$, the algorithm sets $n = 1$ and replaces the current list with a_1. Now $n = 1$, $x = a_1$, so the algorithm outputs "true" and sets $n = 0$. The "while" condition no longer holds, so the algorithm terminates.

Pause 3 Explain how the Binary Search Algorithm would work given $x = 13$ and the list of Example 21.

To determine the complexity of binary search, first suppose that $n = 2^k$ is a power of 2. The algorithm proceeds by progressively halving the length of the list; hence, it terminates after executing the statements between "while" and "end while," in the worst case a total of k times. This involves $3k$ comparisons ($n > 0$? $n = 1$? $x \le a_m$?) and one final comparison ($x = a_1$?) when $n = 1$. If n is not a power of 2, find k such that $2^{k-1} < n \le 2^k$ and increase the length of the input list by adding terms all equal to a_n until the extended list has length 2^k. This list, and hence the original, are searched after at most $3k + 1$ comparisons. Since $2^{k-1} < n$, we have $k - 1 < \log_2 n$, so $k < 1 + \log_2 n$ and $3k + 1 < 4(1 + \log_2 n) + 1 \asymp \log_2 n$. The Binary Search Algorithm is $\mathcal{O}(\log_2 n)$.

We now turn our attention to sorting algorithms. A *sorting algorithm* will put a list of numbers into increasing order or a list of words into alphabetical order. We begin with perhaps the simplest of all sorting algorithms, the *bubble sort*. The Bubble Sort Algorithm makes a number of passes through a list, each time interchanging any consecutive pair of elements that are not in proper order. On the first pass, the largest element is shuffled to the end. On the next pass, the next largest element is shuffled to second from the end. In general, after the kth pass the list looks like this:

$$\underbrace{a_1, a_2, \ldots, a_{n-k}}_{\text{unsorted}} < \underbrace{a_{n-k+1} < \cdots < a_{n-1} < a_n}_{\text{sorted}}$$

Gradually, the largest elements bubble to the end in order.

EXAMPLE 22   Suppose the input list is 6, 3, 1, 4, 9, 2. Initially, the first two numbers are compared and (in this case) interchanged, giving the list 3, 6, 1, 4, 9, 2. Then the second and third elements are compared and, in this case, interchanged, giving 3, 1, 6, 4, 9, 2. Next, the third and fourth elements are compared and switched, giving 3, 1, 4, 6, 9, 2. No interchange of the fourth and fifth numbers is required. The first pass is completed with an interchange of the fifth and last numbers, giving 3, 1, 4, 6, 2, 9. Notice that the largest number, 9, has bubbled to the end.

The second pass through the list is like the first, with one exception. Since the largest element is now at the end, it is not necessary to compare the second last element with the last. Here are the four steps of the second pass in our example. The numbers being compared at each stage are underlined.

$$\underline{3, 1}, 4, 6, 2, 9 \to 1, \underline{3, 4}, 6, 2, 9 \to 1, 3, \underline{4, 6}, 2, 9$$
$$\to 1, 3, 4, \underline{6, 2}, 9 \to 1, 3, 4, 2, 6, 9$$

Notice that the two largest numbers, 6 and 9, are now at the end of the list in correct order. The third pass is like the second, but one step shorter since it is not necessary to compare the fourth and fifth elements. Here are the three steps of the third pass.

$$\underline{1, 3}, 4, 2, 6, 9 \to 1, \underline{3, 4}, 2, 6, 9 \to 1, 3, \underline{4, 2}, 6, 9 \to 1, 3, 2, 4, 6, 9.$$

The fourth pass requires two comparisons,

$$\underline{1, 3}, 2, 4, 6, 9 \to 1, \underline{3, 2}, 4, 6, 9 \to 1, 2, 3, 4, 6, 9$$

and the fifth pass just one,

$$\underline{1, 2}, 3, 4, 6, 9 \to 1, 2, 3, 4, 6, 9.$$

In the general description of the Bubble Sort Algorithm that follows, we use the term *swap* to denote the exchange of values of two variables. For instance, if $a = 4$ and $b = 2$ and we swap a and b, we mean that, henceforth, $a = 2$ and $b = 4$. In the description of any sorting algorithm, we always assume that the elements to be sorted come from a totally ordered set, for example, the real numbers or the words of a language (with lexicographic ordering).

8.3.4 A BUBBLE SORT ALGORITHM

To sort n elements $a_1, a_2, \ldots, a_n$ from least to greatest,
   for $i = n - 1$ down to 1,
      for $j = 1$ to i
         if $a_j > a_{j+1}$, swap a_j and a_{j+1}.

The algorithm consists of a loop inside a loop. In the outer loop, we set $i = n-1$ and then execute the inner loop from $j = 1$ to $j = n - 1$. Then we drop i to $n - 2$ and execute the inner loop from $j = 1$ to $j = n - 2$, and so on, until $i = 1$, at which point the inner loop is executed just once, with $j = 1$. The Bubble Sort Algorithm is popular with beginning programmers because it is short and simple to implement in any language. Let us make sure we understand it.

EXAMPLE 23   For the input list

$$\begin{array}{cccc} 4 & 0 & 3 & 2 \\ a_1 & a_2 & a_3 & a_4 \end{array}$$

we have $n = 4$. The algorithm sets $i = n - 1 = 3$ and runs the inner loop from $j = 1$ to 3. With $j = 1$, we have $a_1 > a_2$, so a_1 and a_2 are swapped, giving the list

$$\begin{array}{cccc} 0 & 4 & 3 & 2 \\ a_1 & a_2 & a_3 & a_4. \end{array}$$

With $j = 2$, we have $a_2 > a_3$, so a_2 and a_3 are swapped, giving

$$\begin{array}{cccc} 0 & 3 & 4 & 2 \\ a_1 & a_2 & a_3 & a_4. \end{array}$$

With $j = 3$, we have $a_3 > a_4$, so a_3 and a_4 are swapped, giving

$$\begin{array}{cccc} 0 & 3 & 2 & 4 \\ a_1 & a_2 & a_3 & a_4. \end{array}$$

Having completed the inner loop, the algorithm returns to the outer, drops i to $i = 2$, and executes the inner loop from $j = 1$ to $j = 2$. With $j = 1$, the inequality $a_1 > a_2$ is not true, so there is no swap. With $j = 2$, we have $a_2 > a_3$, so a_2 and a_3 are swapped, giving

$$\begin{array}{cccc} 0 & 2 & 3 & 4 \\ a_1 & a_2 & a_3 & a_4. \end{array}$$

Again, the algorithm returns to the outer loop, drops i to $i = 1$ and executes the inner loop just for $j = 1$. Since $a_1 > a_2$ is false, there is no swap. The algorithm now terminates.

What is the complexity of a bubble sort? With $i = n - 1$, the inner loop is executed $n - 1$ times and there are $n - 1$ comparisons. With $i = n - 2$, there are $n - 2$ comparisons, and so on. With $i = 1$, just one comparison is required. In all, the number of comparisons is

$$\sum_{i=1}^{n-1}(n - i) = \sum_{i=1}^{n-1} i = \frac{n(n - 1)}{2}$$

so this algorithm is $\mathcal{O}(n^2)$. Note that here our estimate of complexity is not worst case, but best possible: In any bubble sort, all $\frac{1}{2}n(n - 1)$ comparisons must be made before the algorithm terminates.

Many sorting algorithms do better than the bubble sort. On the other hand, it is known that no sorting algorithm has worst-case complexity better than $\mathcal{O}(n \log n)$. With a view toward an eventual discussion of one $n \log n$ algorithm, we first introduce an algorithm for merging two sorted lists, an important task in its own right. Instructors with numerous examination booklets to put into alphabetical order have long since learned that speed can be improved by first dividing the booklets into smaller alphabetized groups and then merging the groups.

Our Merging Algorithm takes two ordered lists and produces a third ordered list comprised of the elements in the two given lists, in order.

EXAMPLE 24

Here is how our Merging Algorithm would sort the ordered lists

$$1, 3, 5, 7, 10, 11 \quad \text{and} \quad 2, 5, 6, 9.$$

We compare the first elements of each list. Since $1 \leq 2$, we start our third list with 1, removing 1 from the first list. This leaves us with

$$3, 5, 7, 10, 11 \qquad 2, 5, 6, 9 \qquad \text{and} \quad 1.$$

We compare the first elements of the first two lists. Since $2 \leq 3$, we place 2 after 1 in the third list and remove 2 from the second list. At this stage, we have the three lists

$$3, 5, 7, 10, 11 \qquad 5, 6, 9 \qquad \text{and} \quad 1, 2.$$

We continue to compare the first elements in the first two lists, appending the smaller to the third list while removing it from the list from which it came. If the first element in the first list equals the first element in the second, we append that element from the first list to the third (and remove it from the first). Here are the next six steps in our merge.

5, 7, 10, 11	5, 6, 9	1, 2, 3
7, 10, 11	5, 6, 9	1, 2, 3, 5
7, 10, 11	6, 9	1, 2, 3, 5, 5
7, 10, 11	9	1, 2, 3, 5, 5, 6
10, 11	9	1, 2, 3, 5, 5, 6, 7
10, 11		1, 2, 3, 5, 5, 6, 7, 9

At this stage the second list is empty, so we simply append the elements 10, 11 of the first list to the third, giving the final list 1, 2, 3, 5, 5, 6, 7, 9, 10, 11.

8.3.5 A MERGING ALGORITHM

To merge two given sorted lists

$$\mathcal{L}_1: a_1 \leq a_2 \leq \cdots \leq a_s \quad \text{and} \quad \mathcal{L}_2: b_1 \leq b_2 \leq \cdots \leq b_t,$$

of lengths s and t, into a single sorted list

$$\mathcal{L}_3: c_1 \leq c_2 \leq \cdots \leq c_{s+t}$$

of length $s + t$, proceed as follows.

Step 1. Set $\mathcal{L}_3$ equal to the empty list.

Step 2. If $\mathcal{L}_1$ is empty, set $\mathcal{L}_3 = \mathcal{L}_2$ and stop. If $\mathcal{L}_2$ is empty, set $\mathcal{L}_3 = \mathcal{L}_1$ and stop.

Step 3. Suppose $a_1 \leq b_1$. Then remove a_1 from $\mathcal{L}_1$ and append it to $\mathcal{L}_3$; if this empties $\mathcal{L}_1$, append the elements of $\mathcal{L}_2$ to $\mathcal{L}_3$ and stop. If $r > 0$ elements remain in $\mathcal{L}_1$, label them $a_1, a_2, \ldots, a_r$ in increasing order and repeat Step 3.

Suppose $a_1 > b_1$. Then remove b_1 from $\mathcal{L}_2$ and append it to $\mathcal{L}_3$; if this empties $\mathcal{L}_2$, append the elements of $\mathcal{L}_1$ to $\mathcal{L}_3$ and stop. If $r > 0$ elements remain in $\mathcal{L}_2$, label them $b_1, b_2, \ldots, b_r$ in increasing order and repeat Step 3.

EXAMPLE 25

We apply the Merging Algorithm to the lists

$$\mathcal{L}_1: \begin{matrix} 3 & 5 & 8 \\ a_1 & a_2 & a_3 \end{matrix} \quad \text{and} \quad \mathcal{L}_2: \begin{matrix} 1 & 7 & 8 \\ b_1 & b_2 & b_3 \end{matrix}.$$

Since neither list is empty, we proceed directly to Step 3. Since $3 = a_1 > b_1 = 1$, we append b_1 to the list $\mathcal{L}_3$, which was initially empty. Then we relabel the remaining elements 7 and 8 of $\mathcal{L}_2$ as b_1, b_2 respectively, so that our lists are

$$\mathcal{L}_1: \begin{matrix} 3 & 5 & 8 \\ a_1 & a_2 & a_3 \end{matrix} \qquad \mathcal{L}_2: \begin{matrix} 7 & 8 \\ b_1 & b_2 \end{matrix} \quad \text{and} \quad \mathcal{L}_3: \begin{matrix} 1 \\ c_1 \end{matrix}.$$

We then repeat Step 3. Since $a_1 \leq b_1$, we append $a_1 = 3$ to $\mathcal{L}_3$ and relabel the remaining elements 5 and 8 of $\mathcal{L}_1$ as a_1 and a_2, respectively. Our lists are now

$$\mathcal{L}_1: \begin{matrix} 5 & 8 \\ a_1 & a_2 \end{matrix} \quad \mathcal{L}_2: \begin{matrix} 7 & 8 \\ b_1 & b_2 \end{matrix} \quad \text{and} \quad \mathcal{L}_3: \begin{matrix} 1 & 3 \\ c_1 & c_2 \end{matrix}.$$

We repeat Step 3. Since $a_1 \leq b_1$, we append $a_1 = 5$ to $\mathcal{L}_3$ and relabel the elements of $\mathcal{L}_1$, obtaining

$$\mathcal{L}_1: \begin{matrix} 8 \\ a_1 \end{matrix} \quad \mathcal{L}_2: \begin{matrix} 7 & 8 \\ b_1 & b_2 \end{matrix} \quad \text{and} \quad \mathcal{L}_3: \begin{matrix} 1 & 3 & 5 \\ c_1 & c_2 & c_3 \end{matrix}.$$

After the next repetition of Step 3, we have

$$\mathcal{L}_1: \begin{matrix} 8 \\ a_1 \end{matrix} \quad \mathcal{L}_2: \begin{matrix} 8 \\ b_1 \end{matrix} \quad \text{and} \quad \mathcal{L}_3: \begin{matrix} 1 & 3 & 5 & 7 \\ c_1 & c_2 & c_3 & c_4 \end{matrix}.$$

Now, since $8 = a_1 \leq b_1 = 8$, we append a_1 to $\mathcal{L}_3$, giving

$$\mathcal{L}_1: \quad \mathcal{L}_2: \begin{matrix} 8 \\ b_1 \end{matrix} \quad \text{and} \quad \mathcal{L}_3: \begin{matrix} 1 & 3 & 5 & 7 & 8 \\ c_1 & c_2 & c_3 & c_4 & c_5 \end{matrix}.$$

Since $\mathcal{L}_1$ is now empty, we append 8, the remaining element of $\mathcal{L}_2$, to $\mathcal{L}_3$, producing the final merged list:

$$\mathcal{L}_3: \begin{matrix} 1 & 3 & 5 & 7 & 8 & 8 \\ c_1 & c_2 & c_3 & c_4 & c_5 & c_6 \end{matrix}.$$

How many comparisons does the Merging Algorithm require to merge ordered lists $\mathcal{L}_1$ and $\mathcal{L}_2$ of lengths s and t into a single ordered list $\mathcal{L}_3$ of length $s + t$? Notice that while elements remain in $\mathcal{L}_1$ and $\mathcal{L}_2$, each element goes into $\mathcal{L}_3$ after one comparison. Eventually, one list is empty and at least one element remains in the other; such remaining elements go to the end of $\mathcal{L}_3$ with no comparisons. It follows that, in all, at most $s + t - 1$ comparisons are needed.

PROBLEM 26. Find ordered lists of total length $s + t = 7$ that require exactly $7 - 1 = 6$ comparisons to merge.

Solution. The maximum number of comparisons, $s + t - 1$, occurs when just one number remains in one of the lists when the other is emptied. Here is such a situation.

$\mathcal{L}_1$	$\mathcal{L}_2$	$\mathcal{L}_3$	Comparisons Needed
1,3,5,7	2,4,6		
3,5,7	2,4,6	1	1
3,5,7	4,6	1,2	1
5,7	4,6	1,2,3	1
5,7	6	1,2,3,4	1
7	6	1,2,3,4,5	1
7		1,2,3,4,5,6	1
		1,2,3,4,5,6,7	0
		Total	6

Pause 4 Find ordered lists of total length 7 that require just three comparisons to merge. ∎

We are now able to describe an algorithm for sorting a list that is not only more efficient than the bubble sort, but, in fact, achieves the theoretical best possible worst-case complexity. Here is the idea.

EXAMPLE 27   Suppose we are given the list

$$7, 11, 5, 9, 11, 4, 10, 15, 17, 3, 9, 6, 21, 1$$

of length 14. We group the elements into seven pairs and order each pair. This gives us seven pairs of ordered lists.

$$7, 11; \quad 5, 9; \quad 4, 11; \quad 10, 15; \quad 3, 17; \quad 6, 9; \quad 1, 21.$$

Next, we merge the first two ordered lists, merge the third and fourth ordered lists, and merge the fifth and sixth. The last ordered list, 1, 21, is unchanged.

$$5, 7, 9, 11; \quad 4, 10, 11, 15; \quad 3, 6, 9, 17; \quad 1, 21.$$

At this point, we have four ordered lists. We merge the first two and the last two, giving

$$4, 5, 7, 9, 10, 11, 11, 15; \qquad 1, 3, 6, 9, 17, 21.$$

Finally, we merge the two lists that remain, obtaining the final ordered list

$$1, 3, 4, 5, 6, 7, 9, 9, 10, 11, 11, 15, 17, 21.$$

In this example, it is useful to think of the given list as 14 ordered lists, each of length 1. After the first step, we were left with seven ordered lists of length 2; after the second, with four ordered lists; after the third, with two ordered lists, and after the fourth, with the desired single ordered list. Since the number of ordered lists is essentially halved at each stage, in general k steps will be needed to sort a list of n elements, where $2^{k-1} < n \leq 2^k$. For example, $2^3 < 14 \leq 2^4$, so four steps are required to sort a list of length 14.

Here is a general description of our Merge Sort Algorithm.

8.3.6 A MERGE SORT ALGORITHM

To sort a list $a_1, a_2, \ldots, a_n$ into increasing order, proceed as follows.

Step 1. set $F = 0$.

Step 2. for $i = 1$ to n, let the list $\mathcal{L}_i$ be the single element a_i.

Step 3. while $F = 0$
        if $n = 1$, set $F = 1$ and output $\mathcal{L}_1$;
        if $n = 2m$ is even
           for $i = 1$ to m
             • merge the sorted lists $\mathcal{L}_{2i-1}$ and $\mathcal{L}_{2i}$
              and label the resulting sorted list $\mathcal{L}_i$;
         set $n = m$.
        if $n = 2m + 1 > 1$ is odd
           for $i = 1$ to m
             • merge the sorted lists $\mathcal{L}_{2i-1}$ and $\mathcal{L}_{2i}$
              and label the resulting sorted list $\mathcal{L}_i$;
             • set $\mathcal{L}_{m+1} = \mathcal{L}_n$;
         set $n = m + 1$.
      end while

The variable F in our algorithm is called a *flag*, a useful parameter to introduce in an algorithm to enable fast termination of a loop. Here, it enables us to exit the while loop as soon as the merging is complete.

PROBLEM 28. What would the merge sort algorithm do with the list

$$2 \quad 9 \quad 1 \quad 4 \quad 6 \quad 5 \quad 3$$
$$a_1 \quad a_2 \quad a_3 \quad a_4 \quad a_5 \quad a_6 \quad a_7$$

?

Solution. Initially, $F = 0$ and lists $\mathcal{L}_1, \mathcal{L}_2, \ldots, \mathcal{L}_7$ are defined, each of length 1.

$$\mathcal{L}_1: 2 \quad \mathcal{L}_2: 9 \quad \mathcal{L}_3: 1 \quad \mathcal{L}_4: 4 \quad \mathcal{L}_5: 6 \quad \mathcal{L}_6: 5 \quad \mathcal{L}_7: 3.$$

At Step 3, since $F = 0$ and $n = 2(3) + 1$ is odd ($m = 3$), we form four new lists $\mathcal{L}_1, \mathcal{L}_2, \mathcal{L}_3, \mathcal{L}_4$ by merging the first six former lists in pairs into three and adding the seventh. We now have

$$\mathcal{L}_1: 2, 9 \quad \mathcal{L}_2: 1, 4 \quad \mathcal{L}_3: 5, 6 \quad \mathcal{L}_4: 3.$$

At this point, n is replaced by $m + 1 = 3 + 1 = 4$ and we repeat Step 3. Since $n = 2(2)$ is even ($m = 2$), we form two lists $\mathcal{L}_1$ and $\mathcal{L}_2$ by merging the former lists $\mathcal{L}_1, \mathcal{L}_2$ and $\mathcal{L}_3, \mathcal{L}_4$, respectively. At this point we have

$$\mathcal{L}_1: 1, 2, 4, 9 \quad \mathcal{L}_2: 3, 5, 6.$$

Now n is replaced by $m = 2$ and we repeat Step 3. Since $n = 2(1)$ is even ($m = 1$), the list $\mathcal{L}_1$ is formed by merging the former $\mathcal{L}_1$ and $\mathcal{L}_2$.

$$\mathcal{L}_1: 1, 2, 3, 4, 5, 6, 9$$

At this point, n is replaced by $m = 1$ and we repeat Step 3. Since $n = 1$, we set $F = 1$, output $\mathcal{L}_1$, the desired sorted list, and stop.

What is the complexity of the Merge Sort Algorithm in terms of the number of comparisons required? As with binary search, it is helpful first to consider the case that the given list has length $n = 2^k$ because then Step 3 is executed exactly k times. Also, we enter Step 3 each time with an even number of lists and exit with an even number, until the last step.

Let us first ignore the, at most, two comparisons required to decide if $n = 1$, $n = 2m$, or $n = 2m + 1 > 1$ each time Step 3 is executed and just count comparisons required by the merging. Initially, we enter Step 3 with 2^k lists, each of length 1, which are merged in pairs. Each merge requires one comparison, for a total of $2^{k-1} = 2^k - 2^{k-1}$ comparisons altogether. We pass through Step 3 a second time, entering with 2^{k-1} lists of length 2, which are merged in pairs. Each pair is merged with at most $2 + 2 - 1 = 4 - 1$ comparisons, for a total of $2^{k-2}(4 - 1) = 2^k - 2^{k-2}$. The third time we execute Step 3, we enter with 2^{k-2} lists of length 4, which are merged in pairs. Each pair is merged with at most $4 + 4 - 1 = 8 - 1$ comparisons, for a total of $2^{k-3}(8 - 1) = 2^k - 2^{k-3}$. Continuing this line of reasoning, we see that pass i through Step 3 requires at most $2^k - 2^{k-i}$ comparisons for the merging. The kth and final pass requires $2^{k-1} + 2^{k-1} - 1 = 2^k - 1$ comparisons, the result of merging two lists, each of length 2^{k-1}.

In total, the merging in the algorithm requires at most

$$(1) \qquad (2^k - 2^{k-1}) + (2^k - 2^{k-2}) + \cdots + (2^k - 4) + (2^k - 2) + (2^k - 1)$$

comparisons. There are k terms here. Since $1 + 2 + 4 + \cdots + 2^{k-1} = 2^k - 1$ (see PAUSE 5), the sum in equation (1) equals $k2^k - (2^k - 1) = k2^k - 2^k + 1$. In addition, two comparisons are required each time the while loop is executed to decide whether $2^k = 1$, $2^k = 2m$, or $2^k = 2m + 1 > 1$. In including the comparison "$F = 0$?" the algorithm requires at most $3k + (k2^k - 2^k + 1) = k2^k - 2^k + 3k + 1$ comparisons.

In general, for a list of n elements, find k such that $2^{k-1} < n \le 2^k$. By extending the list to one of length 2^k (for example, by appending additional elements larger than any number in the list), we see that the given list can be sorted by sorting the larger list and then removing the additional large elements from the end of the list. By the preceding analysis, it follows that the given list can be sorted with at most $k2^k - 2^k + 3k + 1$ comparisons. Since $2^{k-1} < n$, $k < 1 + \log_2 n$ and $2^k < 2n$. So the number of comparisons is at most

$$k2^k - 2^k + 3k + 1 \leq (1 + \log_2 n)2^k - 2^k + 3(1 + \log_2 n) + 1$$
$$= 2^k \log_2 n + 3(1 + \log_2 n) + 1$$
$$< 2n \log_2 n + 3 \log_2 n + 4 \asymp n \log_2 n.$$

Thus, the number of comparisons is $\mathcal{O}(n \log n)$. Referring to Table 8.5, we note that this is a substantial improvement on $\mathcal{O}(n^2)$, the complexity of the bubble sort.

Pause 5　Explain why $1 + 2 + 4 + \cdots + 2^{k-1} = 2^k - 1$.　∎

Answers to Pauses

3. Since $n = 10 \neq 1$, the algorithm sets $m = \lfloor \frac{10}{2} \rfloor = 5$. Since $x = 13 > a_5$, the algorithm replaces n by $n - m = 5$ and changes the list to 12, 15, 17, 19, 20.

Since $n \neq 1$, the algorithm sets $m = \lfloor \frac{5}{2} \rfloor = 2$. Since $x = 13 \leq a_2 = 15$, the algorithm sets $n = m = 2$ and changes the list to 12, 15.

Since $n \neq 1$, the algorithm sets $m = \lfloor \frac{2}{2} \rfloor = 1$. Since $x = 13 > a_1 = 12$, the algorithm replaces n with $n - m = 1$ and changes the list to 15.

Since $n = 1$ and $x \neq a_1$, the algorithm outputs "false," sets $n = 0$, and stops.

4. We want ordered lists with the property that after three comparisons one is empty. Here is an example:

$\mathcal{L}_1$	$\mathcal{L}_2$	$\mathcal{L}_3$	Comparisons Needed
1,3	2,4,6,8,9		
3	2,4,6,8,9	1	1
3	4,6,8,9	1,2	1
	4,6,8,9	1,2,3	1
		1,2,3,4,6,8,9	0
		Total	3

5. The terms in this sum are those of a geometric sequence with $a = 1$, $r = 2$, $n = k$. The sum is $\frac{a(1-r^n)}{1-r}$. [See formula (8) on p. 163.]

True/False Questions

(Answers can be found in the back of the book.)

1. If the list 2, 5, 4, 1 is searched for $x = 4$ using the Linear Search Algorithm, the output is "true" and the final value of i is 3.

2. If the list 2, 5, 4, 1 is searched for $x = 4$ using the Binary Search Algorithm, the output is "true" and the final value of n is 0.

3. Binary Search Algorithm 8.3.3 is more efficient than the Linear Search Algorithm 8.3.1.

4. Merge Sort Algorithm 8.3.6 is more efficient than the Bubble Sort Algorithm 8.3.4.

5. If the list 2, 5, 4, 1 is sorted using the Bubble Sort Algorithm, the first time the list changes it becomes 2, 5, 1, 4.

6. If the list 2, 5, 4, 1 is sorted using the Bubble Sort Algorithm, the first time the list changes it becomes 2, 4, 5, 1.

7. If the lists $\mathcal{L}_1 : 2, 5$ and $\mathcal{L}_2 : 1, 4$ are merged using the Merging Algorithm, the first step is to define a new list $\mathcal{L}_3$ containing no elements.

8. If the list $2, 5, 4, 1$ is sorted using the Merge Sort Algorithm, the final value of F is 0.

9. $1 + 2 + 4 + \cdots + 2^{11} = 2^{12} - 1$ (see PAUSE 5).

10. The median of the numbers $1, 2, 3, 4, 5, 6, 7, 8$ is 5. (See Exercise 16.)

Exercises

*The answers to exercises marked [BB] can be found in the **B**ack of the **B**ook.*

1. (a) [BB] Show the sequence of steps in a binary search to find $x = 2$ in the list $1, 2, 3, 4, 5, 6, 7, 8, 9$. How many times is x compared with an element in the list? How many times would it be compared with an element in the list if we employed a linear search?

   (b) Repeat (a) with $x = 7$.

   (c) Repeat (a) with $x = 10$.

2. (a) Show the sequence of steps in a binary search to find $x = 7$ in the list $3, 5, 7, 10, 12, 15, 17, 22, 24, 30, 31$. How many times is x compared with an element in the list? How many times would it be compared with an element in the list if we employed a linear search?

   (b) Repeat (a) with $x = 30$.

   (c) Repeat (a) with $x = 16$.

3. (a) Describe a *ternary search* algorithm, which searches an ordered list for a given element by successively dividing the list into thirds and determining in which third the element must lie.

   (b) Show that the complexity of the algorithm found in (a) (in terms of comparisons) is $\mathcal{O}(\log_3 n)$.

4. Answer Exercise 1 using a ternary, rather than a binary, search.

5. Answer Exercise 2 using a ternary, rather than a binary, search.

6. (a) [BB] Describe an algorithm that, upon input of k numbers, each in the range 1–100 (inclusive), outputs the complement of this set with respect to $U = \{1, 2, \ldots, 100\}$.

   (b) Repeat (a) if 100 is replaced by n. Find a Big Oh estimate for the complexity of your algorithm in terms of comparisons.

7. [BB] Show the sequence of steps involved in merging the sorted lists $1, 2, 3, 4, 5$ and $2, 4, 6, 8, 10$. How many comparisons are required?

8. Show the sequence of steps involved in merging the sorted lists $2, 4, 4, 6, 8$ and $1, 5, 7, 9, 10$. How many comparisons are required?

9. Show the sequence of steps involved in merging the sorted lists $2, 4, 7, 7, 9, 11$ and $1, 4, 9, 12$. How many comparisons are required?

10. [BB] Find an example of two ordered lists of lengths s and $t \geq 3$ that can be merged with

(a) one comparison;

(b) t comparisons;

(c) exactly $s + t - 1$ comparisons. (For this part, assume also that $s \geq 3$.)

11. Find two ordered lists that require precisely four comparisons to merge.

12. Rewrite the Merging Algorithm using a flag to prevent the program from exiting during Step 1.

13. [BB] Sort the list $3, 1, 7, 2, 5, 4$ into increasing order

    (a) with a bubble sort;

    (b) with a merge sort.

    In each case, how many comparisons are needed? (For the merge sort, ignore comparisons required to check the size and parity of n at each iteration of Step 3.)

14. Repeat Exercise 13 for the list $7, 2, 2, 5, 3, 5, 4$.

15. Repeat Exercise 13 for the list $10, 11, 15, 3, 18, 14, 7, 1$.

16. [BB] The *median* of a list of n numbers is the middle number if n is odd or the average of the two middle numbers (if n is even) after the numbers have been listed from smallest to largest. Describe an algorithm for finding the median of an input list of n numbers. Find a Big Oh estimate of the complexity of your algorithm.

17. Suppose that the eight elements a, b, c, d, u, v, w, x are ordered

$$d < a < u < c < x < b < v < w.$$

(a) [BB] Show the steps in a bubble sort applied to the list a, b, c, d, u, v, w, x. How many comparisons are required?

(b) Repeat (a) using a merge sort.

18. (a) [BB] Show the steps involved in the application of a bubble sort to the list c, a, e, b, d, where these letters have their natural alphabetical order.

(b) Apply the same sequence of interchanges as required in part (a) to the list $1, 2, 3, 4, 5$; that is, if it is necessary to interchange the second and third elements at a certain stage in the bubble sort of (a), then interchange the second and third elements at the same stage in the "sort" of $1, 2, 3, 4, 5$. The final sequence is $2, 4, 1, 5, 3$, which describes the **order** in which the elements of c, a, e, b, d must be taken to list them in order.

(c) Describe an algorithm whose input is a list a_1, a_2, ..., a_n whose natural order is a_{i_1}, a_{i_2}, ..., a_{i_n} and whose output is the sequence of indexes i_1, i_2, ..., i_n (in this order).

19. We explained in the text why the Merging Algorithm requires at most $s + t - 1$ comparisons to merge ordered lists of lengths s and t. For arbitrary s and t, do there exist ordered lists of these lengths for which precisely $s + t - 1$ comparisons are needed to merge? Explain.

20. The Binary Search Algorithm we have presented appears to be more efficient than a linear search, $\mathcal{O}(\log n)$ versus $\mathcal{O}(n)$, but the binary search assumes the input list is ordered. Suppose we modify the Binary Search Algorithm so that it accepts an unordered list as input, uses an efficient sorting algorithm and then applies a binary search described in this section. Is this new algorithm still more efficient than a linear search? Explain.

21. [BB] What is the fewest number of comparisons required to merge ordered lists of lengths s and t? Explain your answer.

22. Ignoring repeated checks as to whether $n = 1$, $n = 2\ell$, or $n = 2\ell + 1 > 1$, we showed in the text that the number of comparisons in any merge sort of 2^k elements is at most $k2^k - 2^k + 1$. Give a specific example of a list of length 2^k, where precisely $k2^k - 2^k + 1$ comparisons are required.

23. [BB] To output the distinct items of a given list a_1, a_2, ..., a_n, the following method is proposed. For each k, search the elements preceding a_k and, if a_k is not found, output a_k. Show that this algorithm can be accomplished with $\mathcal{O}(\log n!)$ comparisons.

24. Modify the Bubble Sort Algorithm to find an algorithm that reverses a sequence; that is, upon input of a_1, a_2, ..., a_n, the algorithm outputs the sequence a_n, a_{n-1}, ..., a_2, a_1. How many swaps are required? Give a Big Oh estimate of complexity.

25. [BB] It is suggested that one way of searching for a number x in a given unordered list is first to sort the list using a merge sort and then to use a binary search algorithm. Is this more or less efficient than a linear search?

26. Given a list a_1, a_2, ..., a_n, each item of which is 0 or 1, it is desired to put the list into increasing order. Would you use one of the sorting methods discussed in this section, or is there a better method? Explain.

8.4   Enumeration of Permutations and Combinations

A truck driver for Deluxe Bakery has to deliver bread to many supermarkets scattered throughout a large metropolitan area. She has a map showing the precise locations of her delivery points. She knows how long it takes to drive from the bakery to each point and how long it takes to drive between any two delivery points. In what order should she deliver bread to minimize total traveling time? This problem, known as the *Traveling Salesman's Problem*, will be encountered again. Here, it serves to illustrate a situation where we would like to enumerate permutations. Assigning the supermarkets the numbers $1, 2, \ldots, n$, the truck driver ideally would like to list all the permutations of $1, 2, \ldots, n$ and, for each permutation, determine the time required for the route that visits supermarkets in the specified order.

To list all the permutations of a set of two or three or even four elements is not difficult. To enumerate all the permutations of larger sets becomes first tedious, and then ridiculous, at least by hand, because $n!$ grows so very rapidly with n: For instance, 15! is roughly 10^{12}. (See 5.1.3 and the paragraph that follows.)

To list all permutations of ten elements, say, it would seem sensible to enlist the support of a computer. For this, of course, a suitable algorithm is required, an algorithm that upon input of a positive integer n, outputs a complete list of all the permutations of $1, 2, \ldots, n$ without omission or repetition. We are confronted with two problems.

- How should the permutations be ordered?
- Given a permutation, how is the next one determined?

Lexicographic order (the way words are ordered in a dictionary) is one way to order permutations. In a dictionary, *terrible* precedes *terrific* because, reading from left to right, the first place where the words differ is at the sixth letter, and there b precedes f in the natural ordering of the letters of the alphabet. So we list the permutation *beadc* before *bedca*, but after *bcaed*. In a similar way, if the symbols are numbers instead of letters, 1357264 precedes 1357624, but follows 1347256.

With respect to lexicographic ordering, there is a procedure for finding the permutation that follows any given permutation.

8.4.1 PROPOSITION   When the permutations of $1, 2, \ldots, n$ are ordered lexicographically, the permutation that follows a particular permutation π is obtained by

- reading the digits in π from right to left,
- noting the first pair xy of consecutive digits where $x < y$,
- replacing x by the smallest of those digits to its right that are larger than x, and then
- writing down in increasing order the digits not yet used.

EXAMPLE 29   The permutation following 1374652 is 1375246 because, reading from right to left, the first consecutive pair xy with $x < y$ is 46, so we replace 4 by 5, the smallest digit to its right that is larger than 4, giving an initial string 1375, which is completed by writing down the unused digits, 2, 4, and 6, in increasing order.   ▧

EXAMPLE 30   The permutations of 1, 2, 3, 4 in lexicographic order are

$$
\begin{array}{cccccccc}
1234 & 1243 & 1324 & 1342 & 1423 & 1432 & 2134 & 2143 \\
2314 & 2341 & 2413 & 2431 & 3124 & 3142 & 3214 & 3241 \\
3412 & 3421 & 4123 & 4132 & 4213 & 4231 & 4312 & 4321.
\end{array}
$$ ▧

To enumerate all permutations of $1, 2, \ldots, n$, the following algorithm can be used.

8.4.2 ALGORITHM FOR ENUMERATING PERMUTATIONS   Given a natural number n, to enumerate the $n!$ permutations of $1, 2, \ldots, n$, proceed as follows.

Step 1. Set $t = 1$. Output Perm$(1) = 123 \ldots n$. If $n = 1$, stop.

Step 2. For $t = 1$ to $n! - 1$, given permutation Perm$(t) = \pi_1 \pi_2 \ldots \pi_n$, determine the next permutation Perm$(t + 1)$ as follows:

- find the largest j such that $\pi_j < \pi_{j+1}$;
- set $m = \min\{\pi_i \mid i > j, \pi_i > \pi_j\}$;
- set $S = \{1, 2, \ldots, n\} \setminus \{\pi_1, \ldots, \pi_{j-1}, m\}$;
- sort the elements of S in increasing order, $b_1 < b_2 < \ldots < b_{n-j}$;
- output Perm$(t + 1) = \pi_1 \ldots \pi_{j-1} m b_1 \ldots b_{n-j}$.   ⬦

With $n = 3$, for example, the permutations of 1, 2, 3 are generated as shown in Table 8.6.

Any algorithm that involves $n!$ steps will take a long time to run, even for relatively small n. For example, at 1 million operations per second, 12! operations require almost 8 minutes. In Exercise 3, we ask you to show that the algorithm just described can be implemented with complexity $\mathcal{O}(n!n)$.

Deluxe Bakery is considering the introduction of bagels to its traditional product lines of bread and pastries and decides to select six of the supermarkets that carry its products for a trial. Toward this effort, it would be helpful for the marketing manager to review a list of all possible choices in order to choose six that have lots of customers. What is required then is a listing of all combinations of supermarkets taken six at a time.

As with permutations, combinations will be listed lexicographically; however, this time we must be careful to avoid listing both 142897 and 218479, for instance, since these represent the same combination. Suppose we agree to list elements

Table 8.6 The permutations of 1, 2, 3 as generated by Algorithm 8.4.2.

t	Perm(t)	j	m	S
1	1 2 3 $\pi_1\pi_2\pi_3$	2	3	$\{\pi_1, m\}^c = \{1, 3\}^c = \{2\}$
2	1 3 2 $\pi_1\pi_2\pi_3$	1	2	$\{m\}^c = \{2\}^c = \{1, 3\}$
3	2 1 3 $\pi_1\pi_2\pi_3$	2	3	$\{\pi_1, m\}^c = \{2, 3\}^c = \{1\}$
4	2 3 1 $\pi_1\pi_2\pi_3$	1	3	$\{m\}^c = \{3\}^c = \{1, 2\}$
5	3 1 2 $\pi_1\pi_2\pi_3$	2	2	$\{\pi_1, m\}^c = \{3, 2\}^c = \{1\}$
6	3 2 1			

in their natural (increasing) order so that, rather than 142897 or 218479, we will write 124789. Imagine that the combination $uvwxyz$ appears in our list. Then $u < v < w < x < y < z$ and so, if these symbols come from $\{1, 2, \ldots, 72\}$, it is apparent, for instance, that y cannot be 72 and x can be neither 71 nor 72. The largest possible value for z is 72, the largest for y is 71, the largest for x is 70, the largest for w is 69, the largest for v is 68, and the largest value for u is 67. Also, the smallest combination is 123456.

When the combinations of $1, 2, \ldots, n$ taken r at a time are ordered lexicographically, the first combination is $123\ldots r$, and the combination that immediately follows a given one is obtained by

- reading the combination from right to left until the first digit that can be increased is found,
- adding 1 to this number (suppose this digit is now k),
- leaving the digits before k as they were, but following k by $k + 1, k + 2, \ldots$ and so on, until r digits in all have been written down.

In the lexicographic ordering of the combinations $1, 2, \ldots, 9$ taken six at a time, what combination follows 134589? Reading from right to left, the first digit that can be increased is 5. Increase this to 6 (so that the combination begins 1346), and complete the combination with 78, giving 134678. What follows 236789? The first digit that can be increased is 3. Increase this to 4 (the next combination begins 24), and complete with 5678, giving 245678.

In the lexicographic ordering of the combinations of 1, 2, 3, 4, 5, 6 taken four at a time, after 1346 come 1356, 1456, 2345, 2346, 2356, and so on. The combinations of 1, 2, 3, 4, 5 taken three at a time are

123, 124, 125, 134, 135, 145, 234, 235, 245, 345.

(Answers can be found in the back of the book.)

1. The Traveling Salesman's Problem is mentioned in this section.
2. Lexicographic order is the way words are ordered in a dictionary.
3. In lexicographic order, the permutation following 152364 is 152634.
4. In lexicographic order, the permutation following 123456 is 123465.
5. In lexicographic order, the permutation following 654321 is 654312.
6. A listing of all permutations of 1, 2, 3, 4, 5, 6 in lexicographic order would contain 720 entries.
7. The algorithm for enumerating permutations takes only a very short time to run.
8. In the lexicographic ordering of the digits $1, 2, \ldots, 9$, taken 6 at a time, the combination following 123569 is 123579.
9. In the lexicographic ordering of the digits $1, 2, \ldots, 9$, taken 6 at a time, the combination following 123456 is 234567.
10. A listing of all combinations of 1, 2, 3, 4, 5, 6, 7, 8, 9 taken six at a time would contain $\binom{9}{6}$ entries.

*The answers to exercises marked [BB] can be found in the **B**ack of the **B**ook.*

1. (a) [BB] With a table like Table 8.6, show the steps involved in the enumeration of the first eight permutations of 1, 2, 3, 4.
   (b) Repeat (a) for the second eight permutations of 1, 2, 3, 4.
   (c) Repeat (a) for the last eight permutations of 1, 2, 3, 4.

2. (a) Use the procedure outlined in this section to list the first 20 permutations of 1, 2, 3, 4, 5.
   (b) [BB] In the lexicographic ordering of the permutations of 1, 2, 3, 4, 5, what five permutations come after 42513?
   (c) In the lexicographic ordering of the permutations of 1, 2, 3, 4, 5, what five permutations precede 42513?

3. (a) [BB] Show that the complexity of Algorithm 8.4.2 for enumerating permutations is $\mathcal{O}(n!n \log n)$ in terms of comparisons.
   (b) Improve the estimate in (a) by showing how to achieve $\mathcal{O}(n!n)$.

4. Let $\pi' = \text{Perm}(t + 1)$ be the permutation derived from $\text{Perm}(t) = \pi$ as in Proposition 8.4.1.
   (a) Prove that $\pi \prec \pi'$, where $\prec$ means precedes in lexicographic order.
   (b) Prove that if σ is a permutation satisfying $\pi \preceq \sigma \prec \pi'$ then $\sigma = \pi$. Thus, π' is the immediate successor of π relative to lexicographic ordering of permutations. (Here $\pi \preceq \sigma$ means $\pi \prec \sigma$ or $\pi = \sigma$.)

5. List, in lexicographic order, all combinations of 1, 2, 3, 4, 5, 6
   (a) [BB] taken four elements at a time;
   (b) taken three elements at a time.

6. In the lexicographic ordering of all combinations of $1, 2, \ldots, 9$ taken five at a time, list, if possible, the three combinations that immediately precede and the three that immediately follow
   (a) [BB] 23469   (b) 13567   (c) 45789

7. (a) List, in lexicographic order, the combinations of 1, 2, 3, 4, 5, 6, 7 taken two at a time.
   (b) [BB] Use Proposition 8.4.3 and Algorithm 8.4.2 to describe an algorithm for enumerating the permutations of $1, 2, \ldots, n$ taken r at a time, not necessarily in lexicographic order.
   (c) Use parts (a) and (b) to list all permutations of 1, 2, 3, 4, 5, 6, 7 taken two at a time.

8. (a) [BB] List, in lexicographic order, all combinations of $1, 2, \ldots, 8$ taken six elements at a time.
   (b) List, in lexicographic order, the first ten and the last ten combinations of $1, 2, \ldots, 8$ taken three at a time.
   (c) Use the list in (b) and the method proposed in Exercise 7(b) to enumerate the first ten and the last ten permutations of $1, 2, \ldots, 8$ taken three at a time.

9. [BB] Prove Proposition 8.4.3.

10. [BB] Suppose $a_1 a_2 a_3 \ldots a_r$ appears in the lexicographic ordering of the combinations of the integers $1, 2, 3, \ldots, n$ taken r at a time, where $a_1 < a_2 < a_3 < \cdots < a_r$.
    (a) What is the biggest possible value for a_r? For a_1? For a_j?
    (b) Under what conditions is this the first combination in the list?

(c) When is it the last?

11. [BB] Describe an algorithm that enumerates all combinations of $1, 2, \ldots, n$ taken r at a time.

12. Suppose a set S has kn elements for natural numbers k and n. Describe an algorithm that will output all k element subsets of S.

Key Terms & Ideas

Here are some technical words and phrases that were used in this chapter. Do you know the meaning of each? If you're not sure, check the glossary or index at the back of the book.

algorithm

Big Oh

same order (functions)

smaller order (functions)

Review Exercises for Chapter 8

1. Describe how Horner's Algorithm evaluates $f(x)$ when
   (a) $f(x) = 2x^3 - 4x + 1$ and $x = -3$,
   (b) $f(x) = x^4 - 2x^3 + x^2 - 5x + 6$ and $x = 2$.

2. Use the Russian peasant method to find
   (a) 149×712,   (b) 1018×72.

3. Let $n > 1$ be an integer, let $S = \{1, 2, \ldots, n\}$, and let $\mathcal{R} = \{(a_1, b_1), (a_2, b_2), \ldots, (a_t, b_t)\}$ be a subset of $S \times S$. Describe algorithms that determine whether the relation $\mathcal{R}$ is
   (a) reflexive;   (b) symmetric;
   (c) antisymmetric;   (d) transitive;
   (e) a function.
   In each case, find a reasonable estimate of the complexity of your algorithm.

4. Suppose we want an algorithm that, for an input of integers $a_1, a_2, \ldots, a_n$, outputs the largest and second largest of these. It is proposed to sort the list in decreasing order and to output the first two integers of the sorted list.
   (a) In terms of comparisons, what is the best complexity function for this algorithm?
   (b) Is there a better way to proceed? Explain and, if the answer is yes, describe a better algorithm.

5. Describe an algorithm that upon input of a list $a_1, a_2, \ldots, a_n$ of integers, outputs the largest and the smallest numbers of the list.

6. Describe an algorithm that implements the floor function; that is, upon input of a real number x, the output is $\lfloor x \rfloor$.

7. (a) Show that $1^k + 2^k + \cdots + n^k = \mathcal{O}(n^{k+1})$ for any $k \geq 1$.
   (b) Show that $1^2 + 2^2 + \cdots + n^2 \asymp n^3$.

8. (a) Show that $3n^3 - 5n^2 + 2n + 1 \asymp n^3$,

   (b) Show that $n^4 - 2n^3 + 3n^2 - 5n + 7 \asymp n^4$.
   Do not merely quote Proposition 8.2.7, but you may use ideas from its proof.

9. (a) (Requires a little knowledge of calculus) Show that $1 + \frac{1}{2} + \frac{1}{3} + \cdots + \frac{1}{n} = \mathcal{O}(\log n)$.
   (b) Show that the Sieve of Eratosthenes, used to find all primes less than or equal to a given integer n, can be implemented with an algorithm that is $\mathcal{O}(n \log n)$. Count comparisons and crossing out an integer as basic operations. (See Section 4.3 and especially paragraph 4.3.5.)

10. Show the sequence of steps in using a binary search to find the number 5 in the list $-8, -5, -1, 0, 1, 2, 4, 5, 8, 9, 12$. How many times is 5 compared with an element in the list? How many times would it be compared with an element in the list if we employed a linear search?

11. Show the sequence of steps involved in merging the sorted lists $-1, 3, 7, 10, 12, 15$ and $-4, -3, -1, 2$. How many comparisons are required?

12. Sort the list $9, -3, 1, 0, -4, 5, 3$ into increasing order
    (a) with a bubble sort;   (b) with a merge sort.
    In each case, how many comparisons are needed? (For the merge sort, ignore comparisons required to check the size and parity of n at each iteration of Step 3.)

13. In the lexicographic ordering of the permutations of $1, 2, 3, 4, 5, 6$, list the 20 permutations that follow 463152.

14. In the lexicographic ordering of all combinations of $1, 2, \ldots, 7$ taken four at a time, list, if possible, the three combinations that immediately precede and the three that immediately follow
    (a) 3467,   (b) 1236,   (c) 2347.

9

Graphs

Many concrete, practical problems can be simplified and solved by looking at them from different points of view. The Königsberg Bridge Problem, which we will soon describe, was a long-standing problem until it was imaginatively solved in 1736 by the great Swiss mathematician Léonhard Euler (1707–1783). Beginning his scientific career shortly after the death of Sir Isaac Newton, Euler spent the last 17 years of his life blind, but still very active. Some of his mathematical contributions were to the theory of convergent sequences and to the calculus of variations. Much of what is taught today about quadratic equations, conic sections, and quadrics in Euclidean space is just as Euler himself laid out. Perhaps less known is that Euler was a superb designer of algorithms; he had the uncanny ability to make order out of chaos, to see simple routes through the most complicated situations. It is because of his imaginative solution to the Königsberg Bridge Problem that Euler is generally considered to be the father of modern-day graph theory.

In the eighteenth century, Königsberg was the capital of East Prussia.[1] The Pregel River flowed through town and split into two branches around Kneiphof island, which is labeled *A* in Fig. 9.1. Seven bridges crossed the river, providing links among the four land masses labeled *A*, *B*, *C*, *D* in the figure. People wondered if it were possible to start on one of the land masses, walk over each of the seven bridges exactly once, and return to the starting point (without getting wet).

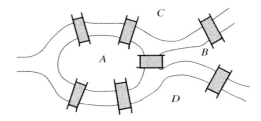

Figure 9.1 The bridges of Königsberg.

---

[1]An ice-free port on the southern coast of the Baltic Sea, Königsberg was completely destroyed during World War II. It was renamed Kaliningrad and transferred to the Soviet Union in 1945. Today, it is the westernmost city in Russia.

To find an abstract mathematical model of a concrete problem can be a difficult task requiring both ingenuity and experience. The primary aim of this chapter is to provide the reader with some of this experience by presenting several real-world problems and showing how they can be formulated in mathematical terms. This process of translation into mathematics forces us to sift through all the details of the problem, deciding which ones are important and which are extraneous. (Those aspects of a "real" problem that make it interesting are sometimes irrelevant and serve primarily to create confusion!) Because the language of mathematics is precise and unambiguous, problems that seem complicated when expressed in ordinary language often have surprisingly straightforward mathematical translations.

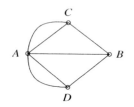

Figure 9.2 A graphical representation of the Königsberg Bridge Problem.

For the Königsberg Bridge Problem, Euler's idea was to realize that the physical layout of land, water, and bridges could be modeled by the graph shown in Fig. 9.2. The land masses are represented by small circles (or vertices) and the bridges by lines (or edges), which can be straight or curved. By means of this graph, the physical problem is transformed into this mathematical one: Given the graph in Fig. 9.2, is it possible to choose a vertex, then to proceed along the edges one after the other and return to the chosen vertex, covering every edge exactly once? Euler was able to show that this was not possible. Can you? (We shall return to this problem and discuss its solution in Section 10.1, in the context of Eulerian circuits.)

The Three Houses–Three Utilities Problem is another physical situation that can be modeled by means of a graph. There are three houses, each of which is to be connected to each of three utilities (water, electricity, and telephone) by means of underground pipes. Is it possible to make these connections without any crossovers? Figure 9.3 shows how to describe this problem with a graph.

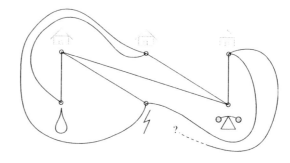

Figure 9.3 The Three Houses–Three Utilities Problem.

The houses and the utilities are represented by vertices and the pipes are the lines drawn between the vertices. When we discuss planar graphs in Chapter 13, we shall see that the answer to our question is no. Can you convince yourself of this now?

Figure 9.4 A way to picture a cube.

For a long time, there has been on the market a popular game called Instant Insanity, which consists of four cubes, each of whose six faces is colored with one of four colors: red, blue, green, white. The object is to stack the cubes in such a way that each of the four colors appears on each side of the resulting column. Since there are over 40,000 possible ways to stack such cubes,[2] it is easy to understand how this game got its name! Certainly, there ought to be a better way to solve this puzzle than trial and error. To illustrate the method we have in mind, we first need a way to picture a three-dimensional cube on paper. We do so as indicated in Fig. 9.4, where we imagine that the cube has been opened and flattened, as if it were a small cardboard box.

[2] The exact number is $\frac{1}{2}(6^4 \times 4^3) = 41{,}472$.

   In Fig. 9.5, we depict the four cubes of one version of Instant Insanity in this way and show a graph that records the pertinent information about them. The graph has four vertices, labeled R, B, G, and W, corresponding, respectively, to the four colors red, blue, green, and white. There is an edge labeled 3 joining vertices W and G, because cube 3 has a white face and a green face on opposite sides of the cube. Cube 3 also has a white and red pair of opposite faces, so vertices W and R are joined with an edge labeled 3. For a similar reason, there is an edge labeled 3 joining vertices B and R. The circle labeled 1 at vertex R corresponds to the fact that cube 1 has a pair of opposite red faces.

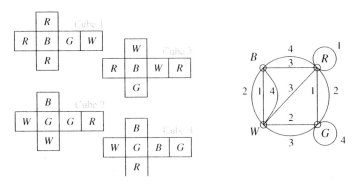

Figure 9.5   Four colored cubes and a graphical representation.

   Once again, a concrete physical problem has been represented by a graph. You do not have to visit Königsberg to simulate the Königsberg Bridge Problem; you do not need to build any houses to simulate the Three Houses–Three Utilities Problem; you do not even have to possess the actual cubes of Instant Insanity in order to play.

   The graph in Fig. 9.5 describes the four cubes of Instant Insanity. Could it also be used to describe a stacking?

   Cube 1 in Fig. 9.6 has its blue face at the front and white face at the back. This orientation can be shown in the graph by emphasizing the edge labeled 1 joining vertices B and W. Similarly, the green–white, red–white, and white–blue front–back faces can be shown by emphasizing three other edges in the graph. The stacking shown on the left of Fig. 9.6 determines the *subgraph* on the right. This stacking does not solve the puzzle, however, because there are too many white faces at the back; moreover, any rotation of any of the cubes through 180° always results in more than one white face at the front or the back. This is more easily seen by observing that in the subgraph there are too many edges joined to vertex W. On the other hand, there are exactly two edges in the subgraph (1 and 4) joined to vertex B, corresponding to the fact that there is just one blue face on the front (part of the B–W pair of faces of cube 1) and just one blue face at the back (part of the W–B pair of faces of cube 4).

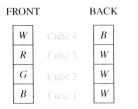
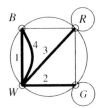

Figure 9.6

When the cubes are stacked with their fronts and backs *correct* (that is, with four different colors on the front and four different colors on the back), the corresponding subgraph will

- contain all four vertices R, B, W, G;
- consist of four edges, one from each cube;
- have exactly two edges or one circle meeting at each vertex.

Figure 9.7 shows two subgraphs, each of which corresponds to a stacking of cubes in which the fronts and backs are correct.

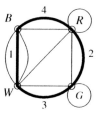 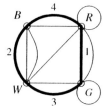

Figure 9.7 Two acceptable subgraphs that are not edge disjoint.

Draw an arrangement of fronts and backs (like that on the left in Fig. 9.6), that is represented by the subgraph on the left in Fig. 9.7. All four colors should appear on the front and on the back. ∎

As anyone who has tried this puzzle knows, getting the front and back of the column correct is easy. It is next getting the **sides** correct that provides the fun(?). Graphically, we require a second subgraph of the type described previously to represent a correct stacking of the sides. Moreover, since a given edge cannot represent both front–back and side–side at the same time, the second subgraph must be *edge disjoint* from the first: No edge can appear in both subgraphs. The subgraphs shown in Fig. 9.7, for instance, are not edge disjoint; they have edges 3 and 4 in common. On the other hand, the subgraphs shown in Fig. 9.8 are indeed edge disjoint and so provide us with a solution to Instant Insanity, as shown in Fig. 9.9.

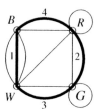 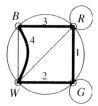

	FRONT	BACK	RIGHT	LEFT
Cube 4	B	R	W	B
Cube 3	G	W	B	R
Cube 2	R	G	G	W
Cube 1	W	B	R	G

Figure 9.8 Two acceptable edge disjoint subgraphs.

Figure 9.9 A solution to the game of Instant Insanity.

9.1.1 REMARK

While our game of Instant Insanity had a unique solution, if we try to make other games by assigning colors to the faces of four cubes in other ways, it is not hard to find games where there are several winning configurations or where there is no solution at all. Also, whereas the subgraphs for our game had certain special properties, such as *connectedness*[3] and a lack of edge crossovers, in general, be on the lookout for other types of subgraphs, three of which are depicted in Fig. 9.10.

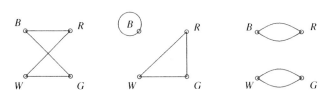

Figure 9.10 Possible subgraphs for other cube games.

Newspapers and magazines often contain mathematical teasers whose solutions can be helped by drawing simple graphs. We close this section with an example of one such puzzle and include another in the exercises for this section.

PROBLEM 1. You and your buddy return home after a semester at college and are greeted at the airport by your mothers and your buddy's two sisters. Not uncharacteristically, there is a certain amount of hugging! Later, the other five people tell you the number of hugs they got and, curiously, these numbers are all different. Assume that you and your buddy did not hug each other, your mothers did not hug each other, and your buddy's sisters did not hug each other. Assume also that the same two people hugged at most once. How many people did you hug? How many people hugged your buddy?

Solution. The conditions on who did not hug whom dictate that no person hugged more than four people. Since the other five hugged different numbers of people, this set of numbers must be $\{0, 1, 2, 3, 4\}$.

Next, it is important to realize that the person who hugged four others could not be your buddy. Why? The graph to the right should help. The four people other than you and your buddy are labeled A_1, A_2, B_1, B_2, and an edge indicates a hug. Think of A_1 and A_2 as sisters (or mothers), and B_1 and B_2 as mothers (or sisters).

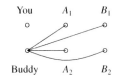

Remembering that you and your buddy did not hug, the graph shows that if your buddy had four hugs it would be impossible for one of the group Buddy, A_1, A_2, B_1, B_2 to have reported no hugs. Thus, your buddy could not have had four hugs.

So the person who got four hugs is among the group A_1, A_2, B_1, B_2. Suppose A_1 got four hugs. (The argument that follows works in precisely the same way if we assume A_2 or B_1 or B_2 was the one with four hugs.) Since A_1 did not hug A_2, the hugging involving A_1 is as depicted in Fig. 9.11(a).

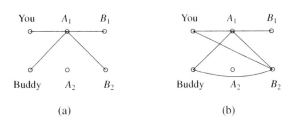

(a)   (b)

Figure 9.11

Since one of the group A_1, A_2, B_1, B_2 received no hugs, it is apparent that this person was A_2. Consider again Fig. 9.11(a). Since you didn't hug your buddy and B_1 didn't hug B_2, the only possible hugs not pictured there are between you or your buddy and B_1 or B_2.

Somebody received three hugs. Who could that be? If it were your buddy, he would have had to hug both B_1 and B_2, leaving nobody with only one hug. We conclude that either B_1 or B_2 received exactly three hugs. There is no loss of generality in assuming it was B_2. Thus, B_2 hugged A_1, you and your buddy. Your buddy now hugged at least two people (A_1 and B_2), so it follows that B_1 must be the person who had one hug. The final situation is shown in Fig. 9.11(b). You and your buddy each hugged two people.

Answer to Pause

1. There are several possibilities for the fronts and backs of cubes that correspond to the subgraph shown in Fig. 9.7. Here is one.

FRONT		BACK
B	Cube 4	R
G	Cube 3	W
R	Cube 2	G
W	Cube 1	B

True/False Questions

(Answers can be found in the back of the book.)

1. The Königsberg Bridge Problem was solved by Léonhard Euler.

2. Sir Isaac Newton is generally considered to be the father of modern-day graph theory.

3. The graph shows that two houses can be connected to each of two utilities with no crossovers.

4. The graph for a Four Houses–Four Utilities problem will have eight vertices and 12 edges.

5. In Instant Insanity, the cube is represented by .

6. In Instant Insanity, the cube is represented by .

7. In Instant Insanity, the graph represents some coloring of a cube.

8. A solution to Instant Insanity depends on certain subgraphs being edge disjoint.

9. A graph with three vertices has a beta index no greater than 1. (See Exercise 5.)

10. There are direct (nonstop) flights among four cities that make it possible to get from any city to any other city by air. It follows that the beta index of the graph of cities and direct flights is at least $\frac{3}{4}$.

Exercises

*The answers to exercises marked [BB] can be found in the **B**ack of the **B**ook.*

1. [BB] (Fictitious) A recently discovered map of the town of Königsberg shows that there was a ferry operating between the banks labeled C and D in Fig. 9.1. Draw a graph in which the vertices are land masses and an edge between two vertices corresponds to a way to move between corresponding land masses.

2. [BB] Draw a configuration of two houses and two utilities, each house connected to each utility, but with no crossovers.

3. One of the owners of the houses in the Three Houses–Three Utilities Problem does not want a telephone. Is it now possible for the houses to be connected to utilities without crossovers? Draw a graph depicting the situation.

4. [BB; (a), (e)] Find solutions, where possible, for the cube games pictured in Figs 9.12 and 9.13.

5. Suppose the vertices of a graph represent cities in a certain region, and an edge joining two vertices indicates that there is a direct (nonstop) flight between those two cities. Geographers define the *beta index* of a graph as the ratio of the number of edges to the number of vertices and view this number as a measure of connectivity of the region. Highly developed countries have high beta indexes; poorly developed countries have low beta indexes. Find the beta index of each of the following graphs.

(a) [BB]

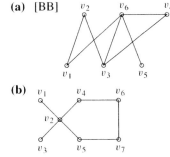

(b)

6. [BB] In the graph, the vertices represent the rooms of a one-story house, and an edge between vertices means that the corresponding rooms have a wall in common. Draw a possible floor plan for this house.

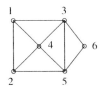

7. You and a friend meet three other couples at a party and several handshakes take place. Nobody shakes hands with himself or herself, there are no handshakes within couples, and no one shakes hands with the same person

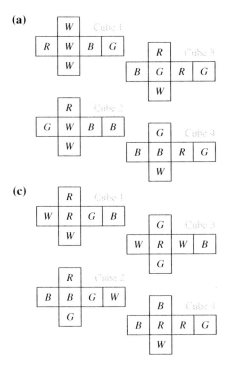

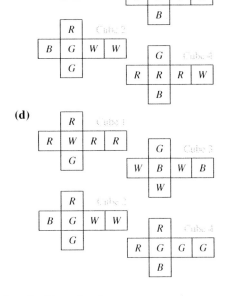

Figure 9.12 Cubes for Exercise 4.

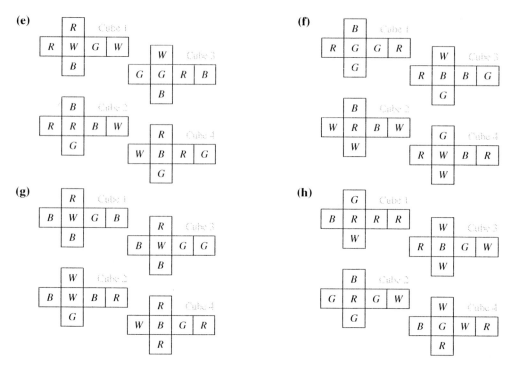

Figure 9.13 More cubes for Exercise 4.

more than once. The numbers of hands shaken by the other seven people (excluding you) are all different. How many hands did you shake? How many hands did your partner shake? Use a graph to aid your solution.

8. **(a)** A graph has six vertices, every two of which are joined by an edge. Each edge is colored red or white. Show that the graph contains a monochromatic triangle (a triangle all of whose vertices have the same color.)

   (b) Is the result of (a) true for a graph with five vertices? Explain.

9. [BB] A graph has six vertices, every two of which are joined by an edge. Each vertex is colored red or white. Show that the graph contains at least **two** monochromatic triangles.

10. A graph has six vertices, every two of which are joined by an edge. Each edge is colored red or white. Show that the graph contains at least **two** monochromatic triangles.

11. A cat and a mouse are at the positions indicated in a maze depicted by the graph of Fig. 9.14.

   (a) Color the cat's and the mouse's positions black. Then color the remaining vertices black and white in such a way that every path in the maze connects vertices of different colors.

   (b) The cat would like to catch the mouse, of course, so the cat changes position to a white vertex. Then the mouse moves, then the cat, and so on, each animal moving alternately one after the other and always to a vertex of the other color. Show that the cat will never get her mouse.

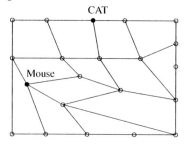

Figure 9.14 For Exercise 11.

9.2 Definitions and Basic Properties

Having used the term *graph* quite a bit already, it is time now to define the word properly and to introduce some of the basic terminology of graph theory.

9.2.1 DEFINITIONS AND NOTATION

A *graph* is a pair $(\mathcal{V}, \mathcal{E})$ of sets, $\mathcal{V}$ nonempty and each element of $\mathcal{E}$ a set of two distinct elements of $\mathcal{V}$. The elements of $\mathcal{V}$ are called *vertices*; the elements of $\mathcal{E}$ are called *edges*. Thus, if e is an edge, then $e = \{v, w\}$, where v and w are different elements of $\mathcal{V}$ called the *end vertices* or *ends* of e. (Colloquially, we often say that the edge $e = \{v, w\}$ *joins* vertices v and w.) We usually abandon set notation and refer to the edge vw; this is, of course, the same as the edge wv. The vertices v and w are said to be *incident* with the edge vw; the edge vw is *incident* with each vertex. Two vertices are *adjacent* if they are the end vertices of an edge; two edges are *adjacent* if they have a vertex in common. The number of edges incident with a vertex v is called the *degree* of that vertex and is denoted deg v. If deg v is an even number, then v is said to be an *even vertex*; if deg v is an odd number, vertex v is *odd*. A vertex of degree 0 is said to be *isolated*. In this text, graphs will always be *finite*, meaning that the set of vertices and, hence, also the set of edges are finite sets. Finally, when we say that $\mathcal{G}(\mathcal{V}, \mathcal{E})$ is a graph, we mean that $\mathcal{G}$ is a graph with vertex set $\mathcal{V}$ and edge set $\mathcal{E}$. ❖

Usually, we draw a picture of a graph, rather than presenting it formally as sets of vertices and edges. For instance, the graph $\mathcal{G}$ with vertices

$$\mathcal{V} = \{v_1, v_2, v_3, v_4, v_5, v_6\}$$

and edges

$$\mathcal{E} = \{v_1v_4, v_1v_6, v_2v_5, v_4v_5, v_5v_6\}$$

can be described as shown in Fig. 9.15.

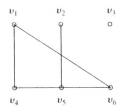

Figure 9.15 A picture of $\mathcal{G}(\mathcal{V}, \mathcal{E})$, where $\mathcal{V} = \{v_1, v_2, v_3, v_4, v_5, v_6\}$ and $\mathcal{E} = \{v_1v_4, v_1v_6, v_2v_5, v_4v_5, v_5v_6\}$.

Many of the graphs presented in Section 9.1 are not graphs at all according to our definition! Many of them have *multiple edges*, that is, several edges incident with the same two vertices. Some of them have a *loop* at a vertex, an edge that is incident with only one vertex. Since most of the graphs of interest to us will have neither multiple edges nor loops, we have opted for the definition of graph presented here. Nevertheless, it is convenient to have a term for more general types of graphs that do arise from time to time. A *pseudograph* is like a graph, but it may contain loops and/or multiple edges.

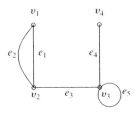

Figure 9.16

Figure 9.16 illustrates a pseudograph with four vertices and five edges. Vertices v_1 and v_2 are incident with edges e_1 and e_2; thus, e_1 and e_2 are multiple edges. Edge e_4 is incident with vertices v_3 and v_4. Edge e_5 is a loop because it is incident only with vertex v_3. Vertices v_2 and v_3 are adjacent, while v_1 and v_3 are not. Edges e_1 and e_3 are adjacent, while e_1 and e_4 are not. Vertex v_1 has degree 2, so v_1 is an even vertex. Counting the loop incident with v_3 twice (as it enters and leaves), v_3 is also an even vertex, with degree 4. Vertices v_2 and v_4 are odd: deg $v_2 = 3$ and deg $v_4 = 1$.

It is unfortunate that there is some lack of standardization of terminology in graph theory, especially in a subject that has more than its share of technical terms. Many words have almost obvious meanings, which are the same from book to book, but other terms are used differently by different authors. It is consequently vital when perusing books or articles on graph theory never to assume that you know the meanings of the graph theoretical terms employed. Always check the author's definitions carefully. For convenience, the definitions that we employ in this book are summarized in a glossary at the end. Readers may have also noticed on the inside covers a description of symbols and notation.

9.2.2 DEFINITION

A graph $\mathcal{G}_1$ is a *subgraph* of another graph $\mathcal{G}$ if and only if the vertex and edge sets of $\mathcal{G}_1$ are, respectively, subsets of the vertex and edge sets of $\mathcal{G}$. ❖

EXAMPLE 2 Each of the three graphs G_1, G_2, and G_3 shown on the right of Fig. 9.17 is a subgraph of the graph G on the left in this figure. (The subgraphs do not have to be drawn the same way they appear in the presentation of G.) ▨

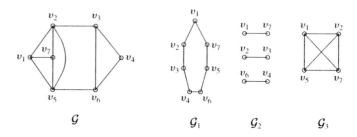

Figure 9.17 A graph and three subgraphs.

EXAMPLE 3 Figure 9.18 depicts a graph G and two subgraphs G_1 and G_2. The last graph in this figure, G_3, is not a subgraph of G because the two vertices of degree 3 in G are not adjacent. ▨

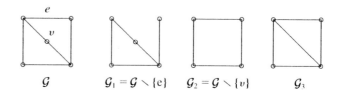

Figure 9.18 A graph G, two subgraphs, G_1 and G_2, and a graph G_3 that is not a subgraph of G.

A useful tool in graph theory is the deletion of an edge or a vertex from a graph. If e is an edge in a graph G, we shall abuse notation and write $G \setminus \{e\}$ to denote the subgraph of $G = G(\mathcal{V}, \mathcal{E})$ that has the same vertex set as G, but whose edge set is $\mathcal{E} \setminus \{e\}$. For example, in Fig. 9.18, the subgraph G_1 is $G \setminus \{e\}$. Similarly, $G \setminus \{v\}$ denotes the graph G with the vertex v removed. The deletion of a vertex requires some care since, when a vertex is removed from a graph, all edges incident with that vertex must also be removed. Again with reference to Fig. 9.18, subgraph $G \setminus \{v\}$ is G_2, not G_3.

Each graph pictured in Fig. 9.19 has as many edges as possible (multiple edges and loops are not permitted in a graph). Such graphs have a name.

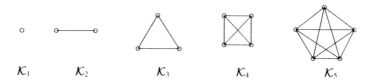

Figure 9.19 The first five complete graphs.

9.2.3 DEFINITION For any positive integer n, the *complete graph on n vertices*, denoted K_n, is that graph with n vertices every two of which are adjacent. ❖

The graphs in Fig. 9.20 are not complete, though they have other interesting properties. In each of them, no two top vertices are adjacent and no two bottom vertices are adjacent (they are examples of *bipartite* graphs), and in the two rightmost graphs every top vertex is adjacent to every bottom vertex (these two are *complete bipartite* graphs).

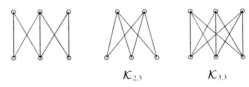

Figure 9.20 Three bipartite graphs, two of which are complete bipartite.

9.2.4 DEFINITIONS A *bipartite graph* is one whose vertices can be partitioned into two (disjoint) sets V_1 and V_2, called *bipartition sets*, in such a way that every edge joins a vertex in V_1 and a vertex in V_2. (In particular, there are no edges within V_1 nor within V_2.) A *complete bipartite graph* is a bipartite graph in which every vertex in V_1 is joined to every vertex in V_2. The complete bipartite graph on bipartition sets of m vertices and n vertices, respectively, is denoted $K_{m,n}$. ❖

Figure 9.20 shows typical pictures of $K_{2,3}$ and $K_{3,3}$. The one-vertex graph K_1 shown in Fig. 9.19 is also bipartite since bipartition sets are not required to be nonempty. It is helpful to note that a graph is bipartite if and only if its vertices can be colored with two colors such that every edge has ends of different colors.

EXAMPLE 4   Consider the graph on the left in Fig. 9.21. Coloring vertex 1 red, vertex 2 white, and continuing to alternate these two colors through the vertices 3, ... , 8 gives every edge differently colored ends. So the graph is bipartite, the bipartition sets being the red vertices and the white vertices. By grouping these bipartition sets, the graph can be redrawn so that it more obviously appears bipartite, as shown on the right in Fig. 9.21.

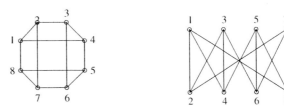

Figure 9.21 A graph and a way to show it is bipartite.

In the graph shown in Fig. 9.21, what are the vertex sets $\{1, 3, 5, 7\}$ and $\{2, 4, 6, 8\}$ called? Is the graph complete? Is it complete bipartite? ∎

It is not hard to show that a bipartite graph can contain no *triangles*.[4] (See Exercise 22.) For instance, graph G_3 in Fig. 9.18 is not bipartite because it contains a triangle (in fact, two triangles).

---

[4]A *triangle* in a graph is a set of three vertices with an edge joining each pair.

Pause 3 Look at the graphs accompanying Exercise 5 in Section 9.1. Are either of these bipartite? Explain. ▮

Two very useful properties of graphs are described in the proposition and corollary that follow. With one proviso, the proofs we present are valid generally, so we state the propositions for pseudographs. The proviso is that a loop at a vertex shall add two to the degree of that vertex. (With reference to the pseudograph in Fig. 9.16, recall that deg $v_3 = 4$.)

9.2.5 PROPOSITION **(Euler)** The sum of the degrees of the vertices of a pseudograph is an even number equal to twice the number of edges. In symbols, if $\mathcal{G}(\mathcal{V}, \mathcal{E})$ is a pseudograph, then

$$\sum_{v \in \mathcal{V}} \deg v = 2|\mathcal{E}|.$$

Proof Adding the degrees of all the vertices involves counting one for each edge incident with each vertex. How many times does an edge get counted? If it is not a loop, it is incident with two different vertices and so gets counted twice, once at each vertex. On the other hand, a loop at a vertex is also counted twice, by convention, in the degree of that vertex. ●

EXAMPLE 5 The graph in Fig. 9.21 has eight vertices each of degree 3. Since

$$\sum_{v \in \mathcal{V}} \deg v = 8(3) = 24 = 2|\mathcal{E}|,$$

it must have 12 edges, and it does. ▨

EXAMPLE 6 The pseudograph in Fig. 9.16 has vertices of degrees 4, 3, 2, 1. Since $4+3+2+1 = 10$, the pseudograph must have five edges, and it does. (Note that a loop is **one** edge, but it adds **two** to the degree.) ▨

PROBLEM 7. How many edges does $\mathcal{K}_{3,6}$ contain?

Solution. This complete bipartite graph has six vertices of degree 3 and three of degree 6. Since

$$\sum_{v \in \mathcal{V}} \deg v = 6(3) + 3(6) = 36 = 2|\mathcal{E}|,$$

$\mathcal{K}_{3,6}$ has 18 edges. ▲

9.2.6 COROLLARY The number of odd vertices in a pseudograph is even.

Proof By Proposition 9.2.5, $\sum_{v \in \mathcal{V}} \deg v = 2|\mathcal{E}|$ is an even number. Since

$$\sum_{v \in \mathcal{V}} \deg v = \sum_{\substack{v \in \mathcal{V} \\ v \text{ even}}} \deg v + \sum_{\substack{v \in \mathcal{V} \\ v \text{ odd}}} \deg v$$

and the first sum on the right, being a sum of even numbers, is even, so also the second sum must be even. Since the sum of an odd number of odd numbers is odd, the number of terms in the sum here, that is, the number of odd vertices, must be even. ●

The pseudograph in Fig. 9.16, for instance, has two odd vertices, v_2 and v_4. The complete bipartite graph $K_{3,6}$ has six odd vertices (each of degree 3).

9.2.7 DEFINITION Suppose that $d_1, d_2, \ldots, d_n$ are the degrees of the vertices of a graph (or pseudograph) G, ordered so that $d_1 \geq d_2 \geq \cdots \geq d_n$. Then $d_1, d_2, \ldots, d_n$ is called the *degree sequence* of G. ❖

EXAMPLE 8
- The degree sequence of the pseudograph in Fig. 9.16 is 4, 3, 2, 1.
- $K_{2,3}$ has degree sequence 3, 3, 2, 2, 2. (See Fig. 9.20.)

Pause 4 Find the degree of each vertex of the pseudograph G shown in Fig. 9.22. What is the degree sequence for G? Verify that the sum of the degrees of the vertices is an even number. Which vertices are even? Which are odd? Verify that the number of odd vertices is even. ∎

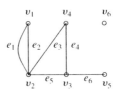

Figure 9.22

Pause 5 Why can there not exist a graph whose degree sequence is 5, 4, 4, 3, 2, 1? ∎

Answers to Pauses

2. The given vertex sets are the bipartition sets of the graph. The graph is not complete since, for example, vertices 1 and 3 are not incident with an edge; it isn't a complete bipartite graph either because, for example, vertices 1 and 6, which lie in different bipartition sets, are not incident with an edge.

3. Neither graph is bipartite. The graph in (a) contains the triangle $v_3 v_4 v_6$. While the graph in (b) does not contain a triangle, it contains the *5-cycle* $v_2 v_4 v_6 v_7 v_5 v_2$, which, like a triangle, causes problems. Try coloring the vertices of the graph in (b) with two colors, say red and white, so that the ends of every edge have different colors. If v_2 were colored white, then v_4 and v_5 would have to be red, so v_6 and v_7 would have to be white. Thus, the edge $v_6 v_7$ would have ends of the same color.

4. Vertices v_1, v_2, v_3, v_4, v_5, and v_6 have degrees 2, 4, 3, 2, 1, and 0, respectively. The degree sequence of G is 4, 3, 2, 2, 1, 0. The sum of the degrees is $4 + 3 + 2 + 2 + 1 + 0 = 12$. The even vertices are v_1, v_2, v_4, and v_6; the odd vertices are v_3 and v_5. There are two odd vertices.

5. The number of odd vertices is 3, which is not even. (Alternatively, the sum of the degrees is 19, which is not an even number.)

True/False Questions

(Answers can be found in the back of the book.)

1. Every graph is a pseudograph.
2. Two vertices are said to be incident if there is an edge joining them.

3. Two edges are said to be adjacent if they have a vertex in common.

4. is a subgraph of □ .

5. ○——○ is a subgraph of ◁▷ .

6. The complete graph $\mathcal{K}_4$ has four vertices and four edges.

7. A complete graph with more than two vertices is not bipartite.

8. The graph $\mathcal{K}_{5,7}$ has 12 vertices and 35 edges.

9. It is not possible for a graph to have degree sequence 4, 4, 3, 3, 2, 2, 2, 1.

10. It is not possible for a graph to have degree sequence 6, 5, 4, 3, 2.

Exercises

*The answers to exercises marked [BB] can be found in the **B**ack of the **B**ook.*

1. [BB] Draw a graph with five vertices v_1, v_2, v_3, v_4, v_5 such that deg $v_1 = 3$, v_2 is an odd vertex, deg $v_3 = 2$, and v_4 and v_5 are adjacent.

2. Draw all possible graphs with three vertices v_1, v_2, v_3. How many edges are there in each graph? What is the degree sequence of each graph? Does this question make sense for pseudographs? Explain.

3. [BB] Give an example of a graph such that every vertex is adjacent to two vertices and every edge is adjacent to two edges.

4. (a) How many vertices and how many edges does the pseudograph contain? What is the degree sequence of this pseudograph?

   (b) Verify Proposition 9.2.5 and Corollary 9.2.6 for this pseudograph.

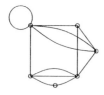

5. [BB] Draw a graph with five vertices and as many edges as possible. How many edges does your graph contain? What is the name of this graph and how is it denoted?

6. (a) What is the maximum degree of a vertex in a graph with n vertices?

   (b) What is the maximum number of edges in a graph with n vertices?

   (c) Given a natural number n, does there exist a graph with n vertices and the maximum possible number of edges?

7. Draw $\mathcal{K}_7$, $\mathcal{K}_{3,4}$, and $\mathcal{K}_{2,6}$.

8. Draw a graph with 64 vertices representing the squares of a chessboard. Two vertices are adjacent if you can move legally between the corresponding squares with a single move of a knight. [The moves of a knight are L-shaped,

two squares vertically (or horizontally) followed by one square horizontally (respectively, vertically).]

   (a) Explain why this graph is bipartite.

   (b) What are the degrees of the vertices?

9. Consider again the graphs accompanying Exercise 5 of Section 9.1, which we reproduce here.

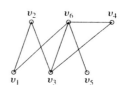 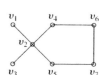

   (a) [BB] For the graph on the left,

   i. Make a table that shows the least number of edges joining each pair of vertices in this graph. (Such a table displays the least number of stops required on air trips between cities in the region depicted by the graph.)

   ii. Add the numbers in each column of the table. Divide each column total by the degree of the corresponding vertex. These ratios are called *accessibility indexes* since they measure the relative accessibility of the cities (by air). Which city is the most accessible? Which is the least accessible?

   iii. Suppose a direct flight joining cities v_1 and v_3 is introduced. What is the new beta index of the graph? What are the new accessibility indexes? Which city is most accessible now? Which city is now least accessible?

   iv. Repeat part (iii), assuming a flight is introduced between cities v_2 and v_6 instead of between v_1 and v_3.

   (b) Repeat the preceding questions for the graph on the right.

10. [BB] Verify Proposition 9.2.5 and Corollary 9.2.6 for the complete graph $\mathcal{K}_n$. What is the beta index of $\mathcal{K}_n$? (See Exercise 5, Section 9.1.)

11. (a) Verify Proposition 9.2.5 for the complete bipartite graph $\mathcal{K}_{m,n}$.

    (b) Verify Corollary 9.2.6 without using the argument given in the proof of that corollary. (Consider the cases corresponding to m and n being odd or even.)

    (c) What is the beta index of $\mathcal{K}_{m,n}$?

12. Does there exist a graph $\mathcal{G}$ with 28 edges and 12 vertices, each of degree

    (a) [BB] 3 or 4?   (b) 3 or 6?

13. [BB] At most social functions, there is a lot of handshaking. Prove that the number of people who shake the hands of an odd number of people is always even.

14. Which of the graphs is a subgraph of the graph in Fig. 9.21?

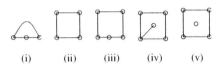

    (i)   (ii)   (iii)   (iv)   (v)

15. [BB; (a)] For each pair of graphs shown, discover whether the graph on the left is a subgraph of the one on the right. If it is not, explain why not. If it is, label the vertices of the subgraph, then use the same symbols to label the corresponding vertices of the graph on the right.

    (a)   (b)

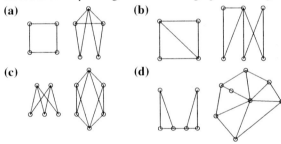

    (c)   (d)

16. [BB; (a)] For each of the graphs, draw pictures of the subgraphs $\mathcal{G} \setminus \{e\}$, $\mathcal{G} \setminus \{v\}$, and $\mathcal{G} \setminus \{u\}$.

    (a)   (b)

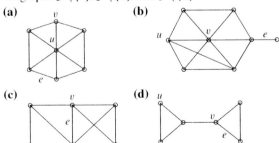

    (c)   (d)

17. [BB] (a) What are the degrees of the vertices?

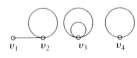

       v_1 v_2 v_3 v_4

    (b) Can there exist a graph with four vertices of degrees 1, 2, 3, and 4?

18. For each of the following sequences, determine if there exists a graph whose degree sequence is the one specified. In each case, either draw a graph or explain why no graph exists.

    (a) [BB] 4, 4, 4, 3, 2

    (b) 100, 99, 98, ... , 3, 2, 2, 2

    (c) [BB] 5, 5, 4, 3, 2, 1

    (d) 1, 1, 1, 1, 1, 1

    (e) 5, 4, 3, 2, 1   (f) 5, 4, 3, 2, 1, 1

    (g) 6, 6, 4, 2, 2, 2, 1, 1   (h) 4, 3, 2, 2, 1

19. Does there exist a graph with five vertices, every vertex incident with at least one edge, but no two edges adjacent? Explain.

20. (a) [BB] A graph has five vertices of degree 4 and two vertices of degree 2. How many edges does it have?

    (b) A graph has degree sequence 5, 5, 4, 4, 3, 3, 3, 3. How many edges does it have?

21. Determine whether each of the graphs in Fig. 9.23 is bipartite. In each case, give the bipartition sets or explain why the graph is not bipartite.

    (a) [BB]   (b)

    (c) [BB]   (d)

    (e)   (f)

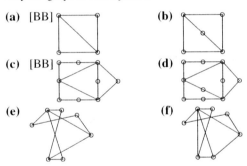

Figure 9.23 Graphs for Exercise 21

22. (a) [BB] Prove that a graph that contains a triangle cannot be bipartite.

    (b) Extend the result of part (a) to a statement about n-cycles, $n \geq 3$. Justify your answer.

23. (a) Must a subgraph of a bipartite graph be bipartite?

    (b) Would your answer to (a) change if, in the definition of a bipartite graph, bipartition sets were required to be nonempty?
    Explain your answers.

24. [BB] (Requires calculus) Prove that the number of edges in a bipartite graph with n vertices is at most $\frac{n^2}{4}$.

25. How many complete bipartite graphs have n vertices?

26. Let $\mathcal{V} = \{1, 2, 3, \ldots, n\}$.

    (a) [BB] How many graphs are there with vertex set $\mathcal{V}$?

    (b) How many of the graphs in (a) contain the triangle 123?

    (c) [BB] What is the total number of triangles in all the graphs with vertex set $\mathcal{V}$?

(d) On average, how many triangles does a graph on n labeled vertices contain?

27. Suppose a graph has nine vertices each of degree 5 or 6. Prove that at least five vertices have degree 6 or at least six vertices have degree 5.

28. [BB] What is the largest possible number of vertices in a graph with 35 edges, all vertices having degree at least 3?

29. Let m and M denote the minimum and the maximum degrees of the vertices of a graph $\mathcal{G}$ with vertex set $\mathcal{V}$ and edge set $\mathcal{E}$. Show that

$$m \leq \frac{2|\mathcal{E}|}{|\mathcal{V}|} \leq M.$$

30. [BB] Suppose all vertices in a graph have odd degree k. Show that the total number of edges in $\mathcal{G}$ is a multiple of k.

31. A graph $\mathcal{G}$ with 17 edges has the property that all its vertices have the same degree d. Find all possible values for d. For each such value, state briefly what the corresponding graph looks like.

32. [BB] Prove that in any graph with more than one vertex there must exist two vertices of the same degree. [*Hint*: Pigeonhole Principle.]

33. Show that a set of nonnegative integers $\{d_1, d_2, \ldots, d_n\}$ is the set of degrees of some pseudograph if and only if $\sum_{i=1}^{n} d_i$ is even.

34. Suppose that $d_1, d_2, \ldots, d_n$ are the degrees of the vertices in some graph. Show that, for any $t < n$,

$$\sum_{i=1}^{t} d_i \leq t(t-1) + \sum_{i=t+1}^{n} \min\{t, d_i\}.$$

Remark: The given condition (holding for all $t < n$) and the requirement that $\sum_{i=1}^{n} d_i$ is even are sufficient as well as necessary for the existence of a graph with a prescribed set $d_1, \ldots, d_n$ of degrees.[5]

35. Can there exist a graph with 13 vertices, 31 edges, 3 vertices of degree 1, and 7 vertices of degree 4? Explain.

9.3 Isomorphism

It is important to know when two graphs are essentially the same and when they are essentially different. When we say graphs are "essentially the same," we mean that they differ only in the way they are labeled or drawn. There should be a one-to-one correspondence between the vertices of the graphs and a one-to-one correspondence between their edges such that corresponding vertices are incident with corresponding edges. The proper term for "essentially the same" is *isomorphic*.

There is a distinction between a graph and its picture. A graph is a set $\mathcal{V}$ and a set $\mathcal{E}$ of unordered pairs of elements of $\mathcal{V}$. A picture of it consists of dots and lines that can be drawn and arranged in many different ways. The bipartite graphs that were pictured in Fig. 9.21, for instance, are isomorphic: The two pictures represent the same graph $\mathcal{G}(\mathcal{V}, \mathcal{E})$, where

$$\mathcal{V} = \{1, 2, 3, 4, 5, 6, 7, 8\}$$

and

$$\mathcal{E} = \{12, 14, 18, 23, 27, 34, 36, 45, 56, 58, 67, 78\}.$$

EXAMPLE 9   Graphs $\mathcal{G}_2$ and $\mathcal{G}_3$ in Fig. 9.24 each consist of two edges incident with a common vertex. They are drawn differently, but the graphs are the same: $\mathcal{G}_2$ and $\mathcal{G}_3$ are isomorphic. The picture of $\mathcal{G}_1$ indicates that this graph has only one edge: $\mathcal{G}_1$ is different from $\mathcal{G}_2$ in an essential way; it is isomorphic to neither $\mathcal{G}_2$ nor $\mathcal{G}_3$.   ▨

EXAMPLE 10   Figure 9.25 illustrates two graphs that are not isomorphic: Each graph consists of four vertices and four edges, but $\mathcal{G}_2$ contains a vertex of degree 1, while $\mathcal{G}_1$ has no such vertex.   ▨

EXAMPLE 11   The graphs in Fig. 9.26 are isomorphic and they have been labeled so as to show corresponding vertices. Either picture represents a graph with four vertices A, B, C, and D and four edges AB, BC, CD, and DA.   ▨

---

[5]P. Erdös and T. Gallai, "Graphs with Prescribed Degrees of Vertices," *Matematikai Lapok* **11** (1960), 264–274.

Figure 9.24 $\mathcal{G}_2$ and $\mathcal{G}_3$ are isomorphic, but neither is isomorphic to $\mathcal{G}_1$.

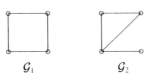

Figure 9.25 Two nonisomorphic graphs.

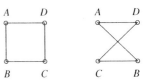

Figure 9.26 Two graphs labeled so as to show that they are isomorphic.

Pause 6 Show that the two graphs to the right are isomorphic by assigning the labels $A, B, C,$ and D to appropriate vertices of the graph on the right. (It might help to think of the edges of $\mathcal{G}_2$ as pieces of string knotted at the vertices. How could $\mathcal{G}_2$ be rearranged to look like $\mathcal{G}_1$? Once you see this, it will be easy to do the required labeling.) ▌

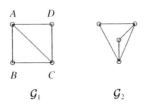

Here is the precise definition of the term *isomorphic*.

9.3.1 DEFINITION Given graphs $\mathcal{G}_1 = \mathcal{G}_1(\mathcal{V}_1, \mathcal{E}_1)$ and $\mathcal{G}_2 = \mathcal{G}_2(\mathcal{V}_2, \mathcal{E}_2)$, we say that $\mathcal{G}_1$ is *isomorphic* to $\mathcal{G}_2$ and write $\mathcal{G}_1 \cong \mathcal{G}_2$ if there is a one-to-one function φ from $\mathcal{V}_1$ onto $\mathcal{V}_2$ such that

- if vw is an edge in $\mathcal{E}_1$, then $\varphi(v)\varphi(w)$ is an edge in $\mathcal{E}_2$, and
- every edge in $\mathcal{E}_2$ has the form $\varphi(v)\varphi(w)$ for some edge $vw \in \mathcal{E}_1$.

We call φ an *isomorphism* from $\mathcal{G}_1$ to $\mathcal{G}_2$ and, abusing notation, say that $\varphi: \mathcal{G}_1 \to \mathcal{G}_2$ is an isomorphism. ❖

The definition of isomorphism is symmetric: If $\mathcal{G}_1$ is isomorphic to $\mathcal{G}_2$, then $\mathcal{G}_2$ is isomorphic to $\mathcal{G}_1$. In fact, if $\varphi: \mathcal{G}_1 \to \mathcal{G}_2$ is an isomorphism, then $\varphi^{-1}: \mathcal{G}_2 \to \mathcal{G}_1$ is an isomorphism. Thus, there is no ambiguity if we simply say that two graphs "are isomorphic."

We often say that graphs are isomorphic if and only if there is a bijection between their vertex sets that "preserves incidence relations." By this, we mean that a vertex v is incident with an edge e in $\mathcal{G}_1$ if and only if $\varphi(v)$ is incident with $\varphi(e)$ in $\mathcal{G}_2$. An isomorphism φ simply relabels vertices without changing any of the incidence relations. If $\varphi(v) = x$, think of x as the new label for v.

EXAMPLE 12 Consider the two graphs shown at the left. We encountered these earlier in Fig. 9.26. Remembering our previous discussion, we see that if vertex u of $\mathcal{G}_2$ is relabeled A, if vertex v is relabeled C, if w is relabeled D, and if x is relabeled B then the pictures represent precisely the same graph. Having seen how to relabel the vertices of $\mathcal{G}_2$ with the labels of $\mathcal{G}_1$, it is easy to write down the isomorphism $\mathcal{G}_2 \to \mathcal{G}_1$ explicitly:

$$\varphi(u) = A, \quad \varphi(v) = C, \quad \varphi(w) = D, \quad \varphi(x) = B.$$

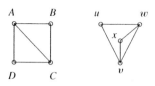

Figure 9.27

Pause 7 Use your solution to PAUSE 6 to find an isomorphism $\varphi\colon \mathcal{G}_2 \to \mathcal{G}_1$ for the graphs $\mathcal{G}_1, \mathcal{G}_2$ shown in Fig. 9.27. ∎

The notion of isomorphism is exceedingly important in mathematics. If the definition looks complicated, the idea is very simple. Isomorphic objects, from a mathematical standpoint, are the same; they differ only in appearance. This idea is not new: $\frac{2}{4}$ and 0.5 look different, but they represent the same real number.

We have remarked that the definition of isomorphism is

symmetric: $\mathcal{G}_1 \cong \mathcal{G}_2$ if and only if $\mathcal{G}_2 \cong \mathcal{G}_1$.

It is also

reflexive: $\mathcal{G} \cong \mathcal{G}$ for any graph $\mathcal{G}$

(because the identity map $\mathcal{G} \to \mathcal{G}$ is an isomorphism) and

transitive: If $\mathcal{G}_1 \cong \mathcal{G}_2$ and $\mathcal{G}_2 \cong \mathcal{G}_3$, then $\mathcal{G}_1 \cong \mathcal{G}_3$

(because, if $\varphi_1\colon \mathcal{G}_1 \to \mathcal{G}_2$ and $\varphi_2\colon \mathcal{G}_2 \to \mathcal{G}_3$ are isomorphisms, then so is the composition $\varphi_2 \circ \varphi_1\colon \mathcal{G}_1 \to \mathcal{G}_3$). Thus, isomorphism is an equivalence relation on the set of all graphs.

The set of all graphs is therefore partitioned into disjoint equivalence classes called *isomorphism classes*. Any two graphs in the same equivalence class are isomorphic; two graphs in different equivalence classes are not isomorphic. The graphs pictured in PAUSE 6 belong to the same equivalence class; the graphs pictured in Fig. 9.25 belong to different equivalence classes. When we casually remark that two graphs are different, we really mean "in different isomorphism classes."

Usually, it is very difficult to prove that two graphs are isomorphic. In principle, we have to list all the one-to-one onto functions between vertex sets and, in each case, check whether the function preserves incidence relations. On the other hand, it is often easy to prove that graphs are not isomorphic. For instance, the graphs $\mathcal{G}_1$ and $\mathcal{G}_2$ in Fig. 9.24 cannot possibly be isomorphic because $\mathcal{G}_2$ is *connected* in the sense that there is a sequence of adjacent edges between any two vertices, while $\mathcal{G}_1$ is not connected.

Since an isomorphism is a one-to-one onto function between vertex sets, isomorphic graphs have the same numbers of vertices. Many other properties are shared by isomorphic graphs.

Suppose $\varphi\colon \mathcal{G}_1 \to \mathcal{G}_2$ is an isomorphism from a graph $\mathcal{G}_1$ to another graph $\mathcal{G}_2$. If v is a vertex of degree k in $\mathcal{G}_1$ and if $v_1, v_2, \dots, v_k$ are the vertices adjacent to v, then, in $\mathcal{G}_2$, $\varphi(v)$ is adjacent to the k vertices $\varphi(v_1), \varphi(v_2), \dots, \varphi(v_k)$, but to no other vertex. Thus, the degree of $\varphi(v)$ is also k. It follows that isomorphic graphs have the same degree sequences and hence also the same numbers of edges, since the number of edges in a graph is one-half the sum of the vertex degrees (Proposition 9.2.5).

9.3.2 PROPOSITION If $\mathcal{G}_1$ and $\mathcal{G}_2$ are isomorphic graphs, then $\mathcal{G}_1$ and $\mathcal{G}_2$ have the

- same number of vertices,
- same number of edges, and
- same degree sequences.

The graphs $\mathcal{G}_1$ and $\mathcal{G}_3$ shown in Fig. 9.17 are not isomorphic because they have different numbers of vertices. The graphs shown in Fig. 9.25 are not isomorphic because $\mathcal{G}_2$ contains a vertex of degree 1 while $\mathcal{G}_1$ does not.

Don't misinterpret Proposition 9.3.2. The proposition asserts three implications of the form

$$\mathcal{G}_1 \cong \mathcal{G}_2 \to \dots$$

which must not be confused with double implications of the form

$$\mathcal{G}_1 \cong \mathcal{G}_2 \leftrightarrow \dots$$

Proposition 9.3.2 says that **if** two graphs are isomorphic **then** they must have certain properties. It does not say that two graphs with the properties listed are isomorphic. In fact, it is possible for two graphs that are not isomorphic to have the same numbers of vertices and edges and the same degree sequences. See Exercises 8 and 9.

Answers to Pauses

6. We show one of several ways in which the vertices of $\mathcal{G}_2$ can be labeled so that it becomes clear that the graph represented by each picture is the same.

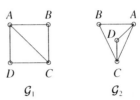

7. $\varphi(u) = B, \varphi(v) = C, \varphi(w) = A, \varphi(x) = D$. The isomorphism φ just relabels vertices of $\mathcal{G}_2$.

True/False Questions

(Answers can be found in the back of the book.)

1. If graphs $\mathcal{G}_1$ and $\mathcal{G}_2$ are isomorphic and pictures are drawn for each of these graphs, then the pictures must look exactly the same.

2. If pictures drawn for graphs $\mathcal{G}_1$ and $\mathcal{G}_2$ look exactly the same, then $\mathcal{G}_1$ and $\mathcal{G}_2$ are isomorphic.

3. $\mathcal{K}_{2,3}$ is isomorphic to $\mathcal{K}_{3,2}$.

4. $\mathcal{K}_{2,3}$ is isomorphic to $\mathcal{K}_5$.

5. If graphs $\mathcal{G}_1$ and $\mathcal{G}_2$ have the same number of vertices, then $\mathcal{G}_1$ and $\mathcal{G}_2$ are isomorphic.

6. If graphs $\mathcal{G}_1$ and $\mathcal{G}_2$ are isomorphic, then $\mathcal{G}_1$ and $\mathcal{G}_2$ have the same number of edges.

7. If graphs $\mathcal{G}_1$ and $\mathcal{G}_2$ are isomorphic, then $\mathcal{G}_1$ and $\mathcal{G}_2$ have the same degree sequences.

8. Isomorphism is an equivalence relation on the set of all graphs.

9. If graphs $\mathcal{G}_1$ and $\mathcal{G}_2$ are isomorphic, $\mathcal{G}_1$ has vertices $\{v_1, v_2, \dots, v_n\}$ and $\mathcal{G}_2$ has vertices $\{w_1, w_2, \dots, w_n\}$, then the degree of vertex v_1 equals the degree of vertex w_1.

10. In Definition 9.3.1, "$\mathcal{V}_1$ **onto** $\mathcal{V}_2$" could be changed to "$\mathcal{V}_1$ **to** $\mathcal{V}_2$" without changing anything.

Exercises

*The answers to exercises marked [BB] can be found in the **B**ack of the **B**ook.*

1. [BB] For each of the ten pairs of graphs that can be obtained from those shown, either label the graphs so as to exhibit an isomorphism or explain why the graphs are not isomorphic.

(i)　　　(ii)　　　(iii)　　　(iv)　　　(v)

2. (a) Draw a graph isomorphic to the one shown on the left, but with no crossover of edges.

(b) Same as (a) for the graph on the right.

3. (a) [BB] Draw all nonisomorphic graphs on $n = 3$ vertices. Give the degree sequence of each.

(b) Repeat part (a) for $n = 4$.

4. [BB; (b)] For each pair of graphs shown,
- if the graphs are not isomorphic, explain why not;
- if the graphs are isomorphic, exhibit an isomorphism from one to the other and relabel the graph on the right so as to show this isomorphism.

(a)

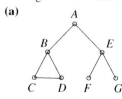 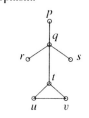

(b)

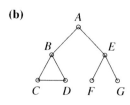 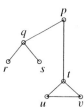

(c)

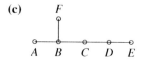 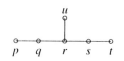

(d)

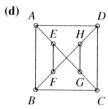 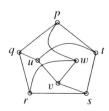

5. (a) [BB] Is the graph on the left isomorphic to $\mathcal{K}_{3,4}$? Explain.

(b) Is the graph on the right isomorphic to $\mathcal{K}_{4,4}$? Explain.

6. Determine whether the two graphs pictured in Fig. 9.28 are isomorphic. (The one on the left is the Petersen graph, which we will encounter again in Chapter 10.)

7. [BB] Explain why any graph is isomorphic to a subgraph of some complete graph.

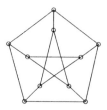 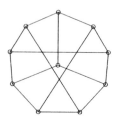

Figure 9.28 Graphs for Exercise 6.

9.3.3 DEFINITION Suppose $v_1, \ldots, v_n$ is a set of n vertices in a graph such that v_i and v_{i+1} are adjacent for $1 \leq i \leq n - 1$ and v_n and v_1 are also adjacent. Then the set of these n vertices and the n edges $v_1 v_2, v_2 v_3, \ldots v_{n-1} v_n, v_n v_1$ is called an *n-cycle*. A 3-cycle is often called a *triangle* and a 4-cycle a *quadrilateral*. ❖

8. (a) [BB] Prove that two graphs that are isomorphic must contain the same number of triangles.

(b) Prove that, for any $n \geq 4$, two isomorphic graphs must contain the same number of n-cycles.

(c) How many edges are there in the graphs $\mathcal{G}_1$ and $\mathcal{G}_2$? How many vertices? What is the degree sequence of each graph? Are the graphs isomorphic? Explain.

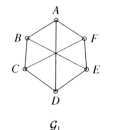 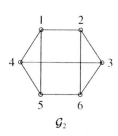

$$\mathcal{G}_1 \qquad\qquad \mathcal{G}_2$$

9. Consider the following three graphs.

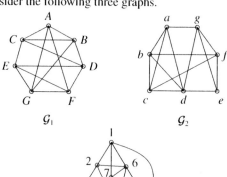

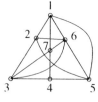

$$\mathcal{G}_3$$

(a) [BB] How many vertices and how many edges are there in each graph? What is the degree sequence of each graph? How many triangles are in each graph?

(b) For each pair of graphs, either exhibit an isomorphism between vertex sets or explain why the graphs are not isomorphic.

10. Show that the following graphs are not isomorphic.

 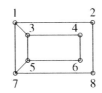

11. (a) [BB] Suppose that graphs G and H have the same numbers of vertices and the same numbers of edges, and suppose that the degree of every vertex in G and in H is 2. Are G and H necessarily isomorphic? Explain.

(b) Suppose that graphs G and H have the same number of vertices and the same number of edges. Suppose that the degree sequences of G and H are the same and that neither graph contains a triangle. Are G and H necessarily isomorphic? Explain.

Key Terms & Ideas

Here are some technical words and phrases that were used in this chapter. Do you know the meaning of each? If you're not sure, check the glossary or index at the back of the book.

adjacent

bipartite graph

bipartition set

complete bipartite

complete graph

degree

degree sequence

edge

even vertex

graph

incident

isolated vertex

isomorphic graphs

isomorphism of graphs

loop

multiple edges

odd vertex

pseudograph

triangle

Review Exercises for Chapter 9

1. In the Königsberg Bridge Problem, a tragic fire destroys the bridge from B to C and also one of the bridges from A to D. (See Fig. 9.1.) Draw a graph representing the new situation. Show that it is now possible for someone to start on land mass B and walk over each of the bridges exactly once, returning to B again.

2. (a) Draw a configuration of four houses and two utilities, each house connected to each utility, but with no crossovers.

(b) Let n be any positive integer. Motivated by 2(a), suggest a general result concerning n houses and 2 utilities. Draw a graph supporting your answer.

3. Find solutions, where possible, for the cube games pictured in Fig. 9.29.

4. (a) Draw a graph with six vertices at least three of which are odd and at least two of which are even.

(b) Draw a graph with six vertices at most three of which are odd and at least two of which are even.

(c) Is it possible to find a graph that satisfies the conditions in both 4a and 4b simultaneously? Explain your answer.

5. For each of the following sequences, determine if there is a graph whose degree sequence is the one specified. In each case, either draw the graph or explain why no such graph can exist.

(a) 3, 3, 3, 3   **(b)** 3, 3, 3, 3, 3

(c) 3, 3, 3, 3, 3, 3   **(d)** 3, 3, 3, 3, 3, 3, 3, 3

6. (a) Does there exist a graph with degree sequence 6, 6, 5, 5, 4, 4, 4, 4, 3? Explain.

(b) Answer part (a) for the sequence 8, 8, 7, 6, 5, 4, 3, 2, 1?

7. Determine whether or not each of the following graphs is bipartite. For any that is bipartite, is the graph complete?

(a)   **(b)**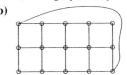

(c)

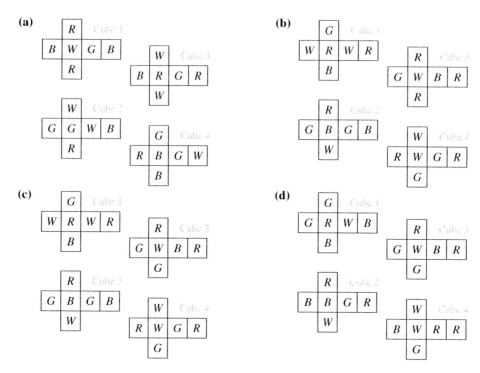

Figure 9.29 Cubes for Exercise 3.

8. Answer these questions for each sequence:
- Does there exist a graph with the given sequence as its degree sequence?
- Does there exist a bipartite graph with the given sequence as its degree sequence?

(a) 2, 2, 2, 2   **(b)** 2, 2, 2, 2, 2

(c) 4, 3, 3, 2, 2, 2   **(d)** 3, 3, 2, 2, 1, 1

9. Find a necessary and sufficient condition for the existence of a bipartite graph with n vertices and every vertex of the same degree d. Justify your answer.

10. Let $\mathcal{G}$ be a graph and let $\mathcal{H}$ be a subgraph of $\mathcal{G}$. Assume $\mathcal{H}$ contains at least three vertices.
- **(a)** Is it possible for $\mathcal{G}$ to be bipartite and for $\mathcal{H}$ to be a complete graph?
- **(b)** Is it possible for $\mathcal{G}$ to be a complete graph and for $\mathcal{H}$ to be bipartite?

Explain your answers.

11. Suppose a graph has 49 vertices, each of degree 4 or 5. Prove that at least 25 vertices have degree 4 or at least 26 vertices have degree 5.

12. Suppose $\mathcal{G}$ is a graph with n vertices, n edges, and no vertices of degree 0 or 1. Prove that every vertex of $\mathcal{G}$ has degree 2.

13. A graph $\mathcal{G}$ has 50 edges, four vertices of degree 2, six of degree 5, eight of degree 4, and the rest of degree 6. How many vertices does $\mathcal{G}$ have?

14. The 24 members of Canada's Olympic Hockey team gather for the first time in Salt Lake City and discover that 78 pairs have played on the same NHL team at some point in their careers.
- **(a)** Show that one player has played on the same team with at least seven of his Olympic teammates.
- **(b)** Show that one player has played on the same team with no more than six of his Olympic teammates.

15. For each pair of graphs shown in Fig. 9.30,
- if the graphs are not isomorphic, explain why not;
- if the graphs are isomorphic, exhibit an isomorphism from one to the other.

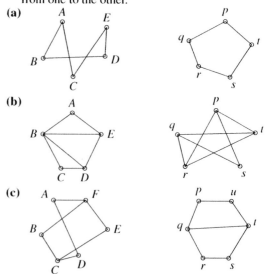

Figure 9.30 Graphs for Exercise 15.

16. Let $S = \{a, b, c, d, e\}$ and let $\mathcal{V}$ be the set of 2-element subsets of S. Let $\mathcal{G}$ be the graph whose vertex set is $\mathcal{V}$ and where, for $A, B \in \mathcal{V}$, AB is an edge if and only if $A \cap B = \emptyset$. Show that $\mathcal{G}$ is isomorphic to the Petersen graph. (See Exercise 6 of Section 9.3.)

17. For each of the following cases, explain why the two graphs are either isomorphic or not.

   (a) $\mathcal{K}_4$ and $\mathcal{K}_{3,8}$ **(b)** $\mathcal{K}_{11}$ and $\mathcal{K}_{3,8}$

   (c) $\mathcal{K}_{4,6}$ and $\mathcal{K}_{2,12}$ **(d)** $\mathcal{K}_{4,6}$ and $\mathcal{K}_{5,5}$

   (e) $\mathcal{K}_{4,6}$ and $\mathcal{K}_{6,4}$

18. George is examining three graphs $\mathcal{G}_1$, $\mathcal{G}_2$, and $\mathcal{G}_3$. He gives correct arguments showing that $\mathcal{G}_1$ is not isomorphic to $\mathcal{G}_2$ and that $\mathcal{G}_2$ is not isomorphic to $\mathcal{G}_3$. Can he conclude that $\mathcal{G}_1$ is not isomorphic to $\mathcal{G}_3$? Explain.

19. Answer Exercise 18 again, assuming that George's correct arguments show that $\mathcal{G}_1$ is not isomorphic to $\mathcal{G}_2$, while $\mathcal{G}_2$ is isomorphic to $\mathcal{G}_3$.

20. Prove that $\mathcal{K}_{a,b} \cong \mathcal{K}_{c,d}$ if and only if $\{a, b\} = \{c, d\}$.

10
Paths and Circuits

Many real problems, when translated to questions about graphs, inquire about the possibility of walking through a graph in a particular way. Although our primary interest is in graphs, the definitions and results of this section are stated for pseudographs, since they apply equally, and with few additional complications, in the more general setting.

10.1.1 DEFINITIONS

A *walk* in a pseudograph is an alternating sequence of vertices and edges, beginning and ending with a vertex, in which each edge is incident with the vertex immediately preceding it and the vertex immediately following it. The *length* of a walk is the number of edges in it. A walk is *closed* if the first vertex is the same as the last and otherwise *open*. A *trail* is a walk in which all edges are distinct; a *path* is a walk in which all vertices are distinct. A closed trail is called a *circuit*. A circuit in which the first vertex appears exactly twice (at the beginning and the end) and in which no other vertex appears more than once is a *cycle*. An *n-cycle* is a cycle with *n* vertices. It is *even* if *n* is even and *odd* if *n* is odd. ❖

There are a lot of words here and, as always, we cannot emphasize too strongly the importance of coming to grips with their meanings. We hope Table 10.1 will help.

Table 10.1

Term	Characteristics
Trail	Distinct edges
Path	Distinct vertices
Circuit	Closed trail
Cycle	Closed trail with distinct vertices (hence distinct edges too)

When thinking about the concepts of path and trail, it is perhaps helpful to note that a path is necessarily a trail: If all the vertices of a walk are different, then all the edges must be different too. As we show in the next example, the converse is not true: A trail need not be a path.

EXAMPLE 1   In the graph shown in Fig. 10.2, $ABCEFCBD$ is a walk of length 7 that is neither a trail nor a path; $ABCEFCD$ is a trail, but not a path; $ABCEFCDBA$ is a closed walk that is not a circuit; $BCEFCDB$ is a circuit that is not a cycle; and $BCDB$ is a 3-cycle and hence an odd cycle. The closed walk $CEFCBDC$ is not a cycle because the first and last vertex appears a third time.

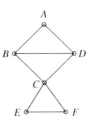

Figure 10.2

Pause 1   Verify each of the assertions just made.   ∎

While, strictly speaking, a walk should be specified by an alternating sequence of vertices and edges, it is often enough to specify only the vertices, as long as consecutive vertices are adjacent, as we have just done.[1] An important type of circuit, known as an *Eulerian circuit*, is one that passes through every vertex and through every edge of a pseudograph.

10.1.2 DEFINITION   An *Eulerian circuit* in a pseudograph is a circuit that contains every vertex and every edge. A pseudograph is *Eulerian* if it contains an Eulerian circuit.   ❖

Note the reference to vertices in the definition of Eulerian circuit, which is crucial to the concept. See Exercise 6.

EXAMPLE 2   In the graph of Fig. 10.2, the circuit $ABCEFCDA$ is not Eulerian because it does not contain the edge BD. As we shall soon see, this graph possesses no Eulerian circuit; it is not an Eulerian graph.   ▨

EXAMPLE 3   Figure 10.3 further illustrates the difference between a circuit and a Eulerian circuit. The circuit $ABCDEFGHFA$ is not Eulerian since, while it encompasses all vertices, it omits four edges. The graph is Eulerian, however: $ABCDEFGHFAD$ BEA is an Eulerian circuit.   ▨

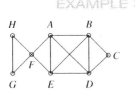

Figure 10.3 A Eulerian graph.

Eulerian circuits are named, of course, after Léonhard Euler, the solver of the Königsberg Bridge Problem, and their study is motivated by that problem. In Section 9.1, we saw that to follow the desired route over the bridges of Königsberg you have to choose a vertex in the pseudograph of Fig. 9.2 and find a walk that includes all the edges exactly once and leads back to the chosen vertex. With our present terminology, the Königsberg Bridge Problem asks if the pseudograph is Eulerian.

---

[1]In a **graph**, there is never a problem specifying just vertices.

In Theorem 10.1.4, we present the remarkably simple test that Euler found for the presence of an Eulerian circuit. First, since an Eulerian circuit provides a walk between every pair of vertices, any Eulerian pseudograph must be *connected*, in the following sense.

10.1.3 DEFINITION

A pseudograph is *connected* if and only if there exists a walk between any two vertices. ❖

As we ask you to show in Exercise 17, if a graph is connected, then there is actually a path between any two vertices, not just a walk.

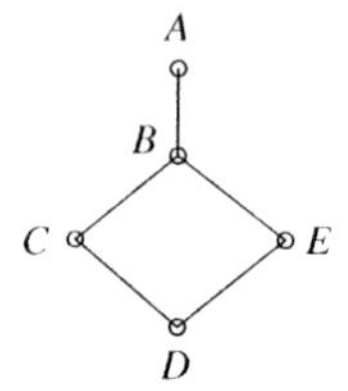

An Eulerian graph must be more than just connected, however, as the graph in Fig. 10.4 illustrates. The basic difficulty with this graph is that there is only one edge incident with A. Any circuit that begins at A cannot return to A without using this edge again, and any circuit that begins at a vertex other than A and attempts to include all edges, after using the edge BA (in the direction B to A), has to repeat it en route back to the starting vertex. The degrees of the vertices play a role in determining whether a graph is Eulerian. It is not hard to see that the degrees of the vertices of an Eulerian graph must be even.

In essence, we have already given the argument. In walking along an Eulerian circuit, every time we meet a vertex (other than the one where we started), either we leave on a loop and return immediately, never traversing that loop again, or we leave on an edge different from that by which we entered and traverse neither edge again. So the edges (other than loops) incident with any vertex in the middle of the circuit can be paired. So also can the edges incident with the first (and last) vertex, since the edge by which we left it at the beginning can be paired with the edge by which we returned at the end. Thus, an Eulerian graph must not only be connected, but also have vertices of even degree. Conversely, a connected graph all of whose vertices are even must be Eulerian. To see why, it will be helpful to examine again the graph of Fig. 10.3 (which is connected and has only even vertices) and to try to construct an Eulerian circuit with a strategy that might apply more generally.

We attempt to find an Eulerian circuit starting at A. To begin, we find **some** circuit that starts and ends at A, for instance, the circuit C_1: $ABCDEFA$. This circuit obviously is not Eulerian because it misses lots of edges. If we delete the edges of C_1 from the graph as well as vertex C, which is isolated after the edges of C_1 have been removed, we are left with graph G_1 on the left of Fig. 10.5.

Figure 10.5

Graph G_1 has a circuit C, FGH, that is connected to C_1 at vertex F. Thus, it can be used to enlarge C_1 as follows: Start at A, follow C_1 as far as F, then pass around C and complete C_1 to A. We obtain a second circuit C_2, $ABCDEFGHFA$, in the original graph, which is larger than C_1, but still not Eulerian because not all edges are yet included. As before, if the edges of C_2 are deleted (from the original graph), together with vertices F, G, and H which have become isolated, we are left with the graph on the right of Fig. 10.5. This graph contains a circuit $ADBEA$, which makes contact with C_2 at A. Piecing together these circuits (follow C_2 to A, then $ADBEA$), we obtain a circuit C_3 that contains all the edges of the original graph,

Figure 10.4 A graph that is not Eulerian.

so C_3 is Eulerian. With the hindsight of this example, we are in a position to prove an important theorem.

10.1.4 THEOREM   A pseudograph (with at least two vertices) is Eulerian if and only if it is connected and every vertex is even.

Proof   ($\longrightarrow$) We have already shown that an Eulerian pseudograph must be connected with each vertex even.

($\longleftarrow$) For the converse, suppose that G is a connected pseudograph with all vertices of even degree. We must prove that G has an Eulerian circuit. Let v be any vertex of G. If there are any loops incident with v, follow these first, one after the other without repetition. Then, since we are assuming that G has at least two vertices and since G is connected, there must be an edge vv_1 (with $v_1 \neq v$) incident with v. If there are loops incident with v_1, follow these one after the other without repetition. Then, since $\deg v_1$ is even and bigger than 0, there must be an edge v_1v_2 different from vv_1. Thus we have a trail from v to v_2, which we continue if possible. Each time we arrive at a vertex not encountered before, follow all the loops without repetition. Since the degree of each vertex is even, we can leave any vertex different from v on an edge not yet covered. Remembering that pseudographs in this book are always finite, we see that the process just described cannot continue indefinitely; eventually, we must return to v, having traced a circuit C_1. Notice that every vertex in C_1 is even since we entered and left on different edges each time it was encountered. If C_1 is Eulerian, we are done. Otherwise, as in the preceding example, we delete from G all the edges of C_1 and all the vertices of G that are left isolated (that is, acquire degree 0) by this procedure. All vertices of the remaining graph G_1 are even (since both G and C_1 have only even vertices) and of positive degree. Also, G_1 and C_1 have a vertex u in common, because G is connected. (See Exercise 20.) Starting at u, and proceeding in G_1 as we did in G, we construct a circuit C in G_1 that returns to u. Now combine C and C_1 by starting at v, moving along C_1 to u, then through C back to u, and then back to v on the remaining edges of C_1. We obtain a circuit C_2 in G that contains more edges than C_1. If C_2 is Eulerian, we are done. Otherwise, we repeat the process, obtaining a sequence of larger and larger circuits. Since our pseudograph is finite, the process must eventually stop, and it stops only with a circuit through all edges and vertices, that is, with an Eulerian circuit.

Pause 2   Why is the graph shown in Fig. 10.2 not Eulerian? ∎

Not only does Theorem 10.1.4 give criteria for a pseudograph to be Eulerian, but its proof gives an algorithm for finding an Eulerian circuit when one exists. We have given one example. Here is another.

Pause 3   A power company's wires in a certain region follow the routes indicated in Fig. 10.6. The vertices represent poles and the edges wires. After a severe storm, all the wires and poles must be inspected. Show that there is a round trip beginning at A, which allows a person to inspect each wire exactly once. Find such a trip. ∎

Sometimes, instead of finding an Eulerian circuit in a pseudograph, we want to find an Eulerian *trail* between two vertices, a trail that passes through every vertex and includes every edge. It is not hard to classify the pseudographs in which such a trail is possible, for adding one additional edge between the two vertices, the enlarged pseudograph is Eulerian. To see this, note that if the two vertices are u and v,

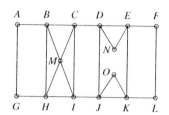

Figure 10.6

then following an Eulerian trail from u to v and going back to u along the extra edge defines an Eulerian circuit. By Theorem 10.1.4, the enlarged pseudograph must be connected with all vertices even. So the original pseudograph must have been connected with all vertices even except u and v, which are necessarily odd. (With the extra edge, they were even.) On the other hand, given a connected pseudograph with all vertices except u and v even, then certainly there is an Eulerian trail from u to v, for adding an extra edge between u and v produces an Eulerian pseudograph. Since an Eulerian circuit can begin at any vertex, imagine the one that begins by going from v to u along the added edge. Removing this added edge from the circuit then gives an Eulerian trail from u to v. We have established the following theorem.

10.1.6 THEOREM

A pseudograph $\mathcal{G}$ possesses an Eulerian trail between two (different) vertices u and v if and only if $\mathcal{G}$ is connected and all vertices except u and v are even.

EXAMPLE 4

Consider the graph in Fig. 10.7. Vertices A and B have degree 3, J and K have degree 2, and all the others have degree 4. Since the graph is connected and A and B are its only odd vertices, there exists an Eulerian trail from A to B. One Eulerian trail is $AGHFDGJHIFELIKLBCADCEB$.

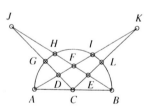

Figure 10.7

Answers to Pauses

1. $ABCEFCBD$ is not a trail (and hence not a path) because BC is a repeated edge; $ABCEFCD$ is a trail because all edges are distinct, but not a path because C is a repeated vertex; $ABCEFCDBA$ is a closed walk because its first and last vertices are the same, but not a circuit because edge AB is repeated; $BCEFCDB$ is a circuit because its edges are distinct and it begins and ends at vertex B, but it is not a cycle because its second and fifth vertices are the same. $BCDB$ is an odd cycle because it contains three edges.

2. The graph in Fig. 10.2 is not Eulerian because not all vertices are even; for example, deg $B = 3$.

3. The desired round trip is just an Eulerian circuit in the graph of Fig. 10.6. Such a circuit exists because the graph is connected and each vertex has even degree; vertices A, F, G, L, N, and O have degree 2; the rest have degree 4. In

the search for an Eulerian circuit, an obvious circuit with which to begin is $ABCDEFLKJIHGA$. Joining this to the circuit $BMCIMHB$ at B gives A-$BMCIMHB$-$CDEFLKJIHGA$. Joining this to the circuit $DJOKEND$ at D gives the following routing for the desired inspection: A-$BMCIMHB$-C--$DJOKEND$-$EFLKJIHGA$.

True/False Questions

(Answers can be found in the back of the book.)

1. A walk in a graph is a trail in which all edges are distinct.

2. A path is a walk in which all vertices are distinct.

3. A trail is a path.

4. A path is a trail.

5. A cycle is a special type of circuit.

6. A cycle is a circuit with no repeated edges.

7. An Eulerian circuit is a cycle.

8. All edges in a circuit must be distinct.

9. A subgraph of a connected graph must be connected.

10. K_8 is Eulerian.

11. $K_{8,10}$ is Eulerian.

12. A pseudograph that possesses an Eulerian trail has exactly two odd vertices.

13. A graph with more than one component cannot be Eulerian. (See 10.1.6 in the Exercises.)

Exercises

*The answers to exercises marked [BB] can be found in the **B**ack of the **B**ook.*

1. (a) [BB] Find a connected graph with as few vertices as possible that has precisely two vertices of odd degree.

   (b) Find a connected graph with as few vertices as possible that has precisely two vertices of even degree.

2. [BB] Answer the Königsberg Bridge Problem and explain.

3. In each case, explain why the graph is Eulerian and find an Eulerian circuit.

   (a) [BB]

   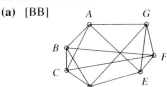

   (b)

   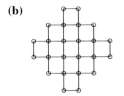

4. [BB; (a)] In each of the pseudographs shown in Fig. 10.8, either describe an Eulerian circuit by numbering the edges or explain why no Eulerian circuit exists.

5. [BB] In the text, we noted that a walk in a graph can be specified by listing a sequence of vertices, each consecutive two of which are adjacent. Gerard suggests that we could replace "vertex" by edge here; that is, a walk in a graph can be defined by a sequence of edges each consecutive two of which are adjacent. Is this true? Comment.

6. Suppose we modify the definition of Eulerian circuit by omitting the reference to vertices. Thus, we propose that an Eulerian circuit be a circuit that contains every edge of a graph. Does Theorem 10.1.4 remain true? Explain.

7. (a) [BB] Is there an Eulerian trail from A to B in the graph shown? If yes, find one; if not, explain why not.

   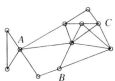

   (b) Same question for A to C.

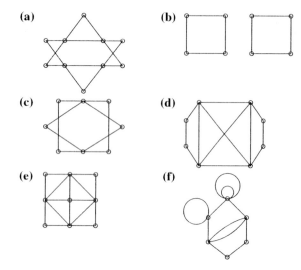

Figure 10.8 Pseudographs for Exercise 4.

8. [BB] (Fictitious) A recently discovered map of the old town of Königsberg shows that there was a ferry operating between the areas labeled C and D in Fig. 9.1.

(a) Is it possible to start on some land area, cross over each bridge exactly once, take the ferry exactly once, and return to the starting point? Explain your answer.

(b) Is it possible to start on some land mass, walk over each bridge exactly once, take the ferry exactly once, and finish on some land mass (possibly different from the starting point)? Explain.

9. Euler's original article about the Königsberg Bridge Problem, which is dated 1736, presents a second similar problem with two islands, four rivers flowing around them, and 15 bridges connecting various land masses, as shown in Fig. 10.9.

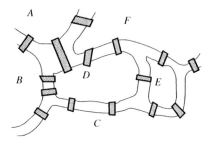

Figure 10.9 Another
Königsberg-type problem.

(a) Is it possible to tour the region starting and finishing in the same area, having walked over every bridge exactly once? Either describe such a tour or explain why none is possible.

(b) Is it possible to tour the region (with perhaps different starting and stopping points), having walked over every bridge exactly once? Either describe such a tour or explain why none is possible.

10. [BB] In Exercise 11 of Section 9.3, you were asked whether graphs $\mathcal{G}$ and $\mathcal{H}$ with the same numbers of vertices and edges and with every vertex in each graph of degree 2 need be isomorphic. Answer this question again, assuming in addition that the graphs are connected.

11. Suppose $\mathcal{G}_1$ and $\mathcal{G}_2$ are Eulerian graphs with no vertices in common. Let v_1 be a vertex in $\mathcal{G}_1$ and let v_2 be a vertex in $\mathcal{G}_2$. Join v_1 and v_2 with a single edge. What can be said about the resulting graph and why? (Is it Eulerian? Is there an Eulerian trail?)

12. (a) [BB] For which values of $n > 1$, if any, is $\mathcal{K}_n$ Eulerian?

(b) [BB] For which values of $n > 1$, if any, does $\mathcal{K}_n$ possess an Eulerian trail? Explain.

13. (a) Find a necessary and sufficient condition on natural numbers m and n in order for $\mathcal{K}_{m,n}$ to be Eulerian. Prove your answer.

(b) Find a necessary and sufficient condition on natural numbers m and n for $\mathcal{K}_{m,n}$ to have an Eulerian trail. Assume $m \le n$. Prove your answer.

14. [**Glenys's Room Problem**] Does there exist any sort of route in and around the figure that crosses every edge exactly once? Explain your answer.

15. [BB] Prove that any circuit in a graph must contain a cycle and that any circuit that is not a cycle contains at least two cycles.

16. [BB] Answer true or false and explain: Any closed walk in a graph contains a cycle.

17. Let u and v be distinct vertices in a graph $\mathcal{G}$. Prove that there is a walk from u to v if and only if there is a path from u to v.

18. [BB] For vertices u and v in a graph $\mathcal{G}$, define $u \sim v$ if $u = v$ or there exists a walk from u to v. Prove that $\sim$ defines an equivalence relation on the vertices of $\mathcal{G}$.

19. Examine the construction of $\mathcal{G}_1$ in the proof of Theorem 10.1.4. We observed that every vertex of this pseudograph is even. Must $\mathcal{G}_1$ also be connected?

20. Complete some details in the proof of Theorem 10.1.4 by establishing the following. Suppose $\mathcal{C}_1(\mathcal{V}_1, \mathcal{E}_1)$ is a circuit in a connected graph $\mathcal{G}$ that does not contain all the edges of $\mathcal{G}$. Let $\mathcal{G}_1$ be that subgraph of $\mathcal{G}$ whose edge set is $\mathcal{E} \setminus \mathcal{E}_1$ and whose vertex set is $\mathcal{V}$ less those vertices of $\mathcal{V}_1$ that become isolated after the removal of the edges in $\mathcal{E}_1$. Prove that $\mathcal{G}_1$ and $\mathcal{C}_1$ have a vertex in common.

21. Suppose $\mathcal{G}_1$ and $\mathcal{G}_2$ are isomorphic graphs. Prove that either both $\mathcal{G}_1$ and $\mathcal{G}_2$ are connected or else neither is connected.

22. [BB] A graph $\mathcal{G}$ has 20 vertices. Any two distinct vertices x and y have the property that $\deg x + \deg y \ge 19$. Prove that $\mathcal{G}$ is connected.

23. Let G be a connected graph with $n > 1$ vertices.
  (a) [BB] If no vertex has degree 1, prove that G has at least n edges.

  (b) Prove that G has at least $n - 1$ edges.

24. Let G be a graph with n vertices and m edges, where $m > \frac{1}{2}(n - 1)(n - 2)$.
  (a) Show that G does not have a vertex of degree 0.

  (b) Show that G is connected.

25. Prove that a graph is bipartite if and only if it contains no odd cycles.

10.1.6 DEFINITION   A *component* of a graph is a maximal connected subgraph, that is, a connected subgraph that is properly contained in no other connected subgraph that has more vertices or more edges.   ❖

A graph with just one component is connected. Figure 10.10 shows graphs with two and three components.

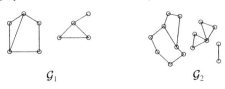

G_1 G_2

Figure 10.10 G_1 has two components; G_2 has three components.

26. Let G be a graph all of whose vertices have even degree. How can the Eulerian circuit algorithm described in Theorem 10.1.4 be modified to determine the number of components in G?

27. [BB] Prove that isomorphic graphs have the same number of components.

10.2 Hamiltonian Cycles

An Eulerian circuit passes through every edge of a graph exactly once. In this section, we discuss circuits that pass through each **vertex** of a graph exactly once. Unlike the situation in Section 10.1, the definitions and results of this section apply only to graphs, not to pseudographs.

10.2.1 DEFINITION   A *Hamiltonian cycle* in a graph is a cycle that contains every vertex of the graph. A *Hamiltonian graph* is one with a Hamiltonian cycle.   ❖

Some authors define a *Hamiltonian circuit* as a circuit in which every vertex except the first and last appears exactly once. A circuit with no repeated vertices (except the first and the last) is a cycle, so a Hamiltonian circuit is a cycle. Thus the terms *Hamiltonian circuit* and *Hamiltonian cycle* are synonymous.

EXAMPLE 5   Graph G_1 in Fig. 10.11 is Hamiltonian: The cycle $ABCDEA$, for instance, is Hamiltonian. On the other hand, graph G_2 is not Hamiltonian, but how can we convince ourselves of this fact?

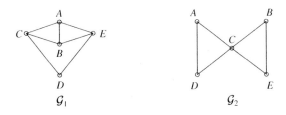

G_1 G_2

Figure 10.11 G_1 is Hamiltonian; G_2 is not.

Suppose that G_2 has a cycle $\mathcal{H}$ that contains every vertex. Then $\mathcal{H}$ will contain A, which we note is a vertex of degree 2. Since we cannot enter and leave A on the same edge (edges of a cycle are distinct), it follows that both edges incident with A have to be part of $\mathcal{H}$. In particular, edge CA is in $\mathcal{H}$. The same argument applied to B shows that CB is part of $\mathcal{H}$ and, similarly, CD and CE are in $\mathcal{H}$: All four edges incident with C are part of $\mathcal{H}$. This situation is impossible, however: Since

$\mathcal{H}$ is a cycle, vertex C can appear only once unless the cycle begins and ends at C. In either case, since $\mathcal{H}$ cannot use the same edge twice, exactly two edges incident with C can be part of $\mathcal{H}$. ▨

While it is possible to decide precisely which graphs possess Eulerian circuits (Theorem 10.1.4), it is noteworthy that there has not yet been found a way to classify Hamiltonian graphs; in other words, there is no known theorem of the sort "$\mathcal{G}$ is Hamiltonian if and only if ...." There are, however, some properties of cycles that are helpful in trying to find Hamiltonian cycles and that sometimes allow us to conclude that a particular graph is not Hamiltonian.

10.2.2 PROPERTIES OF CYCLES IN GRAPHS

Suppose $\mathcal{H}$ is a cycle in a graph $\mathcal{G}$.

1. For each vertex v of $\mathcal{H}$, precisely two edges incident with v are in $\mathcal{H}$; hence, if $\mathcal{H}$ is a Hamiltonian cycle of $\mathcal{G}$ and a vertex v in $\mathcal{G}$ has degree 2, then both edges incident with v must be part of $\mathcal{H}$.
2. The only cycle contained in $\mathcal{H}$ is $\mathcal{H}$ itself. (We say that $\mathcal{H}$ contains no *proper cycles*.)

We have, in essence, already explained why each vertex of a cycle is incident with exactly two edges: Any vertex (except the first and last) appears exactly once in a cycle. If the cycle $\mathcal{H}$ is Hamiltonian, then every vertex is in $\mathcal{H}$, so both edges incident with any vertex of degree 2 must be in $\mathcal{H}$. This establishes Property 1. Property 2 asserts that, if $\mathcal{C}$ is a cycle contained in another cycle $\mathcal{H}$, then $\mathcal{C} = \mathcal{H}$. We prove this by contradiction.

Suppose $\mathcal{C}$ is a cycle contained in $\mathcal{H}$ and $\mathcal{C} \neq \mathcal{H}$. Then there is a vertex y in $\mathcal{H}$ that is not in $\mathcal{C}$. Let x be any vertex in $\mathcal{C}$. Since $\mathcal{H}$ contains both x and y, there is a path using edges of $\mathcal{H}$ from x to y. Thus, $\mathcal{H}$ contains some edge vw where vertex v is in $\mathcal{C}$, but w is not. (See Fig. 10.12.) So $\mathcal{H}$ contains the two edges of $\mathcal{C}$ that are incident with v together with the edge vw. Altogether, there are three edges incident with v that must be part of $\mathcal{H}$. This contradicts Property 1. Thus $\mathcal{H}$ is not a cycle.

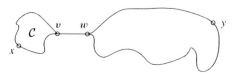

Figure 10.12

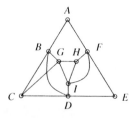
Pause 4

Answer true or false and explain: The graph shown is not Hamiltonian because it contains the cycle $GHIG$. ▮

10.2.3 THE PETERSEN GRAPH

As a deeper application of the properties of Hamiltonian graphs described in 10.2.2, we introduce a famous graph named after the Danish mathematician Julius Petersen (1839–1910).[2] We show that this graph (Fig. 10.13), is not Hamiltonian.

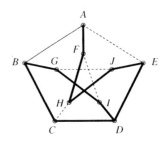

Figure 10.13 The Petersen graph is not Hamiltonian.

Figure 10.14

Suppose $\mathcal{H}$ is a Hamiltonian cycle. Then $\mathcal{H}$ must contain at least one of the five edges connecting the outer to the inner vertices. Since the graph is symmetric, there is no loss of generality in assuming that AF is part of $\mathcal{H}$. (Refer to Fig. 10.14.) By Property 1, precisely one of the two edges FH and FI is in $\mathcal{H}$. Again, by symmetry, we may assume FH is part of the cycle while FI is not.

Since FI is not in $\mathcal{H}$, but two edges incident with I must be in $\mathcal{H}$ (Property 1), IG and ID are in $\mathcal{H}$. Now precisely one of the edges GB, GJ is in $\mathcal{H}$.

Suppose first that GB is in and GJ is out. Because precisely two edges incident with J are in $\mathcal{H}$ and JG is not, both JH and JE are part of $\mathcal{H}$. Thus, CH is out and both BC and CD are in $\mathcal{H}$. At this point, however, $\mathcal{H}$ contains the proper cycle $BCDIGB$, a contradiction. We conclude that GB cannot be part of $\mathcal{H}$ and hence that GJ is. An argument similar to the one just given now leads again to the false conclusion that $\mathcal{H}$ contains a proper cycle.

Pause 5

Give the details of this argument. ∎

Pause 6

Look at the graph pictured in Fig. 10.15. Show that no Hamiltonian cycle can contain edges 1, 2, 3, 4. ∎

Hamiltonian graphs take their name from Sir William Rowan Hamilton (1805–1865), a contemporary and personal friend of William Wordsworth and Samuel Taylor Coleridge and indeed a man of many talents. By the age of 13, he had mastered one language for each year of his life, including Latin, Greek, Hebrew, Chinese, and Sanskrit! At 17, he had a firm grasp of calculus. He studied astronomy at Trinity College, Dublin, and later made important contributions to the study of optics. He is perhaps best known within the sphere of mathematics as the inventor of the *quaternions*, the first noncommutative *field* to be discovered. Hamilton's quaternions is an algebraic structure like the real numbers in which one can add, subtract, multiply, and divide (by any nonzero number), but in which multiplication is not commutative: There are quaternions a and b for which $ab \neq ba$. The reader may have encountered noncommutative systems before; for example, the set of all $n \times n$ matrices over the real numbers is not commutative. A basic difference between matrices and quaternions, however, and the thing that made Hamilton's discovery so

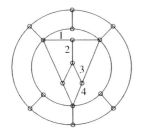

Figure 10.15 No Hamiltonian cycle contains edges 1, 2, 3, 4.

[2]J. Petersen, "Die Theorie der regulären Graphen," *Acta Mathematica* **15** (1891), 193–220.

remarkable, is the lack of divisibility in matrices. There are many nonzero matrices that are not invertible; on the other hand, every nonzero quaternion has an inverse.

Hamilton also invented a game that made use of a wooden regular *dodecahedron*, that is, a solid with 12 congruent faces, each of which is a regular pentagon. The vertices of the dodecahedron were labeled with the names of 20 cities of the world, and the object of the game was to find a route "around the world," along the edges of the solid, which passed through each city exactly once and led back to the city where the tour started.

Imagine that the pentagon on which the dodecahedron sits is stretched so that the solid collapses until it is flat. The result is a graph in the plane. (See Fig. 10.16.) Hamilton's world tour is possible if and only if the graph contains what we now call a Hamiltonian cycle. The graph in fact is Hamiltonian; a Hamiltonian cycle is marked with the heavy lines in Fig. 10.16.

Figure 10.16 A dodecahedron and its associated Hamiltonian graph.

In some graphs a Hamiltonian cycle always exists (the complete graph on n vertices, for instance). Assigning the vertices of $\mathcal{K}_n$ the labels $v_1, v_2, \ldots, v_n$, then $v_1 v_2 \cdots v_n v_1$ is a cycle because we are assured of an edge between each pair of vertices. The cycle clearly passes through each vertex (except the first and the last) exactly once, so it is Hamiltonian. It would seem that a graph with many edges should have a good chance of being Hamiltonian. The following theorem, published by G. A. Dirac in 1952, provides further evidence in support of this idea.

10.2.4 THEOREM

(Dirac[3]) If a graph $\mathcal{G}$ has $n \geq 3$ vertices and every vertex has degree at least $\frac{n}{2}$, then $\mathcal{G}$ is Hamiltonian.[4]

Proof

Among all the possible paths in $\mathcal{G}$, suppose that $\mathcal{P}: v_1 v_2 \cdots v_t$ is longest in the sense that it uses the most vertices. Thus, there is no walk in $\mathcal{G}$ that uses more than t vertices without repeating some vertex. If some vertex w adjacent to v_1 is not in $\mathcal{P}$, then the walk $w v_1 v_2 \cdots v_t$ does not have repeated vertices and is longer than $\mathcal{P}$. Since this is contrary to the way $\mathcal{P}$ was chosen, every vertex adjacent to v_1 is in $\mathcal{P}$. (Similarly, every vertex adjacent to v_t is in $\mathcal{P}$.) Since $\deg v_1 \geq \frac{n}{2}$, $t \geq \frac{n}{2} + 1$, the "+1" counting v_1 itself. Since $n \geq 3$ and t is an integer, we conclude that $t \geq 3$ also.

Claim: There is a pair of vertices v_k, v_{k+1} in $\mathcal{P}$ $(1 \leq k < t)$ such that v_1 is adjacent to v_{k+1} and v_t is adjacent to v_k, as suggested in Fig. 10.17.

If this were not the case, then each of the vertices of $\mathcal{P}$ adjacent to v_1 would determine a vertex **not** adjacent to v_t (its predecessor in $\mathcal{P}$). Since the vertices

Figure 10.17

---

[3] G. A. Dirac, "Some Theorems on Abstract Graphs," *Proceedings London Mathematical Society* **2** (1952), 69–81.

[4] There is a stronger version of this theorem, due to Oystein Ore, which says that a graph with $n \geq 3$ vertices is Hamiltonian as long as the sum of the degrees of any two nonadjacent vertices is at least n. See Exercise 16.

$v_2, \ldots, v_t$ are all different, there would be in $\mathcal{G}$ at least $\frac{n}{2}$ vertices not adjacent to v_t. These vertices, together with the vertices adjacent to v_t, account for at least n vertices in $\mathcal{G}$. Including v_t itself, we have found more than n vertices, which cannot be. This establishes the validity of our claim, from which it follows that $\mathcal{G}$ contains the cycle

$$\mathcal{C}: v_1 v_{k+1} v_{k+2} \cdots v_t v_k v_{k-1} \cdots v_1.$$

We show that $\mathcal{C}$ contains all vertices of $\mathcal{G}$ and hence is the desired Hamiltonian cycle. Remember that $\mathcal{C}$ contains at least $\frac{n}{2} + 1$ vertices, so there are less than $\frac{n}{2}$ vertices not in $\mathcal{C}$. Hence, any vertex w that is not in $\mathcal{C}$ must be adjacent to some vertex v_s of $\mathcal{C}$. Then w, v_s, and the remaining vertices of $\mathcal{C}$ in sequence would define a path longer than $\mathcal{P}$, contradicting the definition of $\mathcal{P}$.

Show that Dirac's Theorem is false if $\frac{n}{2}$ is replaced by $\frac{n-1}{2}$ in its statement. [*Hint*: Examine graphs presented in this section that are not Hamiltonian.] ∎

10.2.5 REMARK   A graph $\mathcal{G}$ is called *pancyclic* if it contains cycles of all lengths $1, 2, \ldots, n$, $n = |\mathcal{V}(G)|$. The following result has been proved by J. A. Bondy.[5]

10.2.6 THEOREM   **(Bondy)** Let $\mathcal{G}$ be Hamiltonian and suppose that $\mathcal{G}$ has at least $\frac{n^2}{4}$ edges. Then either

(i) $\mathcal{G}$ is pancyclic, or
(ii) n is even and $\mathcal{G}$ is isomorphic to the complete bipartite graph $\mathcal{K}_{\frac{n}{2},\frac{n}{2}}$.

If a graph has $n \geq 3$ vertices each of degree at least $\frac{n}{2}$, show that the conditions of Theorem 10.2.6 are satisfied. ∎

Pause 8 and Bondy's Theorem tell us that the conditions of Dirac's Theorem can be used to prove much more about a graph than simply that it is Hamiltonian. While a proof of Bondy's Theorem is beyond the scope of this text, the reader is asked to prove the special cases of 3-cycles and 4-cycles in the exercises (under the assumptions of Dirac's Theorem). See Exercises 19 and 20.

Application: Gray Codes[6]

One way in which Hamiltonian cycles are important in the real world is in the construction of *Gray codes*. A Gray code of length n is a list of all 2^n sequences of 0's and 1's with the property that each sequence in the list differs from the next in precisely 1 digit (bit) and the last number differs from the first in precisely 1 bit. For example, $00, 01, 11, 10$ is a Gray code of length 2.

It is virtually clear that a Gray code is just a Hamiltonian cycle in a certain graph, that is, the graph with 2^n vertices labeled with all possible sequences of n 0's and 1's and where an edge joins vertices whose labels differ in just 1 bit. For example, if $n = 2$, we draw a graph with $2^2 = 4$ vertices. One possibility is shown to the left, and an obvious Hamiltonian cycle is $00, 01, 11, 10, 00$, giving the Gray code $00, 01, 11, 10$. If $n = 3$, we draw a graph with $2^3 = 8$ vertices labeled $000, 001, 010, 100, 011, 101, 110, 111$, as shown on the left of Fig. 10.18, and we find the Hamiltonian cycle

$$000, 010, 011, 111, 110, 100, 101, 001, 000,$$

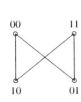

---

[5]"Pancyclic Graphs," *Journal of Combinatorial Theory* **11** (1971), 80–84.
[6]After Frank Gray, a researcher at Bell Lab, who patented a vacuum tube using Gray encoding in 1953.

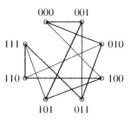
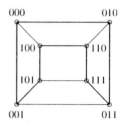

Figure 10.18 A Hamiltonian cycle gives a Gray code of length 3.

which gives the Gray code 000, 010, 011, 111, 110, 100, 101, 001 of length 3. The graph here is usually drawn as on the right (think of flattening a cube; see Exercise 12), but to draw the graph at the outset this way seems to us like presupposing the answer.

 **Pause 9**

Can you think of a way to create a Gray code of length $n + 1$ from one of length n? Find a Gray code of length 4. ∎

Answers to Pauses

4. False! The graph is Hamiltonian: $AFEDIHGCBA$ is a Hamiltonian cycle. It is not the entire **graph** that must not contain a proper cycle, but any **Hamiltonian cycle**.

5. We are assuming that both AF and FH are in a Hamiltonian path $\mathcal{H}$. As before, FI is not in $\mathcal{H}$; therefore, both IG and ID are. Since edge GJ is also in $\mathcal{H}$, while GB is out, both BA and BC are in because two edges adjacent to B are part of $\mathcal{H}$ and BG is not in $\mathcal{H}$, as shown on the left. Using Property 2, we see that CH cannot be part of $\mathcal{H}$; otherwise $\mathcal{H}$ contains the proper cycle $ABCHFA$. So both CD and HJ are in. Now $\mathcal{H}$ contains the proper cycle $ABCDIGJHFA$, a contradiction.

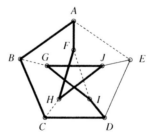
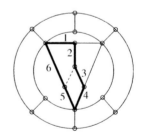

6. If a Hamiltonian cycle $\mathcal{H}$ contains edges 2 and 3 (see the graph on the right), then the third edge at the center could not be part of $\mathcal{H}$ (Property 1), so the edges labeled 5 and 6 would have to belong to $\mathcal{H}$ (Property 1 again). Now edges 1, 2, 3, 4, 5, and 6 form a proper cycle within $\mathcal{H}$. This contradicts Property 2.

7. The graph $\mathcal{G}_2$ in Fig. 10.11, which is **not** Hamiltonian, has $n = 5$ vertices each of degree at least $2 = \frac{n-1}{2}$.

8. Dirac's Theorem says that the graph is Hamiltonian. Also, the sum of the degrees of the vertices is at least $n(\frac{n}{2}) = \frac{n^2}{2}$. Proposition 9.2.5 then says that $2|\mathcal{E}| \geq \frac{n^2}{2}$, so $|\mathcal{E}| \geq \frac{n^2}{4}$. (As usual, $\mathcal{E}$ is the set of edges of the graph.)

9. Put a 0 in front of each sequence in a Gray code of length n; then write down the list of length n **in reverse order** and put a 1 in front of each of these sequences.

For example, putting a 0 in front of each sequence in the Gray code of length 3 given in the text gives us

0000, 0010, 0011, 0111, 0110, 0100, 0101, 0001.

Now write down the Gray code of length 3 with a 1 in front of each sequence,

1001, 1101, 1100, 1110, 1111, 1011, 1010, 1000,

and concatenate the two lists.

True/False Questions

(Answers can be found in the back of the book.)

1. A Hamiltonian cycle is a circuit.

2. $\mathcal{K}_8$ is Hamiltonian.

3. $\mathcal{K}_{8,10}$ is Hamiltonian.

4. A graph with more than one component cannot be Hamiltonian.

5. A graph that contains a proper cycle cannot be Hamiltonian.

6. The problem of classifying Hamiltonian graphs is still open.

7. A pseudograph $\mathcal{G}$ is Hamiltonian if and only if it contains a Hamiltonian subgraph $\mathcal{H}$ that contains all the vertices of $\mathcal{G}$.

8. If a graph $\mathcal{G}$ contains a cycle that does not pass through all the vertices of $\mathcal{G}$, then $\mathcal{G}$ is not Hamiltonian.

9. Hamiltonian graphs are named after the famous Canadian graph theorist George Hamilton.

10. If a graph $\mathcal{G}$ has $n \geq 3$ vertices and every vertex has degree at most $\frac{n}{2}$, then $\mathcal{G}$ is Hamiltonian.

Exercises

*The answers to exercises marked [BB] can be found in the **B**ack of the **B**ook.*

1. [BB] Is the graph Hamiltonian? Is it Eulerian? Explain your answers.

2. [BB; (b), (d)] Determine whether or not each of the graphs of Exercise 4 of Section 10.1 is Hamiltonian. In each case, either label the edges with numbers so as to indicate a Hamiltonian cycle or explain why no such cycle exists.

10.2.7 DEFINITION   A *Hamiltonian path* in a graph is a path that passes through every vertex exactly once.

❖

3. Determine whether each of the graphs shown is Hamiltonian. Determine also whether each graph has a Hamilto-

nian path. In each case, either number the vertices so as to indicate a Hamiltonian cycle or path or explain why no such cycle or path exists.

(a)   **(b)**

(c)

(d)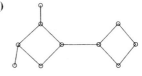

(e) **(f)**

(g) **(h)**

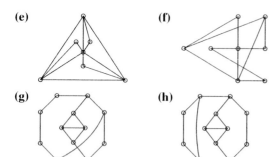

4. Is the graph Hamiltonian? If no, why not? If yes, find all Hamiltonian cycles.

5. Consider the graph shown.

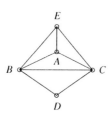

(a) [BB] Is it Hamiltonian?

(b) Is there a Hamiltonian path?

(c) [BB] Is it Eulerian?

(d) Is there an Eulerian trail?
Explain your answers.

6. (a) (The Knight's Tour) Is it possible for a knight to tour a chessboard visiting every square exactly once and returning to its initial square? (See Exercise 8 of Section 9.2.)

(b) Is the sort of tour described in 6a possible on a 7×7 "chessboard"?
(For a complete classification of those $m \times n$ boards on which knight's tours are possible, the reader is directed to the interesting article by Allen J. Schwenk that appeared in the December 1991 issue of *Mathematics Magazine*.)

7. Is the graph of Fig. 10.15 Hamiltonian? Display a Hamiltonian cycle or explain clearly why no such cycle exists.

8. (a) Does the graph have a Hamiltonian cycle that excludes edges a and ℓ. Explain.

(b) Is the graph Hamiltonian? Explain.

9. The figure shows the floor plan of a single-story house with various doorways between rooms and other doorways leading outside.

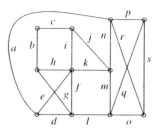

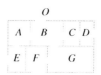

(a) [BB] Is it possible to start outside, then to enter the house and walk through every room exactly once (without leaving the house), and finally to return outside? If yes, exhibit the route on a copy of the floor plan.

(b) Is there is a route that starts outside and leads through every doorway in the house exactly once? (You are allowed to return outside or to reenter rooms as often as you want.)

10. [BB] In a group of $2n$ people, each person has at least n friends. Prove that the group can be seated in a circle, each person next to a friend.

11. (a) [BB] How many edges must a Hamiltonian cycle in $\mathcal{K}_n$ contain?

(b) How many Hamiltonian cycles does $\mathcal{K}_n$ have?

(c) [BB] What is the maximum number of *edge disjoint* Hamiltonian cycles in $\mathcal{K}_n$?[7] (Cycles are *edge disjoint* if no two of them have an edge in common.)

(d) Find all the Hamiltonian cycles in $\mathcal{K}_n$ for $n = 1, 2, 3, 4, 5$. In each case, exhibit a maximum number that are edge disjoint.

12. [BB] Draw a picture of a cube. By imagining that the bottom square is stretched until it is flat, draw a graph of the flattened cube. Is this graph Hamiltonian? If so, draw a Hamiltonian cycle. If not, explain why not.

13. The picture on the left of Fig. 10.19 is that of an icosahedron, a solid object whose faces consist of 20 congruent equilateral triangles. By stretching the base triangle and flattening, the icosahedron determines a graph in the plane (as shown on the right side of the figure). Find a Hamiltonian cycle in this graph.

[7] In fact, any complete graph actually has this maximum number of edge disjoint cycles.

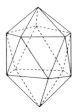 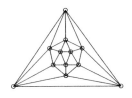

Figure 10.19 An icosahedron and its associated graph.

14. Make a model of a dodecahedron (Fig. 10.16) and trace a Hamiltonian cycle along its edges. Do the same for the icosahedron. (*Suggestion*: Look for ideas in geometry texts, in their discussions of the Platonic solids. One such book is the wonderful work of H. S. M. Coxeter, *Introduction to Geometry*, Wiley, New York, 1961.)

15. (a) [BB] Suppose $\mathcal{G}$ is a graph with n vertices, each of which has degree $d \geq \frac{n-1}{2}$. Prove that $\mathcal{G}$ contains a Hamiltonian path. [*Hint*: Add an extra vertex to $\mathcal{G}$ that is adjacent to every vertex and use Dirac's Theorem.]

(b) Does the graph shown on the left have a Hamiltonian path? If so, find it. If it doesn't have one, explain why not.

(c) Repeat (b) for the graph on the right.

(d) Does the converse of (a) hold; that is, if a graph has a Hamiltonian path, must the degree of every vertex be at least $\frac{n-1}{2}$? Explain your answer. What about the converse of Dirac's Theorem?

(e) [BB] Give an example of a graph that has a Hamiltonian path, but no Hamiltonian cycle.

16. (Ore's Theorem) Suppose $\mathcal{G}$ is a graph with $n \geq 3$ vertices and that the sum of the degrees of any two nonadjacent vertices is at least n. Prove that $\mathcal{G}$ is Hamiltonian by starting with a path $\mathcal{P}: v_1 v_2 \cdots v_t$ of greatest length,

as in the proof of Dirac's Theorem, and then considering separately the cases where

(a) [BB] v_1 and v_t are adjacent, and

(b) v_1 and v_t are not adjacent.

17. Suppose $\mathcal{G}$ is a graph with $n \geq 3$ vertices and at least $\binom{n-1}{2} + 2$ edges. Show that $\mathcal{G}$ is Hamiltonian. [*Hint*: Exercise 16.]

18. [BB] Suppose $\mathcal{G}$ is a graph with $n \geq 2$ vertices such that the sum of the degrees of any two nonadjacent vertices is at least $n - 1$. Prove that $\mathcal{G}$ has a Hamiltonian path.

19. Let $\mathcal{G}$ be a graph with n vertices, each of degree at least $\frac{n}{2}$. Show that either $\mathcal{G}$ contains a triangle or n is even and $\mathcal{G}$ is isomorphic to $\mathcal{K}_{\frac{n}{2}, \frac{n}{2}}$.

20. [BB] Let $\mathcal{G}$ be a graph with $n \geq 4$ vertices, each of degree at least $\frac{n}{2}$. Show that $\mathcal{G}$ contains a 4-cycle.

21. Answer true or false and in each case either give a proof or provide a counterexample.

(a) A Hamiltonian graph contains no proper cycles.

(b) Every vertex in a Hamiltonian graph has degree 2.

(c) [BB] Every Eulerian graph is Hamiltonian.

(d) Every Hamiltonian graph is Eulerian.

22. Let $\mathcal{G}$ be a graph with at least three vertices.

(a) [BB] If there is a Hamiltonian path between any two vertices of $\mathcal{G}$, must $\mathcal{G}$ contain a Hamiltonian cycle? Explain.

(b) If, at every vertex v in $\mathcal{G}$, there is a Hamiltonian path that starts at v, must $\mathcal{G}$ contain a Hamiltonian cycle? Explain.

(c) Is it possible for there to exist an Eulerian trail between any two vertices of $\mathcal{G}$? If so, must $\mathcal{G}$ contain an Eulerian circuit? Explain.

23. A connected graph $\mathcal{G}$ has 11 vertices and 53 edges. Show that $\mathcal{G}$ is Hamiltonian, but not Eulerian.

24. (a) Find a necessary and sufficient condition on m and n for $\mathcal{K}_{m,n}$ to be Hamiltonian. Prove your answer.

(b) Determine whether the graph shown is Hamiltonian.

10.3 The Adjacency Matrix

Graphs occur with increasing frequency in modern-day problems. While theoretically, any problem associated with a finite graph is solvable, in practice, the number of cases to consider is often so large and the time needed to deal with each case so great that an exhaustive search of all possibilities is impossible. Accordingly, the discovery of new graph-based algorithms and ways to improve efficiency are flourishing areas of mathematical research today. To write an algorithm that requires the input of a graph, we first must decide how to code the pertinent information that describes a graph. For this purpose, the *adjacency matrix* is commonly used.

10.3.1 DEFINITION

Let G be a graph with n vertices labeled $v_1, v_2, \ldots, v_n$. For each i and j with $1 \le i, j \le n$, define

$$a_{ij} = \begin{cases} 1 & \text{if } v_i v_j \text{ is an edge} \\ 0 & \text{if } v_i v_j \text{ is not an edge.} \end{cases}$$

The *adjacency matrix* of G is the $n \times n$ matrix $A = [a_{ij}]$ whose (i, j) entry is a_{ij}. ❖

EXAMPLE 6 Figure 10.20 shows a graph G and its adjacency matrix A.

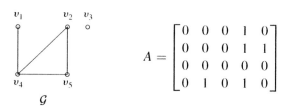

$$A = \begin{bmatrix} 0 & 0 & 0 & 1 & 0 \\ 0 & 0 & 0 & 1 & 1 \\ 0 & 0 & 0 & 0 & 0 \\ 0 & 1 & 0 & 1 & 0 \end{bmatrix}$$

Figure 10.20 A graph and its adjacency matrix.

EXAMPLE 7 The adjacency matrix of the complete bipartite graph on the sets $V_1 = \{v_1, v_2\}$ and $V_2 = \{v_3, v_4, v_5\}$ is

$$\begin{bmatrix} 0 & 0 & 1 & 1 & 1 \\ 0 & 0 & 1 & 1 & 1 \\ 1 & 1 & 0 & 0 & 0 \\ 1 & 1 & 0 & 0 & 0 \\ 1 & 1 & 0 & 0 & 0 \end{bmatrix}.$$

Since the adjacency matrix records all the incidence relations in a graph, it is not surprising that it gives a lot of information about the graph. We list here some of the basic properties of an adjacency matrix. Some are obvious, others not quite so, and perhaps the most curious of all, due to Gustav Kirchhoff, we leave to Chapter 12.

10.3.2 PROPERTIES OF AN ADJACENCY MATRIX

Let G be a graph with vertices $v_1, v_2, \ldots, v_n$ and let $A = [a_{ij}]$ be the adjacency matrix of G.

1. The diagonal entries of A are all 0; that is, $a_{ii} = 0$ for $i = 1, \ldots, n$. This follows because an edge from vertex v_i to v_i is a loop and loops are not allowed in graphs. (Actually, we can define the adjacency matrix of a pseudograph and show that it has most of the properties given here, but we shall restrict our attention to graphs.)

2. The adjacency matrix is *symmetric*, that is, $a_{ij} = a_{ji}$ for all i, j.
   Conversely, given any symmetric matrix A that contains only 0's and 1's and only 0's on its diagonal, there exists a graph G whose adjacency matrix is A. Thus, there is a one-to-one correspondence between graphs and symmetric 0, 1 matrices with only 0's on the diagonal.

The next three properties are less obvious than the first two. We will discuss them in some detail after a couple of PAUSEs.

3. deg v_i is the number of 1's in row i; this is also the number of 1's in column i since row i and column i are the same, by symmetry.
4. The (i, j) entry of A^2 is the number of different walks of length 2 from v_i to v_j; in particular, the degree of v_i is the ith main diagonal entry of A^2.
5. In general, for any $k \geq 1$, the (i, j) entry of A^k is the number of walks of length k from v_i to v_j.

Can the 4×4 identity matrix $I = \begin{bmatrix} 1 & 0 & 0 & 0 \\ 0 & 1 & 0 & 0 \\ 0 & 0 & 1 & 0 \\ 0 & 0 & 0 & 1 \end{bmatrix}$ be the adjacency matrix of a graph?   ∎

Find a graph whose adjacency matrix is $A = \begin{bmatrix} 0 & 0 & 0 & 1 \\ 0 & 0 & 1 & 0 \\ 0 & 1 & 0 & 0 \\ 1 & 0 & 0 & 0 \end{bmatrix}$.   ∎

As mentioned, the powers of an adjacency matrix A have special significance. To understand why the (i, j) entry of A^2 is the number of walks of length 2 between v_i and v_j in the graph corresponding to A, remember that this entry is the dot product of row i and column j of A. Since A contains only 0's and 1's, this dot product is just the number of coordinates in which row i and column j each have a 1. For example, if row i of A were the vector $[0, 0, 1, 0, 1, 1, 0]$ and column j the vector $[1, 1, 1, 0, 0, 1, 0]$, then the dot product (row i) · (row j) $= 2$, corresponding to the two coordinates (third and sixth) where each vector has a 1. How does it happen that a row and a column have a 1 in the same coordinate? In our example, row i and column j each have third coordinate 1; this corresponds to the fact that there is an edge in the graph between v_i and v_3 and an edge between v_j and v_3. There is a walk in the graph from v_i to v_j that uses two edges, $v_i v_3 v_j$. The dot product of row i and column j is therefore the number of walks of length 2 from v_i to v_j.

In general, there is one walk of length 2 from a vertex to itself for each edge incident with that vertex. Thus, the degree of vertex v_i is the diagonal entry a_{ii} of the square of the adjacency matrix, as asserted in Property 4. The rest of Property 4 and Property 5 can be justified with similar arguments.

EXAMPLE 8   Referring to Fig. 10.20, $A^2 = \begin{bmatrix} 1 & 1 & 0 & 0 & 1 \\ 1 & 2 & 0 & 1 & 1 \\ 0 & 0 & 0 & 0 & 0 \\ 0 & 1 & 0 & 3 & 1 \\ 1 & 1 & 0 & 1 & 2 \end{bmatrix}$.

The $(4, 2)$ entry of A^2 is 1 corresponding to the fact that there is precisely one walk of length 2 between v_4 and v_2 in the associated graph: $v_4 v_5 v_2$. The $(4, 4)$ entry of A^2 is 3; there are three walks of length 2 from v_4 back to v_4, one for each edge incident with v_4.

The third power of the matrix A in Fig. 10.20 is $A^3 = \begin{bmatrix} 0 & 1 & 0 & 3 & 1 \\ 1 & 2 & 0 & 4 & 3 \\ 0 & 0 & 0 & 0 & 0 \\ 3 & 4 & 0 & 2 & 4 \\ 1 & 3 & 0 & 4 & 2 \end{bmatrix}$.

The $(4, 5)$ entry of A^3 is 4. Thus, there are four walks of length 3 from v_4 to v_5 in the graph. What are they? ∎

Since the adjacency matrix of a graph records the number of vertices and the adjacencies between them, the following theorem is straightforward.

10.3.3 THEOREM   Two graphs are isomorphic if and only if their vertices can be labeled in such a way that the corresponding adjacency matrices are equal.

EXAMPLE 9   The graphs in Fig. 10.21 have been labeled so that each has the adjacency matrix

$$\begin{bmatrix} 0 & 1 & 0 & 1 \\ 1 & 0 & 1 & 0 \\ 0 & 1 & 0 & 1 \\ 1 & 0 & 1 & 0 \end{bmatrix}.$$

(These are the graphs that appeared in Fig. 9.27, with the labels A, B, C, D replaced by v_1, v_2, v_3, v_4, respectively.) As we earlier noted, these graphs are isomorphic. ∎

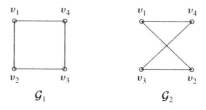

Figure 10.21 Two graphs labeled so as to show that they are isomorphic.

Suppose we are presented with two graphs that are already labeled. Can we tell from the adjacency matrices whether the graphs are isomorphic? Consider again the graphs of Fig. 10.21, but labeled as in Fig. 10.22.

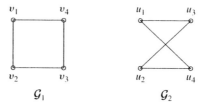

Figure 10.22 Two isomorphic graphs.

The adjacency matrices A_1 and A_2 of $\mathcal{G}_1$ and $\mathcal{G}_2$, respectively, are

$$A_1 = \begin{bmatrix} 0 & 1 & 0 & 1 \\ 1 & 0 & 1 & 0 \\ 0 & 1 & 0 & 1 \\ 1 & 0 & 1 & 0 \end{bmatrix} \quad \text{and} \quad A_2 = \begin{bmatrix} 0 & 0 & 1 & 1 \\ 0 & 0 & 1 & 1 \\ 1 & 1 & 0 & 0 \\ 1 & 1 & 0 & 0 \end{bmatrix}.$$

Although these graphs are isomorphic, their matrices are not equal simply because of the way the graphs were presented to us, their labels already in place. Observe, however, that the following reassignment of labels to $\mathcal{G}_1$ defines an isomorphism $\mathcal{G}_1 \to \mathcal{G}_2$.

$$
\begin{aligned}
v_1 &\to u_1 \\
v_2 &\to u_4 \\
v_3 &\to u_2 \\
v_4 &\to u_3
\end{aligned}
$$

(1)

We use this isomorphism to obtain a *permutation matrix* P, that is, a matrix whose rows are the rows of the identity matrix, but not necessarily in their natural order. Precisely, let P be that 4×4 matrix with row 1 of the 4×4 identity matrix as its first row, row 2 of the identity as its fourth row, row 3 of the identity as its second row, and row 4 of the identity as its third row. In other words,

$$
P = \begin{bmatrix} 1 & 0 & 0 & 0 \\ 0 & 0 & 1 & 0 \\ 0 & 0 & 0 & 1 \\ 0 & 1 & 0 & 0 \end{bmatrix}.
$$

Notice how the isomorphism in (1) determines P. If the isomorphism maps v_i to u_j, we put row i of the identity matrix into row j of P. Just as the relabeling of the vertices of $\mathcal{G}_1$ given by (1) transforms $\mathcal{G}_1$ into $\mathcal{G}_2$, the matrix P transforms the adjacency matrix of $\mathcal{G}_1$ into the adjacency matrix of $\mathcal{G}_2$ in the sense that $PA_1P^T = A_2$. The notation P^T means the *transpose* of the matrix P, that is, the matrix obtained from P by interchanging rows and columns.

$$
PA_1P^T = \begin{bmatrix} 1 & 0 & 0 & 0 \\ 0 & 0 & 1 & 0 \\ 0 & 0 & 0 & 1 \\ 0 & 1 & 0 & 0 \end{bmatrix} \begin{bmatrix} 0 & 1 & 0 & 1 \\ 1 & 0 & 1 & 0 \\ 0 & 1 & 0 & 1 \\ 1 & 0 & 1 & 0 \end{bmatrix} \begin{bmatrix} 1 & 0 & 0 & 0 \\ 0 & 0 & 0 & 1 \\ 0 & 1 & 0 & 0 \\ 0 & 0 & 1 & 0 \end{bmatrix}
$$

$$
= \begin{bmatrix} 0 & 1 & 0 & 1 \\ 0 & 1 & 0 & 1 \\ 1 & 0 & 1 & 0 \\ 1 & 0 & 1 & 0 \end{bmatrix} \begin{bmatrix} 1 & 0 & 0 & 0 \\ 0 & 0 & 0 & 1 \\ 0 & 1 & 0 & 0 \\ 0 & 0 & 1 & 0 \end{bmatrix}
$$

$$
= \begin{bmatrix} 0 & 0 & 1 & 1 \\ 0 & 0 & 1 & 1 \\ 1 & 1 & 0 & 0 \\ 1 & 1 & 0 & 0 \end{bmatrix} = A_2.
$$

Pause 13

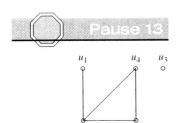

Graph $\mathcal{G}_1$ shown at the left is the same as $\mathcal{G}$ in Fig. 10.20, except that the labels v_1, v_2, v_3, v_4, v_5 have been replaced by u_1, u_4, u_3, u_2, u_5, respectively. Find the adjacency matrix A_1 of $\mathcal{G}_1$. Then find a permutation matrix such that $PAP^T = A_1$. ∎

The proof of the following theorem, which we have been illustrating, is not especially interesting and will not be included. The key idea is that, if $\mathcal{G}$ is a graph with adjacency matrix A, then an isomorphism from $\mathcal{G}$ to another graph just amounts to renumbering the vertices of $\mathcal{G}$. Renumbering vertices corresponds to permuting the rows (equivalently, computing PA) and permuting the columns of A (equivalently, computing AP^T), hence, changing A to the matrix PAP^T. See the Exercises for more details.

10.3.4 THEOREM

Labeled graphs $\mathcal{G}_1$ and $\mathcal{G}_2$, with adjacency matrices A_1 and A_2, respectively, are isomorphic if and only if $A_2 = PA_1P^T$ for some permutation matrix P.

10. No, by Property 1.

11. Here is a graph with adjacency matrix $A = \begin{bmatrix} 0 & 0 & 0 & 1 \\ 0 & 0 & 1 & 0 \\ 0 & 1 & 0 & 0 \\ 1 & 0 & 0 & 0 \end{bmatrix}$.

12. There are four walks of length 3 from v_4 to v_5: $v_4v_5v_2v_5$, $v_4v_1v_4v_5$, $v_4v_5v_4v_5$, and $v_4v_2v_4v_5$.

13. $A_1 = \begin{bmatrix} 0 & 1 & 0 & 0 & 0 \\ 1 & 0 & 0 & 1 & 1 \\ 0 & 0 & 0 & 0 & 0 \\ 0 & 1 & 0 & 0 & 1 \\ 0 & 1 & 0 & 1 & 0 \end{bmatrix}$ $P = \begin{bmatrix} 1 & 0 & 0 & 0 & 0 \\ 0 & 0 & 0 & 1 & 0 \\ 0 & 0 & 1 & 0 & 0 \\ 0 & 1 & 0 & 0 & 0 \\ 0 & 0 & 0 & 0 & 1 \end{bmatrix}$

The equation $PAP^T = A_1$ corresponds to the reassignment of labels to the graph $\mathcal{G}$, whose adjacency matrix is A. The matrix P is therefore the 5×5 matrix, where row 1 of the identity is in row 1, row 2 of the identity is in row 4, row 3 of the identity is in row 3, row 4 of the identity is in row 2, and row 5 of the identity is in row 5.

True/False Questions

(Answers can be found in the back of the book.)

1. $\begin{bmatrix} 0 & 1 & 0 \\ 1 & 1 & 1 \\ 0 & 1 & 0 \end{bmatrix}$ is the adjacency matrix of a graph.

2. $\begin{bmatrix} 0 & 1 & 0 \\ 0 & 0 & 1 \\ 1 & 0 & 0 \end{bmatrix}$ is the adjacency matrix of a graph.

3. If a graph $\mathcal{G}$ has adjacency matrix $\begin{bmatrix} 0 & 1 & 1 \\ 1 & 0 & 0 \\ 1 & 0 & 0 \end{bmatrix}$, there are two walks from v_1 back to itself that include two edges.

4. If A is the adjacency matrix of a graph and $\deg v_1 = 0$, then the $(1, j)$ entry of A^k is 0 for all j and all k.

5. Let A be the adjacency matrix of a graph. If the $(3, 4)$ entry of A is 1 and the $(3, 4)$ entry of A^2 is 2, then $\deg v_3 \geq 3$.

6. Let A be the adjacency matrix of a graph. In general, for any $n \geq 1$, the (i, j) entry of A^n is the number of walks from v_i to v_j that include at least n edges.

7. If A is the adjacency matrix of a graph and $A^n = 0$ (the zero matrix) for some n, then A contains no cycles.

8. If A is the adjacency matrix of the graph K_5, then the $(2, 4)$ entry of A^2 is 4.

9. Two graphs are isomorphic if and only if their adjacency matrices are equal, no matter how the vertices are labeled.

10. $\begin{bmatrix} 0 & 1 & 0 \\ 1 & 0 & 0 \\ 0 & 1 & 0 \end{bmatrix}$ is a permutation matrix.

Exercises

*The answers to exercises marked [BB] can be found in the **B**ack of the **B**ook.*

1. Find the adjacency matrices of the graphs in Figs. 10.2 [BB] and 10.4.

2. What is the adjacency matrix of K_n? Label the vertices of $K_{m,n}$ so that the adjacency matrix has an especially nice form.

3. (a) [BB] Let A be the adjacency matrix of the graph $\mathcal{G}_2$ shown in Fig. 10.11. Determine the $(3, 5)$ entry of A^3 by inspection of the graph, that is, without writing down A explicitly. Determine the $(2, 2)$ entry of A^3 by similar means.

   (b) Repeat part (a) for the graph $\mathcal{G}_1$ of Fig. 10.11.

4. [BB] What is the significance of the total number of 1's in the adjacency matrix of a graph?

5. Let A be the adjacency matrix of a graph $\mathcal{G}$ whose vertex set is $\{v_1, \dots, v_n\}$. Prove that the ith entry on the diagonal of A^3 equals twice the number of different triangles that contain vertex v_i.

6. Suppose that $\mathcal{G}$ is a graph with adjacency matrix A.
   (a) [BB] Show that the number of walks of length 2 in $\mathcal{G}$ is the sum of the entries of the matrix A^2.
   (b) Let d_i denote the degree of the vertex v_i in $\mathcal{G}$. Show that the sum of the entries of A^2 is also $\sum d_i^2$.

7. Find the adjacency matrices A_1 and A_2 of the graphs $\mathcal{G}_1$ and $\mathcal{G}_2$ shown. Find a permutation matrix P such that $A_2 = P A_1 P^T$, thus proving that $\mathcal{G}_1$ and $\mathcal{G}_2$ are isomorphic. [*Hint:* See PAUSE 6 of Section 9.3.]

$\mathcal{G}_1$

$\mathcal{G}_2$

8. (a) [BB] Find the adjacency matrices A_1 and A_2 of the graphs $\mathcal{G}_1$ and $\mathcal{G}_2$ shown.

$\mathcal{G}_1$

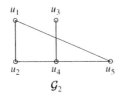
$\mathcal{G}_2$

   (b) [BB] Explain why the function $\varphi \colon \mathcal{G}_1 \to \mathcal{G}_2$ defined by
   $$\varphi(v_1) = u_4, \quad \varphi(v_2) = u_5, \quad \varphi(v_3) = u_1,$$
   $$\varphi(v_4) = u_3, \quad \varphi(v_5) = u_2$$
   is an isomorphism.

   (c) [BB] Find a permutation matrix P that corresponds to the isomorphism in (b) such that $P A_1 P^T = A_2$.

9. Repeat Exercise 8 for the graphs $\mathcal{G}_1$ and $\mathcal{G}_2$ shown. For φ, take the function $\mathcal{G}_1 \to \mathcal{G}_2$ defined by
   $$\varphi(v_1) = u_4, \quad \varphi(v_2) = u_1, \quad \varphi(v_3) = u_5$$
   $$\varphi(v_4) = u_6, \quad \varphi(v_5) = u_3, \quad \varphi(v_6) = u_2.$$

$\mathcal{G}_1$ $\mathcal{G}_2$

10. Repeat Exercise 8 for the graphs $\mathcal{G}_1$ and $\mathcal{G}_2$ shown. For φ, take the function $\mathcal{G}_1 \to \mathcal{G}_2$ defined by
    $$\varphi(v_1) = u_1, \quad \varphi(v_2) = u_2, \quad \varphi(v_3) = u_6, \quad \varphi(v_4) = u_8,$$
    $$\varphi(v_5) = u_4, \quad \varphi(v_6) = u_3, \quad \varphi(v_7) = u_7, \quad \varphi(v_8) = u_5.$$

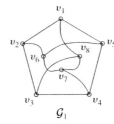
$\mathcal{G}_1$

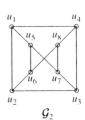
$\mathcal{G}_2$

11. Let $A = \begin{bmatrix} a & b & c \\ p & q & r \\ x & y & z \end{bmatrix}$ and let $P = \begin{bmatrix} 0 & 1 & 0 \\ 0 & 0 & 1 \\ 1 & 0 & 0 \end{bmatrix}$.
    Thus P is a permutation matrix whose rows are those of the 3×3 identity matrix in the order 2, 3, 1.
    (a) [BB] Compute PA and compare with A.
    (b) Compute AP^T and compare with A.
    (c) Compute PAP^T and compare with A.

12. Let $A = \begin{bmatrix} a & b & c & d \\ p & q & r & s \\ x & y & z & w \\ \alpha & \beta & \gamma & \delta \end{bmatrix}$ and let P be the permutation
    matrix $\begin{bmatrix} 0 & 0 & 1 & 0 \\ 1 & 0 & 0 & 0 \\ 0 & 0 & 0 & 1 \\ 0 & 1 & 0 & 0 \end{bmatrix}$.
    Find PA, AP^T, and PAP^T without calculation but with explanations.

13. For each pair of matrices A_1, A_2 shown, decide whether there is a permutation matrix P with $A_2 = P A_1 P^T$. Either find P or explain why no such P exists.

(a) [BB] $A_1 = \begin{bmatrix} 0 & 1 & 0 & 0 \\ 1 & 0 & 1 & 1 \\ 0 & 1 & 0 & 1 \\ 0 & 1 & 1 & 0 \end{bmatrix}$,

$A_2 = \begin{bmatrix} 0 & 1 & 0 & 0 \\ 1 & 0 & 1 & 1 \\ 0 & 1 & 0 & 0 \\ 0 & 1 & 0 & 0 \end{bmatrix}$

(b) $A_1 = \begin{bmatrix} 0 & 0 & 0 & 1 & 1 \\ 0 & 0 & 1 & 0 & 0 \\ 0 & 1 & 0 & 1 & 0 \\ 1 & 0 & 1 & 0 & 1 \\ 1 & 0 & 0 & 1 & 0 \end{bmatrix}$,

$A_2 = \begin{bmatrix} 0 & 1 & 1 & 0 & 0 \\ 1 & 0 & 0 & 1 & 1 \\ 1 & 0 & 0 & 0 & 0 \\ 0 & 1 & 0 & 0 & 1 \\ 0 & 1 & 0 & 1 & 0 \end{bmatrix}$

(c) $A_1 = \begin{bmatrix} 0 & 1 & 0 & 1 & 0 & 1 \\ 1 & 0 & 1 & 0 & 1 & 0 \\ 0 & 1 & 0 & 1 & 0 & 1 \\ 1 & 0 & 1 & 0 & 1 & 0 \\ 0 & 1 & 0 & 1 & 0 & 1 \\ 1 & 0 & 1 & 0 & 1 & 0 \end{bmatrix}$,

$A_2 = \begin{bmatrix} 0 & 1 & 0 & 1 & 1 & 0 \\ 1 & 0 & 1 & 0 & 0 & 1 \\ 0 & 1 & 0 & 1 & 0 & 1 \\ 1 & 0 & 1 & 0 & 1 & 0 \\ 1 & 0 & 0 & 1 & 0 & 1 \\ 0 & 1 & 1 & 0 & 1 & 0 \end{bmatrix}$

14. [BB] Let A be the adjacency matrix of a bipartite graph. Prove that the diagonal entries of A^{37} are all equal to 0.

15. Let A be the adjacency matrix of a graph $\mathcal{G}$.
    (a) [BB] Find a necessary and sufficient condition for the matrix A^2 to be the adjacency matrix of some graph.

    (b) Find a necessary and sufficient condition for A^3 to be an adjacency matrix.

16. Let A be the adjacency matrix of a graph $\mathcal{G}$ with at least two vertices. Prove that $\mathcal{G}$ is connected if and only if, for some natural number n, the matrix $B = A + A^2 + \cdots + A^n$ has no zero entries.

17. Suppose A_1 and A_2 are the adjacency matrices of isomorphic graphs $\mathcal{G}_1$ and $\mathcal{G}_2$, respectively. Show that A_1 and A_2 have the same characteristic polynomial. [*Hint*: First show that if P is a permutation matrix then $P^T = P^{-1}$.]

18. [BB] Discuss other ways, besides the adjacency matrix, that a graph could be stored in a computer.

10.4 Shortest Path Algorithms

In this section, we consider graphs whose edges have numbers attached to them. Typically, the number associated with an edge is a unit of time, distance, cost, or capacity in some sense.

10.4.1 DEFINITION

A *weighted graph* is a graph $\mathcal{G}(V, \mathcal{E})$ together with a function $w : \mathcal{E} \to [0, \infty)$. If e is an edge, the nonnegative real number $w(e)$ is called the *weight* of e. The *weight of a subgraph* of $\mathcal{G}$ (often a path or a trail) is the sum of the weights of the edges of the subgraph. ❖

One famous problem concerning weighted graphs is known as the Traveling Salesman's Problem.

The Traveling Salesman's Problem

On a typical business trip, a traveling salesman visits various towns and cities. If he wants to avoid having to pass through the same community twice, he needs a Hamiltonian cycle through the map of towns and air routes. This map can be thought of as a graph in an obvious way. Assigning to each edge a weight equal to the travel time between the cities at the ends, the traveling salesman's graph becomes a weighted graph. Among all Hamiltonian cycles (assuming there are any), what our salesman would like to find is one whose weight is a minimum to minimize total travel time. To find the Hamiltonian cycle of least weight in a weighted (Hamiltonian) graph is called the *Traveling Salesman's Problem* (TSP). It can be solved by laboriously calculating all Hamiltonian cycles and then selecting the shortest. While this approach is extremely inefficient, it is unknown whether anything better is possible. The Traveling Salesman's Problem is many people's favorite example of an *NP-complete* problem: It is an open question as to whether or not there exists an efficient (polynomial time) algorithm for its solution.[8]

Our aim in the rest of this section is to discuss a certain problem concerning weighted graphs for which, unlike the Traveling Salesman's Problem, complete and efficient solutions exist. A *shortest path* between two vertices in a weighted graph is a path of least weight. (In an unweighted graph, a shortest path means one with the fewest number of edges.) Numerous algorithms for finding shortest paths have been discovered, and efficient ones are widely used. Anybody who has ever visited **www.MapQuest.com**, for instance, has to have been impressed at the lightning speed with which it finds any address in North America and also the quickest route there from wherever you happen to be. The algorithms at the base of the software that MapQuest uses are due to Holland's Edsger Dijkstra (1930–), who apparently created one of his more widely known algorithms at a Dutch café in 1956. (Mathematicians are famous for their love of coffee. The great Paul Erdös once defined a mathematician as a person who turns coffee into theorems.)

The algorithm we first describe[9] finds the shortest path from a specified vertex A in a weighted graph to another specified vertex, say E. If continued indefinitely, it gives shortest paths from A to all other vertices in the graph. Where no path exists, this is also identified by the algorithm. The algorithm proceeds by progressively assigning to each vertex v in the graph an ordered pair (x, d), where d is the shortest distance from A to v and xv is the last edge on the shortest path. Thus, if E is eventually labeled (w, t), the shortest path from A to E is t units long and the last edge of the shortest path is wE. The first coordinate of the label for w determines the second last edge of the shortest path, and by continuing to work backward, the entire path can be found. If vertex E never gets labeled, there is no path from A to E; the graph is not connected.

10.4.2 DIJKSTRA'S ALGORITHM

To find a shortest path from vertex A to vertex E in a weighted graph, carry out the following procedure.

Step 1. Assign to A the label $(-, 0)$.

Step 2. Until E is labeled or no further labels can be assigned, do the following.

(a) For each labeled vertex $u(x, d)$ and for each unlabeled vertex v adjacent to u, compute $d + w(e)$, where $e = uv$.

(b) Find the minimum value d' of all the numbers $d + w(e)$ found in (a).

(c) For each u and v for which $d + w(e) = d'$, assign to v the label (u, d'). If a vertex can be labeled (x, d') for various vertices x, make any choice. ❖

Here is how Dijkstra's algorithm works for the graph in Fig. 10.23 that we might view as a map with the vertices representing towns; the edges, roads; and the weights of the edges, distances.

First, give A the label $(-, 0)$. There are three edges incident with A with

---

[8]For more information on this most interesting problem, we refer the reader to **www.math.princeton/edu/tsp**. There, for instance, you'll discover that as of May 2004, the largest instance of the Traveling Salesman Problem to be solved involves visits to all 24,978 cities in Sweden, a tour of approximately 72,500 kilometers. (It has also been proved that there is no shorter tour.) This surpasses the previous record of 15,112 cities through Germany set in April 2001. The calculations leading to the solution of the problem for the cities of Sweden took approximately 8 years of computation time (running in parallel on a network of Linux workstations).

[9]E. W. Dijkstra, "A Note on Two Problems in Connection with Graphs," *Numerische Mathematik* **1** (1959), 269–271.

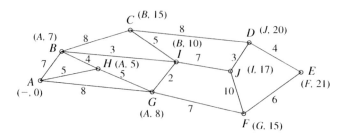

Figure 10.23 Dijkstra's shortest path algorithm applied to a weighted graph.

weights 7, 5, and 8. Since $d = 0$, vertex H gives the smallest value of $d + w(e)$, so H acquires the label $(A, 5)$. Now we repeat Step 2 for the two vertices labeled so far.

There are two unlabeled vertices adjacent to the already labeled vertex A. The numbers $d + w(e)$ are $0 + 7 = 7$ and $0 + 8 = 8$. There are also two unlabeled vertices adjacent to the other labeled vertex, H, and, for these, the numbers $d + w(e)$ are $5 + 4 = 9$ and $5 + 5 = 10$. The smallest $d + w(e)$ is 7, corresponding to the labeled vertex $u = A$ and the unlabeled $v = B$. Thus, B is labeled $(A, 7)$. Again we repeat Step 2.

Now there are three labeled vertices. There is one unlabeled vertex adjacent to the labeled vertex A and, for this, $d + w(e) = 0 + 8 = 8$. There is also just one unlabeled vertex adjacent to the labeled H, and here, $d + w(e) = 5 + 5 = 10$. There are two unlabeled vertices adjacent to the third labeled vertex B; for C, $d + w(e) = 7 + 8 = 15$ and for I, $d + w(e) = 10$. The smallest $d + w(e)$ is 8, corresponding to edge AG. So G acquires the label $(A, 8)$.

We repeat Step 2. There are four labeled vertices, A, B, H, and G, and the algorithm requires that we look at all unlabeled vertices adjacent to each of these. Since all vertices adjacent to A and to H have already been labeled, we have, in fact, only to look at B and G. There are two unlabeled vertices adjacent to B. For C, $d + w(e) = 7 + 8 = 15$; for I, $d + w(e) = 7 + 3 = 10$. There are two unlabeled vertices adjacent to G. For I, $d + w(e) = 8 + 2 = 10$; for F, $d + w(e) = 8 + 7 = 15$. The minimum $d + w(e)$ occurs with I and either edge BI or GI. We can therefore assign to I either the label $(B, 10)$ or the label $(G, 10)$; we opt for $(B, 10)$.

Repeating Step 2, we have only to look at vertices B, G and I. The only unlabeled vertex adjacent to B is C, for which $d + w(e) = 7 + 8 = 15$. The only unlabeled vertex adjacent to G is F, for which $d + w(e) = 8 + 7 = 15$. There are two unlabeled vertices adjacent to I. For C, $d + w(e) = 10 + 5 = 15$, and for J, $d + w(e) = 10 + 7 = 17$. Vertices C and F, which tie for the minimum $d + w(e)$, are each labeled. Vertex F is labeled $(G, 15)$, and C can be labeled either $(B, 15)$ or $(I, 15)$; we choose $(B, 15)$.

Continuing in this way, the vertices of the graph acquire the labels shown in Fig. 10.23. The shortest route from A to E has weight 21. A shortest path is $AGFE$, as we see by working backward from E. Since E was labeled last, the algorithm has actually found the length of a shortest route from A to any vertex. For instance, $ABIJ$ is a shortest path to J, of weight 17.

What is the complexity of Dijkstra's algorithm? We take as our basic operation an addition or comparison (which we weight equally). Assume k vertices have been labeled. Each of these vertices is conceivably adjacent to $n - k$ unlabeled vertices. For each such vertex there is one addition. After at most $k(n-k)$ additions in all, we must find the minimum of at most $k(n-k)$ numbers, a process requiring $k(n-k) - 1$

comparisons.[10] So the number of additions and comparisons is a sum of terms of the form $2k(n - k) - 1$, the largest sum being

$$f(n) = \sum_{1}^{n-1} [\, 2k(n - k) - 1\,] = \frac{n^3}{3} - \frac{4}{3}n + 1$$

corresponding to the worst-case where just one vertex is labeled at each iteration of Step 2. This algorithm has worst case complexity $\mathcal{O}(n^3)$. Note that $f(n)$ is also an upper bound for the total number of operations required if the algorithm runs until all vertices are labeled. [This was our assumption in computing $f(n)$.]

With a few minor modifications, the efficiency of Dijkstra's algorithm can be substantially increased. We present an improved version here and apply it, as with the former, to determine the weight of a shortest path from A to E in the graph of Fig. 10.23.

In the new version, the starting point A is assigned a permanent label of 0, while all other vertices initially are assigned temporary labels of ∞. At each iteration, the temporary labels are decreased or left unchanged, and one additional vertex is assigned a permanent label: the shortest distance from A to that particular vertex. This procedure continues until the required terminal point E acquires a permanent label or until some iteration results in no temporary labels (including that of E) being changed. In the latter case, we can conclude that there is no path from A to E.

10.4.3 DIJKSTRA'S ALGORITHM (IMPROVED)

To find the length of a shortest path from vertex A to vertex E in a weighted graph, proceed as follows:

Step 1. Set $v_1 = A$ and assign to this vertex the permanent label 0. Assign every other vertex a temporary label of ∞, where ∞ is a symbol that, by definition, is deemed to be larger than any real number.

Step 2. Until E has been assigned a permanent label or no temporary labels are changed in (a) or (b), do the following:

(a) Take the vertex v_i that most recently acquired a permanent label, say d. For each vertex v that is adjacent to v_i and has not yet received a permanent label, if $d + w(v_i v) < t$, the current temporary label of v, change the temporary label of v to $d + w(v_i v)$.

(b) Take a vertex v that has a temporary label smallest among all temporary labels in the graph. Set $v_{i+1} = v$ and make its temporary label permanent. If there are several vertices v that tie for smallest temporary label, make any choice.

Here is how the algorithm works for the graph of Fig. 10.23. We will describe the first few iterations in words, draw a figure summarizing the state we have reached, and then describe the remaining iterations. Readers might well wish to follow our description with their own diagrams.

At the start, $A = v_1$ is given the permanent label 0; all others are given temporary labels ∞. Next, H, B, and G have their temporary labels decreased to 5, 7, and 8, respectively, while all other temporary labels stay at ∞. Since 5 is the minimum of 5, 7, 8, we set $v_2 = H$ and make 5 its permanent label.

Now examine those vertices with temporary labels adjacent to v_2. For B, $5 + w(e) = 5 + 4 = 9$, but this is larger than its temporary label of 7, so no change occurs. For G, $5 + w(e) = 5 + 5 = 10$, again larger than the older temporary label

---

[10]Finding the minimum of t numbers requires $t - 1$ comparisons. (See Exercise 4 of Section 8.2.)

of 8. Hence, no temporary labels are changed. The smallest temporary label in the graph at this point is 7, so this becomes the next permanent label and $v_3 = B$.

Next, we examine temporary vertices adjacent to v_3. This will assign to C a new temporary label of $7 + 8 = 15$ and, to I, a new temporary label of $7 + 3 = 10$. The smallest temporary label is 8, on G; so $v_4 = G$ and this vertex acquires the permanent label 8. Figure 10.24 shows the present state of affairs. Permanent labels are circled; temporary labels are in parentheses.

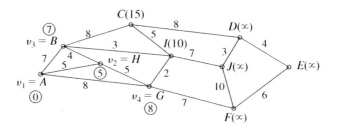

Figure 10.24 Dijkstra's algorithm, improved version.

Next, we focus on v_4. For I, we obtain $8 + 2 = 10$, the current label, so there is no change. For F, we get $8 + 7 = 15$, so F gets a temporary label of 15 and $v_5 = I$ is assigned the permanent label of 10. At the next iteration, we have a choice of C or F for v_6 and J gets a temporary label of 17. Assuming $v_6 = C$, then F will be v_7 and D will obtain a temporary label of 23.

At the next step, E gets a temporary label of 21 and $v_8 = J$. Then D gets its temporary label lowered to 20 and becomes v_9. Finally, $v_{10} = E$ with a permanent label of 21. Note that the permanent labels are exactly the second coordinates of the labels assigned to the vertices in Fig. 10.23.

As stated, this algorithm gives the length of the shortest path but not the path itself. If at each choice of a permanently labeled vertex v_i, however, we also make note of the vertex v_ℓ from which its permanent label arose, using

$$\text{(permanent label of } v_\ell) + \text{(weight of edge } v_\ell v_i) = \text{permanent label of } v_i,$$

then we can easily trace back the shortest path. Also, and the original algorithm has the same property; if allowed to continue until all vertices are labeled, the improved version will give the shortest distances from A to all other vertices.

Before introducing another shortest path algorithm, we justify the adjective *improved*, which we applied to the second version of Dijkstra's algorithm by showing that the complexity function for the second version indeed has smaller order than that for the original.

In the second version, exactly one vertex is given a permanent label at each iteration of Step 2. Assume v_k has just been identified and received a permanent label. At worst, there are $n - k$ vertices adjacent to v_k, none of which as yet has acquired a permanent label. For each such vertex, one addition is required and then one comparison to determine whether to change a temporary label. This process requires $2(n - k)$ operations. Finally, to choose the smallest among $n - k$ temporary labels requires an additional $n - k - 1$ comparisons. In all, at most

$$f(n) = \sum_{k=1}^{n-1} [\, 2(n-k) + (n-k-1)\,]$$

$$= \sum_{1}^{n-1} [\, 3(n-k) - 1\,]$$

$$= \frac{3}{2}n^2 - \frac{5}{2}n + 1 = \mathcal{O}(n^2)$$

operations are required. Recalling that the original version of Dijsktra's algorithm was $\mathcal{O}(n^3)$, we see that the second is indeed more efficient than the original. Again, we also observe that the complexity function is still $\mathcal{O}(n^2)$ even if it runs until all vertices get labeled.

If our goal is to find the shortest path between every pair of vertices in a weighted graph with n vertices, we can employ either version of Dijkstra's algorithm, letting it run until all vertices have acquired their final labels and repeating this procedure for each of the n possible starting points. The complexity functions increase by a factor of n to $\mathcal{O}(n^4)$ in the original version and to $\mathcal{O}(n^3)$ in the improved case. There is also an algorithm, due to R. W. Floyd[11] and S. Warshall,[12] that determines the shortest distances between all pairs of vertices in a graph. This algorithm is popular because it is so easy to describe.

10.4.4 THE FLOYD–WARSHALL ALGORITHM

To find the shortest distances between all pairs of vertices in a weighted graph where the vertices are $v_1, v_2, \ldots, v_n$, carry out the following procedure:

Step 1. For $i = 1$ to n, set $d(i, i) = 0$. For $i \neq j$, if $v_i v_j$ is an edge, let $d(i, j)$ be the weight of this edge; otherwise, set $d(i, j) = \infty$.

Step 2. For $k = 1$ to n,
   for $i, j = 1$ to n, let $d(i, j) = \min\{d(i, j), \; d(i, k) + d(k, j)\}$

The final value of $d(i, j)$ is the shortest distance from v_i to v_j.

Initially, the algorithm sets the shortest distance from v_i to v_j to be the length of edge $v_i v_j$, if this is an edge. After the first iteration of Step 2 ($k = 1$), this shortest distance has been replaced by the length of the path $v_i v_1 v_j$, if this is a path. In general, after stage k, the algorithm has determined the shortest distance from v_i to v_j via the vertices $v_1, v_2, \ldots, v_k$. This distance is the true shortest distance after $k = n$. In Fig. 10.25, we show a graph, the initial values of $d(i, j)$, and the values of $d(i, j)$ after each change in k.

The Floyd–Warshall algorithm is very efficient from the point of view of storage since it can be implemented by just updating the matrix of distances with each change in k; there is no need to store different matrices. In many specific applications, it is faster than either version of Dijkstra's algorithm although, like the improved version, it too is $\mathcal{O}(n^2)$.

[11]R. W. Floyd, "Algorithm 97: Shortest Path," *Communications of the Association for Computing Machinery* **5** (1962), 345.
[12]S. Warshall, "A Theorem on Boolean Matrices," *Journal of the Association for Computing Machinery* **9** (1962), 11–12.

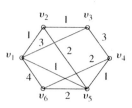

	Initial values of $d(i, j)$					
	v_1	v_2	v_3	v_4	v_5	v_6
v_1	0	1	3	∞	1	4
v_2	1	071	∞	2	∞	
v_3	3	1	0	3	∞	∞
v_4	1	2	∞	1	0	2
v_5	1	2	∞	1	0	2
v_6	4	∞	∞	2	2	0

After $k = 1$

$$
\begin{matrix}
0 & 1 & 3 & \infty & 1 & 4 \\
1 & 0 & 1 & \infty & 2 & 5 \\
3 & 1 & 0 & 3 & 4 & 7 \\
\infty & \infty & 3 & 0 & 1 & 2 \\
1 & 2 & 4 & 1 & 0 & 2 \\
4 & 5 & 7 & 2 & 2 & 0
\end{matrix}
\longrightarrow
$$

After $k = 2$

$$
\begin{matrix}
0 & 1 & 2 & \infty & 1 & 4 \\
1 & 0 & 1 & \infty & 2 & 5 \\
2 & 1 & 0 & 3 & 3 & 6 \\
\infty & \infty & 3 & 0 & 1 & 2 \\
1 & 2 & 3 & 1 & 0 & 2 \\
4 & 5 & 6 & 2 & 2 & 0
\end{matrix}
\longrightarrow
$$

After $k = 3$

$$
\begin{matrix}
0 & 1 & 2 & 5 & 1 & 4 \\
1 & 0 & 1 & 4 & 2 & 5 \\
2 & 1 & 0 & 3 & 3 & 6 \\
5 & 4 & 3 & 0 & 1 & 2 \\
1 & 2 & 3 & 1 & 0 & 2 \\
4 & 5 & 6 & 2 & 2 & 0
\end{matrix}
$$

After $k = 4$

$$
\longrightarrow
\begin{matrix}
0 & 1 & 2 & 5 & 1 & 4 \\
1 & 0 & 1 & 4 & 2 & 5 \\
2 & 1 & 0 & 3 & 3 & 5 \\
5 & 4 & 3 & 0 & 1 & 2 \\
1 & 2 & 3 & 1 & 0 & 2 \\
4 & 5 & 5 & 2 & 2 & 0
\end{matrix}
\longrightarrow
$$

After $k = 5$

$$
\begin{matrix}
0 & 1 & 2 & 2 & 1 & 3 \\
1 & 0 & 1 & 3 & 2 & 4 \\
2 & 1 & 0 & 3 & 3 & 5 \\
2 & 3 & 3 & 0 & 1 & 2 \\
1 & 2 & 3 & 1 & 0 & 2 \\
3 & 4 & 5 & 2 & 2 & 0
\end{matrix}
\longrightarrow
$$

After $k = 6$

$$
\begin{matrix}
0 & 1 & 2 & 2 & 1 & 3 \\
1 & 0 & 1 & 3 & 2 & 4 \\
2 & 1 & 0 & 3 & 3 & 5 \\
2 & 3 & 3 & 0 & 1 & 2 \\
1 & 2 & 3 & 1 & 0 & 2 \\
3 & 4 & 5 & 2 & 2 & 0
\end{matrix}
$$

Figure 10.25 An application of the Floyd–Warshall algorithm.

True/False Questions

(Answers can be found in the back of the book.)

1. In a weighted graph, it is possible that some edges might have weight 0.
2. The Traveling Salesman's Problem is the problem of finding a maximum Hamiltonian cycle in a weighted (Hamiltonian) graph.
3. It is an open question as to whether there exists an efficient (polynomial time) algorithm for the solution of the Traveling Salesman's Problem.
4. In the weighted graph

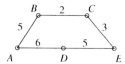

the shortest path between A and E is ADE.

5. In the weighted graph in Question 4, the shortest path between C and D is CED.
6. Dijkstra's algorithm was named after a Dutch computer scientist.
7. Dijkstra's algorithm (original version), when used to find a shortest path from vertex A to vertex E, terminates if E is assigned a label.
8. Dijkstra's algorithm (improved version), when used to find a shortest path from vertex A to vertex E, terminates if E is assigned a label.
9. The Floyd-Warshall algorithm, when used to find a shortest path from vertex A to vertex E, terminates when E is assigned a label.

10. All the algorithms in this section, when used to find the shortest paths between all pairs of vertices in a weighted graph, are $\mathcal{O}(n^3)$.

Exercises

*The answers to exercises marked [BB] can be found in the **B**ack of the **B**ook.*

1. The Traveling Salesman's Problem is that of finding the Hamiltonian cycle of least weight in a Hamiltonian graph. Is this what a traveling salesman necessarily wants to do? Discuss.

2. [BB] Apply both forms of Dijkstra's algorithm to the graph.

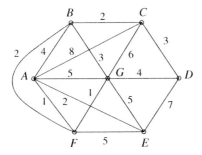

3. Apply the first form of Dijkstra's algorithm to find a shortest path from A to E in the graph shown. Label all vertices.

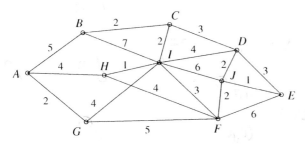

4. (a) [BB] Apply the original version of Dijkstra's algorithm to find the length of the shortest path from A to every other vertex in the graph. Show the final labels on all vertices. Also, find the shortest path from A to E.

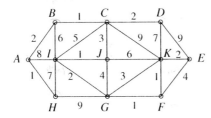

(b) Apply the original version of Dijkstra's algorithm to find the length of the shortest path from H to every other vertex in the graph. Show the final labels on all vertices. Find the shortest path from H to D.

5. Apply the improved version of Dijkstra's algorithm to find the length of a shortest path from A [BB] and from H to every other vertex in the graph of Exercise 4. In each case, exhibit an order in which permanent labels might be assigned.

6. Use the first form of Dijkstra's algorithm to find the shortest path from A to R (and its length) in the graph shown. Show the final labels on all vertices.

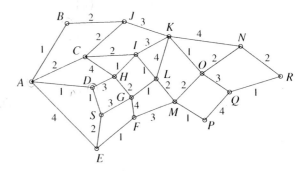

7. [BB] Use the improved version of Dijkstra's algorithm to find the length of a shortest path from A to R in the graph of Exercise 6. Also, exhibit an order in which permanent labels might be assigned.

8. Use the original form of Dijkstra's algorithm to find the shortest path from A to T in the graph shown. Label all vertices.

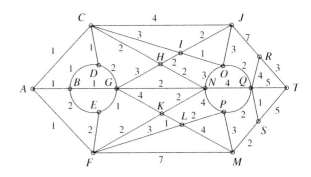

9. Use the original form of Dijkstra's algorithm to find a shortest path from A to every other vertex in the graph. Label the vertices on a shortest path from A to M and state the length of this path.

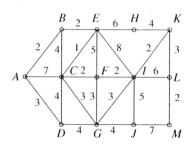

10. [BB] Use the improved version of Dijkstra's algorithm to find the shortest path from A to E (and its length) in the graph. Label all vertices.

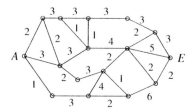

11. Use the improved version of Dijkstra's algorithm to find the shortest path from A to E in the graph shown. Show the final labels on all vertices.

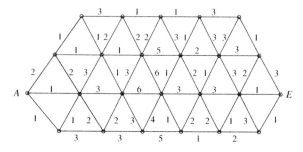

12. [BB] Could Dijkstra's algorithm (original version), employed to determine a shortest path from A to E in a weighted graph, terminate before E is labeled? Could the improved algorithm terminate before E acquires a permanent label? Explain.

13. Andrew suggests a "new improved" improved Dijkstra algorithm. In Step 2(b) of the algorithm described in 10.4.3, make permanent **all** temporary labels that tie for having smallest temporary label and then, as in 10.4.3, choose one to call v_{i+1} and continue. Comment on this suggestion.

14. (a) If weights were assigned to the edges of the graph shown in Exercise 1 of Section 10.2, the Traveling Salesman's Problem would not have a solution. Why not?

(b) Despite this observation, our salesman still has to complete the trip. Assigning weights as shown and assuming the salesman starts at A and does not wish to travel along the same edge more than once, find a most efficient route for the trip.

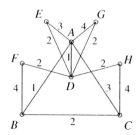

(c) Suppose the salesman is willing to cover the same edge more than once. Is the route found in (b) still the most efficient?

(d) Use the original form of Dijkstra's algorithm to find the shortest paths from E to each of the other vertices in the above graph. Label all vertices.

15. (a) [BB] How could any of the algorithms presented in this section be used to find the path requiring the fewest number of edges between two specified vertices in an **unweighted** graph?

(b) Use one of Dijkstra's algorithms to find the shortest path from A to B in the graph.

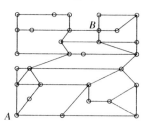

16. [BB] Suppose the improved version of Dijsktra's algorithm is used to find the shortest distances between all pairs of vertices in a graph on n vertices by being permitted to run until all vertices acquire their final labels. Why is this procedure $\mathcal{O}(n^3)$ (in terms of comparisons)?

17. [BB] Suppose the Floyd–Warshall algorithm is applied to the graph shown.

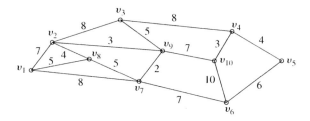

(a) What are the final values of $d(1, 1)$, $d(1, 2)$, ..., $d(1, 10)$?

(b) Find the values of $d(1, 5)$, $d(1, 6)$, $d(3, 4)$, and $d(8, 5)$ after $k = 4$.

(c) What is the initial value of $d(2, 5)$? How does this value change as k increases from 1 to 10?

18. The Floyd–Warshall algorithm is applied to the graph shown.

(a) Find the final values of $d(7, 1), d(7, 2), \ldots, d(7, 8)$.

(b) Find the values of $d(1, 2)$, $d(3, 4)$, $d(2, 5)$, and $d(8, 6)$ after $k = 4$.

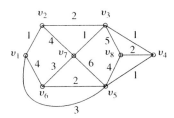

(c) Find the values of $d(6, 8)$ at the start and as k varies from 1 to 8.

19. Inadvertently, David reverses the order of the k and the i, j loops in Step 2 of the Floyd–Warshall algorithm, implementing Step 2 in the form

For $i, j = 1$ to n,
   for $k = 1$ to n,

let $d(i, j) = \min\{d(i, j), \ d(i, k) + d(k, j)\}$

Does this affect the algorithm? Explain.

20. [BB] Suppose the values of the $d(i, j)$ for two consecutive values of k are the same in an implementation of the Floyd–Warshall algorithm. Is it necessary to continue; that is, can it be assumed that the values will now remain constant?

21. Prove that the Floyd–Warshall algorithm works. Specifically, assume that $\mathcal{G}$ is a weighted graph with vertices $v_1, v_2, \ldots, v_n$ and assume that there is a path from v_i to v_j. Prove that, when the algorithm terminates, $d(i, j)$ is the length of a shortest path from v_i to v_j.

22. Show that the Floyd–Warshall algorithm requires $\mathcal{O}(n^3)$ additions and comparisons.

23. Discover what you can about Edsger Dijkstra and write a short note about him.

24. Discover what you can about R. W. Floyd and write a short note about him.

A lot of terminology has been introduced in this chapter. As preparation for the review exercises that follow, the student may find the following summary useful.

Walk	Alternating sequence of vertices and edges, beginning and ending with a vertex, each edge incident with the vertex immediately preceding it and the vertex immediately following it
Closed walk	First and last vertices are the same
Open walk	First and last vertices different
Trail	Walk with distinct edges
Path	Walk with distinct vertices
Circuit	Closed trail
Eulerian circuit	Circuit containing every vertex and every edge
Cycle	Circuit with no repeated vertices except the first (which is the same as the last)
Hamiltonian cycle	Cycle containing every vertex
Hamiltonian graph	Graph with a Hamiltonian cycle

Key Terms & Ideas

Here are some technical words and phrases that were used in this chapter. Do you know the meaning of each? If you're not sure, check the glossary or index at the back of the book.

adjacency matrix

circuit

component

connected

cycle

Eulerian circuit

Eulerian pseudograph

even cycle

Hamiltonian cycle

Hamiltonian graph

length (of a walk)

n-cycle

odd cycle

path

trail

Traveling Salesman's Problem

walk (in a pseudograph)

weighted graph

Review Exercises for Chapter 10

1. In the Königsberg Bridge Problem (see Fig. 9.1), two new bridges are constructed, one joining A to C and the other B to D. Use Theorem 10.1.4 to show that the answer to the question is now yes.

2. One of the mayoralty candidates in Königsberg says that he can obtain a positive solution to the bridge problem by building only one new bridge. Is he telling the truth?

3. Suppose $\mathcal{G}_1$ and $\mathcal{G}_2$ are graphs with no vertices in common and assume that each graph possesses an Eulerian trail. Show that it is possible to select vertices v and w of $\mathcal{G}_1$ and $\mathcal{G}_2$, respectively, such that if v and w are joined by a new edge the resulting graph will possess an Eulerian trail.

4. True or false? Explain your answers in each case.
   (a) Every trail is a path.
   (b) Every open trail is a path.
   (c) If there is an open trail from vertex v to vertex w, then there is a path from v to w.
   (d) Every path is an open trail.
   (e) If there is a path from vertex v to vertex w, then there is an open trail from v to w.

5. Let $\mathcal{G}$ be a connected graph with at least two vertices. Assume that every edge of $\mathcal{G}$ belongs to a unique cycle. Prove that $\mathcal{G}$ is Eulerian.

6. Is the graph Hamiltonian? Is it Eulerian? Explain your answers.

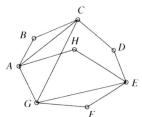

7. Determine, with reasons, whether each of the following graphs is Hamiltonian.
   (a)

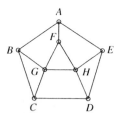

   (b)

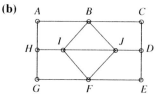

8. Determine whether the graph is Hamiltonian.

9. Determine whether the graph is Hamiltonian.

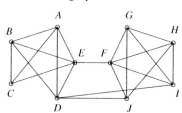

10. Let $\mathcal{G}$ be the graph of Exercise 9 with edge EF removed. (For convenience, we draw $\mathcal{G}$.)

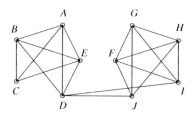

    (a) If $\mathcal{H}$ is a Hamiltonian cycle in $\mathcal{G}$, precisely one of the edges BC, AC, CE is not in $\mathcal{H}$. Why?
    (b) Is $\mathcal{G}$ Hamiltonian? Answer by considering the three cases described in part (a).

11. (a) How many edges must a Hamiltonian cycle in $\mathcal{K}_{n,n}$ contain?
    (b) How many Hamiltonian cycles does $\mathcal{K}_{n,n}$ have? Assume $n \geq 2$.
    (c) What is the maximum number of edge-disjoint Hamiltonian cycles in $\mathcal{K}_{n,n}$?
    (d) When $n = 4$, show that the maximum number of edge-disjoint Hamiltonian cycles predicted in 11c is realized.

12. True or false? Explain your answers in each case.

  (a) In a Hamiltonian graph, every edge belongs to some Hamiltonian cycle.

  (b) In a Hamiltonian graph, every edge belongs to a cycle.

  (c) Every Eulerian graph contains a subgraph that is Hamiltonian.

  (d) Every Hamiltonian graph contains a subgraph that is Eulerian.

13. Let $n \geq 3$ and let $3 \leq t \leq n$. How many t-cycles are there in $\mathcal{K}_n$? Explain.

14. A connected graph $\mathcal{G}$ has 14 vertices and 88 edges. Show that $\mathcal{G}$ is Hamiltonian, but not Eulerian.

15. A connected graph $\mathcal{G}$ has 10 vertices and 41 edges.

  (a) Show that $\mathcal{G}$ is not Eulerian.

  (b) Show that $\mathcal{G}$ is Hamiltonian.

16. The following questions refer to the graph $\mathcal{G}$ drawn on the left.

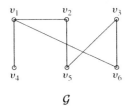
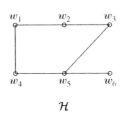

$$\mathcal{G} \qquad\qquad \mathcal{H}$$

  (a) Find the adjacency matrix A of $\mathcal{G}$.

  (b) Without any calculation, determine the $(1, 5)$ entries of A^2, A^3, A^4, and A^5.

  (c) Find an isomorphism $\varphi \colon \mathcal{G} \to \mathcal{H}$, where $\mathcal{H}$ is the graph on the right.

  (d) If B is the adjacency matrix of $\mathcal{H}$, find a permutation matrix P such that $PAP^T = B$. Check your answer by writing down B and computing the product PAP^T.

17. Let $v_1, v_2, \ldots, v_8$ and $w_1, w_2, \ldots, w_{12}$ be the bipartition sets of the complete bipartite graph $\mathcal{K}_{8,12}$. Let A be the adjacency matrix of this graph, where the vertices are listed in the order $v_1, \ldots, v_8, w_1, \ldots, w_{12}$. What is the

  (a) $(1, 5)$ entry of A?

  (b) $(8, 9)$ entry of A?

  (c) $(10, 12)$ entry of A^2?

  (d) $(5, 5)$ entry of A^2?

  (e) $(20, 6)$ entry of A^2?

  (f) $(5, 7)$ entry of A^4?

  (g) $(5, 7)$ entry of A^{15}?

18. Suppose $\mathcal{G}$ is a connected graph. Is it possible to determine from the adjacency matrix of $\mathcal{G}$ whether $\mathcal{G}$ is Eulerian? Explain.

19. Martha claims that a graph with adjacency matrix

$$A = \begin{bmatrix} 0 & 1 & 1 & 1 & 0 & 1 & 1 \\ 1 & 0 & 1 & 0 & 1 & 0 & 1 \\ 1 & 1 & 0 & 0 & 0 & 1 & 1 \\ 1 & 0 & 0 & 0 & 1 & 1 & 1 \\ 0 & 1 & 0 & 1 & 0 & 1 & 1 \\ 1 & 0 & 1 & 1 & 1 & 0 & 0 \\ 1 & 1 & 1 & 1 & 1 & 0 & 0 \end{bmatrix}$$

must be Hamiltonian. How can she be so sure?

20. If A is the adjacency matrix of a graph $\mathcal{G}$ and $A^2 = [b_{ij}]$, find $\frac{1}{2} \sum_i b_{ii}$.

21. **(a)** Which of the following three matrices (if any) is the adjacency matrix of a graph? In each case, either sketch a corresponding graph or explain why no such graph exists.

$$\begin{bmatrix} 0 & 0 & 1 \\ 0 & 1 & 0 \\ 1 & 0 & 0 \end{bmatrix} \quad \begin{bmatrix} 0 & 1 & 0 & 1 \\ 1 & 0 & 1 & 0 \\ 0 & 1 & 0 & 1 \\ 1 & 0 & 1 & 0 \end{bmatrix} \quad \begin{bmatrix} 0 & 0 & 0 \\ 0 & 0 & 1 \\ 1 & 1 & 0 \end{bmatrix}$$

  (b) Let A be the adjacency matrix of the graph shown. Explain how the $(1, 3)$ and $(2, 4)$ entries in A^3 can be found without computing A^3 by matrix multiplication. Determine the values of these entries in this way.

  (c) Let B be the adjacency matrix of a connected graph. Prove that there is a natural number m such that $C = B + B^2 + \cdots + B^m$ has no zero entries. Your answer should specify the minimum possible value of m (in terms of a property of the graph).

22. Apply the first form of Dijkstra's algorithm to the following graph, showing the shortest distances from A to every other vertex. Exhibit an order in which a shortest path from A to E might be realized.

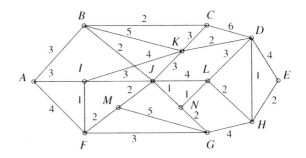

23. Apply the improved version of Dijkstra's algorithm to the graph of Exercise 22 to find the length of a shortest path from A to every other vertex.

24. Apply the original form of Dijkstra's algorithm to find the length of the shortest path from A to every other vertex in the graph shown. Show the final labels on all vertices. Also find the shortest path from A to H.

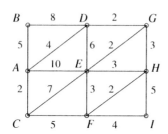

25. Apply the improved version of Dijkstra's algorithm to answer Exercise 24.

26. Apply the Floyd–Warshall algorithm to the graph, showing the initial values of $d(i, j)$ and the values of $d(i, j)$ at the end of every step.

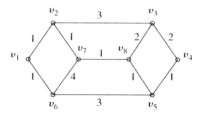

27. Apply the Floyd-Warshall algorithm to the graph in Exercise 24. Show the initial values of the $d(i, j)$, $i, j = 1, 2, \ldots, 9$; the values after $k = 1$, $k = 3$, and $k = 5$; and the final values. Explain how the algorithm can be used to find the shortest path from A to H.

28. An encyclopedia salesman, traveling by car, wishes to visit ten towns and return home without passing through the same town twice. He knows that one, but only one, of the towns has a direct connection to each of the other towns (that is, connections passing through no other towns). He also knows that there are a total of 39 such direct road connections between pairs of towns. Why is he confident that he will be able to find such a route?

11

Applications of Paths and Circuits

11.1 The Chinese Postman Problem

In this chapter, we present various applications of the ideas developed in Chapter 10. We use what we know about Eulerian graphs to solve the Chinese Postman Problem and to reconstruct RNA chains. The latter subject requires the concept of a digraph, a graph in which the edges have directions. We show how Hamiltonian paths can be used in the study of tournaments and, finally, we will see how shortest path algorithms can be applied to scheduling problems.

A mail carrier who begins his route at the post office must deliver letters to each block in a certain part of town and then return to the post office. What is the least amount of walking the mail carrier must do? This problem, a version of which was first solved by H. E. Dudeney in 1917,[1] is today known as the *Chinese Postman Problem* because it was studied in most general form by the Chinese mathematician, Mei-ko Kwan (also known as Meigo Guan).[2] It is clear that the same problem is faced by paper boys, street repair crews, snow plow operators, and so on.

We represent the mail carrier's problem by a weighted graph G with each vertex denoting a street corner and each edge a street of length the weight of that edge. If we assume that the post office is on a corner, then any route the postman follows corresponds to a closed walk in the graph that uses each edge at least once. If the graph G has an Eulerian circuit, then we have an optimal solution since every block will be walked exactly once. If not, then the postman will have to walk certain blocks more than once, but his aim is to plan these extra trips so that the total distance walked is as small as possible.

11.1.1 THE CHINESE POSTMAN PROBLEM

Given a connected and possibly weighted graph, find the shortest closed walk that covers every edge at least once.

The first step in the solution to this problem is the realization that the postman's walk will follow an Eulerian circuit in a pseudograph obtained from the given graph by the duplication of certain edges.

---

[1] See Angela Newing, "The Life and Work of H. E. Dudeney," *Mathematical Spectrum* **21** (1988/89), 37–44.
[2] M. K. Kwan, "Graphic Programming Using Odd or Even Points," *Chinese Math* **1** (1962), 273–277.

Suppose that the graph G shown in Fig. 11.1 represents the streets that a postman must cover and suppose that all streets have the same length.

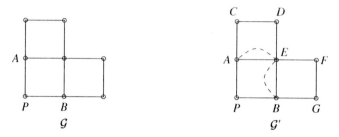

Figure 11.1

Since the postman's route covers all streets, it doesn't matter where the post office is, so assume it is at vertex P. Since G has vertices of odd degree (A and B), G is not Eulerian, so the postman cannot service this area by walking each block exactly once. Our problem is to determine the least number of edges that should be duplicated to obtain an Eulerian pseudograph. Since all vertices of an Eulerian pseudograph must have even degree, we will have to add an extra copy (or extra copies) of certain of the edges incident with A and with B. If A and B were joined by an edge, then a single extra copy of that edge would certainly suffice. Since, however, A and B are not joined by an edge, we need at least two additional edges. The pseudograph G' shown on the right in Fig. 11.1 (extra edges shown as dashed lines) is Eulerian and a solution to the Chinese Postman Problem. One Eulerian circuit is $PACDEAEBGFEBP$.

Unlike many graph theoretical problems, the Chinese Postman Problem has been solved: Procedures have been found for determining which edges of a graph must be duplicated to obtain the Eulerian pseudograph of least weight.[3]

EXAMPLE 1   We illustrate with reference to the graph G in Fig. 11.2, where we again assume that all streets have the same length.

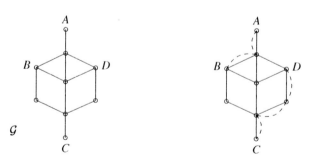

Figure 11.2

There are four odd vertices in G, labeled A, B, C, D in the figure. Consider all the partitions of these vertices into pairs and, for each partition, calculate the sum of the lengths of shortest paths between pairs.

[3]See J. Edmonds, "The Chinese Postman Problem," *Operations Research* **13** Suppl. 1 (1965), 353; J. Edmonds and E. L. Johnson, "Matching, Euler Tours and the Chinese Postman," *Mathematical Programming* **5** (1973), 88–124; E. L. Lawler, *Combinatorial Optimization Networks and Matroids*, Holt, Rinehart and Winston, New York, 1975; and E. Minieka, *Optimization Algorithms for Networks and Graphs*, Marcel Dekker, New York, 1978.

Table 11.3

Partition into pairs	Sum of lengths of shortest paths
$\{A, B\}, \{C, D\}$	$2 + 3 = 5$
$\{A, C\}, \{B, D\}$	$4 + 2 = 6$
$\{A, D\}, \{B, C\}$	$2 + 3 = 5$

As the calculations in Table 11.3 show, the minimum sum of lengths is 5, and this is achieved with two partitions either of which yields a solution to the problem. If we choose, for instance, $\{A, B\}, \{C, D\}$, then a pseudograph of minimum weight is obtained by duplicating the edges along the shortest path from A to B and along the shortest path from C to D, as shown on the right of Fig. 11.2. As before, many people could have obtained our solution by inspection. Computers cannot see, however. Our intent has been to illustrate a concrete procedure that works in all cases and does not depend on a picture.

11.1.2 THE CHINESE POSTMAN PROBLEM—AN ALGORITHM

To find an Eulerian pseudograph of minimum weight by duplicating edges of a weighted connected graph $\mathcal{G}$,

Step 1. Find all the odd vertices in $\mathcal{G}$.

Step 2. For each partition of the odd vertices into pairs of vertices,

$$\{v_1, w_1\}, \{v_2, w_2\}, \ldots, \{v_m, w_m\},$$

find the length of a shortest path between each v_i and w_i and add these lengths.

Step 3. Take a partition for which the sum of lengths in Step 2 is minimum and, for each pair $\{v_i, w_i\}$ of vertices in this partition, duplicate the edges along a shortest path from v_i to w_i.

Pause 1 Step 2 of this algorithm assumes that the odd vertices of a graph can always be partitioned into pairs. Why should this be the case?

Pause 2 In the implementation of the algorithm, will it ever be necessary to duplicate an edge more than once? In other words, if an edge e has been duplicated for inclusion in the shortest path from v_i to w_i, will it perhaps be necessary later to duplicate it for inclusion in the shortest path from v_j to w_j?

In the Exercises, we ask you to show that the pseudograph produced by this algorithm is Eulerian and, furthermore, that given any Eulerian pseudograph obtained from $\mathcal{G}$ by duplicating certain edges, the odd vertices can be paired such that there are edge disjoint paths of new edges between them. From this, it follows that our algorithm does indeed produce an Eulerian pseudograph of minimum weight.

Suppose we attach some weights to the edges of the graph we considered before, as shown in Fig. 11.4. There are still four odd vertices and three partitions of these into pairs, but the lengths of shortest paths between pairs of odd vertices have changed.

As the calculations in Table 11.5 show, the minimum sum of lengths is now 9, corresponding to the partition $\{A, D\}, \{B, C\}$. Duplicating the edges on a shortest path from A to D and from B to C, as shown on the right of Fig. 11.4, we obtain an Eulerian pseudograph of minimum weight and a solution to the Chinese Postman Problem for the graph $\mathcal{G}$.

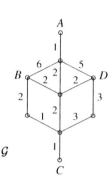

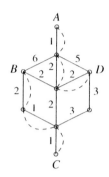

Figure 11.4

Table 11.5

Partition into pairs	Sum of lengths of shortest paths
$\{A, B\}, \{C, D\}$	$5 + 5 = 10$
$\{A, C\}, \{B, D\}$	$6 + 4 = 10$
$\{A, D\}, \{B, C\}$	$5 + 4 = 9$

Answers to Pauses

1. The number of odd vertices in a graph is even (Corollary 9.2.6).

2. No, it won't. To see why not, think about how the partition

$$\mathcal{P} = \{ \{v_1, w_1\}, \{v_2, w_2\}, \dots, \{v_m, w_m\} \}$$

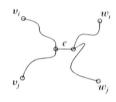

was determined. Denoting by ℓ_i the length of the shortest path between v_i and w_i, the sum, $L = \sum_i \ell_i$, is least among all similar sums arising from all partitions of the odd vertices into pairs.

If an edge e is duplicated because it is part of the shortest path between v_i and w_i, and it is later required again because it is part of the shortest path between v_j and w_j, then the partition obtained from $\mathcal{P}$ by replacing the pairs $\{v_i, w_i\}, \{v_j, w_j\}$ by the pairs $\{v_i, v_j\}, \{w_i, w_j\}$ has the sum of shortest path lengths less than or equal to $L - 2w(e)$, contradicting the minimality of L.

True/False Questions

(Answers can be found in the back of the book.)

1. The Chinese Postman Problem can always be solved in Hamiltonian graphs without repeating any edges.

2. In the unweighted graph ▭ the Chinese Postman Problem can be solved by repeating one edge.

3. In the weighted graph 3 ▭ 1 the Chinese Postman Problem can be solved by repeating one edge.

4. In a graph $\mathcal{G}$ with two odd vertices, v_1 and v_2, the Chinese Postman Problem is solved by finding the shortest path from v_1 to v_2.

5. If a graph $\mathcal{G}$ has six odd vertices, to solve the Chinese Postman Problem, we must first divide the odd vertices into two groups of three.

6. The odd vertices of a graph can always be partitioned into pairs.

7. In the graph the Chinese Postman Problem has a unique solution.

8. In the weighted graph the Chinese Postman Problem has a unique solution.

9. In the unweighted graph $\mathcal{K}_n$, n even, the Chinese Postman Problem is solved by repeating $\frac{n}{2}$ edges.

10. In the unweighted graph $\mathcal{K}_n$, n odd, the Chinese Postman Problem is solved by repeating $\frac{n-1}{2}$ edges.

Exercises

*The answers to exercises marked [BB] can be found in the **B**ack of the **B**ook.*

1. Solve the Chinese Postman Problem for each of the graphs shown.
   (a) [BB]
   (b)
   (c)
   (d)
   (e)
   (f)

   graphs shown.

   5. Solve the Chinese Postman Problem for each of the graphs shown in Fig. 11.6.
   (a)
   (b)
   (c)
   (d)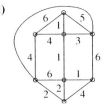

   Figure 11.6 Graphs for Exercise 5

2. [BB; $\mathcal{K}_5$] Solve the Chinese Postman Problem for $\mathcal{K}_5$, $\mathcal{K}_6$, and $\mathcal{K}_{3,5}$.

3. [BB] Solve the Chinese Postman Problem for the weighted graph shown.

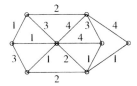

4. [BB] Solve the Chinese Postman Problem for the two

6. [BB] Suppose X and Y are any two vertices of a weighted connected graph $\mathcal{G}$. Explain why the shortest mail car-

rier's route from X to X has the same length as the shortest route from Y to Y.

7. Solve the Chinese Postman Problem for the unweighted graph shown.

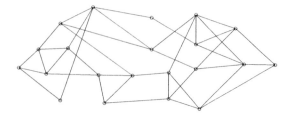

8. Solve the Chinese Postman Problem for the weighted graph.

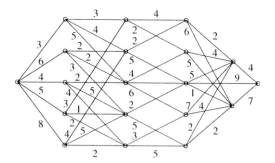

The remaining exercises concern the algorithm presented in this section for obtaining an Eulerian pseudograph of minimum weight from a given non-Eulerian connected graph G by duplicating certain edges.

9. [BB] In the solution to the Chinese Postman Problem, every odd vertex is the end of a path between odd vertices. Is it possible, however, for an odd vertex also to be an intermediate vertex on a path between (other) odd vertices?

10. [BB] Prove that the pseudograph G' that the algorithm finds is Eulerian.

11. Suppose G has n odd vertices. In how many ways can these be partitioned into $\frac{n}{2}$ pairs?

12. Suppose that G'' is any Eulerian pseudograph obtained from G by duplicating certain edges.

   (a) Prove that each odd vertex of G is the initial vertex of a path consisting entirely of new edges (in G'') and leading to another odd vertex.

   (b) Improve the result of (a) by showing that the odd vertices of G can, in fact, be partitioned into two equal sets, $\{v_1, v_2, \ldots, v_m\}$ and $\{w_1, w_2, \ldots, w_m\}$, with edge disjoint paths consisting entirely of new edges between each v_i and w_i.

   (c) Conclude that of all the pseudographs obtainable from G by duplicating edges, the algorithm yields an Eulerian pseudograph of minimum weight.

11.2 Digraphs

When graphs are used to model real-life situations, the edges often represent lines of communication, such as roads or pipes. In such situations, it is not unusual for the flow through an edge to have an associated direction.

11.2.1 DEFINITION A *digraph* is a pair $(\mathcal{V}, \mathcal{E})$ of sets, $\mathcal{V}$ nonempty and each element of $\mathcal{E}$ an ordered pair of distinct elements of $\mathcal{V}$. The elements of $\mathcal{V}$ are called *vertices* and the elements of $\mathcal{E}$ are called *arcs*. ❖

Loosely speaking, a digraph is just a graph in which each edge has an orientation or direction assigned to it. (We use the words *orientation* and *direction* synonymously.) It can be pictured like a graph, with the orientation of an arc indicated by an arrow: We draw an arrow $u \longrightarrow v$ if $(u, v) \in \mathcal{E}$. Some digraphs are pictured in Fig. 11.7.

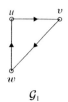

$\mathcal{G}_1$

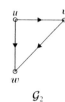

$\mathcal{G}_2$

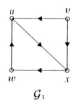

$\mathcal{G}_3$

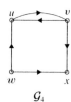

$\mathcal{G}_4$

Figure 11.7

As with most aspects of graph theory, there is a rather extensive terminology used for digraphs and, as we have noted before, different textbooks employ the same words with slight variations in meaning. The policy in this text is to use the same terms for graphs and digraphs whenever possible, with one exception: In a digraph, we use the term *arc* instead of *edge*. An edge is just a set, an unordered pair of vertices $\{u, v\}$; an arc is an ordered pair (u, v) or (v, u) (as ordered pairs, these are different). Just as it has been our custom when naming edges of a graph not to use set notation, we omit parentheses when naming arcs of a digraph, thus referring to "the arc uv" rather than "the arc (u, v)."

As with the term *graph*, our definition of *digraph* precludes the existence of loops and multiple arcs. Note the subtle distinction between multiple edges and multiple arcs, however. Since the arcs uv and vu are different, they may both appear in a digraph. All the pictures in Fig. 11.7 represent digraphs, in particular $\mathcal{G}_4$, which, without the arrows, would not be a graph. There are multiple edges, but not multiple arcs, between u and v.

In the same way that the vertices of a graph have degrees, a vertex of a digraph has an *indegree* and an *outdegree*, these being, respectively, the number of arcs directed into and away from that vertex. Considering the graph $\mathcal{G}_3$ in Fig. 11.7, vertices u and x have indegree 2 and outdegree 1, vertex v has indegree 0 and outdegree 2, and vertex w has indegree 1 and outdegree 1. The *indegree sequence* of $\mathcal{G}_3$ is 2, 2, 1, 0, and the *outdegree sequence* of $\mathcal{G}_3$ is 2, 1, 1, 1. The following result can be proved with a routine modification of the argument used to prove Proposition 9.2.5.

11.2.2 PROPOSITION (cf. Proposition 9.2.5) The sum of the indegrees of the vertices of a digraph equals the sum of the outdegrees of the vertices, this common number being the number of arcs.

As might be expected, when considering the possible isomorphism of digraphs, the direction of arcs must be taken into account. In Fig. 11.7, $\mathcal{G}_1$ and $\mathcal{G}_2$ are not isomorphic because every vertex in $\mathcal{G}_1$ has outdegree 1, whereas in $\mathcal{G}_2$ outdeg $u = 2$. The indegree sequences of isomorphic digraphs must be equal, as must be their outdegree sequences. With this small change in property 2, Proposition 9.3.2 is equally valid for digraphs.

By convention, any walk in a digraph respects orientation of arcs; that is, each arc is followed in the direction of its arrow. For example, digraph $\mathcal{G}_1$ in Fig. 11.7 is Eulerian because $uvwu$ is an Eulerian circuit. This is also a Hamiltonian cycle. Digraph $\mathcal{G}_2$ has neither an Eulerian circuit nor a Hamiltonian cycle (the arc is uw, not wu), although it does have a Hamiltonian path uvw.

 Explain why neither digraph $\mathcal{G}_3$ nor $\mathcal{G}_4$ of Fig. 11.7 is Hamiltonian. ∎

In Theorem 10.1.4, we established necessary and sufficient conditions for a graph to be Eulerian. This theorem can be adapted to the situation of digraphs with a suitable strengthening of the concept of connectedness.

11.2.3 DEFINITION A digraph is called *strongly connected* if and only if there is a walk from any vertex to any other vertex that respects the orientation of each arc. ❖

Imagine a city where every street is one-way. The digraph of streets and intersections of this city is connected if it is possible to drive from any intersection to any other intersection, perhaps by moving the wrong way down a one-way street, and strongly connected if such travel is always possible without breaking the law!

The proof of the following theorem is left to the Exercises.

(cf. Theorem 10.1.4) A digraph is Eulerian if and only if it is strongly connected and, for every vertex, the indegree equals the outdegree.

Is digraph G_3 in Fig. 11.7 Eulerian? What about the digraph in Fig. 11.8? ∎

Figure 11.8 A digraph associated with K_3.

The adjacency matrix A of a digraph G with vertices $v_1, v_2, \ldots, v_n$ is defined by setting $a_{ij} = 1$ if there is an arc from vertex v_i to vertex v_j and 0 otherwise. Unlike the adjacency matrix of a graph (see Section 10.3), the adjacency matrix of a digraph is generally not symmetric, since an arc from v_i to v_j does not imply an arc from v_j to v_i. Most assertions made in Section 10.3 apply, with appropriate changes. For example, the (i, j) entry of A^2 is the number of different walks of length 2 from v_i to v_j (respecting the orientation of arcs). This number need not be the same as the number of walks of length 2 from v_j to v_i, obviously. The ith entry of the diagonal of A^2, being the number of walks of length 2 from v_i to v_i, is the number of vertices v_j such that there exists a circuit of the form $v_i v_j v_i$. (See Fig. 11.9.)

v_i ⚬⟷⚬ v_j

Figure 11.9

Theorems 10.3.3 and 10.3.4 hold for digraphs. Digraphs are isomorphic if and only if their vertices can be labeled in such a way that their adjacency matrices are equal. Labeled digraphs G_1 and G_2 with adjacency matrices A_1 and A_2, respectively, are isomorphic if and only if $A_2 = P A_1 P^T$ for some permutation matrix P.

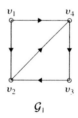
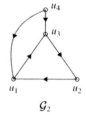

Figure 11.10 Two isomorphic digraphs.

EXAMPLE 2 Consider the digraphs of Fig. 11.10. The adjacency matrices of G_1 and G_2 are

$$A_1 = \begin{bmatrix} 0 & 1 & 0 & 1 \\ 0 & 0 & 0 & 1 \\ 0 & 1 & 0 & 0 \\ 0 & 0 & 1 & 0 \end{bmatrix} \quad \text{and} \quad A_2 = \begin{bmatrix} 0 & 0 & 1 & 0 \\ 1 & 0 & 0 & 0 \\ 0 & 1 & 0 & 0 \\ 1 & 0 & 1 & 0 \end{bmatrix}.$$

The map $\varphi: G_1 \to G_2$ defined by

$$\varphi(v_1) = u_4, \quad \varphi(v_2) = u_1, \quad \varphi(v_3) = u_2, \quad \varphi(v_4) = u_3$$

is an isomorphism, and the permutation matrix

$$P = \begin{bmatrix} 0 & 1 & 0 & 0 \\ 0 & 0 & 1 & 0 \\ 0 & 0 & 0 & 1 \\ 1 & 0 & 0 & 0 \end{bmatrix}$$

determined by φ (as in Section 10.3) has the property that $P A_1 P^T = A_2$.

The shortest path algorithms described in Section 10.4 can be applied to digraphs, with obvious modifications that take into account the orientation of arcs. Examples appear in our discussion of scheduling problems in Section 11.5.

Here is another algorithm, due to Richard Bellman (1920–1984) and Lester R. Ford Jr. (1927–) that, for a directed graph with vertices $v_1, v_2, \dots, v_n$, computes successively the length $d_i(j)$ of a shortest path from v_1 to v_j using at most i arcs. Since no path in such a digraph can have more than $n - 1$ arcs, the final values of $d_{n-1}(j)$, $j = 2, \dots, n$, are the lengths of shortest paths from v_1 to all other vertices.

11.2.5 THE BELLMAN–FORD ALGORITHM

Given a weighted digraph with vertices labeled $v_1, v_2, \dots, v_n$, to find the shortest distances from v_1 to all other vertices, proceed as follows.

Step 1. for $i, j = 1, 2, \dots, n$,

- if $i = j$, set $w(i, i) = 0$; if $i \neq j$ and $v_i v_j$ is an arc, set $w(i, j)$ equal to the weight of $v_i v_j$; otherwise, set $w(i, j) = \infty$.
- set $d_0(1) = 0$ and, for $j = 2, 3, \dots, n$, set $d_0(j) = \infty$.
- for $i = 2$ to n, set $p(i) = v_1$.

Step 2. for $i = 1$ to n
    for $j = 1$ to n
- find the k for which $\min = d_{i-1}(k) + w(v_k, v_j)$ is least;
- if $\min < d_{i-1}(j)$, set $d_i(j) = \min$ and $p(j) = v_k$
    else set $d_i(j) = d_{i-1}(j)$.

Step 3. if $d_n(j) = d_{n-1}(j)$ for $j = 1, 2, \dots, n$,
    for $j = 1$ to n output $d_n(j)$;
    else output "No shortest paths. There is a negative weight cycle."

If there are no negative weight cycles, the value of $d_n(j) = d_{n-1}(j)$ that is output in Step 3 is the length of a shortest path from v_1 to v_j, and $p(j)$ is the second last vertex on a shortest path to v_j.

We apply this algorithm to the graph shown in Fig. 11.11. After initialization in Step 1, the process begins with Step 2. Setting $i = 1$, the algorithm computes the weight of a shortest one-arc path to vertices v_2, v_3, v_4, v_5. The shortest path to v_2 has weight 1, and the last vertex on this path is v_1. The shortest path to v_5 has weight 4, and the last vertex on this path is v_1. Shortest paths to v_3 and v_4, using at most one arc, have infinite length. The first column of Table 11.12 records these data.

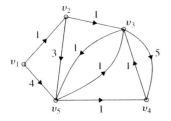

Figure 11.11

Table 11.12 Results of applying the Bellman–Ford algorithm to the digraph shown in Fig. 11.11. The (i, j) entry is ∞ or, when $d_i(j)$ is finite, the pair $d_i(j)$, $p(j)$.

| | | \multicolumn{5}{c}{Max. no. of arcs} | | | | |
		1	2	3	4	5
	v_2	$1, v_1$	$1, v_1$	$1, v_1$	$1, v_1$	$1, v_1$
Vertices	v_3	∞	$2, v_2$	$2, v_2$	$2, v_2$	$2, v_2$
	v_4	∞	$5, v_5$	$5, v_5$	$4, v_5$	$4, v_5$
	v_5	$4, v_1$	$4, v_1$	$3, v_3$	$3, v_3$	$3, v_3$

Now $i = 2$ and the algorithm computes the length of a shortest path to v_2, v_3, v_4, v_5 using at most two arcs. For each $j = 2, 3, 4, 5$, the algorithm first computes the minimum $d_1(k) + w(v_k, v_j)$; that is, the length of a shortest path to v_k using one arc plus the weight of arc $v_k v_j$. This number (min) is compared with $d_1(k)$, the length of the shortest one-arc path to v_k. The smaller of these two numbers becomes $d_2(j)$. If the shortest path had length min, the algorithm also sets the *predecessor* vertex $p(2) = v_k$, thus remembering that v_k is the vertex preceding v_j on a shortest at most two-arc path to v_j. The shortest at most two-arc path to v_2 is still a one-arc path, and the same is true for v_5. The shortest at most two-arc path to v_3 has length 2, and the last vertex on such a path is v_2. The shortest at most two-arc path to v_4 has length 5, and the last vertex on such a path is v_5. We leave it to you to check the remaining columns of the table.

In this example, all vertices eventually have finite labels. Will this always be the case?

∎

In contrast to the algorithms of Dijkstra, the Bellman–Ford algorithm works perfectly well on weighted digraphs where some arcs have negative weight. In Fig. 11.13, we show the result of applying the original form of Dijkstra's algorithm to the digraph of Fig. 11.11, with different (and some negative) arc weights. Since neither version of Dijkstra's algorithm examines a vertex again after it has acquired its permanent label, vertex v_3 is incorrectly determined to be at distance 3 from v_1. The correct length of a shortest path from v_1 to v_3 is 2, along $v_1 v_5 v_4 v_3$, and this is found by the Bellman–Ford algorithm, as shown in Table 11.14.

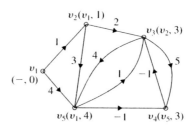

Figure 11.13 An application of Dijkstra's algorithm (first form) to a weighted digraph with some negative weights. The final labeling at v_3 is wrong.

Table 11.14 Results of applying the Bellman–Ford algorithm to the digraph shown in Fig. 11.13.

		Max. no. of arcs				
		1	2	3	4	5
	v_2	$1, v_1$	$1, v_1$	$1, v_1$	$1, v_1$	$1, v_1$
Vertices	v_3	∞	$3, v_2$	$2, v_4$	$2, v_4$	$2, v_4$
	v_4	∞	$3, v_5$	$3, v_5$	$3, v_5$	$3, v_5$
	v_5	$4, v_1$	$4, v_1$	$4, v_1$	$4, v_1$	$4, v_1$

Any path in a digraph with n vertices cannot contain more than $n - 1$ arcs. So in Step 2 of the Bellman–Ford algorithm, why does the outer for loop run from $i = 1$ to n and not to $i = n - 1$? (Remember that i is the number of arcs in a path.) The answer is to detect negative weight cycles (which can be reached from v_1). This is also the reason for the inclusion of Step 3. If a weighted digraph has a cycle of negative total weight, there is no shortest path to any vertex on this cycle that is reachable from v_1, since by going around the cycle, lengths can be decreased as much as desired. Suppose the value of $d_n(j)$ is different (and hence less) than the value of $d_{n-1}(j)$ for some vertex v_j. Thus there is a walk $\mathcal{W}$ of n edges from v_1 to v_j of total weight less than any walk that uses fewer than n edges. Such a walk must contain a repeated vertex, and hence a cycle $\mathcal{C}: u_1 u_2 \cdots u_1$, so the walk is $\mathcal{W}: v_1 \cdots \mathcal{C} \cdots v_j$. Notice that the cycle must have negative total weight since the weight of $\mathcal{W}$ is, by assumption, less than the weight of $v_1 \cdots u_1 \cdots v_j$ (omitting $\mathcal{C}$). It can be shown that any negative weight cycle will be detected by Bellman–Ford since, in this case, for some vertex v_j, the value of $d_n(j)$ must be less than $d_{n-1}(j)$. [See Exercise 29b.]

Pause 6   In Fig. 11.13, change the weight of $v_3 v_5$ from 4 to 1. Make a table like that in Table 11.12. Examine the values of $d_4(j)$ and $d_5(j)$ and comment.   ∎

Weighted digraphs are helpful in settings where graphs are not appropriate; specifically, in any situation where travel between two vertices can proceed in only one direction. We provide examples in the next three sections.

Answers to Pauses

3. In $\mathcal{G}_3$, vertex v has indegree 0. Since there is no way of reaching v on a walk respecting orientation of edges, no Hamiltonian cycle can exist. In $\mathcal{G}_4$, vertex x has outdegree 0, so no walk respecting orientations can leave x.

4. The digraph $\mathcal{G}_3$ is not Eulerian. It is not strongly connected (there is no way to reach v). Also, the indegrees and outdegrees of three vertices (u, v, and x) are not the same. The digraph in Fig. 11.8 is Eulerian, however. It is strongly connected (there is a circuit $uvwu$ that permits travel in the direction of arrows between any two vertices), and the indegree and outdegree of every vertex are 2. (An Eulerian circuit is $uwvuvwu$.)

5. If there is no directed path from v_1 to some vertex v_i, the label for v_i will always be ∞.

6.

		Max. no. of arcs			
		1	2	3	4	5
	v_2	1, v_1	1, v_1	1, v_1	1, v_1	1, v_1
Vertices	v_3	∞	3, v_2	2, v_4	2, v_4	2, v_4
	v_4	∞	3, v_5	3, v_5	3, v_5	2, v_5
	v_5	4, v_1	4, v_1	4, v_1	3, v_3	3, v_3

Since $d_4(v_4) = 3$ and $d_5(v_4) = 2$, the algorithm has detected the negative cycle $v_3 v_5 v_4 v_3$.

True/False Questions

(Answers can be found in the back of the book.)

1. If you remove the arrows from the arcs of a digraph, what's left will always be a graph.

2. The indegree sequence and the outdegree sequence of a digraph are the same.

3. The sum of the indegrees of the vertices of a digraph equals the number of vertices of the digraph.

4. A digraph is Eulerian if and only if, for every vertex, the indegree equals the outdegree.

5. The adjacency matrix of a digraph must be symmetric.

6. The adjacency matrix of a digraph always has 0's on the diagonal.

7. If A is the adjacency matrix of a digraph and outdeg $v_1 = 0$, then the $(1, j)$ entry of A^k is 0 for all j and for all k.

8. Let A be the adjacency matrix of a digraph. If the $(3, 4)$ entry of A is 1 and the $(3, 4)$ entry of A^2 is 2, then outdeg $v_1 \geq 3$.

9. If A is the adjacency matrix of a Hamiltonian digraph, then, for any natural number n, $A^n \neq 0$.

10. The Bellman–Ford algorithm does not work on weighted digraphs when some arcs have negative weight.

Exercises

*The answers to exercises marked [BB] can be found in the **B**ack of the **B**ook.*

1. Which of the following pairs of digraphs are isomorphic? Explain your answers.

    (a) [BB]

    (b)

    (c)

    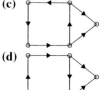

    (d)

    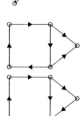

2. Must the indegree and the outdegree sequences of a digraph be the same? Explain.

3. [BB] Prove Proposition 11.2.2: The sum of the indegrees of the vertices of a digraph equals the sum of the outdegrees, and this number is the number of arcs.

4. Exhibit a digraph that is strongly connected, but not Eulerian.

5. [BB] Let $\mathcal{G}$ be a connected graph with all vertices of even degree. Can the edges of $\mathcal{G}$ be oriented so that the resulting digraph is Eulerian? Explain.

6. Suppose a digraph with n vertices has no (directed) cycles. What is the maximum number of arcs on a (directed) walk between two vertices? Explain.

7. Let A be the adjacency matrix of a digraph $\mathcal{G}$. What does the sum of the entries in row i of A represent? What

about the sum of the entries in column i?

8. [BB] Let A be the adjacency matrix of the illustrated digraph.

    (a) Find A.

    (b) Determine the $(3, 3)$ and $(1, 4)$ entries of A^2 without calculating the matrix A^2 and explain your reasoning.

    (c) Determine the $(4, 2)$ entry of A^3 and the $(1, 3)$ entry of A^4 without calculating A^3 or A^4 and explain your reasoning.

    (d) Is the digraph strongly connected? Explain.

    (e) Is the digraph Eulerian? Explain.

9. Repeat Exercise 8 for the digraph shown here.

10. Prove Theorem 11.2.4: A digraph is Eulerian if and only if it is strongly connected and, for every vertex, the indegree equals the outdegree.

11. [BB] Find necessary and sufficient conditions for a digraph to have an Eulerian trail. Explain your answer.

12. Let A be the adjacency matrix of a digraph $\mathcal{G}$. Explain why A^T is also the adjacency matrix of a digraph $\mathcal{G}^T$. Is it possible for $\mathcal{G}$ and $\mathcal{G}^T$ to be isomorphic? Explain.

13. [BB; (a)] Label the vertices of each pair of digraphs in Exercise 1 and then give the adjacency matrices corresponding to your labeling. (For any pair of graphs that are isomorphic, label in such a way that the two graphs have the same adjacency matrix.)

14. [BB] Consider the digraphs $\mathcal{G}_1$, $\mathcal{G}_2$ shown.

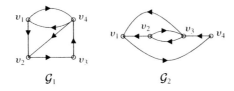

$$\mathcal{G}_1 \qquad\qquad \mathcal{G}_2$$

(a) Find the adjacency matrix A_1 of $\mathcal{G}_1$ and the adjacency matrix A_2 of $\mathcal{G}_2$.

(b) Explain why the map $\varphi: \mathcal{G}_1 \to \mathcal{G}_2$ defined by

$$\varphi(v_1) = u_2, \quad \varphi(v_2) = u_1,$$
$$\varphi(v_3) = u_4, \quad \varphi(v_4) = u_3$$

is an isomorphism.

(c) Find the permutation matrix P that corresponds to φ and satisfies $P A_1 P^T = A_2$.

(d) Are these digraphs strongly connected?

(e) Are these digraphs Eulerian?

15. Repeat Exercise 14 for the digraphs shown and the map $\varphi: \mathcal{G}_1 \to \mathcal{G}_2$ defined by

$$\varphi(v_1) = u_3, \quad \varphi(v_2) = u_4, \quad \varphi(v_3) = u_2,$$
$$\varphi(v_4) = u_5, \quad \varphi(v_5) = u_1.$$

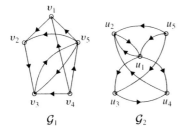

$$\mathcal{G}_1 \qquad\qquad \mathcal{G}_2$$

16. In each of the following cases, find a permutation matrix P such that $A_2 = P A_1 P^T$.

(a) $A_1 = \begin{bmatrix} 0 & 1 & 0 & 1 \\ 0 & 0 & 1 & 0 \\ 0 & 0 & 0 & 1 \\ 0 & 0 & 0 & 0 \end{bmatrix}$, $A_2 = \begin{bmatrix} 0 & 0 & 1 & 1 \\ 0 & 0 & 1 & 0 \\ 0 & 0 & 0 & 0 \\ 0 & 1 & 0 & 0 \end{bmatrix}$

(b) $A_1 = \begin{bmatrix} 0 & 0 & 1 & 0 \\ 0 & 0 & 0 & 1 \\ 1 & 0 & 0 & 0 \\ 0 & 1 & 0 & 0 \end{bmatrix}$, $A_2 = \begin{bmatrix} 0 & 0 & 0 & 1 \\ 0 & 0 & 1 & 0 \\ 0 & 1 & 0 & 0 \\ 1 & 0 & 0 & 0 \end{bmatrix}$

(c) $A_1 = \begin{bmatrix} 0 & 1 & 0 & 1 & 1 \\ 0 & 0 & 1 & 0 & 0 \\ 0 & 0 & 0 & 1 & 1 \\ 0 & 0 & 0 & 0 & 1 \\ 0 & 1 & 0 & 0 & 0 \end{bmatrix}$,

$$A_2 = \begin{bmatrix} 0 & 0 & 0 & 0 & 1 \\ 0 & 0 & 0 & 1 & 0 \\ 1 & 1 & 0 & 1 & 0 \\ 1 & 0 & 0 & 0 & 0 \\ 0 & 1 & 0 & 1 & 0 \end{bmatrix}$$

17. [BB; (a)] Which of the digraphs in Exercise 1 are strongly connected? Explain your answers.

18. An orientation of a graph can be achieved by replacing each edge $\{x, y\}$, an unordered pair of vertices, by one of the ordered pairs (x, y) or (y, x); that is, you put an arrow on each edge of the graph.

(a) [BB] Find all nonisomorphic orientations of $\mathcal{K}_3$.

(b) Find all nonisomorphic orientations of $\mathcal{K}_4$.

(c) Find all nonisomorphic orientations of $\mathcal{K}_{2,3}$.

19. [BB] If a graph $\mathcal{G}$ is connected and some orientation is put on the edges of $\mathcal{G}$, must the resulting digraph be strongly connected? Explain.

20. [BB] Answer true or false and explain: If a digraph $\mathcal{G}$ with at least two vertices is strongly connected, then every vertex of $\mathcal{G}$ is part of a circuit (consisting of more than a single vertex).

21. (a) Use a version of Dijkstra's algorithm to find the length of shortest paths from v_1 to each of the other vertices. What is the shortest path from v_1 to v_5?

(b) Apply the Bellman–Ford algorithm to the given graph, answering by means of a table like Table 11.12.

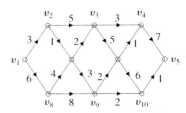

22. [BB; (a)] Apply the Bellman–Ford algorithm to the digraphs shown, answering by means of a table like Table 11.12.

(a)

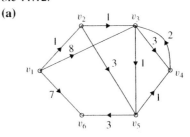

$$A_2 = \begin{bmatrix} 0 & 0 & 0 & 0 & 1 \\ 0 & 0 & 0 & 1 & 0 \\ 1 & 1 & 0 & 1 & 0 \\ 1 & 0 & 0 & 0 & 0 \\ 0 & 1 & 0 & 1 & 0 \end{bmatrix}$$

(b)

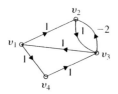

23. [BB] Would it be sensible to use the Bellman–Ford algorithm on undirected graphs? Comment.

24. (a) [BB] Apply the original form of Dijkstra's algorithm to determine the lengths of shortest paths from v_1 to every other vertex in the graph at the right. Does it work correctly? Explain.

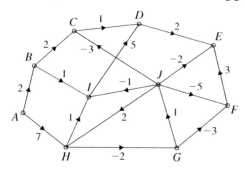

   (b) [BB] Would Bellman–Ford work? Explain.

25. Answer both parts of Exercise 24 for the following graph.

26. Add an arc CI of weight 1 and an arc IH of weight 2 to the digraph of Exercise 25 and answer both parts of that question again.

27. [BB] When the Bellman–Ford algorithm has finished, explain how to find a shortest path from v_1 to v_j.

28. When the Bellman–Ford algorithm detects the presence of a negative weight cycle, can it be adapted to exhibit such a cycle? Explain.

29. (a) [BB] The Bellman–Ford algorithm can be terminated as soon as two successive columns are the same; that is, if for two successive values of i, the numbers $d_i(2), \ldots, d_i(n)$ are identical. Explain.

   (b) Show that the Bellman–Ford algorithm will detect the presence of any negative weight cycle in a weighted digraph (assuming there is at least one directed path from v_1 to every other vertex).

30. If a digraph contains arcs with negative weights, is it possible for there to exist a shortest walk from one vertex to another that is not a path? Explain.

31. Find a reasonable estimate of the complexity of the Bellman–Ford algorithm in terms of comparisons.

32. In an attempt to get the algorithms of Dijkstra to work correctly on digraphs with negative weight edges, the following idea is proposed. Determine the highest negative weight k of an arc, add $|k|$ to the weight of every arc (now all arcs have nonnegative weights), use Dijkstra to find shortest paths, and finally subtract from each final weight $|k|$ times the number of arcs required on a shortest path. Comment.

33. Discover what you can about Bellman and Ford and write a short note about these men.

11.3 RNA Chains

In October 1989, it was announced that Sidney Altman, a Canadian-born professor at Yale University, and Thomas Cech of the University of Colorado had won jointly the Nobel Prize in chemistry for research on ribonucleic acid that "could help explain the origins of life" and "probably provide a new tool for gene technology."

Ribonucleic (pronounced rī-bō-nōo-clā-ĭc) acid (RNA for short) and deoxyribonucleic acid (DNA) are genetic materials carried in the cells of the human body. In fact, RNA is a chain each link of which is one of four chemicals: uracil, cytosine (sī-tō-zēn), adenine, and guanine. Throughout this section, we will use the letters U, C, A, and G, respectively, to represent these chemicals. Here, for example, is one RNA chain:

(1)   UCGAGCUAGCGAAG.

Two kinds of enzymes can break the links in an RNA chain. The first, called a G-enzyme, breaks a chain after each G-link. For example, this enzyme would break the preceding chain into the following *fragments*:

G-fragments: UCG, AG, CUAG, CG, AAG.

The second enzyme, called a U,C-enzyme, breaks the chain after each U- and after each C-link. Thus, it would break the chain in (1) into the fragments

U,C-fragments: U, C, GAGC, U, AGC, GAAG.

It is apparently not possible to discover directly the sequence of U's, C's, A's, and G's that comprise a particular chain, but using the enzymes just described, the collection of fragments of the chain, the *complete enzyme digest*, can be determined. The problem is then how to recover an RNA chain from its complete enzyme digest. In this section, we show how to solve this problem with a method that makes use of graph theory.

There are 5! possible RNA chains with the G-fragments just listed. (In real situations, the number is much larger.[4]) Our aim is to find which of these 120 chains also gives rise to the given set of U,C-fragments. Our method involves associating with any complete listing of G- and U,C-fragments a directed pseudograph (it is seldom a graph) and hunting for Eulerian circuits or trails, each of which corresponds to an RNA chain with the specified fragments. If no suitable circuit or trail is found, then no such chain exists. (Perhaps an error was made in listing the fragments.)

In any recovery problem, we may assume that there are at least two G-fragments and two U,C-fragments. (Otherwise, it's not hard to discern the original chain!) Also, it is straightforward to determine the fragment with which the chain ends. In the preceding listing of fragments, for example, the U,C-fragment GAAG is *abnormal*: U,C-fragments should end in U or C but GAAG does not. The only way this could happen is for GAAG to be at the end of the chain.

Pause 7

Using the fact that GAAG must come last in the sought after RNA chain, lower the previous estimate of 120 possible chains with the given fragment lists by determining how many RNA chains have the set of U,C-fragments listed previously.   ∎

The initial lists of fragments will always contain at least one abnormal fragment (at the end). If this is a G-fragment ending in U or C or a U,C-fragment ending in G, there will be only one abnormal fragment and, in this case, the final fragment is uniquely determined. The only way in which there can be two abnormal fragments is if they both end in A. In this case, however, one will be identifiable as contained within the other; it is the longer of the two with which the chain ends. Again, the final fragment is uniquely determined.

Pause 8

There can never be more than two abnormal fragments. Why?   ∎

To illustrate the general procedure, we consider the example described previously. We assume that we know only the fragments and, to make things amusing, change the order of the fragments and start with these lists:

G-fragments: CUAG, AAG, AG, UCG, CG
U,C-fragments: U, U, AGC, C, GAAG, GAGC

Imagine splitting the G-fragments further using the U,C-enzyme and splitting the U,C-fragments further with the G-enzyme. For example, UCG in the first list

---

[4]The first chain successfully recovered contained 77 links. See Robert W. Holley, Jean Apgar, George A. Everett, James T. Madison, Mark Marquisse, Susan H. Merrill, John Robert Penswick, and Ada Zamir, "Structure of a Ribonucleic Acid," *Science* **147** (1965), 1462–1465.

would become U, C, G, while AGC in the second list would become AG, C. A fragment like AAG wouldn't split further. The resulting bits are called *extended bases*.

Now we will see how graph theory comes into play. Consider any fragment in one of the lists that splits under the action of the other enzyme, UCG for example. Draw two vertices labeled U and G for the first and last extended bases in this G-fragment and join them by an arc labeled UCG going from the first extended base to the last, as shown in Fig. 11.15.

Figure 11.15

Similarly, the G-fragment CG determines an arc labeled CG from a vertex labeled C to one labeled G. Repeating for all fragments that split, we obtain the digraph shown in Fig. 11.16. (In general, the procedure described could yield a directed pseudograph.)

To find the RNA chain, we look for Eulerian circuits or trails that end with the arc GAAG corresponding to the abnormal fragment. Here, an Eulerian trail can be found. We obtain the original chain by writing down the labels of the arcs on this trail in order, noting that each vertex encountered is listed twice on the arc labels, so one of these occurrences should be discarded. If there is more than one such Eulerian trail or circuit, then there is more than one chain with the given fragments. If, by some chance, no appropriate Eulerian trail or circuit exists, then the original fragments contradicted each other; there is no RNA chain with these fragments.

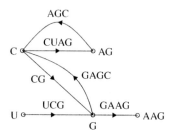

Figure 11.16 A digraph determining an RNA chain.

In the digraph of Fig. 11.16, there is just one Eulerian trail: UCG, GAGC, CUAG, AGC, CG, GAAG. Eliminating overlap at each vertex, we obtain the RNA chain UCGAGCUAGCGAAG.

The method just described works whenever there is an abnormal fragment that splits; in the example, the abnormal fragment GAAG splits under the action of the G-enzyme into G and AAG. It follows that the method always works when there are two abnormal fragments since the longer abnormal fragment must split. This is illustrated in our next problem.

PROBLEM 3. Determine the RNA chain or chains (if any) that give rise to the following complete enzyme digest.

G-fragments: AACUG, UAG, A, AG, AG, AG, G
U,C-fragments: U, AGAAC, AGAGA, GGAGU.

Solution. There are two abnormal fragments, A and AGAGA. The longer is AGAGA, so this is the fragment with which the chain ends. In Fig. 11.17, we show the digraph that depicts this situation. The unique answer is AGAACUGGAGUAGAGA.

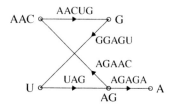

Figure 11.17

A slight variation is required when there is a single abnormal fragment that does not split. In this case, the abnormal fragment will be a vertex, rather than an arc, in the related directed pseudograph, and solutions can be obtained from all Eulerian trails or circuits that end at this vertex. We illustrate.

PROBLEM 4. Determine the RNA chain or chains (if any) that give rise to the following complete enzyme digest.

G-fragments: CUAG, G, UG, C, CACG, AG
U,C-fragments: AC, AGC, GGAGC, C, U, GU.

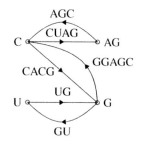

Figure 11.18

Solution. The only abnormal fragment is C, so this is the end of the chain. In Fig. 11.18, the corresponding digraph is shown and we note that it is Eulerian. In fact, there are two Eulerian circuits that end at vertex C and these lead to two answers: CUAGCACGUGGAGC and CACGUGGAGCUAGC.

Here is a summary of the method outlined in this section.

11.3.1 RECOVERY OF AN RNA CHAIN FROM ITS COMPLETE ENZYME DIGEST

1. Determine the fragment with which the chain ends. It is the abnormal fragment if there is only one and, otherwise, the longer of the two abnormal fragments.
2. Form a directed pseudograph by drawing an arc for each fragment that splits under the action of the other enzyme. Such an arc is drawn from a vertex labeled with its first extended base to a vertex labeled with its last extended base. Label the arc with the name of the fragment.
3. If there is an abnormal fragment that splits, determine all Eulerian trails or circuits whose final arc is labeled with that abnormal fragment. Otherwise, determine all Eulerian trails or circuits whose final vertex is labeled with the abnormal fragment. Then, for each such trail or circuit, write down in order the labels of the arcs without repeating the label of common vertices.

The connection between graph theory and the problem of recovering RNA chains from their enzyme digests does not seem to be well known. It came first to our attention in a book on combinatorics by Fred Roberts,[5] although the ideas seem to have originated in work of James E. Mosimann.[6] We are indebted to George Hutchinson[7] for making available some additional material to complement his and Mosimann's journal articles.

We would also like to thank Daniel Kobler for making us aware of the fact that graph theory techniques similar to those described in this section have been used recently to study problems of recovering DNA chains from other types of information about fragments.[8]

Answers to Pauses

7. Since GAAG comes last, we seek the number of arrangements of the fragments U, C, GAGC, U, AGC. Since U appears twice, the answer is $\frac{1}{2}5! = 60$. (See Section 7.5.)
8. There can be at most one abnormal G-fragment and at most one abnormal U,C-fragment.

True/False Questions

(Answers can be found in the back of the book.)

1. The RNA chain GCUAGUUGCGUC has four G-fragments.
2. The RNA chain GCUAGUUGCGUC has seven U,C-fragments.
3. The G-fragments UCG, G, CAG, UG, AC could come from $5! = 120$ different RNA chains.
4. The U,C-fragments GC, C, GAC, GU, AC could come from $5! = 120$ different RNA chains.
5. The RNA chain GCUAGUUGCGUC has an abnormal U,C-fragment.

[5]Fred S. Roberts, *Applied Combinatorics*, Prentice Hall, Upper Saddle River, NJ, 1984.

[6]James E. Mosimann, *Elementary Probability for the Biological Sciences*, Appleton-Century-Crofts, New York, 1968.

[7]George Hutchinson, "Evaluation of Polymer Sequence Fragment Data Using Graph Theory," *Bulletin of Mathematical Biophysics* **31** (1969), 541–562, and *Evaluation of Polymer Sequence Data from Two Complete Digests*, Internal Report, Laboratory of Applied Studies, Division of Computer Research and Technology, National Institute of Health, Maryland (1968).

[8]For example, see J. Blazewicz, A. Hertz, D. Kobler, and D. de Werra, "On Some Properties of DNA Graphs," *Discrete Applied Mathematics* **98** (1999), 1–19.

6. An RNA chain can never have two abnormal fragments.

7. An RNA chain always begins with an abnormal fragment.

8. An Eulerian trail or circuit determining an RNA chain must end with an arc labeled with an abnormal fragment.

9. Graph theory techniques similar to those demonstrated in this section have also been used to study problems of recombining DNA chains from other types of information about fragments.

Exercises

*The answers to exercises marked [BB] can be found in the **B**ack of the **B**ook.*

1. Answer the following questions for each pair of fragment lists given.

   i. From how many RNA chains could the given list of G-fragments arise? From how many chains could the given list of U,C-fragments arise? Which of these numbers provides a better estimate of the number of RNA chains whose G-fragments and U,C-fragments are as described?

   ii. Find all RNA chains with the given complete enzyme digests.

   (a) [BB] G-fragments: CUG, CAAG, G, UC
         U,C-fragments: C, C, U, AAGC, GGU

   (b) G-fragments: G, UCG, G, G, UU
        U,C-fragments: GGGU, U, GU, C

   (c) G-fragments: UCACG, AA, CCG, AAAG, G
        U,C-fragments: C, GGU, GAAAGAA, C, AC, C

   (d) G-fragments: UUCG, G, ACG, CUAG
        U,C-fragments: G, C, GGAC, U, AGU, C, U

   (e) [BB] G-fragments: UG, CC, ACCAG, G, AUG
         U,C-fragments: C, GAU, C, AGC, GAC, GU

   (f) G-fragments: CACG, AUG, UCAG, AG, UG
        U,C-fragments: AC, C, GU, G, AGAU, GAGC, U

   (g) G-fragments: UCG, AUAG, AG, UCAAUAG, G
        U,C-fragments: C, AGU, AG, GGAU, C, AGU, AAU

   (h) G-fragments: UAG, CUAAG, UA, G, UCAG, UAG
        U,C-fragments: C, U, U, AGGC, AAGU, AGU, AGU, A

2. [BB] (a) Why must there always exist an abnormal fragment?

   (b) Give a necessary and sufficient condition for there to exist two abnormal fragments.

3. [BB] Find the length of the smallest RNA chain with the property that its G- and U,C-fragments are the same as those of another RNA chain. (Assume that these chains contain no A's and are of length greater than 1.)

4. (a) [BB] Show that an abnormal fragment that contains a G cannot also contain a U or a C. (Similarly, an abnormal fragment that contains a U or a C cannot also contain a G.)

   (b) If there are two abnormal fragments, show that the shorter of the two must be just a series of As.

5. Explain why every RNA chain determines an Eulerian trail or circuit in the corresponding directed pseudo-graph.

11.4 Tournaments

In this section, we consider another kind of digraph called a *tournament*, which is just a complete graph with an orientation.

11.4.1 DEFINITION

A *tournament* is a digraph with the property that, for every two distinct vertices u and v, exactly one of uv, vu is an arc. The *score* of a vertex in a tournament, denoted $s(v)$, is the outdegree of the vertex. The *score sequence* of a tournament is the list of outdegrees in nonincreasing order. ❖

Pause 9

Suppose that a tournament T has n vertices, each of which has a different score. What is the score sequence of T? ∎

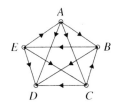

Figure 11.19 A tournament of size 5.

Tournaments arise in many different situations, the most obvious giving rise to their name. A round-robin competition in sport is one in which every competitor plays every other competitor once. Such a competition can be represented by a tournament in which the players are vertices and an arc directed from vertex v to vertex u indicates that player v defeats player u. In this context, the score of a vertex is the number of wins achieved by that player in the tournament and the score sequence is the sequence of wins by all the players, arranged in decreasing order. An example of a tournament involving five players and with score sequence $3, 3, 2, 2, 0$ appears in Fig. 11.19.

There are other less obvious applications of tournaments. In psychology, subjects are sometimes presented with alternatives two at a time and asked to express a preference for one of them. Representing the various alternatives as the vertices of a digraph and assuming all possible pairs of alternatives are presented to the subject, the person's preferences can be represented as a tournament in a natural way.

Tournaments arise in biology as well. It is sometimes the case that, for every pair of animals of a certain species, one is dominant over the other. This relation defines a pecking order in the species and can be analyzed by means of tournaments.

It is usually desired to rank the members of a tournament. In the round-robin competition pictured in Fig. 11.19, the numbers of wins recorded by A, B, C, D, and E are 3, 2, 2, 0, and 3, respectively. Since A and E have the best records, these players should finish ahead of the rest. Since E defeated A, perhaps E should be ranked first, although A might resent this since A defeated B, who in turn defeated E. A Hamiltonian path provides one way of settling rankings: rank v ahead of u if vertex v occurs before vertex u in the Hamiltonian path. Such a ranking may seem reasonable since a player will always have beaten the person ranked immediately below him or her. In Fig. 11.19, for example, $EACBD$ is a Hamiltonian path and E, A, C, B, and D is the corresponding ranking of players. The following theorem, due to the Hungarian mathematician L. Rédei, tells us that this procedure is available in any tournament.

11.4.2 THEOREM

(Rédei[9]) Every tournament has a Hamiltonian path.

Proof

Suppose T is a tournament with n vertices. We proceed by induction on n. The result is trivial for $n = 1$, and for $n = 2$ the only tournament is ○——○ , which clearly has a Hamiltonian path. So assume that $k \geq 2$ and that the result is true for $n = k$. Let T be a tournament with $k + 1$ vertices, let u be any vertex of T, and let $T \setminus \{u\}$ be that subgraph of T obtained by deleting u (and all arcs incident with u). This subgraph has k vertices and is a tournament, since each pair of vertices is still joined by an arc. By the induction hypothesis, we conclude that $T \setminus \{u\}$ has a Hamiltonian path $v_1 v_2 \cdots v_k$. Now there is an arc between u and v_1 (see Fig. 11.20). If this arc is uv_1 (that is, directed from u to v_1), then $uv_1 v_2 \cdots v_k$ is a Hamiltonian path in T.

Suppose, on the other hand, that the arc is $v_1 u$ and consider the arc between u and v_2. If this arc is uv_2, then $v_1 u v_2 v_3 \cdots v_k$ is a Hamiltonian path in T and again we have the desired result. In general, if there is a minimal integer $i > 1$ such that the arc between u and v_i is uv_i, then $v_{i-1}u$ is an arc (by minimality of i), and $v_1 v_2 \cdots v_{i-1} u v_i \cdots v_k$ is a Hamiltonian path [see Fig. 11.20(b)]. If there is no such minimal i, all arcs between u and v_i are of the type $v_i u$, and $v_1 v_2 \cdots v_k u$ is a Hamiltonian path. In every case, there is a Hamiltonian path. ●

[9]L. Rédei, "Ein kombinatorischer Satz," *Acta Litterarum ac Scientiarum Szeged* **7** (1934), 39–43.

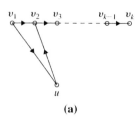

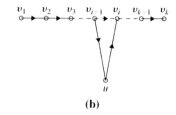

(a)   **(b)**

Figure 11.20

Unfortunately, there is no reason why a Hamiltonian path in a tournament should be unique, so disputes over ranking can still exist. In our earlier example concerning the tournament in Fig. 11.19, for instance, $ABECD$ is another Hamiltonian path.

Find a third Hamiltonian path. ∎

The point is that with more than one Hamiltonian path there is no unique ranking of the players. Certain tournaments, however, do have unique Hamiltonian paths.

11.4.3 DEFINITION

A tournament is *transitive* if and only if whenever uv and vw are arcs then uw is also an arc. ❖

Figure 11.21 No 3-cycle can appear in a transitive tournament.

Transitive tournaments are precisely those that have no subtournaments of the form illustrated in Fig. 11.21. For instance, the tournament in Fig. 11.19 is not transitive because $ABEA$ is a 3-cycle like that in Fig. 11.21.

It turns out that we can characterize those tournaments with unique Hamiltonian paths in terms of the concepts of transitivity and scores.

11.4.4 THEOREM

The following properties of a tournament T are equivalent.

1. T has a unique Hamiltonian path.
2. T is transitive.
3. Every player in T has a different score.

Proof

We show (1) → (2), that a tournament with a unique Hamiltonian path must be transitive, and leave the rest of the proof to Exercise 9. So assume that T has a unique Hamiltonian path and order the vertices so that this path is $v_{n-1}v_{n-2}\cdots v_0$. It is sufficient to show that v_jv_i is an arc whenever $j > i$. Suppose, by way of contradiction, that this is not the case. Then there must be some arc v_iv_j with $j > i$. (See Fig. 11.22.)

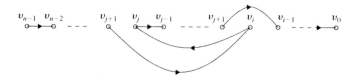

Figure 11.22

Choose i as small as possible such that an arc of this type exists (for some j) and, with that i fixed, choose j as large as possible such that the arc $v_i v_j$ exists. If $j \neq n - 1$ and $i \neq 0$ (as depicted in the figure), then

$$v_{n-1} \cdots v_{j+1} v_i v_j v_{j-1} \cdots v_{i+1} v_{i-1} \cdots v_0$$

is a second Hamiltonian path. If $i = 0$ and $j \neq n - 1$, then

$$v_{n-1} \cdots v_{j+1} v_0 v_j v_{j-1} \cdots v_1$$

is a second Hamiltonian path. If $j = n - 1$ and $i \neq 0$,

$$v_i v_{n-1} v_{n-2} \cdots v_{i+1} v_{i-1} \cdots v_0$$

is a second Hamiltonian path and, if $i = 0$ and $j = n - 1$, then

$$v_0 v_{n-1} v_{n-2} \cdots v_1$$

is a second Hamiltonian path. In all cases, we contradict the uniqueness of the Hamiltonian path.

Since we don't need graph theory to rank n players all of whose scores are different, the import of Theorem 11.4.4, sadly, is that Hamiltonian paths are not very helpful in ranking the vertices in tournaments.

 **Pause 11**

In a tournament of n players $v_0, v_1, \ldots, v_{n-1}$ suppose the score of player v_i is i. Find a Hamiltonian path. ∎

Answers to Pauses

9. Since each player in a tournament of n players can achieve at most $n - 1$ victories, the score of each vertex is at most $n - 1$. The score of each vertex is nonnegative, so any score s satisfies $0 \leq s \leq n - 1$. The only set of n distinct scores in this range is $\{0, 1, 2, \ldots, n - 1\}$, so the score sequence is $n - 1, n - 2, \ldots, 2, 1, 0$.

10. $ACBED$ is a third Hamiltonian path in Fig. 11.19.

11. Player v_{n-1} wins all $n - 1$ games; so there is an arc from v_{n-1} to each other v_i, in particular to v_{n-2}. Player v_{n-2} wins $n - 2$ games (losing only to v_{n-1}), so there is an arc from v_{n-2} to each of $v_0, v_1, \ldots, v_{n-3}$. Continuing in this way, we see that there is an arc from v_i to v_{i-1} for each i, $1 \leq i \leq n - 1$. Thus, $v_{n-1} v_{n-2} \cdots v_0$ is a path and, since it contains all vertices, Hamiltonian.

True/False Questions

(Answers can be found in the back of the book.)

1. 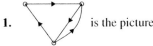 is the picture of a tournament.

2. The score sequence of 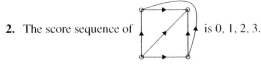 is 0, 1, 2, 3.

3. 4, 2, 2, 2, 2 is the score sequence of a tournament.

4. A tournament cannot have two vertices with score 0.

5. There is a tournament of size 3 in which all players have the same score.

6. There is a tournament of size 4 in which all players have the same score.

7. For every natural number n, there is a tournament of size n in which all players have different scores.

8. If $s_1, \ldots, s_n$ is the score sequence of a tournament, then $n - 1 - s_n, n - 1 - s_{n-1}, \ldots, n - 1 - s_1$ is the score sequence of another tournament.

9. Every tournament has a Hamiltonian cycle.

10. is the picture of a transitive tournament.

Exercises

*The answers to exercises marked [BB] can be found in the **B**ack of the **B**ook.*

1. **(a)** [BB] Draw all nonisomorphic tournaments with three vertices and give the score sequence of each. Which of these are transitive?

   (b) Repeat part (a) for tournaments with four vertices.

2. [BB] Let A be the adjacency matrix of a tournament. Describe $A + A^T$ and explain.

3. (For students of linear algebra)

   (a) Prove that A is the adjacency matrix of a tournament with n players if and only $A + A^T = J - I$, where I is the $n \times n$ identity matrix and J is the $n \times n$ matrix consisting entirely of 1's.

   (b) If A is the adjacency matrix of a tournament, so is its transpose. Why?

   (c) Let P be an $n \times n$ permutation matrix, that is, a matrix obtained from the $n \times n$ identity matrix by rearranging its rows. If A is the adjacency matrix of a tournament, so is PAP^T. Why?

4. **(a)** Find all Hamiltonian paths in the tournament of Fig. 11.19.

   (b) Suppose the arc in Fig. 11.19 is DB, not BD. Find all Hamiltonian paths in this tournament.

5. Suppose $s_1, s_2, \ldots, s_n$ are the scores in a tournament.

   (a) [BB] Prove that $\sum_{i=1}^{n} s_i = \sum_{i=1}^{n} (n - 1 - s_i)$ and interpret this result in the context of a round-robin tournament.

   (b) Prove that $\sum_{i=1}^{n} s_i^2 = \sum_{i=1}^{n} (n - 1 - s_i)^2$ and interpret this result in the context of a round-robin tournament.

6. [BB] Let $\mathcal{T}$ be a tournament and let v be any vertex of $\mathcal{T}$ having maximum score. Show that the length of the shortest path from v to any other vertex of $\mathcal{T}$ is 1 or 2.

7. **(a)** [BB] Could 3, 2, 1, 1 be the score sequence of a tournament?

   (b) Could 6, 6, 6, 6, 1, 1, 1, 1 be the score sequence of a tournament?

8. Let S be the set of scores in a tournament $\mathcal{T}$ with n vertices.

   (a) Prove that $\sum_{s \in S} s = \frac{1}{2}n(n - 1)$.

   (b) Let t be a natural number less than n and let $s_1, s_2, \ldots, s_t \in S$.

   Prove that $\sum_{i=1}^{t} s_i \geq \frac{1}{2}t(t - 1)$.

   [*Remark*: H. G. Landau has proved that the two conditions in (a) and (b) are sufficient as well as necessary for the existence of a tournament with a prescribed set of scores.[10]]

9. Complete the proof of Theorem 11.4.4 as follows.

   (a) Prove that the scores in a transitive tournament of n vertices are all different. Thus, (2) → (3).

   (b) Suppose every player in a tournament $\mathcal{T}$ has a different score. Show that $\mathcal{T}$ has a unique Hamiltonian path. Thus, (3) → (1). [*Hint*: PAUSES 9 and 11]

10. Find all Hamiltonian paths in the tournament shown.

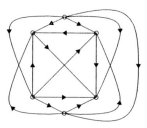

11. [BB; →] Prove that a tournament is transitive if and only if it contains no cycles.

12. Suppose $\mathcal{G}$ is a digraph on a vertex set $\mathcal{V}$. Put a binary relation on $\mathcal{V}$ by defining $v \preceq v$ for each $v \in \mathcal{V}$ and, for vertices $u \neq v$, $u \preceq v$ if uv is an arc.

   (a) Does $\preceq$ define a partial order on $\mathcal{V}$?

   (b) Find a necessary and sufficient condition for $\preceq$ to define a partial order when $\mathcal{G}$ is a tournament. Is this partial order a total order?

   Explain your answers.

[10]H. G. Landau, "On Dominance Relations and the Structure of Animal Societies, III: The Condition for a Score Structure," *Bulletin of Mathematical Biophysics* **15** (1955), 143–148.

11.5 Scheduling Problems

The shortest path algorithms for weighted graphs discussed in Section 10.4 have many obvious applications. Often, the weight on an edge represents distance (or cost), and the shortest path is just the shortest (or cheapest) route between the distinguished points. There is also a large area of application to weighted digraphs, where the arcs represent tasks that must be performed in a certain order and the weight of an arc represents the time required to carry out the task. The problem in which we are interested is to determine the order in which the tasks should be undertaken so that they all are completed in the shortest possible time. We present two types of such *scheduling problems* in this section.

We assume throughout that the weights of arcs in digraphs are integers. Such digraphs are also called *directed networks*.

11.5.1 DEFINITION

A *directed network* is a digraph with an integer weight attached to each arc. ❖

**11.5.2 A TYPE I
SCHEDULING PROBLEM**

The construction of a fence involves four tasks: setting posts (Po), cutting wood (C), painting (Pa), and nailing (N). Setting posts must precede painting and nailing, and cutting must precede nailing. Suppose that setting posts takes 3 units of time, cutting wood takes 2 units of time, painting takes 5 units of time for uncut wood and 4 units of time otherwise, and nailing takes 2 units of time for unpainted wood and 3 units of time otherwise. In what order should these tasks be carried out to complete the project in the shortest possible time?

This problem can be easily analyzed. There are five ways in which the fence can be completed:

$$Po—C—N—Pa$$
$$Po—C—Pa—N$$
$$Po—Pa—C—N$$
$$C—Po—N—Pa$$
$$C—Po—Pa—N$$

and it is a simple matter to compute the time for each. We can also illustrate the situation with the directed network shown in Fig. 11.23. The arcs in the digraph represent tasks and the vertices represent stages in the process. The direction of an arc indicates passage from one stage to another. For instance, the arc with weight 2 from D to F represents nailing, while the two arcs leaving vertex A represent

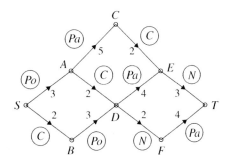

Figure 11.23 A directed network for a scheduling problem.

cutting and painting. Vertex E represents the stage where all tasks except nailing have been completed

A path corresponds to a certain order of tasks; thus, the three different paths from S to E represent three different ways to cut, paint, and set posts. Note that the weight given to an arc may depend on which tasks precede it; for example, arcs DF and ET each represent nailing, but they have different weights.

The shortest path from S to T shows us how to complete the project in the least amount of time. Applying Dijkstra's algorithm (first version) to the digraph, we obtain the labels shown in Fig. 11.24.

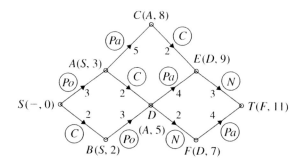

Figure 11.24

One shortest path is $SADFT$, completing the job in 11 units of time. This path corresponds to first setting posts, then cutting, then nailing, and finally painting. Notice that there was a choice in the labeling of vertex D; it could equally well have been labeled $(B, 5)$. There is, therefore, a second shortest path that completes the job in 11 units of time, $SBDFT$. So we could equally well cut, then set posts, then nail, and finally paint.

The procedure just described is important in the management sciences and has been thoroughly studied. Methods for solving such networks are often called *critical path methods* (CPMs) or *project evaluation and review techniques* (PERTs), and a great deal of specialized terminology has been developed. For example, a shortest path such as $SADFT$ (or $SBDFT$) is called a *critical path*.

In the scheduling problem discussed previously, one task had to be completed before another could start. Such would be the case in a one-person project, for example. Also, the time required for a task depended on what tasks had already been completed. In other situations, however, several different tasks can be pursued simultaneously and the time of a given task is independent of the other tasks. Think of the construction of a house or office building. Such a project often requires the services of a large number of people. While the order of tasks is sometimes important (plumbing before carpets!), sometimes it isn't (plumbing and electrical work). Also, and unlike building a fence, in a large construction project the times of the tasks are often determined only by the nature of the task.

As before, our aim is to plan the project so as to minimize the time required. While strictly speaking, the procedure we outline is not a shortest path method, it does fit naturally into this section.

11.5.3 A TYPE II SCHEDULING PROBLEM

To finish a basement, a contractor must arrange for certain tasks to be completed. These are shown in Table 11.25 together with brief codes for referring to them and the times required for each.

Table 11.25

Task	Code	Time
Floor installation	F	4
Plumbing	Pl	3
Electrical work	E	5
Wallboard	W	3
Varnish doors and moldings	V	1
Paint	Pa	2
Install doors and moldings	D	1
Lay carpet	C	2

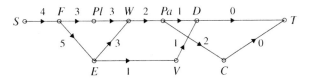

Figure 11.26

We represent this problem by the digraph in Fig. 11.26. This time the vertices represent tasks, and an arc from u to v means that task u precedes task v. It is necessary to install the floor (F) before any other tasks can commence. The electrical work (E) and plumbing (Pl) must both be completed before the wallboard can go in, but neither the plumbing nor the electrical work is a prerequisite for the other; these two tasks can occur simultaneously. The order in which other tasks are carried out is shown in the digraph. Note that, while the electrical work must precede the painting, we do not show an arc from E to Pa since this precedence can be inferred from the arcs EW and WPa.

The weight assigned to an arc is the time it takes to complete the task represented by the terminal vertex of the arc. Both EW and PlW are assigned a weight of 3 since both E and Pl must be completed before W can commence and W requires 3 units of time. The last two arcs, leading to the finish of the project, are assigned a weight of 0 because the job is completed once D and C are finished.

When the job is completed, all paths from start to finish will have been followed. Thus, in this situation, it is the time required for the longest path that is the shortest time for the entire project. To find this path, we modify in two ways the first version of Dijkstra's algorithm. No vertex is labeled until all prerequisite vertices have been labeled, and each vertex is always labeled with the **largest** value of $d + w(e)$. The final labels in our example are shown in Fig. 11.27.

The job can be completed in 16 units of time, and $FEWPaC$ is the critical path. Note that the tasks not on the critical path (Pl, V, and D) can be delayed somewhat without delaying the project. For example, plumbing could take 5 time units instead of 3 and the label $(E, 12)$ for W would still be correct: The critical path would not be affected. Varnishing could take as much as 6 units of time without delaying the project because, if this were to occur, only the label for D would change, to $(V, 16)$: The project could still be completed in 16 units of time. On the other

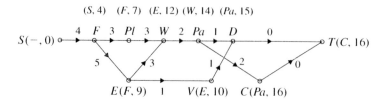

Figure 11.27

hand, if more than 6 units of time was spent on varnishing, the project would be delayed. This extra $6 - 1 = 5$ units of time that could be spent on V is called the *slack* of the task V. As we have seen, the slack of Pl is 2 and the slack of D is 1. Knowledge of these values allows the contractor to complete the project more quickly by transferring workers to other tasks on the critical path.

| **11.5.4 DEFINITION** | In a project that requires the completion of various tasks, the slack in a particular task is the length of time that task can be delayed without delaying the entire project. ❖ |

In projects more complicated than the one just presented, a given task may lie on several paths that are not critical. In such cases, special care must be taken in determining slack. There are examples in the exercises.

True/False Questions

(Answers can be found in the back of the book.)

1. Every digraph is a directed network.

2. When using a directed network to analyze a type I scheduling problem, vertices represent tasks and arcs represent stages in the process.

3. Dijkstra's algorithm is often used to help solve type I scheduling problems.

4. In type I scheduling problems, several different tasks can be carried out simultaneously.

5. A critical path in a type I scheduling problem is a shortest path from start to finish.

6. PERT and CPM are acronyms that sometimes appear in management science texts when discussing type I scheduling problems.

7. When using a directed network to analyze a type II scheduling problem, vertices represent tasks.

8. A modified version of Dijkstra's algorithm is often used to help solve type II scheduling problems.

9. A critical path in a type II scheduling problem is a shortest path from start to finish.

10. In a type II scheduling problem, a vertex that is not on any critical path will have nonzero slack.

Exercises

*The answers to exercises marked [BB] can be found in the **B**ack of the **B**ook.*

1. [BB] Solve the fence problem described in paragraph 11.5.2, assuming that the setting of posts takes 3 units of time if the wood has not yet been cut and 4 units of time otherwise. (All other aspects of the project are unchanged.)

2. [BB] The construction of a certain part in an automobile engine involves four activities: pouring the mold, calibration, polishing, and inspection. The mold is poured first; calibration must occur before inspection. Pouring the mold takes 8 units of time, calibration takes 3 units, polishing takes 6 units for an uncalibrated product and 8 units for a calibrated one, and inspection takes 2 units of time for a polished product and 3 units for an unpolished one.
   (a) What type of scheduling problem is this (type I or II)? Why? Represent the paths to completion of this job by drawing the appropriate directed network.
   (b) What is the shortest time required for this job? Describe the critical path.

3. In Exercise 2, suppose polishing takes 9 units of time for an uncalibrated product. (All other conditions remain the same.) Find the new critical path and the length of the revised project.

4. Repeat Exercise 2, assuming that, in addition to the tasks stated, the workers will take a coffee break. The coffee break must take place after calibration and before inspection. If it occurs before polishing, it requires 2 time units; after polishing, it requires 6 time units.

5. [BB] Change the basement project described in paragraph 11.5.3 by supposing that
   • plumbing requires 4 units of time;
   • the doors and moldings will be installed before they are varnished;
   • the carpets cannot be installed until the doors and moldings have been varnished; and
   • there are kitchen cabinets to be installed in 1 unit of time after painting.
   Draw the appropriate directed network that depicts the paths to completion of this revised project. Describe all critical paths and the slack in each task.

6. The building of a plastic model ship involves
   • detaching and sorting out the pieces (D),
   • gluing (G),
   • painting (P),
   • applying the decals (A).
   The decals must be applied last and the pieces must be detached and sorted before they are glued together. Detaching and sorting takes 2 units of time for unpainted pieces and otherwise 3 units of time. Gluing takes 12 units of time for unpainted pieces and 15 otherwise. Painting takes 10 units of time for pieces without glue; 12 otherwise. It takes 5 units of time to apply the decals.

   (a) What type of scheduling problem is this? Draw a network that describes the possible routes to completion of the model.
   (b) Applying Dijsktra's algorithm (first version) to your network, discover the fastest way this ship can be assembled. How long will this take?

7. [BB] Suppose we want to build a Klein bottle. The tasks involved in this project and the time required for each are recorded in the following table.

Code	Tasks	Time (in months)
G	blow glass	7
Po	polish	5
Sh	shape	9
A	add hole	4
H	affix handles	5
Tw	twist	2
R	remove hole	4
Pa	paint	6

   The glass must be blown before anything else. Polishing precedes all but G and Sh; shaping precedes all but G and Po. The hole must be added before it is removed (!) and before the bottle is twisted. The handles go on before Tw and Pa. Once Tw, R, and Pa are completed, the project is finished.
   (a) What type of scheduling problem is this (type I or II)? Draw the appropriate directed network.
   (b) Find all critical paths for this project.
   (c) Find the slack of Po, Sh, A, Tw, and R for each of the critical paths found in (b).
   (d) Suppose that tasks Po and A are each delayed 3 months. Will the completion of the project be delayed? Explain.

8. Repeat Exercise 7 if, in addition to all the conditions stated there, A must also precede H.

9. Repeat Exercise 7 if A takes 6 months to complete instead of 4, and R takes 7 months to complete instead of 4.

10. What's a Klein bottle? Find out what you can about this thing and write a short note.

11. [BB] To complete her master's thesis, a geology student must perform fieldwork (F) and laboratory analysis (L), conduct a library search (S) of the literature, create a database of relevant articles (D), and write the thesis (W). The write-up cannot begin until all tasks except for the laboratory analysis are complete. It takes 3 units of time if it is the last task and otherwise 5 units. The fieldwork, which takes 4 units of time, must precede both the laboratory analysis and the database creation. The library

search takes 2 units of time. The laboratory analysis takes 2 units of time if it is undertaken after the library search and otherwise 3 units. Creation of the database takes 1 unit of time if it is delayed until the library search is complete and otherwise 4 units.

(a) What type of scheduling problem is this (I or II)? Draw the appropriate directed network.

(b) What is the shortest possible time in which this student can complete her thesis?

(c) In what order should she perform her thesis-related tasks to achieve this minimum time?

12. Fred and Wilma Noseworthy are planning a dinner party. The things they must do before their guests arrive and the time required for each are shown in the following table. The fish must be caught and the wine purchased before the table is set. The Noseworthys are not fond of raw fish or raw vegetables and do not use wine in their cooking. The table must be dusted before it can be set. Vacuuming is never done until the table is set. Fortunately, Fred and Wilma have the full support of their student daughter and son, who are always very willing to help their parents with whatever jobs need to be done (so up to four jobs can be done simultaneously). The entire family greets their guests together after all tasks have been completed.

Dust house	D	3
Vacuum house	V	2
Set table	T	1
Buy wine	W	4
Catch fish	F	6
Pick vegetables	P	2
Cook food	C	4
Greet guests	G	2

(a) What type of scheduling problem is this (I or II)? Why? Draw the appropriate directed network.

(b) What is the shortest possible time in which dinner preparations can be accomplished? Describe the critical path and illustrate with a directed network, showing all labels.

(c) Find the slack in W, C, and D.

13. Repeat Exercise 12 under the additional assumption that wine is used in the cooking.

14. Before going to school, John must take a shower, get dressed, eat breakfast, and finish his math assignment. John will take his shower before getting dressed or eating breakfast and he will get dressed before finishing his assignment, but there are no other restrictions. Taking a shower requires 9 minutes; getting dressed takes 9 minutes if John has first eaten breakfast, but otherwise 12 minutes. Finishing his assignment takes 12 minutes if

John has eaten breakfast, but 18 minutes otherwise. Eating breakfast takes 9 minutes if John has finished his assignment and 18 minutes otherwise.

(a) [BB] What type of scheduling problem is this (I or II)? Draw the appropriate directed network.

(b) Find all possible ways in which John can carry out his tasks before school so that he can leave in the shortest possible time.

15. Repeat Exercise 14, removing the restriction that John must dress before finishing his assignment.

16. A manufacturing company imports basic widgets and upgrades them into super deluxe widgets. The process involves six operations A, B, C, D, E, and F. Although no two operations can be carried out simultaneously, there is some flexibility concerning the order in which they are done. The requirements are that C cannot be started until B is finished, D cannot be started until both A and B are finished, E cannot be started until A, B, and C are finished, and F cannot be commenced until A, B, C, and D are all complete. A costs \$300, B costs \$200 if carried out before A and \$300 otherwise, and C costs \$500 if done before A and \$200 otherwise. D and F both cost \$600 irrespective of when they are done. E costs \$400 if done before F, but only \$100 if done after F. What is the least possible cost of the overall process? Specify the critical path or paths involved.

17. The computer systems manager in a mathematics department is asked to schedule two large projects. The tasks involved and the time required for each are shown in the table.

Task	Code	Units of Time
Load project 1	$P1$	8
Load project 2	$P2$	15
Mount tape backup for project 1	Tp	11
Purge printer queue	Q	10
Find printer for project 2	P	10
Establish connection between the projects	C	5
Update project 1	U	20
Send printer jobs to buffer	B	25

The tape backup for project 1 cannot be mounted until project 1 is loaded. The printer for project 2 will not be found until project 2 is loaded and the printer queue is purged. The connection between the projects cannot be established until both projects are loaded. Project 1 will not be updated until it is loaded, and the printer jobs will not be buffered until the printer queue is purged.

(a) What kind of a scheduling problem is this? Explain.

(b) Draw a network describing this project. Apply Dijsktra's algorithm (first version) to find the least amount of time it will require to complete the project.

(c) Describe the critical path. Also find the maximum amount of slack in each activity.

Key Terms & Ideas

Here are some technical words and phrases that were used in this chapter. Do you know the meaning of each? If you're not sure, check the glossary or index at the back of the book.

arc

Chinese Postman Problem

digraph

directed graph

directed network

indegree

outdegree

score

score sequence

slack

strongly connected

tournament

transitive tournament

Review Exercises for Chapter 11

1. Solve the Chinese Postman Problem for the two graphs.

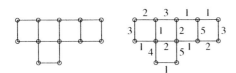

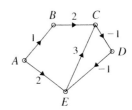

2. Solve the Chinese Postman Problem for the weighted graph given in Exercise 24 of the Chapter 10 Review Problems.

3. Solve the Chinese Postman Problem for the unweighted graph $K_{3,6}$.

4. Explain how to solve the Chinese Postman Problem for a graph $\mathcal{G}$ that has an Eulerian trail.

5. Let $\mathcal{G}$ be a strongly connected digraph with the property that no vertex has indegree equal to its outdegree. Prove that at least two vertices have indegrees greater than their outdegrees.

6. (a) Find two different orientations on the edges of K_4 that lead to nonisomorphic digraphs.

(b) Find two different orientations on the edges of K_4 that lead to isomorphic digraphs.

7. If A is the adjacency matrix of a digraph and $A^2 = [b_{ij}]$, find $\frac{1}{2} \sum b_{ii}$ and explain.

8. (a) Show that Dijkstra's algorithm fails for the digraph shown and explain why it fails. Start at vertex A.

(b) Apply the Bellman–Ford algorithm to the digraph. Your answer should make clear that you understand this algorithm by showing how the labels on vertices change as the algorithm proceeds.

9. Find all RNA chains with the given complete enzyme digests.

(a) G-fragments: G, AUG, UCAG, CCUG
    U,C-fragments: G, GGAU, C, C, U, AGC, U

(b) G-fragments: G, G, AUU, UCG, G, UG, G
    U,C-fragments: GGGGU, C, U, GAU, GU

(c) G-fragments: UG, CUAAG, AG, CG, UCG
    U,C-fragments: GU, AAG, GAGC, GC, U, U, C

(d) G-fragments: CG, UAAUAG, AUCG, AAG
    U,C-fragments: GAAGC, AAU, AG, GGU, C, AU

10. Let $n \geq 3$ and assume that the complete graph K_n has vertices labeled $w_1, w_2, \ldots, w_n$ and arc $w_i w_j$ directed w_i to w_j if and only $i < j$. Show that the tournament on this digraph is transitive.

11. (a) Could 5, 5, 4, 3, 2, 2, 2 be the score sequence of a tournament?

(b) Could 8, 8, 8, 6, 6, 3, 3, 1, 1, 1 be the score sequence of a tournament?

12. Let T be a tournament and let v be any vertex of T having minimum score. Show that the length of the shortest path from any other vertex to v is 1 or 2.

13. In a round-robin tennis tournament, we know that Alice is the clear winner, George is the clear loser, and all other players are tied for second. Show that the number of players competing must have been odd.

14. An industrial process involves six tasks, A, B, C, D, E, and F. Both A and B must come before C; C and D must come before F; B must come before D; and D before E. A takes 6 hours unless it comes after B, in which case it takes only 5. C takes 7 hours if it comes after D, but only 4 if before D. D takes 3 hours if it comes before A and 2 if after A. E takes 7 hours if it precedes C, but only 5 if it comes after C. Tasks B and F require 2 hours each. What is the shortest time required for this process? Describe the critical path or paths.

15. (a) Use a version of Dijkstra's algorithm to find a shortest path from A to J. Arcs should be used only in the directions indicated.

(b) Viewing the network as representing a type II scheduling problem and the weights as representing times in days, find a critical path from A to J and determine the overall time required to complete such a project.

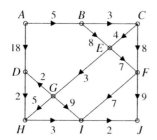

16. Consider the directed network.

(a) Use a version of Dijkstra's algorithm to find a shortest path from A to F. Arcs should be used only in the directions indicated.

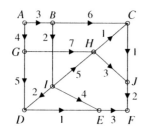

(b) Viewing the network as representing a type II scheduling problem and the weights as representing times in days, find a critical path from A to F and determine the overall time required to complete such a project.

17. George has to do four things before his mathematics exam tomorrow morning: study, sleep, eat pizza, and check his e-mail. He intends to spend two different periods of time studying, 3 hours on each occasion. While the sessions could be back to back, at least one session must occur before he sleeps. Eating pizza requires 1 hour, but it also takes 1 hour for the order to arrive (and something else could be done during this interval). Eating pizza must precede sleeping and also at least one of the study

sessions. George will get 6 hours of sleep if he sleeps after all study has been completed, but he is willing to settle for 5 hours otherwise. If George checks his e-mail between study sessions, he will do so quickly and take only 1 hour; otherwise, he will spend 2 hours at this activity.

(a) Find the shortest possible time in which George can complete his activities and a way in which he can order them and complete them in this time.

(b) Assume that George decides to read his e-mail before eating his pizza. Does this change the answer to (a)? If so, how?

(c) Assume that George decides to read his e-mail before ordering his pizza. Does this change the answer to (a)? If so, how?

18. When a customer places an order with a food delivery service, a phone operator keys (K) in the order. This requires 3 units of time and must be done first. Other employees of the store then shop for the frozen goods (F), the dry goods (D), and the produce (P) that have been ordered. The frozen goods are bagged (BF) separately from the produce and dry goods (PD), and then everything is loaded (L) onto the delivery truck. Shopping for the frozen goods requires 3 units of time if done right after the order is taken, and otherwise 5 units of time. It takes 4 units of time to shop for the dry goods. The produce is selected immediately after the dry goods and takes 7 units of time. It takes 2 units of time to pack the frozen goods if this occurs immediately after they are selected, and otherwise 3 units of time. Packing the dry goods requires 2 units of time if the frozen goods have not yet been packed, and otherwise 3 units. Loading the truck takes 8 units of time if the frozen goods were packed before the dry goods, and otherwise 11 units of time.

(a) What type of scheduling problem is this? Why?

(b) Draw a network that describes this situation.

(c) Apply Dijsktra's algorithm (first form) to discover how to get the groceries on their way to the customer as quickly as possible. What is the shortest amount of time this process will take?

19. Viewing the network as representing a type II scheduling problem and the weights as representing times in days, find a critical path from A to E and determine the overall time required to complete such a project. Determine the slack at all vertices that are off the critical path.

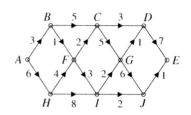

20. The following chart lists a number of tasks that must be completed for a crew of workers to construct a glynskz.

Task	A	B	C	D	E	F	G	H	I	J
Time (in days)	2	2	3	1	1	2	3	4	3	3

Task A must be carried out before any other tasks can commence. Task B must precede tasks E and F, and both E and F must be completed before H can begin. Tasks C and D must precede task G, which in turn must precede I. Task J must be carried out last. It is assumed that there are enough workers to carry out any number of tasks simultaneously.

(a) What is the fewest number of days needed to construct this glynskz? Find all critical paths.

(b) Find the slack in C, D, and E.

21. Dan and Jeff decided to cook a meal for their friends. The table shows the tasks involved and the time each requires. The food must be bought first, and all chopping of vegetables for the salad has to be done before making the salad. Similarly, all chopping of vegetables for the stir fry must be done before cooking the stir fry. The chicken wings can be cooked anytime (after purchase), while the rice must be cooked before it is drained. The stirfry will sit on the rice, so the rice must be drained before the stir fry is cooked. Finally, everything is arranged on the plates.

Task	Code	Units of Time
Buy groceries	B	10
Cook chicken wings	W	8
Chop vegetables for salad	CVS	3
Chop vegetables for stir fry	CVF	2
Cook rice	R	4
Cook stir fry	SF	7
Make salad	S	1
Drain rice	DR	1
Arrange plates	A	1

(a) What kind of scheduling problem is this? Explain.

(b) Draw a network that illustrates the routes to completion of dinner preparations. Apply Dijkstra's algorithm (first version) to your network to find the shortest time that Dan and Jeff must allow to prepare dinner?

(c) What is the critical path? Where is the slack and how much is there in each case?

12

Trees

12.1 Trees and their Properties

One kind of graph that we frequently encounter is called a *tree*, perhaps because it can be drawn so that it looks a bit like an ordinary tree. In this section, we introduce this concept with a variety of examples.

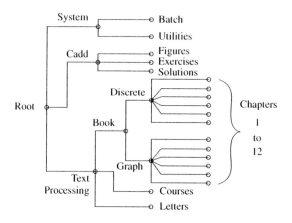

Figure 12.1 A partial computer directory structure.

The operating system on a computer organizes files into directories and subdirectories in the same way that people gather together pieces of paper into folders and put them into the drawers of a filing cabinet. The computer on which this text was first prepared had a directory called Book partitioned into two subdirectories called Discrete and Graph, each in turn containing a number of subdirectories, one for each chapter. Each chapter subdirectory had one file for each section in that chapter. Part of the organization of these computer files is depicted in Fig. 12.1.

Suppose you wanted to write down all the increasing subsequences that can be formed from the sequence 4, 8, 5, 0, 6, 2: 4, 5, 6 is one such subsequence, as is 0, 2, but not 2, 4 because it is not a subsequence of the given sequence. The order of the elements in a subsequence must be the same as in the sequence itself. To ensure that no subsequences are inadvertently omitted, some systematic method of enumeration is required. The graph drawn in Fig. 12.2 indicates such a method. In the figure, the desired subsequences correspond to paths from Start to each vertex.

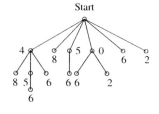

Figure 12.2

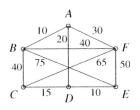

List all the monotonically increasing subsequences of the sequence 4, 8, 5, 0, 6, 2. ∎

Figure 12.3

Suppose the vertices of the graph shown in Fig. 12.3 represent towns and the edges roads, and the label on a road gives the time it takes to travel the road. Is it possible for a salesperson to drive to all the towns and return to his or her starting point, having visited each town exactly once? If it is, what is the shortest distance required for such a trip? In Section 10.4, we introduced this Traveling Salesman's Problem and mentioned that there is no efficient algorithm known for solving it. In reasonably small graphs, of course, we can exhaustively enumerate all the possibilities. Figure 12.4 indicates how we can use a graph to search systematically for Hamiltonian cycles, if they exist. We assume that the salesperson starts at A. The graph makes it apparent that there are in fact 12 Hamiltonian cycles in the graph of Fig. 12.3.

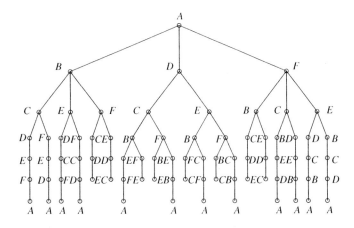

Figure 12.4 A hunt for Hamiltonian cycles in the graph of Fig. 12.3.

Answer the Traveling Salesman's Problem for the graph of Fig. 12.3. Find a shortest Hamiltonian cycle and its length. ∎

John and David are going to play a few games of chess. They agree that the first person to win two games in a row or to win a total of three games will be declared the winner. The possible outcomes can be conveniently pictured with the graph shown in Fig. 12.5.

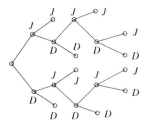

Figure 12.5

How many outcomes are possible? What is the maximum number of games John and David will play? ∎

With the exception of that in Fig. 12.3, all the graphs that have appeared in this section are *trees*.

12.1.1 DEFINITION A *tree* is a connected graph that contains no circuits. ❖

There are several alternative definitions.

12.1.2 PROPOSITION Let $\mathcal{G}$ be a graph. Then the following statements are equivalent.

(1) $\mathcal{G}$ is a tree.
(2) $\mathcal{G}$ is connected and *acyclic*, that is, without cycles.
(3) Between any two vertices of $\mathcal{G}$ there is precisely one path.

Proof (1) → (2): Since a cycle is a circuit, statement (1) immediately implies statement (2).

(2) → (3): If there are two different paths $\mathcal{P}_1$, $\mathcal{P}_2$ from some vertex v to another, w, then the closed walk from v to v obtained by following the vertices of $\mathcal{P}_1$ and then those of $\mathcal{P}_2$ in reverse order would contain a cycle, contradicting (2). (See Exercise 12.)

(3) → (1): Since there is a path between any two vertices of $\mathcal{G}$, certainly $\mathcal{G}$ is connected. Moreover, it can contain no circuits. Otherwise, it would contain a cycle (Exercise 15, Section 10.1) and a cycle determines **two** paths between any two vertices of it.

The sequence of implications (1) → (2) → (3) → (1) just established proves the equivalence of (1), (2), and (3). ◉

12.1.3 DEFINITION A tree is *rooted* if it comes with a specified vertex, called the *root*. ❖

This may not seem like much of a definition, but the concept is useful. Also, there is a convention for picturing rooted trees. Suppose v is a root in a tree T. By Proposition 12.1.2, there is a unique path from v to any other vertex. Thus, the concept of *level*, meaning length of a path from v (number of edges), is well defined. When drawing a rooted tree then, we agree to put the root v at the top (in contrast to the way we draw trees that grow out of doors); we put all level 1 vertices (those adjacent to v) on a horizontal line just below v, those of level 2 (reachable from v along a path of two edges) on a horizontal line below the level 1 vertices, and so on. The tree in Fig. 12.2 is drawn so as to show the vertex "start" as root. Vertex A in Fig. 12.4 is a root. Vertices B, D, and F have level 1; the vertices labeled C, E, F, C, E, B, C, E in the next row have level 2; and so on.

The way in which a rooted tree is drawn clearly depends on which vertex is the root. In Fig. 12.6, we show two pictures of the same tree, rooted at A on the left and at B on the right.

In this section, we derive a number of properties of trees and discuss a connection with the isomers of a certain kind of hydrocarbon.

12.1.4 PROPOSITION Suppose $\mathcal{G}$ is a graph each of whose vertices has degree at least 2. Then $\mathcal{G}$ contains a circuit.

Proof Let v_1 be any vertex of $\mathcal{G}$. Since $\deg v_1 \neq 0$, we may proceed to an adjacent vertex v_2. Since $\deg v_2 \geq 2$, we may proceed to an adjacent vertex v_3 along a new edge. Note that $v_1v_2v_3$ is a path. In general, suppose $k \geq 3$ and that we have found a

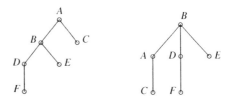

Figure 12.6 The same tree rooted at A on the left and B on the right.

path through distinct vertices $v_1, v_2, \ldots, v_k$. Since deg $v_k \geq 2$, v_k is adjacent to a vertex $v_{k+1} \neq v_{k-1}$. If $v_{k+1} \in \{v_1, v_2, \ldots, v_{k-2}\}$, we have a circuit; otherwise, $v_1 v_2 \cdots v_{k+1}$ is a path. Since there are only finitely many vertices in $\mathcal{G}$, we cannot continue to find paths of increasing length, so eventually we find a circuit.

In a trivial way, a graph with a single vertex (of degree 0) is a tree. A tree with more than one vertex can have no vertices of degree 0 (because it is connected), so all its vertices have degree at least 1. If they all had degree at least 2, there would be a circuit. Thus, we obtain a basic property of trees.

A tree with more than one vertex must contain a vertex of degree 1. (Such a vertex is called a *leaf.*)

Pause 4

What is a leaf? ∎

Pause 5

Modify the argument used to prove Proposition 12.1.4 to prove that a tree with more than one vertex must contain at least two leaves. ∎

In Exercise 23(b) of Section 10.1, you were asked to prove that a connected graph with n vertices has at least $n-1$ edges. It turns out that a connected graph with n vertices and exactly $n-1$ edges is a tree; moreover, this property characterizes trees.

A connected graph with n vertices is a tree if and only if it has $n-1$ edges.

Proof

($\longrightarrow$) First, by mathematical induction, we prove that a tree with n vertices has $n-1$ edges. This is clear for $n = 1$, so assume that $k \geq 1$ and that any tree with k vertices has $k-1$ edges. Let $\mathcal{T}$ be a tree with $k+1$ vertices. We must prove that $\mathcal{T}$ has k edges. For this, let v be a vertex in $\mathcal{T}$ of degree 1. Remove v and the single edge e with which it is incident. The point to appreciate is that the *pruned tree* $\mathcal{T}_0 = \mathcal{T} \setminus \{v\}$ that remains is itself a tree. It has no circuits since the original tree had no circuits. Why is it connected? If w and u are vertices in $\mathcal{T}_0$, they are joined by a path $\mathcal{P}$ in $\mathcal{T}$. Since you enter and leave each vertex of $\mathcal{P}$ along different edges, each vertex of $\mathcal{P}$ between w and u has degree at least 2. Thus, v and the lone edge e with which it is adjacent are not part of the path $\mathcal{P}$. So $\mathcal{P}$ must lie entirely in $\mathcal{T}_0$. Therefore, $\mathcal{T}_0$ is connected and hence a tree. Since $\mathcal{T}_0$ has k vertices, it has $k-1$ edges, by the induction hypothesis. Since $\mathcal{T}$ has one more edge than $\mathcal{T}_0$, $\mathcal{T}$ has k edges, which is what we wanted to show.

($\longleftarrow$) For the converse, we suppose that $\mathcal{G}$ is a connected graph with n vertices and $n-1$ edges and prove that $\mathcal{G}$ is a tree. We have only to establish the absence

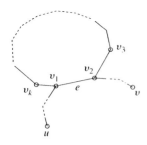

Figure 12.7

of circuits. Suppose that G contains a circuit $v_1 v_2 \cdots v_k v_1$. (Since graphs have no loops and no multiple edges, $k \geq 3$.) Remove the edge $e = v_1 v_2$. The remaining graph $G \setminus \{e\}$ has all n vertices of G but $n - 2$ edges; moreover, $G \setminus \{e\}$ is connected because any two vertices u, v of G that were connected via a path that included e are still connected via a walk in which $v_1 v_k v_{k-1} \cdots v_3 v_2$ is substituted for e. (See Fig. 12.7.)

If $G \setminus \{e\}$ contains a circuit we delete an edge from this and obtain a connected graph that still contains n vertices, but has just $n - 3$ edges. Since G is finite, eventually all circuits will be deleted and we shall be left with a connected graph with n vertices, fewer than $n - 1$ edges, and no circuits. Such a graph is a tree. We showed earlier that a tree with n vertices must have $n - 1$ edges. Thus, there can be no circuit in G; G is indeed a tree. ⊚

Pause 6 The tree in Fig. 12.1 has 26 vertices and $25 = 26 - 1$ edges, as predicted by Theorem 12.1.6. Verify this theorem for the trees in Figs. 12.2 and 12.5. ∎

Two other properties of trees follow quickly from Theorem 12.1.6. The first has already been noted.

12.1.7 COROLLARY A tree with more than one vertex has at least two leaves, that is, at least two vertices of degree 1.

Proof Suppose T is a tree with n vertices $v_1, v_2, \ldots, v_n$ and $n - 1$ edges. By Proposition 9.2.5, $\sum_{i=1}^{n} \deg v_i = 2(n - 1) = 2n - 2$. We already know that some vertex, say v_1, has degree 1. If the remaining $n - 1$ vertices each have degree 2 or more, then the sum of all the degrees would be at least $1 + 2(n - 1) = 2n - 1$, a contradiction. So there has to be another vertex, in addition to v_1, that also has degree 1. ⊚

In fact, there is a precise formula for the number of leaves that clearly shows that this number is at least 2. See Exercise 20.

12.1.8 COROLLARY Any edge added to a tree must produce a cycle.

Proof The new graph remains connected and it is not a tree because it has an equal number of edges and vertices. So it must contain a cycle. ⊚

Pause 7 Is it possible for two cycles to be formed when a single edge is added to a tree? Is it possible for two circuits to be formed? ∎

The identification of a tree as an important type of graph is credited to the English mathematician Arthur Cayley (1821–1895), a lawyer, a contemporary of Sir William Rowan Hamilton, and arguably the leading English mathematician of the nineteenth century. Cayley did fundamental work in the theory of matrices and is considered by many to be the founder of abstract group theory. In chemistry, chemical compounds with the formula $C_k H_{2k+2}$ are known as *paraffins*. The molecule $C_k H_{2k+2}$ contains k carbon atoms and $2k + 2$ hydrogen atoms. Each hydrogen atom is bonded to exactly one atom, a carbon atom; each carbon atom is bonded to four atoms. It is not hard to see that there is just one possible structure for each of the first three paraffins: methane, ethane, and propane. (See Fig. 12.8.)

On the other hand, for $k \geq 4$, various arrangements of $C_k H_{2k+2}$ are possible. Each arrangement is called an *isomer*. Arthur Cayley wanted to know the number of

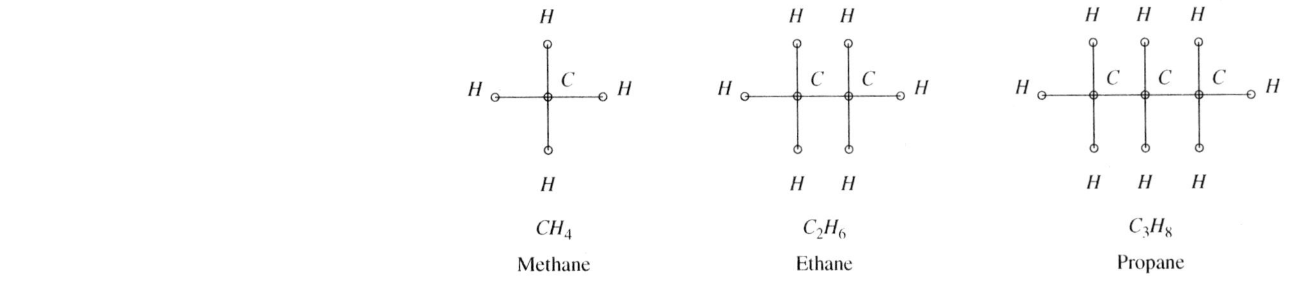

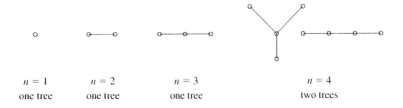

Figure 12.8

isomers of each paraffin. Each isomer is clearly associated with a connected graph, which is, in fact, a tree. Here is why.

Each of the k carbon atoms in C_kH_{2k+2} corresponds to a vertex of degree 4 in the associated graph, and each of the $2k+2$ hydrogen atoms, to a vertex of degree 1. The total number of vertices in the graph is $k+(2k+2)=3k+2$, and the total number of edges is one-half the sum of the degrees; that is, $\frac{1}{2}(4k+(2k+2))=3k+1$. Since the graph is connected and the number of edges is 1 less than the number of vertices, it is a tree (by Theorem 12.1.6).

Cayley also noted that an isomer of C_kH_{2k+2} is completely determined by the arrangement of the carbon atoms and that these form a tree with each vertex of degree at most 4. (See Exercise 21.) Note the tree of carbons in each of the molecules in Fig. 12.8. To draw an isomer of C_kH_{2k+2}, we draw a tree with k vertices labeled C, each of degree at most 4, and then add new edges with end vertices labeled H, of degree 1, at each C vertex where necessary so that each C vertex acquires degree 4. (It can be shown that $2k+2$ edges must be added. See Exercise 22.)

To enumerate all trees with n vertices, as Cayley was attempting to do, is very difficult unless n is small. The situation for $n \leq 4$ is shown in Fig. 12.9.

$n = 1$
one tree

$n = 2$
one tree

$n = 3$
one tree

$n = 4$
two trees

Figure 12.9 The unlabeled trees with $n \leq 4$ vertices.

Pause 8

Draw graphs of all possible isomers of butane (whose chemical formula is C_4H_{10}). How many are there? ∎

There is no closed formula for the number of trees with n vertices, although these numbers (for various n) appear as the coefficients of a certain generating function that begins

$$x + x^2 + x^3 + 2x^4 + 3x^5 + 6x^6 + 11x^7 + 23x^8,$$

but whose derivation would take us too far afield.[1] On the other hand, as we shall see in the next section, there are precisely n^{n-2} *labeled* trees on n vertices (Theorem 12.2.3). As the name implies, a labeled tree is one in which each vertex has a

[1] The interested reader might consult Frank Harary's book, *Graph Theory*, Addison-Wesley (1969).

distinct label attached to it. Figure 12.10 shows graphs of the $3^{3-2} = 3$ different labeled trees with vertices A, B, and C.

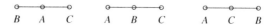

Figure 12.10 The three labeled trees on three vertices.

12.1.9 DEFINITION

Trees T_1 and T_2 whose vertices are labeled with the same set of labels are *isomorphic* if and only if, for each pair of labels v and w, vertices v and w are adjacent in T_1 if and only if they are adjacent in T_2. ❖

In Fig. 12.10, no two of the labeled trees are isomorphic. The situation is different, however, in Fig. 12.11. Here the labeled trees T_1 and T_2 are isomorphic, although neither is isomorphic to T_3. The adjacencies between the labeled vertices of T_1 and T_2 are identical. On the other hand, whereas vertices B and C are adjacent in T_1 (and T_2), such is not the case in T_3.

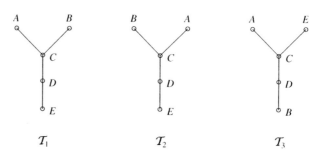

Figure 12.11 T_1 and T_2 are isomorphic labeled trees that are not isomorphic to T_3.

Answers to Pauses

1. There are 13 in all.

    4; 4, 8; 4, 5; 4, 5, 6; 4, 6; 8; 5; 5, 6; 0; 0, 6; 0, 2; 6; 2

2. A shortest Hamiltonian cycle is $ABCDEFA$ of length 155.

3. There are ten possible outcomes, corresponding to the ten vertices of degree 1 in Fig. 12.5. As many as five games could be required to decide a winner.

4. A leaf is a vertex of degree 1.

5. Let v_1 be a leaf in a tree and start a path, as described in Proposition 12.1.4, with v_1. Since there are no circuits in a tree, the path $v_1, v_2, v_3, \ldots$ obtained in the proposition can be extended to a longer path as long as each vertex we meet has degree at least 2. By finiteness, it must eventually terminate with a second vertex of degree 1, that is, another leaf.

6. The tree in Fig. 12.2 has 14 vertices and $13 = 14 - 1$ edges; the tree in Fig. 12.5 has 19 vertices and $18 = 19 - 1$ edges.

7. If an additional edge uv produced two cycles, there would be two paths between u and v, contradicting Proposition 12.1.2. The answer is also no for circuits. To see why, note that when an edge is added to a tree T any circuit that is produced must be a cycle. Why? Suppose the addition of edge v_1v_2 produces a circuit

$v_1v_2v_3 \cdots v_nv_1$. If this circuit is not a cycle, there is a repeated vertex. This vertex must be v_1 or v_2 because $\mathcal{T}$ contains no circuits. If the repeated vertex is v_1 (the argument in the case of v_2 is similar), then our circuit has the form $v_1v_2 \cdots v_1w \cdots v_nv_1$. Since the edge v_1w is not v_1v_2, $v_1w \cdots v_nv_1$ is a circuit in $\mathcal{T}$, a contradiction. Thus, if an edge v_1v_2 is added to a tree, it is in fact only a cycle that is produced. Thus an additional edge cannot produce two circuits because, as observed at the beginning, it cannot produce two cycles.

8. Since there are two nonisomorphic trees with four vertices, and in each of these all vertices have degree at most 4, there are two isomers of butane. These are pictured in Fig. 12.12. (Note the two trees of four carbon atoms and compare with the two trees on the right of Fig. 12.9.)

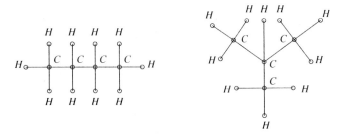

Figure 12.12

(Answers can be found in the back of the book.)

1. If $\mathcal{G}$ is a tree and $\mathcal{H}$ is a subgraph of $\mathcal{G}$, then $\mathcal{H}$ must also be a tree.

2. If $\mathcal{G}$ is not a tree and $\mathcal{H}$ is a subgraph of $\mathcal{G}$, then $\mathcal{H}$ must also not be a tree.

3. Every tree possesses an Eulerian trail.

4. If A is the adjacency matrix of a tree, then $A^n = 0$ for some n.

5. If A is the adjacency matrix of a graph $\mathcal{G}$ and $A^n = 0$ for some n, then $\mathcal{G}$ must be a tree.

6. A tree with eight vertices has seven edges.

7. A graph with 20 edges and 21 vertices must be a tree.

8. A tree with more than one vertex has at most two leaves.

9. C_3H_6 is a paraffin.

10. Labeled trees $\overset{A}{\circ}—\overset{B}{\circ}—\overset{C}{\circ}—\overset{D}{\circ}$ and $\overset{D}{\circ}—\overset{C}{\circ}—\overset{B}{\circ}—\overset{A}{\circ}$ are isomorphic.

Exercises

The answers to exercises marked [BB] can be found in the Back of the Book.

1. [BB] Suppose eight teams qualify for the playoffs in a local softball league. In the first round of playoffs, Series A pits the best team against the team that finished eighth, Series B has the second best team playing the team that finished seventh, and Series C has the third place team playing the sixth. In Series D, the teams that finished fourth and fifth play. In the second round, the winners of Series A and C compete, as do the winners of Series B and D, in Series E and F. Finally, the winners of these series play to determine the league champion. Draw a tree that summarizes the playoff structure in this league.

2. Edward VII, eldest son among Queen Victoria's nine children, finally ascended to the throne of England in 1901 (after 60 years as Prince of Wales). Upon his death in

1910, he was succeeded by King George V. George V had six children, perhaps the most infamous of whom was Edward VIII, who abdicated to marry a twice divorced American. Upon this abdication, George VI, father of the present Queen of England, became king. Queen Elizabeth has four children, Charles, Anne, Andrew, and Edward. Her sister, Princess Margaret, has two, Sarah and David. Prince Charles has two boys, William and Harry, marking the first time since the death of Edward VII that there have been two males in direct succession to the English throne. Draw that portion of Prince William's family tree that shows the people discussed in this short narrative.

3. Make a tree (like that in Fig. 12.2) that displays all monotonically increasing subsequences of $3, 2, 8, 0, 9, 1, 5$. How many are there altogether? Taking "start" to be the root, how many vertices are at each possible level?

4. John does not play chess very well, so the next time he plays David he says he will quit after winning a game or after five games in all have been played. Make a graph showing all possible outcomes. How many possible outcomes are there? In how many of these does John win a game?

5. [BB] It's the weekend and Harry has several ways to spend his Friday and Saturday evenings. He can study, read, watch television, or go out with the boys. Draw a tree that shows all possible ways Harry can spend his Friday and Saturday evenings.

6. Mary can travel from St. John's to Corner Brook by car, bus, or plane and from Corner Brook to Goose Bay by plane or boat. Draw a tree showing all the possible ways Mary can go from St. John's to Goose Bay via Corner Brook. In how many of these ways does she avoid the bus?

7. [BB] In how many ways can a committee of three people be chosen from the following group of people: Bruce, Philomena, Irene, Tom, and Dave? Draw a tree that shows all possible committees and the way each was chosen.

8. Draw the tree with root A and with root B.

9. The vertices in the graph represent towns; the edges, roads; and the labels on the roads, costs of paving the roads.

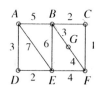

(a) Make a tree that shows all paths beginning at vertex A. List the paths that terminate at C. Indicate which, if any, are Hamiltonian.

(b) Is the graph Hamiltonian? Explain.

(c) Which roads should be paved so that one may drive from A along paved roads to as many towns as possible at minimal cost? Justify your answer. What is this minimal cost?

10. Solve the Traveling Salesman's Problem for each of the following graphs by making trees that display all Hamiltonian cycles. (Start at A in each case.)

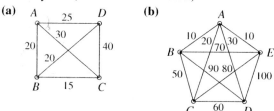

11. (a) Given that a tree has 100 vertices of degree 1 and 20 of degree 6 and that one-half of the remaining vertices are of degree 4 and the rest of degree 2, determine the number of vertices of degree 2.

(b) Prove that a tree as specified in (a), except that the number of vertices of degree 1 must be less than 80, cannot exist.

12. [BB] Suppose $\mathcal{P}_1$ and $\mathcal{P}_2$ are two paths from a vertex v to another vertex w in a graph. Prove that the closed walk obtained by following $\mathcal{P}_1$ from v to w and then $\mathcal{P}_2$ in reverse from w to v contains a cycle.

13. [BB] (a) Draw the graphs of all nonisomorphic unlabeled trees with five vertices.

(b) How many isomers does pentane (C_5H_{12}) have? Why?

14. (a) Draw the graphs of all nonisomorphic unlabeled trees with six vertices.

(b) How many isomers does hexane (C_6H_{14}) have? Why?

15. [BB] Suppose $\mathcal{G}$ is a graph whose vertices represent cities in a country. An edge in $\mathcal{G}$ represents a direct (nonstop) air flight between the corresponding cities. What does a beta index less than 1 say about air travel in the country? There are two possibilities to consider. (See Exercise 5 of Section 9.1.)

16. Prove that a connected graph with n vertices is a tree if and only if the sum of the degrees of the vertices is $2(n-1)$.

17. [BB] Recall that a graph is *acyclic* if it has no cycles. Prove that a graph with n vertices is a tree if and only if it is acyclic with $n-1$ edges.

18. Suppose a graph $\mathcal{G}$ has two connected components, $\mathcal{T}_1$, $\mathcal{T}_2$, each of which is a tree. Suppose we add a new edge to $\mathcal{G}$ by joining a vertex of $\mathcal{T}_1$ to a vertex in $\mathcal{T}_2$. Prove that the new graph is a tree.

19. (a) [BB] Let e be an edge in a tree T. Prove that the graph consisting of all the vertices of T, but with the single edge e deleted, is not connected.

    (b) Without assuming the existence of vertices of degree 1, use the result of (a) and the strong form of mathematical induction to prove that a tree with n vertices has $n - 1$ edges.

20. Let T be a tree with n vertices $v_1, v_2, \ldots, v_n$. Prove that the number of leaves in T is $2 + \sum_{\deg v_i \geq 3} [\deg v_i - 2]$.

21. [BB] Prove that the subgraph of a $C_k H_{2k+2}$ tree T consisting of the k carbon vertices and all edges from T among them is itself a tree.

22. (a) Suppose T is a tree with k vertices labeled C, each of degree at most 4. Enlarge T by adjoining sufficient vertices labeled H so that each vertex C has degree 4 and each vertex H has degree 1. Prove that the number of H vertices adjoined to the graph must be $2k + 2$.

    (b) Can you prove (a) without assuming that T is a tree?

23. We have noted in this section that there are n^{n-2} labeled trees on n vertices.

    (a) Verify this formula for $n = 4$ by drawing the nonisomorphic unlabeled trees on four vertices and dis-

covering how many different labeled trees each determines. (See Fig. 12.9.)

    (b) Repeat (a) for $n = 5$.

24. Prove that a tree with $n \geq 2$ vertices is a bipartite graph.

25. [BB] Find necessary and sufficient conditions for a tree to be a complete bipartite graph. Prove your answer.

26. A *forest* is a graph every component of which is a tree or, equivalently, a graph without cycles.

    (a) [BB] Explain why a forest is the disjoint union of trees.

    (b) Show that a forest with c components, each containing at least two vertices, has at least $2c$ vertices of degree 1.

    (c) Is the result of (b) true without the stipulation that each component contain at least two vertices? Explain.

    (d) Find a formula for the number of edges in a forest with n vertices and c components and prove your answer.

27. (a) [BB] Show that a tree with two vertices of degree 3 must have at least four vertices of degree 1.

    (b) Show that the result of (a) is the best possible: A tree with two vertices of degree 3 need not have five vertices of degree 1.

12.2 Spanning Trees

Figure 12.13 represents a map: The vertices correspond to towns and the labels on the edges represent distances along existing gravel roads between adjacent towns. The province plans to pave certain roads in such a way that one can get between any two towns on pavement. What roads should be paved so as to minimize the total length of pavement required? In the language of graph theory, this problem, known as the Minimum Connector Problem, asks for a minimum spanning tree for the graph.

12.2.1 DEFINITION   A *spanning tree* of a connected graph $\mathcal{G}$ is a subgraph that is a tree and that includes every vertex of $\mathcal{G}$. A *minimum spanning tree* of a weighted graph is a spanning tree of least weight, that is, a spanning tree for which the sum of the weights of all its edges is least among all spanning trees.   ❖

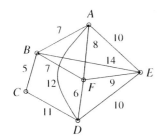

Figure 12.13

The concept of spanning tree exists only for a connected graph $\mathcal{G}$ and, if $\mathcal{G}$ has n vertices, any spanning tree must necessarily contain $n - 1$ edges.

Finding a spanning tree in a connected graph $\mathcal{G}$ is not hard. If $\mathcal{G}$ has no cycles, then it is already a tree, so $\mathcal{G}$ is a spanning tree for $\mathcal{G}$. If $\mathcal{G}$ does contain a cycle, then, just as in the proof of the second half of Theorem 12.1.6, we can delete an edge (without deleting any vertex) so as to remove the cycle, but leave the graph connected. By repeating this procedure, we eventually find a connected subgraph without cycles containing all the vertices of $\mathcal{G}$, that is, a spanning tree. Figure 12.14 shows a graph and three of its spanning trees. Spanning trees are considered to be *different* if they make use of different edges of the graph. Trees T_1 and T_2 in Fig. 12.14 are isomorphic, but they are different spanning trees of $\mathcal{G}$.

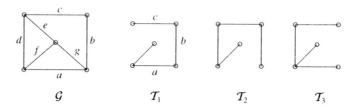

Figure 12.14 A graph $\mathcal{G}$ and three of its spanning trees.

There is a procedure for obtaining additional spanning trees from a given spanning tree. In Fig. 12.14, $\mathcal{T}_2$ and $\mathcal{T}_3$ were obtained from $\mathcal{T}_1$ as follows: First edge d was added to $\mathcal{T}_1$, giving the cycle $abcd$; removing a gives $\mathcal{T}_2$ and removing b gives $\mathcal{T}_3$. Removing c would give a fourth spanning tree, and, if we wanted more, we could return to $\mathcal{T}_1$ and add edge e, say, thereby completing another cycle $abcef$. Successively removing each of the edges a, b, c, and f of this cycle would give four new spanning trees. Remember that adding an edge to a tree always produces a cycle (Corollary 12.1.8). In Exercise 14, we ask you to show how the procedure described in this paragraph can be adapted to show that all the spanning trees in a graph can be obtained from a given one.

How many spanning trees does a connected graph possess? For this, there is a pretty result established in 1847 by the German physicist Gustav Kirchhoff (1824–1887), who was studying electrical networks.

To understand and apply Kirchhoff's result, and especially if it has been a while since you had a course in linear algebra, we suggest you consult Appendix A, especially the section on determinants, before continuing.

12.2.2 THEOREM

(Kirchhoff) Let M be the matrix obtained from the adjacency matrix of a connected graph $\mathcal{G}$ by changing all 1's to -1's and each diagonal 0 to the degree of the corresponding vertex. Then the number of spanning trees of $\mathcal{G}$ is the value of any cofactor of M.

It is surprising that there is such a simple formula, because it is often a difficult problem to count graphs of a specified type. In particular, counting the number of **nonisomorphic** spanning trees in a graph is a complicated affair.

The proof of Kirchhoff's Theorem (which is also known as the *Matrix-Tree Theorem*) will not be included here.[2] Instead, we content ourselves with an illustration.

EXAMPLE 1   Consider the graph whose adjacency matrix is

$$A = \begin{bmatrix} 0 & 1 & 1 & 1 \\ 1 & 0 & 1 & 1 \\ 1 & 1 & 0 & 0 \\ 1 & 1 & 0 & 0 \end{bmatrix}.$$

[2]See Chapter 12 of J. A. Bondy and U. S. R. Murty, *Graph Theory with Applications*, North-Holland, New York, 1981.

The matrix specified in Kirchhoff's Theorem is

$$M = \begin{bmatrix} 3 & -1 & -1 & -1 \\ -1 & 3 & -1 & -1 \\ -1 & -1 & 2 & 0 \\ -1 & -1 & 0 & 2 \end{bmatrix}.$$

The $(1, 1)$ cofactor of M is

$$+ \det \begin{bmatrix} 3 & -1 & -1 \\ -1 & 2 & 0 \\ -1 & 0 & 2 \end{bmatrix} = 3 \begin{vmatrix} 2 & 0 \\ 0 & 2 \end{vmatrix} - (-1) \begin{vmatrix} -1 & 0 \\ -1 & 2 \end{vmatrix} + (-1) \begin{vmatrix} -1 & 2 \\ -1 & 0 \end{vmatrix}$$

$$= 3(4) + 1(-2) + (-1)2 = 8$$

(expanding by cofactors of the first row). Kirchhoff's Theorem guarantees that all the cofactors of M equal 8. For example, the $(2, 3)$ cofactor of M is

$$- \det \begin{bmatrix} 3 & -1 & -1 \\ -1 & -1 & 0 \\ -1 & -1 & 2 \end{bmatrix} = -[(-1)(0) + 2(-3 - 1)] = -(-8) = 8$$

(expanding by cofactors of the third column). Thus, there are eight spanning trees in the graph. ▨

Draw the graph discussed in Example 1 and show each of its eight spanning trees. ∎

How many spanning trees has the graph in Fig. 12.14 and why? ∎

Now follows a remarkable application of Kirchhoff's Theorem. The proof involves the calculation of a certain determinant. Readers may like to consult Appendix A, where we mimic the calculation in the case $n = 5$.

12.2.3 THEOREM   The number of labeled trees with $n \geq 3$ vertices is n^{n-2}.

Proof   After the vertices of the complete graph $\mathcal{K}_n$ are labeled, any spanning tree of $\mathcal{K}_n$ is a labeled tree on n vertices. Conversely, any tree with these n vertices is a spanning tree for $\mathcal{K}_n$ because $\mathcal{K}_n$ contains all possible edges.[3] Thus, the number of labeled trees on n vertices is the number of spanning trees for $\mathcal{K}_n$, and the latter number can be determined by Kirchhoff's Theorem.

The adjacency matrix of $\mathcal{K}_n$ contains 0's on the diagonal and 1's everywhere off the diagonal. So the matrix whose equal cofactors count the number of trees is the $n \times n$ matrix

$$M = \begin{bmatrix} n-1 & -1 & \cdots & -1 \\ -1 & n-1 & \cdots & -1 \\ -1 & -1 & \cdots & -1 \\ \vdots & \vdots & \ddots & \vdots \\ -1 & -1 & \cdots & -1 \\ -1 & -1 & \cdots & n-1 \end{bmatrix}.$$

---

[3]Here Fig. 12.15 may help. The tree on the left is a spanning tree of $\mathcal{K}_4$, but not of $\mathcal{G}$, since BD is not an edge in $\mathcal{G}$.

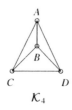
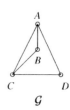

K_4 $\mathcal{G}$

Figure 12.15

The $(1, 1)$ cofactor of M is the determinant of an $(n-1) \times (n-1)$ matrix that looks exactly like M. Recall that the determinant of a matrix is not changed if a row is added to another row. Adding to the first row in turn each of the rows below it gives the matrix

$$\begin{bmatrix} 1 & 1 & 1 & \cdots & 1 \\ -1 & n-1 & -1 & \cdots & -1 \\ -1 & -1 & n-1 & & -1 \\ \vdots & \vdots & & \ddots & \\ -1 & -1 & -1 & \cdots & n-1 \end{bmatrix}$$

and then adding the first row of this matrix to each of the rows below it gives the matrix

$$\begin{bmatrix} 1 & 1 & 1 & \cdots & 1 \\ 0 & n & 0 & \cdots & 0 \\ 0 & 0 & n & & 0 \\ \vdots & \vdots & & \ddots & \vdots \\ 0 & 0 & 0 & \cdots & n \end{bmatrix},$$

which is an upper triangular $(n-1) \times (n-1)$ matrix with $n-2$ n's on the diagonal. Its determinant is n^{n-2}.

Answers to Pauses

9. The graph and its eight spanning trees are shown.

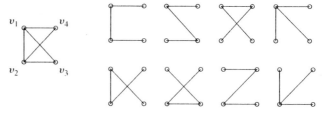

As spanning trees, the eight are all different, although they are partitioned into just two isomorphism classes, the left six in one class, the rightmost two in the other.

10. Labeling the graph as shown, the matrix specified in Kirchhoff's Theorem is

$$M = \begin{bmatrix} 3 & -1 & 0 & -1 & -1 \\ -1 & 3 & -1 & 0 & -1 \\ 0 & -1 & 3 & -1 & -1 \\ -1 & 0 & -1 & 2 & 0 \\ -1 & -1 & -1 & 0 & 3 \end{bmatrix}.$$

The value of any cofactor is 24, so the graph in Fig. 12.14 has 24 spanning trees.

(Answers can be found in the back of the book.)

1. The graph pictured by ▢ has four different spanning trees.

2. Any two spanning trees of ▢ are isomorphic.

3. The (weighted) graph pictured by ▢ has a unique minimum spanning tree.

4. Every connected graph has a spanning tree.

5. If a graph $\mathcal{G}$ has a unique spanning tree, then $\mathcal{G}$ is a tree.

6. Kirchhoff's Theorem tells us how to find the number of nonisomorphic spanning trees.

7. The $(1, 2)$ cofactor of $\begin{bmatrix} 3 & -1 & -1 & -1 \\ -1 & 3 & -1 & -1 \\ -1 & -1 & 2 & 0 \\ -1 & -1 & 0 & 2 \end{bmatrix}$ is $\det \begin{bmatrix} -1 & -1 & -1 \\ -1 & 2 & 0 \\ -1 & 0 & 2 \end{bmatrix}$.

8. The number of labeled trees with five vertices is $5^3 = 125$.

9. The number of spanning trees for $\mathcal{K}_6$ is $6! = 720$.

Exercises

*The answers to exercises marked [BB] can be found in the **B**ack of the **B**ook.*

1. [BB] This exercise concerns the graph $\mathcal{G}$ shown in Fig. 12.14. Delete edges a, c, and e to obtain a new spanning tree T for $\mathcal{G}$. Reinsert edge a to obtain the circuit afg. Draw two other spanning trees for $\mathcal{G}$ by removing first f and then g from this circuit.

2. [BB; (a)] For each of the graphs shown,
   - find three spanning trees representing two isomorphism classes of graphs;
   - find the total number of spanning trees.

   (a)

   (b)

   (c)

   (d)

3. Let e be an edge of the complete graph $\mathcal{K}_n$. Prove that the number of spanning trees of $\mathcal{K}_n$ that contain e is $2n^{n-3}$.

4. [BB] How many labeled trees are there on n vertices for $1 \le n \le 6$?

5. [BB] Draw all the labeled trees on four vertices.

6. How many spanning trees does $\mathcal{K}_7$ have? Why?

7. (a) [BB] Draw all the spanning trees of $\mathcal{K}_{2,2}$ and indicate the isomorphism classes of these. How many isomorphism classes are there?

   (b) Repeat (a) for $\mathcal{K}_{2,3}$.

8. Determine the number of spanning trees of the complete bipartite graph $\mathcal{K}_{2,n}$.

9. [BB] Suppose some edge of a connected graph $\mathcal{G}$ belongs to every spanning tree of $\mathcal{G}$. What can you conclude and why?

10. Let $\mathcal{G}$ be a tree. Describe all the spanning trees of $\mathcal{G}$ and explain.

11. If $\mathcal{G}$ is a graph and e is an edge that is not part of a circuit, then e must belong to every spanning tree of $\mathcal{G}$. Why?

12. (a) [BB] Prove that every edge in a connected graph is part of some spanning tree.

    (b) Prove that any two edges of a connected graph are part of some spanning tree.

    (c) [BB] Given three edges in a connected graph, is there always a spanning tree containing these edges? Explain your answer.

13. Let $\mathcal{G}$ be a connected graph with at least two vertices. Show that $\mathcal{G}$ has a vertex v such that $\mathcal{G} \setminus \{v\}$ is still connected. Show that $\mathcal{G}$ has at least two vertices with this property.

14. Suppose that T_0 and T are two different spanning trees for a graph $\mathcal{G}$.

    (a) [BB] Let e be an edge in T that is not in T_0. Prove that there is an edge f in T_0 that is not in T such that $(T_0 \cup \{e\}) \setminus \{f\}$ is a spanning tree.

(b) Describe a procedure for obtaining T from T_0.

15. Let C_n be the cycle with n vertices labeled $1, 2, \ldots, n$ in the order encountered on the cycle.

(a) Find the number of spanning trees for C_n (in two ways).

(b) Find a general formula for the number of spanning trees for $C_n \cup \{e\}$, where e joins 1 to a ($3 \leq a \leq n - 1$).

16. [BB] How many graphs have n vertices labeled $v_1, v_2, \ldots, v_n$ and $n - 1$ edges? Compare this number with the number of trees with vertices $v_1, \ldots, v_n$, for $2 \leq n \leq 6$.

17. Show that any shortest path algorithm can be used to construct a spanning tree for an unweighted connected graph. (Caution! A shortest path algorithm requires a weighted graph. How are you going to get started?)

12.3 Minimum Spanning Tree Algorithms

In this section, we answer the Minimum Connector Problem suggested by the town and road map in Fig. 12.13. The problem requires us to find a minimum spanning tree, and we would like to find one efficiently. In theory, we could enumerate all the spanning trees of a weighted graph and simply choose the tree of least weight; but if the graph is at all complicated, this is not an easy chore. In this section, we discuss two better ways discovered in the 1950s by J. B. Kruskal[4] and R. C. Prim.[5] Both algorithms are in some sense "obvious." They produce a minimum weight spanning tree an edge at a time, at each stage making the best choice of next edge without thought to what has happened already or what will ensue. For this reason, they are called *greedy* algorithms.

12.3.1 KRUSKAL'S ALGORITHM

To find a minimum spanning tree in a connected weighted graph with $n > 1$ vertices, carry out the following procedure.

Step 1. Find an edge of least weight and call this e_1. Set $k = 1$.

Step 2. While $k < n$

if there exists an edge e such that $\{e\} \cup \{e_1, e_2, \ldots, e_k\}$ does not contain a circuit,
   • let e_{k+1} be such an edge of least weight;
      replace k by $k + 1$;
else output $e_1, e_2, \ldots, e_k$ and stop.

end while

EXAMPLE 2 We illustrate with reference to the graph of Fig. 12.16. Kruskal's algorithm initially picks an edge of lowest weight. There are several edges of weight 2 and none with less weight. Any of these may be selected. Suppose we begin with edge $e_1 = AJ$. There still remain edges of weight 2, so we choose any other, say $e_2 = GM$. Among those edges that do not form a circuit with e_1 and e_2 (at this point, there are no edges that do), we choose one of lowest weight, say DE, and call this e_3. Continuing, we might select edges $AJ, GM, DE, MF, FE, LK, HJ, KM, CK, BC$. At this stage, there remains an edge (GL) of weight 4, but this edge would complete a circuit with LK, KM, GM already selected, and so we choose an edge of weight 5, say JL, and another, IA. Now any of the remaining edges will complete a circuit with those selected, so we must stop; the algorithm assures us we have the desired minimum spanning tree. It has weight 39.

---

[4]J. B. Kruskal, Jr., "On the Shortest Spanning Subtree of a Graph and the Traveling Salesman Problem," *Proceedings of American Mathematical Society* **7** (1956), 48–50.

[5]R. C. Prim, "Shortest Connection Networks and Some Generalizations," *Bell System Technical Journal* **36** (1957), 1389–1401.

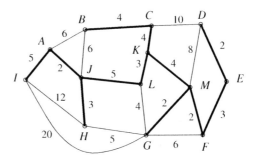

Figure 12.16 An application of Kruskal's algorithm might select, in this order, edges $AJ, GM, DE, MF, FE, LK, HJ, KM,$ CK, BC, JL, IA.

Why does the algorithm work? Suppose G is the given connected graph and T_K is the subgraph produced by Kruskal's algorithm. The algorithm terminates only when the inclusion of any edge of G not in T_K produces a circuit in T_K. We must prove that T_K is a spanning tree and that it is minimum.

First, note that T_K contains every vertex of G. Why? Suppose, to the contrary, that some vertex v is not in T_K. Since G is connected, there exists some edge incident with v. Adding this edge to T_K cannot produce a circuit in T_K since none of the edges incident with v is in T_K. Thus, the algorithm could continue, a contradiction. By its construction T_K contains no circuits. To see that it is connected, let v and w be any two vertices of T_K. There is a path in G from v to w and any edge of this path not in T_K can be replaced by a path in T_K, since adding to T_K any edge of G not in T_K produces a circuit. Thus, T_K is a spanning tree. It is more difficult to establish that T_K is minimum.

Let T_m be a minimum spanning tree in G. We wish to show that the weight of T_K equals the weight of T_m. Suppose that G (hence, also T_m and T_K) has n vertices. Then T_K contains $n-1$ edges. Suppose these were determined by the algorithm in the order $e_1, e_2, \ldots, e_{n-1}$. If $T_K = T_m$, there is nothing to prove; otherwise, we may suppose that there are edges of T_K not in T_m. Let e_k be the first such edge. Since T_m is also a spanning tree, with an argument similar to that used to solve Exercise 14(a) of Section 12.2, there is an edge e in T_m, but not in T_K, such that $T = (T_m \cup \{e_k\}) \setminus \{e\}$ is a spanning tree. The weight of T is

$$(1) \qquad w(T) = w(T_m) + w(e_k) - w(e) \geq w(T_m)$$

since T_m has minimum weight. Therefore, $w(e_k) \geq w(e)$.

If $k = 1$, $w(e_k) \leq w(e)$ since e_1 was the first edge chosen and so has minimum weight. So $w(e) = w(e_k)$. If $k > 1$, the edges $e, e_1, e_2, \ldots, e_{k-1}$ do not contain a circuit because they are all part of the tree T_m. Again, $w(e) = w(e_k)$; otherwise, $w(e) < w(e_k)$ and the algorithm would have chosen an edge of weight $w(e)$ instead of e_k. In all cases, this makes T a minimum spanning tree since, by (1), its weight is the same as the weight of the minimum spanning tree T_m. Also, T is *closer* to T_K than was T_m in the sense that T has edges $e_1, \ldots, e_k$ in common with T_K. Now, if $T = T_K$, then T_K is minimum (which is what we want to show); otherwise, we apply to T and T_K the procedure just applied to T_m and T_K and obtain another minimum spanning tree with yet another edge in common with T_K. Continuing in this way, we eventually arrive at a minimum spanning tree with edges $e_1, \ldots, e_{n-1}$ in common with T_K (and so equal to T_K), proving that T_K is indeed a minimum spanning tree.

What is the complexity of Kruskal's algorithm in terms of comparisons? To estimate the number of comparisons, we must first decide how we are going to determine, at a particular stage, whether a given edge forms a circuit with some of the edges already selected.

At each stage, Kruskal's algorithm has selected certain edges. Think of the subgraph determined by these edges and all n vertices of $\mathcal{G}$. This subgraph has a certain number of connected components, each of which is a tree. The first such subgraph has n components; the final minimum spanning tree has just one component. To begin, assign the labels $1, 2, \ldots, n$ to the vertices of $\mathcal{G}$. If the first edge selected is uv, with u labeled i, v labeled j, and $i < j$, change the label of v to i. The subgraph consisting of this edge and all n vertices has $n - 1$ components and, as at the outset, all the vertices in each component have the same label. If we could preserve this feature of our labeling, then the edges eligible for selection at a certain stage (that is, those edges not forming a circuit with edges already chosen) would be simply those whose end vertices have different labels.

Suppose, at a certain stage, vertices have the same label if and only if they lie in the same component of the subgraph whose vertices are all those of $\mathcal{G}$ and whose edges are those the algorithm has chosen so far and that each such component is a tree. We seek an edge that does not complete a circuit with previously chosen edges, hence an edge with end vertices lying in different components. Select an edge $e = xy$ whose end vertices x and y have different labels and that has least weight among such edges. If x is labeled k and y is labeled ℓ and $k < \ell$, then x belongs to a component all of whose vertices are labeled k, and y belongs to a component all of whose vertices are labeled ℓ. By changing to k the labels on all the vertices labeled ℓ, the next subgraph once again has the property that the vertices have the same label if and only if they lie in the same connected component. Moreover, each new component is again a tree, since a circuit cannot be produced by joining two vertices in different components.

Pause 11 Describe the labels on the final minimum spanning tree. ∎

This is our suggested procedure for ensuring no circuits. How many comparisons does it require? First, sort the edges $e_1, e_2, \ldots, e_N$ of $\mathcal{G}$ so that $w(e_1) \leq w(e_2) \leq \cdots \leq w(e_N)$. Using an efficient algorithm such as the merge sort discussed in Section 8.3, this can be accomplished with $\mathcal{O}(N \log N)$ comparisons. In the worst case (that the last edge e_N appears in Kruskal's tree) the ends of every edge must be compared to change the higher label to the lower. This part of the algorithm could require as many as N comparisons. Also, for each of the $n - 1$ edges that are eventually selected, the labels on $n - 2$ vertices must be examined to see which must be changed. This contributes a further $(n - 1)(n - 2)$ comparisons. By the approach outlined here, Kruskal's algorithm is $\mathcal{O}(N \log N + N + n^2) = \mathcal{O}(N \log N + n^2)$. In fact, the rule by which the labels of vertices are changed can be modified so that Kruskal's algorithm can be completed with just $\mathcal{O}(N \log N)$ comparisons. (See Exercise 12.)

We now turn our attention to another algorithm, a popular one, for finding a minimum spanning tree. *Prim's algorithm* is like Kruskal's insofar as it selects an edge of least weight at each stage. This time, however, instead of merely guarding against circuits, the algorithm requires that the subgraph determined by selected edges always be a tree.

EXAMPLE 3 We illustrate Prim's approach as it would apply to the graph of Fig. 12.16, which we have shown again in Fig. 12.17. Start at any vertex, say K, and select the edge

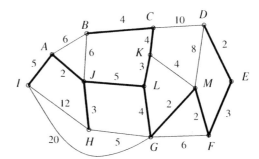

Figure 12.17 An application of Prim's algorithm might begin with vertex K and then select, in this order, edges KL, LG, GM, MF, FE, DE, KC, BC, JL, AJ, JH, AI.

incident with K of least weight. Thus, we select edge KL of weight 3. The next edge chosen is the edge of least weight adjacent to KL. Any of LG, KM, or KC is eligible. Suppose we select LG. Then we select the edge of least weight among those edges forming a tree with the two edges already selected (GM, for instance). We continue to select, in succession, the edge of least weight among those edges, as yet unselected, that form a tree with those already chosen and continue until we have a spanning tree. You should verify that the spanning tree shown in Fig. 12.17 is one that Prim's algorithm might identify.

12.3.2 PRIM'S ALGORITHM

To find a minimum spanning tree in a connected weighted graph with $n > 1$ vertices, proceed as follows.

Step 1. Choose any vertex v and let e_1 be an edge of least weight incident with v. Set $k = 1$.

Step 2. While $k < n$
    if there exists a vertex that is not in the subgraph T whose edges are
        $e_1, e_2, \ldots, e_k$,
            • let e_{k+1} be an edge of least weight among all edges of the form
            ux, where u is a vertex of T and x is a vertex not in T;
            • replace k by $k + 1$;
    else output $e_1, e_2, \ldots, e_k$ and stop.
    end while

Perhaps the best way to see that Prim's algorithm succeeds in finding a minimum spanning tree in a connected graph $\mathcal{G}$ is to prove that at each stage the algorithm has found a tree that is a subgraph of some minimum spanning tree.

Initially, the algorithm has selected a vertex v and an edge e_1 of least weight incident with v. We claim that e_1 is contained in some minimum spanning tree.

Justify this claim.   ∎

Continuing inductively, suppose that after k steps the algorithm has produced a tree T that is a subgraph of a minimum spanning tree T_m for the graph. At the next stage, the algorithm produces another subgraph T_1 by adding a vertex x and an edge ux to T, where the weight of ux is least among all edges joining vertices

$x \notin T$ to vertices $u \in T$. Since T contains no circuits and the additional vertex x is incident with only one edge in T_1, the subgraph T_1 also contains no circuits. It is also connected and hence a tree. Why is it contained in a minimum spanning tree for G? This is surely the case if it is contained in T_m. If it is not contained in T_m, then the subgraph T_m with edge ux adjoined contains a circuit, $uxx_1x_2 \cdots x_r u$. Such a circuit must contain an edge of the form yw, with $y \notin T$ and $w \in T$.[6] It follows that $w(ux) \leq w(yw)$, since yw was also eligible for selection by the algorithm when ux was chosen. Thus, the spanning tree $(T_m \cup \{ux\}) \setminus \{yw\}$, having weight not exceeding that of T_m, is also a minimum spanning tree, and it contains T_1. By the Principle of Mathematical Induction, it follows that each subgraph produced by Prim's algorithm is a tree contained in a minimum spanning tree. In particular, the last tree selected is itself a minimum spanning tree.

We now show how to implement Prim's algorithm with complexity $\mathcal{O}(n^3)$ and leave to the exercises an implementation that is $\mathcal{O}(n^2)$. (See Exercise 13.) Recalling that Kruskal's algorithm is $\mathcal{O}(N \log N + n^2)$, where N is the number of edges, we see that the choice between Kruskal's and Prim's algorithms depends primarily on the relative sizes of N and n.

Suppose G is a connected graph with n vertices. In Prim's algorithm, we select a vertex v and find the minimum weight of the potentially $n-1$ edges incident with v. For this, at most $n-2$ comparisons are required. Suppose vu is the edge selected. Next, we find the edge of least weight among those that are incident with u or with v (excluding the edge vu). In the worst case, in which every vertex is adjacent to each of these vertices, we would have to find the minimum of $2(n-2)$ numbers, a process requiring $2(n-2)-1$ comparisons. After k edges (and $k+1$ vertices) have been selected, we seek the edge of least weight among those incident with one of the vertices already selected. In the worst case, the remaining $n-(k+1)$ vertices are adjacent to each of the first $k+1$, and we must find the minimum of $(k+1)(n-k-1)$ numbers. This would require $(k+1)(n-k-1)-1$ comparisons. In all, then, we require

$$\sum_{k=0}^{n-2}[(k+1)(n-k-1)-1] = \sum_{k=0}^{n-2}(nk+n-k^2-2k-2)$$

comparisons. Recalling that

$$\sum_{k=0}^{n} k = \frac{n(n+1)}{2} \quad \text{and} \quad \sum_{k=0}^{n} k^2 = \frac{n(n+1)(2n+1)}{6},$$

we find that the number of comparisons is

$$n\frac{(n-2)(n-1)}{2} + n(n-1) - \frac{(n-2)(n-1)(2n-3)}{6}$$

$$-2\frac{(n-2)(n-1)}{2} - 2(n-1) = \frac{1}{6}n^3 - \frac{7}{6}n + 1.$$

The procedure is $\mathcal{O}(n^3)$.

A Bound for a Minimum Hamiltonian Cycle

There is an interesting connection between the Traveling Salesman's Problem (Section 10.4) and minimum spanning trees in a weighted graph. Recall that the Traveling Salesman's Problem is to find a Hamiltonian cycle of minimum weight in a

---

[6]The edge yw is xx_1 if $x_1 \in T$; otherwise, x_1x_2 if $x_2 \in T$; and so on. This process eventually leads to edge yw, as described, because the last vertex u is in T.

weighted Hamiltonian graph. Our ability to find minimum spanning trees gives us a way to determine lower bounds for the weight of a minimum Hamiltonian cycle.

Suppose $\mathcal{G}$ is a weighted Hamiltonian graph with Hamiltonian cycle $\mathcal{H}$. Removing any vertex v of $\mathcal{G}$ (and the edges with which it is incident) gives us a subgraph $\mathcal{G}'$ of $\mathcal{G}$ and a subgraph $\mathcal{H}'$ of $\mathcal{H}$ that is a spanning tree for $\mathcal{G}'$; in fact, $\mathcal{H}'$ is a path through all vertices of $\mathcal{G}$ except v. It follows that the weight of $\mathcal{H}$ is the weight of $\mathcal{H}'$ plus the sum of the weights of the two edges in $\mathcal{H}$ incident with v. Hence,

$$w(\mathcal{H}) \geq w(\text{minimum spanning tree for } \mathcal{G}')$$
$$+ \text{ smallest sum of weights of two edges incident with } v.$$

By choosing several different vertices v, we can obtain various lower bounds for the weight of the Hamiltonian cycle $\mathcal{H}$ and so, in particular, for the weight of a minimum Hamiltonian cycle.

Considering again the graph in Fig. 12.16 (which is Hamiltonian), if we remove vertex H (and the three edges with which it is incident), it is easily checked that all the edges of the spanning tree indicated in Fig. 12.16, except for HJ, comprise a minimum spanning tree for the subgraph, of weight $39 - 3 = 36$. The smallest two weights of edges incident with H are 3 and 5. Therefore, we obtain $36 + 3 + 5 = 44$ as a lower bound for the weight of any Hamiltonian cycle.

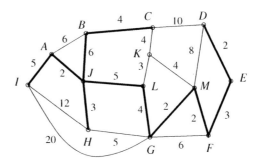

Figure 12.18 A graph $\mathcal{G}$ and a spanning tree for $\mathcal{G} \setminus \{K\}$ with weight 38.

Suppose we remove K instead of H. This time the heavy edges in Fig. 12.18 form a minimum spanning tree in the subgraph, of weight 38. The two smallest weights of edges incident with K are 3 and 4, so we obtain $38 + 3 + 4 = 45$ as a lower bound for the weight of any Hamiltonian cycle, a better estimate than before.

Find a Hamiltonian cycle in the graph of Fig. 12.16. What is its weight? ∎

Answers to Pauses

11. Each time an edge is added, we changed the labels on its end vertices to the lower of the two previous labels (and all the vertices in a certain component to the lower as well). All vertices are eventually labeled 1.

12. Let $\mathcal{T}$ be any minimum spanning tree. If e_1 is not in $\mathcal{T}$, then $\mathcal{T} \cup \{e_1\}$ contains a circuit and, removing a second edge e ($\neq e_1$) of this circuit incident with v, we obtain another spanning tree $\mathcal{T}' = (\mathcal{T} \cup \{e_1\}) \setminus \{e\}$. Since the weight of $\mathcal{T}$ was minimum, $w(\mathcal{T}) \leq w(\mathcal{T}')$, so $w(e_1) \geq w(e)$. Since e_1 was an edge of least weight incident with v, it follows that $w(e_1) = w(e)$ and hence that $\mathcal{T}'$ is also a minimum spanning tree, and one that contains e_1.

13. $IHJABCDEFMKLGI$ is a Hamiltonian cycle of weight 75. Note how the path $JA \cdots GI$ that results when H is removed is a spanning tree for the sub-

graph without H and how the path $LG \cdots FM$ that results when K is removed is a spanning tree for the subgraph without K.

True/False Questions

(Answers can be found in the back of the book.)

1. If Kruskal's algorithm is applied to [graph] 3 ⬜ 3 after one application of Step 2, we will have [graph].

2. If Kruskal's algorithm is applied to [graph] 3 ⬜ 3 we might end up with 3 [graph] 2.

3. If Kruskal's algorithm is applied to [graph] 3 ⬜ 3 we might end up with [graph] 3.

4. If Prim's algorithm is applied to [graph] 3 ⬜ 3 after one application of Step 2, we will have [graph].

5. If Prim's algorithm is applied to [graph] 3 ⬜ 3 we might end up with 3 [graph].

6. If Prim's algorithm is applied to [graph] 3 ⬜ 3 we might end up with [graph] 3.

7. In Prim's algorithm, Step 1 will always select the edge of least weight in the graph.

8. The decision whether to use Kruskal's algorithm or Prim's on a graph G depends on the relative magnitude of the vertex set and edge set of G.

9. Kruskal's algorithm can be used on unweighted graphs.

10. Prim's algorithm can be used on unweighted graphs.

Exercises

*The answers to exercises marked [BB] can be found in the **B**ack of the **B**ook.*

1. [BB; (a)] Use Kruskal's algorithm to find a spanning tree of minimum total weight in each of the graphs in Fig. 12.19. Give the weight of your minimum tree and show your steps.

2. [BB; (a)] For each of the graphs of Exercise 1, apply Prim's algorithm to find a minimum spanning tree. Try to find a tree different from the one found before. Start at vertex E in each graph, explain your reasoning, and draw the tree.

3. [BB] Find a minimum spanning tree for the graph in Fig. 12.13. What is the smallest length of pavement re-

quired to connect the towns in this graph?

4. (a) Explain how Kruskal's algorithm could be modified so that it finds a spanning tree of **maximum** weight in a connected graph.

   (b) Apply the modified algorithm described in (a) to find a maximum spanning tree for each of the graphs and give the maximum weight of each.

      i. [BB] Exercise 1(a)   **ii.** Exercise 1(b)
     iii. Exercise 1(c)   **iv.** Exercise 1(d)
       v. Fig. 12.16

(a)

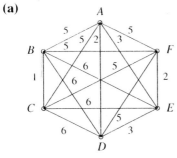

(b)

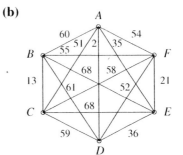

(c)

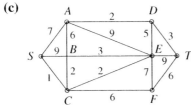

(d)

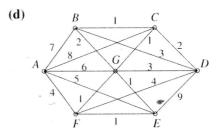

Figure 12.19   Graphs for Exercise 1.

5. Repeat Exercise 4 for Prim's algorithm. For each part of (b), start at vertex A.

6. [BB] Explain how a minimum spanning tree algorithm can be used to find a spanning tree in a connected graph where the edges are **not** weighted.

7. How could a minimum spanning tree algorithm be used to find a spanning tree in an unweighted graph that **excludes** a given edge, assuming such spanning trees exist?

8. (a) [BB] Suppose we have a connected graph G and we want to find a spanning tree for G that contains a given edge e. How could Kruskal's algorithm be used to do this? Discuss both the weighted and unweighted cases.

   (b) Use Kruskal's algorithm to show that if G is a connected graph, then any (not necessarily connected) subgraph that contains no circuits is part of some spanning tree for G. Consider both the weighted and unweighted cases.

9. Answer Exercise 8 using Prim's algorithm instead of Kruskal's.

10. [BB] Prove that at each vertex v of a weighted connected graph Kruskal's algorithm always includes an edge of lowest weight incident with v.

11. (a) Prove that any minimum weight spanning tree in a connected weighted graph can be obtained by Kruskal's algorithm. [*Hint*: Look at the argument on page 385 showing that Kruskal's algorithm selects a minimum spanning tree.]

    (b) [BB] If all the weights in a connected weighted graph are distinct, show that the graph has a unique spanning tree of minimum weight.

12. In our discussion of the complexity of Kruskal's algorithm, we suggested a certain system of labeling vertices (p. 386). Consider the following modification.

    Suppose that vertex x is labeled k and vertex y is labeled ℓ and that we have just selected edge xy. Compare the relative sizes of the components to which x and y belong, and change the labels of all vertices in the **smaller** of these components to the label of the larger. (If the components have equal size, label with the smaller number.)

    With reference to Example 2, (p. 384), we begin with 13 components each containing a single vertex. After the selection of AJ, component 1 contains two vertices, A and J, and component 10 is empty; the remaining components are unchanged. Figure 12.20 shows how the components change as the edges GM, DE, MF, and FE are successively selected.

    (a) Continue the scheme shown in this figure to show the relabeling of vertices until the spanning tree of Fig. 12.16 is obtained.

    (b) [BB] Show that in the general case the number of times the label on any vertex is changed is at most $\log_2 n$, n the number of vertices of G.

    (c) [BB] Show that Kruskal's algorithm can be implemented with a number of comparisons that is $\mathcal{O}(N \log N)$, N the number of edges of G.

13. In the implementation of Prim's algorithm discussed on page 388 it is not really necessary at each stage to find the minimum of so many numbers. Consider the following alternative. Select any vertex v_1 and label every other vertex v with the weight of edge vv_1 if vv_1 is an edge and ∞ otherwise. Then select edge v_1v_2 such that the label on v_2 is a minimum. For each vertex v adjacent to v_2, change the label of v to the minimum of its old label and the weight of edge vv_2. Select v_3 with minimum la-

Component	Size	Vertices
1	1	A
2	1	B
3	1	C
4	1	D
5	1	E
6	1	F
7	1	G
8	1	H
9	1	I
10	1	J
11	1	K
12	1	L
13	1	M

add AJ →

Component	Size	Vertices
1	2	A, J
2	1	B
3	1	C
4	1	D
5	1	E
6	1	F
7	1	G
8	1	H
9	1	I
11	1	K
12	1	L
13	1	M

add GM →

Component	Size	Vertices
1	2	A, J
2	1	B
3	1	C
4	1	D
5	1	E
6	1	F
7	2	G, M
8	1	H
9	1	I
11	1	K
12	1	L

add DE →

Component	Size	Vertices
1	2	A, J
2	1	B
3	1	C
4	2	D, E
6	1	F
7	2	G, M
8	1	H
9	1	I
11	1	K
12	1	L

add MF →

Component	Size	Vertices
1	2	A, J
2	1	B
3	1	C
4	2	D, E
7	3	G, M, F
8	1	H
9	1	I
11	1	K
12	1	L

add FE →

Component	Size	Vertices
1	2	A, J
2	1	B
3	1	C
7	5	G, M, F, D, E
8	1	H
9	1	I
11	1	K
12	1	L

Figure 12.20 Components not listed are empty.

bel and add the corresponding edge (v_3v_1 or v_3v_2). The graph on the left shows the labels on the vertices of the graph of Fig. 12.16 just after $v_1 = K$ has been selected; the graph on the right depicts the situation just after v_2 has been selected.

(a) Show the labels just after $v_3 = G$ has been selected.

(b) Explain carefully how the process started here should be continued to produce the next edge. Illustrate by showing the labels on the graph just after v_4 has been chosen.

(c) Show that the implementation of Prim's algorithm described here is $\mathcal{O}(n^2)$, in terms of comparisons.

14. By considering the subgraphs determined by deleting each vertex in the graph, find the best (greatest) lower bound for the weight of a minimum Hamiltonian cycle. Find a minimum Hamiltonian cycle.

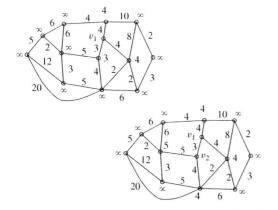

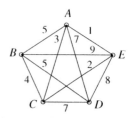

15. This exercise concerns the graph in Exercise 1(a).

   (a) [BB] Find a Hamiltonian cycle of lowest weight. What is the weight?

   (b) [BB] By removing vertex A, use the method discussed in this section to find a lower bound for the weight of any Hamiltonian cycle.

   (c) [BB] Repeat part (b), removing vertex B instead of A.

   (d) Try to improve (increase) the lower bounds found in parts (b) and (c) by removing some other vertex.

16. Repeat Exercise 15 for the graph in Exercise 1(b). Use vertices D and F in parts (b) and (c).

17. Repeat Exercise 15 for the graph in Exercise 1(c). Use vertices B and T in parts (b) and (c).

18. Repeat Exercise 15 for the graph in Exercise 1(d). Use vertices E and G in parts (b) and (c).

12.4   Acyclic Digraphs and Bellman's Algorithm

A (directed) graph is *acyclic* if it contains no (directed) cycles. For example, the digraph on the left of Fig. 12.21 is acyclic, but the one on the right is not; there is a cycle around the outer vertices. Is there any easy way to see that there are no cycles in $\mathcal{G}$, on the left? This is where the vertex labels help. The digraph has been labeled so that $v_i v_j$ is an arc only when $i < j$. For example, there are no arcs of the form $x v_0$, the only arc $x v_1$ is $v_0 v_1$, the only arcs $x v_2$ are with $x = v_0$ and $x = v_1$, and so on. So it is clear why there is no cycle: In any path, the subscripts on the vertices v_i must increase, so there is never an arc on which to return to the first vertex. A labeling of the vertices such as that shown for $\mathcal{G}$ has a special name.

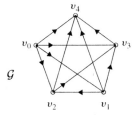

Figure 12.21   The digraph on the left is acyclic; the digraph on the right is not.

12.4.1 DEFINITION   A labeling $v_0, v_1, \ldots, v_{n-1}$ of the vertices of a digraph is called *canonical* if the only arcs have the form $v_i v_j$ with $i < j$. A canonical labeling of vertices is also called a *canonical ordering*. ❖

As we shall see, a digraph has a canonical ordering of vertices if and only if it is acyclic. It is interesting that the converse of this statement is also true: Any acyclic digraph has a canonical labeling of vertices. To prove this, we require a preliminary result.

12.4.2 LEMMA   Let S be a nonempty set of vertices of an acyclic digraph $\mathcal{G}$. Then there exists $v \in S$ such that $S_v = \{x \in S \mid xv \text{ is an arc}\} = \emptyset$.

Proof   We establish this result by contradiction. Assume the result is false. Thus, for each $v \in S$, there is an arc of the form xv with $x \in S$. Let v_0 be any vertex in S and let $v_1 v_0$ be an arc, $v_1 \in S$. There exists an arc $v_2 v_1$, $v_2 \in S$; in general, having found vertices $v_1, v_2, \ldots, v_k$ in S with $v_{i+1} v_i$ an arc, $i = 1, 2, \ldots, k - 1$, there exists an arc $v_{k+1} v_k$ with $v_{k+1} \in S$. Since $\mathcal{G}$ has only a finite number of vertices, eventually, $v_{k+1} \in \{v_1, v_2, \ldots, v_k\}$, say $v_{k+1} = v_i$, $1 \leq i \leq k$. If k is minimal with this occurring, $v_{k+1} v_k v_{k-1} \cdots v_i$ is a cycle, contradicting the fact that $\mathcal{G}$ is acyclic.

12.4.3 THEOREM   A digraph is acyclic if and only if it has a canonical labeling of vertices.

Proof   ($\leftarrow$) If $v_0, v_1, \ldots v_{n-1}$ is a canonical labeling of the vertices of a digraph and $v_{i_1} v_{i_2} \cdots v_{i_k}$ is a walk, then $i_1 < i_2 < \cdots < i_k$. It follows that such a walk cannot be closed.

($\rightarrow$) Suppose $\mathcal{G}$ is an acyclic digraph with vertex set $\mathcal{V}$. We may assume $|\mathcal{V}| = n > 1$. Applying the lemma to $\mathcal{S} = \mathcal{V}$, we obtain a vertex v_0 with the property that there are no arcs of the form $x v_0$. Applying Lemma 12.4.2 to $\mathcal{S} = \mathcal{V} \setminus \{v_0\}$, we obtain a vertex v_1 with the property that there are no arcs of the form $x v_1$ with $x \in \mathcal{S}$; that is, the only possible arc $x v_1$ is with $x = v_0$. Now apply the lemma to $\mathcal{S} = \mathcal{V} \setminus \{v_0, v_1\}$. We obtain a vertex v_2 with the property that the only possible arcs of the form $x v_2$ are $v_0 v_2$ and $v_1 v_2$. Continuing in this manner, we obtain vertices $v_0, v_1, \ldots, v_{n-1}$ with the property that for any j, the only arcs $x v_j$ are with $x = v_i$ and $i < j$. Thus $v_0, v_1, \ldots, v_{n-1}$ is a canonical labeling.

We want to discuss a second algorithm to which the name of Richard Bellman is attached.

Pause 14   Name the first algorithm described in this book to which Bellman's name is attached. ∎

The algorithm we have in mind takes as input an acyclic digraph whose vertices have been labeled canonically, together with a specified vertex v, and outputs the lengths of shortest paths from v to every other vertex. The algorithm also describes the shortest path from v to any other vertex by means of a *rooted* spanning tree. Remember that a root in a tree is simply a designated vertex. In a digraph, the concept is stronger. There is only one possible root.

12.4.4 DEFINITION   A digraph $\mathcal{T}$ is a *rooted tree* with vertex v as the *root* if the unoriented graph (ignoring orientations of arcs) is a tree, if v has indegree 0, and v is the only such vertex of $\mathcal{T}$. ❖

For example, if the edges of the tree shown in Fig. 12.2 are directed down, then we have a rooted tree with "start" as root. On the other hand, the digraph to the left is not a rooted tree because there is more than one vertex of indegree 0.

In Proposition 12.1.2, we showed that any two vertices of a tree are joined by a unique path. This is clearly not the case if the edges of the tree are oriented (and we require paths to respect orientation). There is, however, a unique path from the root to every other vertex.

The notion of a rooted undirected tree appeared earlier (see Definition 12.1.3.) We will see later that there is no conflict in these notions. (See Exercise 15 in Section 12.6.)

12.4.5 PROPOSITION   In a rooted (directed) tree with root v, there is a unique path from v to every other vertex.

Proof   Uniqueness is straightforward: If there were two different directed paths $\mathcal{P}_1$, $\mathcal{P}_2$ from v to some vertex u, then, ignoring orientations, we would have two different paths from v to u, contradicting the fact that the undirected graph T is a tree. We now show the existence of a directed path from v to any other vertex. So, let u be a vertex of T different from v. Since indeg $u \neq 0$, there is a directed edge $u_1 u$. If $u_1 = v$, we have a path from v to u; otherwise, since indeg $u_1 \neq 0$, we have a directed edge $u_2 u_1$. Note that $u_2 \neq u$ since the arc between u and u_1 is $u_1 u$. Thus $u_2 u_1 u$ is a path and if $u_2 = v$ we are done. In general, suppose $k \geq 2$ and we have found a path $u_k u_{k-1} \cdots u_1 u$ with no $u_i = v$. Since indeg $u_k \neq 0$, there is a directed arc $u_{k+1} u_k$. Also, $u_{k+1} \notin \{u, u_1, u_2, \ldots, u_k\}$ because the undirected graph T has no cycles. Thus $u_{k+1} u_k \cdots u_1 u$ is a path and, if $u_{k+1} = v$, we have a directed path from v to u. Since our tree is finite, this process cannot continue indefinitely, so eventually some $u_k = v$.

12.4.6 COROLLARY   In a rooted (directed) tree, every vertex other than the root has indegree 1.

Proof   Let T be a rooted tree with root v and suppose $u \neq v$ is a vertex with indeg $u \neq 1$. Since indeg $u \neq 0$, we have indeg $u \geq 2$, so there are distinct arcs $u_1 u$ and $u_2 u$. The proposition says there is a path $\mathcal{P}_1$ from v to u_1 and also a path $\mathcal{P}_2$ from v to u_2. Thus we obtain two different paths from v to u (with final arcs $u_1 u$ and $u_2 u$). This contradicts uniqueness of a directed path from v to u.

12.4.7 BELLMAN'S ALGORITHM   Given a weighted acyclic digraph $\mathcal{G}$ with nonnegative weights and a canonical labeling $v_0, v_1, \ldots, v_{n-1}$, to find the shortest paths from v_0 to every other vertex,

Step 1. Set $d_0 = 0$ and $d_i = \infty$ for $i = 1, 2, \ldots, n-1$.
Set $p_i = -1$ for $i = 0, 1, \ldots, n-1$.

Step 2. For t from 1 to $n - 1$,
let $d_t = \min\{d_j + w(v_j, v_t) \mid j = 0, \ldots, t-1\}$, and let p_t be a j that gives this minimum.

As with previous shortest path algorithms, a final value $d_t = \infty$ simply indicates that there is no directed path from v_0 to v_t.

Consider the acyclic canonically labeled graph $\mathcal{G}$ with arcs weighted as shown on the left in Fig. 12.22. We show the values of d_t and p_t (p for predecessor) at the beginning and after each iteration of the loop in Step 2. The final values of d_1 and p_1 are 2 and 0, respectively. Thus the shortest distance to v_1 has length 2, and the last arc on a shortest path is $v_0 v_1$. The final values of d_2 and p_2 are 4 and 1, respectively, showing that the shortest path to v_2 has length 4, and the last arc on the corresponding path is $v_1 v_2$. The final values of d_3 and p_3 are 2 and 0, respectively, asserting the facts that a shortest path to v_3 has length 2 and $v_0 v_3$ is the last arc on such a path. On the right in Fig. 12.22, we show just those arcs that are used last on shortest paths from v_0 to each vertex. It is not a coincidence that these form a spanning tree rooted at v_0. In the Exercises, we ask you to explain why.

Answer to Pause   **14.** In Section 11.2, we met the Bellman-Ford shortest path algorithm.

True/False Questions

(Answers can be found in the back of the book.)

1. The digraph pictured by is acyclic.

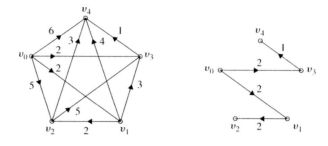

	d_0, p_0	d_1, p_1	d_2, p_2	d_3, p_3	d_4, p_4
Initially	$0, -1$	$\infty, -1$	$\infty, -1$	$\infty, -1$	$\infty, -1$
$t = 1$	$0, -1$	$2, 0$	$\infty, -1$	$\infty, -1$	$\infty, -1$
$t = 2$	$0, -1$	$2, 0$	$4, 1$	$\infty, -1$	$\infty, -1$
$t = 3$	$0, -1$	$2, 0$	$4, 1$	$2, 0$	$\infty, -1$
$t = 4$	$0, -1$	$2, 0$	$4, 1$	$2, 0$	$3, 3$

Figure 12.22

2. If every edge in an acyclic undirected graph is given a direction, the resulting digraph is acyclic.

3. If a digraph is acyclic, then the underlying undirected graph must be acyclic.

4. The digraph pictured by [figure] is a canonical labeling of the digraph in Question 1.

5. A digraph is acyclic if and only if every labeling of its vertices is canonical.

6. The graph pictured by [figure] is a rooted tree with some vertex as its root.

7. In a rooted (directed) tree with root v, there is a unique path from v to every other vertex.

8. In a rooted (directed) tree, every vertex other than the root has outdegree 1.

9. Bellman's name has appeared twice so far in this book.

10. In Bellman's algorithm, if there is a directed path from v_0 to v_t, then the final value of d_t is finite.

Exercises

*The answers to exercises marked [BB] can be found in the **B**ack of the **B**ook.*

1. [BB; (a)] For each of the digraphs in Fig. 12.23, either show that the digraph is acyclic by finding a canonical labeling of vertices or exhibit a cycle.

2. Suppose $v_0, v_1, \ldots, v_{n-1}$ is a canonical labeling of a digraph $\mathcal{G}$. What can be said about the indegree and outdegree of v_0, if anything? Explain.

3. [BB] Find an $\mathcal{O}(n^2)$ algorithm that computes the indegrees of a digraph with n vertices. (The addition of two numbers is the basic operation.)

4. (a) Describe an algorithm that finds a canonical labeling for the vertices of an acyclic digraph.

   (b) Find a Big Oh estimate for your algorithm in terms of some reasonable basic operation (or operations).

   (c) Write a computer program that implements your algorithm.

(a)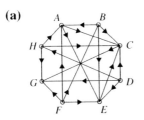

(b)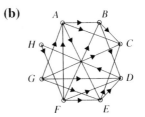

(c)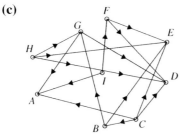

(d)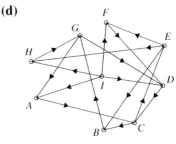

Figure 12.23 Digraphs for Exercise 1.

5. The algorithm described in the proof of Theorem 12.4.3 can in fact be adapted to find a cycle in a digraph that is not acyclic.
   (a) [BB] Explain how this can be accomplished.
   (b) Describe an algorithm that implements your idea.
   (c) Write computer code that implements your algorithm.

6. How many shortest path algorithms can you name? How many of these can you describe?

7. [BB] Suppose T is a rooted (directed) tree with n vertices. How many arcs does T have? Why?

8. Let G be a connected graph and suppose we orient the edges in such a way that the digraph we obtain has a unique vertex of indegree 0. Must this digraph be a rooted tree?

9. The following digraphs are acyclic and canonical labelings are shown. Apply Bellman's algorithm to each digraph to find the lengths of shortest paths from v_0 to each other vertex. Find a shortest path to v_t and the predecessor vertex v_{p_t}.
   (a) [BB]

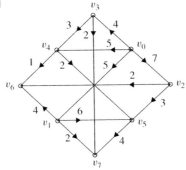

(b)

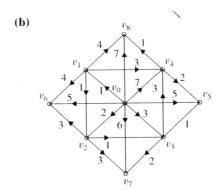

10. Show that Bellman's algorithm works; that is, if G is an acyclic digraph with vertices $v_0, v_1, \ldots, v_{n-1}$ canonically labeled, then the final value of d_t is the length of a shortest path from v_0 to v_t, and there is a path of this length whose final arc is $v_{p_t} v_t$.

11. [BB] Suppose we apply Bellman's algorithm to an acyclic digraph with a canonical ordering of vertices. Explain why the arcs $v_{p_t} v_t$ produce a spanning tree rooted at v_0.

12. Find the complexity of Bellman's algorithm in terms of additions and comparisons.

13. [BB] Explain how Bellman's algorithm can be modified to find the length of a shortest path to each v_t from a given vertex v_k that is not necessarily v_0.

14. [BB; (a)] For each of the digraphs that accompany Exercise 9, find the shortest distance to each v_t and the corresponding value of p_t,
   i. when paths start at v_1 and,
   ii. when paths start at v_2.

12.5 Depth-First Search

In this section, we describe a procedure called *depth-first search*, which is simple, efficient, and the basis for a number of important computer algorithms in graphs. It quickly tests whether a graph is connected, produces a spanning tree in the connected case, and is the key to solving a problem about turning graphs into digraphs.

12.5.1 THE DEPTH-FIRST SEARCH ALGORITHM

Let G be a graph with n vertices.

Step 1. Choose any vertex and label it 1. Set $k = 1$.

Step 2. While there are unlabeled vertices
    if there exists an unlabeled vertex adjacent to k, assign to it the smallest
        unused label ℓ from the set $\{1, 2, \ldots, n\}$ and set $k = \ell$.
    else if $k = 1$, stop;
        else backtrack to the vertex ℓ from which k was labeled and set $k = \ell$.

Step 3. end while

When the algorithm terminates, there is a path from vertex 1 to each labeled vertex that uses only edges required by the algorithm (Exercise 3). Thus, if the algorithm successfully labels all n vertices of the graph G, the graph must have been connected. The converse is also true (Exercise 4). Thus, depth-first search is an algorithm that tests connectedness in a graph.

EXAMPLE 4   We consider how the depth-first search algorithm might proceed with the graph in Fig. 12.24(a). Starting at vertex 1, one possible forward procedure in the depth-first search yields the labels shown in Fig. 12.24(a). All the vertices adjacent to vertex 4 have been labeled and $k = 4 \neq 1$, so the algorithm backtracks first to 3, the vertex from which 4 acquired its label. All vertices adjacent to 3 have also been labeled, so

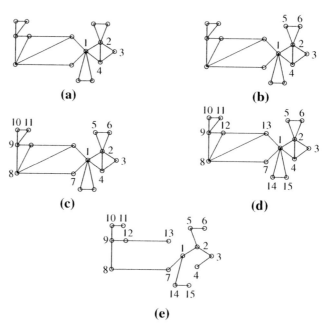

(a)

(b)

(c)

(d)

(e)

Figure 12.24 A depth-first search and the corresponding spanning tree.

it backtracks to 2. Vertex 2 has an unlabeled adjacent vertex. The smallest unused label so far is 5, so the algorithm would label 5 some vertex adjacent to 2, say the one shown. Vertex 5 has an adjacent unlabeled vertex, so this gets labeled 6. The current assignment of labels is depicted in Fig. 12.24(b). The algorithm now backtracks until it finds a vertex with an adjacent unlabeled vertex. It finds vertex 1 in this way and, since this vertex has adjacent unlabeled vertices, the algorithm could conceivably assign labels as far as 11, as shown in Fig. 12.24(c). Since all vertices adjacent to 11 have been labeled, the algorithm backtracks through vertex 10 to vertex 9 and then assigns labels 12 and 13. From vertex 13, the algorithm backtracks to 12, then to 9 (from which 12 received its label), then to 8, to 7, and to 1, after which vertices 14 and 15 are labeled. Finally, the algorithm backtracks to 14, then to 1, and stops. The final labels are shown in Fig. 12.24(d). Since 15 labels were used and the graph had 15 vertices, the graph was connected, a fact admittedly obvious by sight, but not to a computer.

In addition to testing for connectedness, depth-first search has another use. If the graph is connected, the edges that were used in the search form a spanning tree for the graph (see Exercise 5). Applied to the graph in the preceding example, the algorithm produces the spanning tree shown in Fig. 12.24(e).

Carry out a depth-first search for the graph given in Fig. 12.24(a) different from the one in the text, and draw the corresponding spanning tree. Start at vertex 1 as before. ∎

Show that the complexity function for depth-first search applied to a graph with n vertices is $\mathcal{O}(n^2)$. [*Hint*: Think of edges instead of vertices.] ∎

One critical advantage that a person has over a computer in solving elementary graph problems is sight. The reader with little experience writing computer programs may well wonder from time to time at the rather detailed way we describe some "obvious" procedures. When a person, for instance, applies the depth-first search algorithm to a simple graph that he or she can see, some ways of labeling the vertices are much more sensible than others. Furthermore, a person can **see** when all the vertices are labeled and hence stop without backtracking to vertex 1, as required by the algorithm.

This section concludes by considering a problem that some readers may have seen previously in a different context. Our solution involves moving without thought around the vertices of a graph that is never fully seen, just the way a computer does. On the other hand, when we stop, we can be confident that we have indeed explored **every** vertex.

PROBLEM 5. An Innkeeper has a full 8-pint flagon of wine and empty flagons that hold 5 and 3 pints, respectively. The three flagons are unmarked and no other measuring devices are available. Explain how the innkeeper can divide the wine into two equal amounts in the fewest number of steps.

Solution. We imagine the graph whose vertices and edges are as follows: There is a vertex labeled (a, b, c) if and only if it is possible for the innkeeper to hold, with certain knowledge, a pints of wine in the 8-pint flagon, b pints in the 5-pint flagon, and c pints in the 3-pint flagon. Thus, vertex $(8, 0, 0)$ corresponds to the initial state. There is an edge joining (a, b, c) and (a', b', c') if it is possible to reach the state (a', b', c') from (a, b, c), or vice versa, by pouring all the wine from one of the three flagons into another. For example, from the initial state, the innkeeper can reach $(3, 5, 0)$ by emptying the 8-pint flagon into the 5-pint flagon; thus, there is an edge between $(8, 0, 0)$ and $(3, 5, 0)$. We explore the vertices of this graph with a procedure much like depth-first search. Continue from $(3, 5, 0)$. Emptying the remainder of the 8-pint flagon into the 3-pint flagon takes us to $(0, 5, 3)$, emptying the 5-pint flagon into the 8-pint flagon takes us to $(5, 0, 3)$, then emptying the 3-pint flagon into the 5-pint flagon takes us to $(5, 3, 0)$. (See Fig. 12.25.)

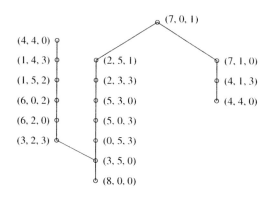

Figure 12.25 The spanning tree for a problem of flagons and wine.

We continue to visit, in order, vertices $(2, 3, 3)$, $(2, 5, 1)$, $(7, 0, 1)$, $(7, 1, 0)$, $(4, 1, 3)$, and finally $(4, 4, 0)$. This state is what the innkeeper sought; it has been reached in ten steps.

Now we backtrack, first to $(4, 1, 3)$. Emptying the contents of the 8-pint flagon into the 5-pint flagon takes us to a previously labeled vertex on the path to $(4, 1, 3)$, that is, $(0, 5, 3)$. If we could get from $(0, 5, 3)$ to $(4, 1, 3)$ in fewer than seven steps, then the path to $(4, 4, 0)$ could be shortened, but that issue will be decided when we have backtracked to $(0, 5, 3)$ and can be ignored for now. Note, however, that we must be careful, because an edge in our graph only signifies that you can go from one of the end vertices to the other, not necessarily in both directions (see Exercise 9). We continue to investigate vertices adjacent to $(4, 1, 3)$. Emptying the 1 pint remaining in the 5-pint flagon into the 8-pint flagon leads to $(5, 0, 3)$, again a vertex already labeled. There are no other vertices adjacent to $(4, 1, 3)$, so we backtrack to $(7, 1, 0)$. We leave it to you to confirm that all vertices adjacent to those on the route from $(7, 1, 0)$ back to $(3, 5, 0)$ have already been labeled lower on the path. The vertex $(3, 5, 0)$, however, has an adjacent vertex not yet labeled, $(3, 2, 3)$. From this, we move in order to $(6, 2, 0)$, $(6, 0, 2)$, $(1, 5, 2)$, $(1, 4, 3)$, and then $(4, 4, 0)$. We have found a route to the desired state that requires just seven steps. Backtracking again from $(4, 4, 0)$, we come first to $(1, 4, 3)$ and find two adjacent vertices on the first path, $(5, 0, 3)$ and $(0, 5, 3)$, and hence two more routes to $(4, 4, 0)$; for example,

$$(8, 0, 0) \to (3, 5, 0) \to (3, 2, 3) \to \cdots$$
$$\to (1, 4, 3) \to (5, 0, 3) \to (5, 3, 0) \to \cdots \to (4, 4, 0).$$

Since each of these routes is (much) longer than the current shortest route, we do not display them on the graph. Continuing to backtrack from $(1, 4, 3)$, we find that $(1, 5, 2)$ is adjacent to $(0, 5, 3)$ and $(6, 0, 2)$ is adjacent to $(5, 0, 3)$, but, as before, we do not display these adjacencies since the routes they give to $(4, 4, 0)$ are longer than the current shortest route. Eventually, we reach the initial vertex $(8, 0, 0)$ and discover that all adjacent vertices have been labeled, so we know that all vertices of the graph have been visited. We also discover that we can pass from $(8, 0, 0)$ to $(5, 0, 3)$ in one step, giving yet another route to the desired vertex $(4, 4, 0)$, a route requiring eight steps. The shortest route, however, remains at seven steps.

Answers to Pauses

15. One possible answer is given, along with the associated spanning tree.

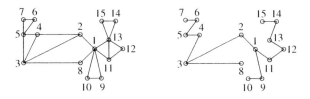

16. Depth-first search proceeds by deciding at each stage either to proceed along a particular edge to the next unlabeled vertex or not to proceed (because the edge joins two labeled vertices). If all edges incident with a given vertex are rejected, then the algorithm backtracks. Hence, focusing our attention on the edges, each edge need be considered at most twice. (Note that once an edge has been rejected or used in backtracking, it is never considered again.) Hence, the total number of steps is at most twice the number of edges, this number being at most $\binom{n}{2} = \frac{1}{2}n(n-1)$. So the complexity of depth-first search is $\mathcal{O}(n^2)$.

True/False Questions

(Answers can be found in the back of the book.)

1. At any stage during a depth-first search, the vertices that have been labeled are all connected by edges.

2. Depth-first search has assigned labels 1 and 2 as shown:

The next vertex to be labeled will be B.

3. Depth-first search has assigned labels 1 and 2 as shown:

The next vertex to be labeled will be A.

4. If $\mathcal{G}$ is a graph with ten vertices and depth-first search stops after eight vertices have been labeled, $\mathcal{G}$ is not connected.

5. If a graph $\mathcal{G}$ is connected, the edges that are used in a depth-first search on $\mathcal{G}$ will form a spanning tree for $\mathcal{G}$.

6. If depth-first search is applied to a a tree starting at some designated vertex 1, the resulting labeling must be unique.

7. Every spanning tree of $\mathcal{K}_n$ is obtainable as a depth-first search spanning tree.

8. The complexity function from a depth-first search applied to a graph with n vertices is $\mathcal{O}(n^2)$.

9. Breadth-first search (see Exercise 10) has assigned labels 1 and 2 as shown:

The next vertex to be labeled will be B.

10. Every spanning tree of $\mathcal{K}_n$ is obtainable as a breadth-first search spanning tree.

Exercises

*The answers to exercises marked [BB] can be found in the **B**ack of the **B**ook.*

1. [BB; (a)] For each of the following graphs, carry out a depth-first search starting at vertex a. Show all labels and list those used, in order, on the final backtracking. Highlight any resulting spanning tree.

2. [BB; (a)] In each of the graphs shown in Fig. 12.26, a depth-first search has labeled several vertices. Show all labels, list in order those used on the final backtracking, and show any resulting spanning tree.

3. Use mathematical induction to show that when the depth-first search algorithm terminates there is a path from vertex 1 to each labeled vertex that uses only edges required by the algorithm.

4. (a) [BB] Let v be a vertex in a graph $\mathcal{G}$ that is labeled by the depth-first search algorithm. Prove that the algorithm labels all the vertices adjacent to v.

(b) Prove that if $\mathcal{G}$ is connected the depth-first algorithm labels every vertex of $\mathcal{G}$.

5. Suppose the depth-first algorithm is applied to a connected graph $\mathcal{G}$. Prove that the vertices of $\mathcal{G}$ together with the edges used by the algorithm form a spanning tree. [*Hint*: Exercises 3 and 4]

6. [BB] Give an example of a connected graph $\mathcal{G}$ that has a spanning tree not obtainable as a depth-first spanning tree for $\mathcal{G}$.

7. (a) [BB] Explain how to change the depth-first search algorithm so that it can count the number of connected components of a graph.

(b) Table 12.27 shows the adjacencies in a graph with vertices $v_1, v_2, \ldots, v_{13}$. **Without drawing the graph**, apply a depth-first search and use the method discovered in part (a) to determine the number of components. Give the labels that the search assigns to the vertices.

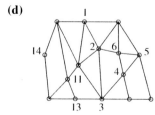

Figure 12.26

Table 12.27

	1	2	3	4	5	6	7	8	9	10	11	12	13
1	0	1	0	0	0	1	0	0	0	0	1	0	0
2	1	0	0	0	0	0	0	0	0	0	1	0	0
3	0	0	0	0	0	0	0	1	0	0	0	0	1
4	0	0	0	0	1	0	1	0	0	0	0	1	0
5	0	0	0	1	0	0	0	0	0	1	0	0	0
6	1	0	0	0	0	0	0	0	0	0	1	0	0
7	0	0	0	1	0	0	0	0	1	1	0	0	0
8	0	0	1	0	0	0	0	0	0	0	0	0	1
9	0	0	0	0	0	0	1	0	0	0	0	1	0
10	0	0	0	0	1	0	1	0	0	0	0	0	0
11	1	1	0	0	0	1	0	0	0	0	0	0	0
12	0	0	0	1	0	0	0	0	1	0	0	0	0
13	0	0	1	0	0	0	0	1	0	0	0	0	0

8. Given a full 12-ounce flagon of wine and two empty flagons holding 8 and 5 ounces, respectively, explain how to divide the wine into two equal 6-ounce portions in the fewest number of steps. The flagons are unmarked. No other measuring devices are at hand.

9. [BB] In our wine-pouring Problem 5, if it is possible to move from (a, b, c) to (a', b', c') in a single step, is it always possible to move in the other direction, (a', b', c') to (a, b, c), in a single step?

10. [BB] What might the phrase *breadth-first search* mean? Design such a procedure.

11. [BB; (a)] Apply a breadth-first search to each of the graphs shown in Exercise 1 (starting at vertex a in each case).

12. Suppose the breadth-first search algorithm is applied to an arbitrary graph $\mathcal{G}$.
    (a) Prove that when the algorithm terminates there is a path from vertex 1 to every other labeled vertex using only edges required by the algorithm.
    (b) Prove that if $\mathcal{G}$ is connected every vertex is labeled.
    (c) Prove that if $\mathcal{G}$ is connected then the vertices of $\mathcal{G}$ together with the edges used by the algorithm form a spanning tree.

13. Let $\mathcal{G}$ be a connected graph with $n \geq 2$ vertices, one of which is u. Show that $\mathcal{G}$ has a spanning tree with the property that, for any vertex v, the edges of the tree that connect u and v define a shortest path between u and v. [*Hint*: Think of the spanning tree produced by the breadth-first search algorithm. See Exercise 10.]

14. Prove that the complete bipartite graph $\mathcal{K}_{2,n}$ has the property that every spanning tree is obtainable as a depth-first search spanning tree if and only if $n = 2, 3, 4$.

12.6 The One-Way Street Problem

Over the years, the amount of traffic on the streets of a small town has increased enormously and the town planners are trying to decide what should be done. One suggestion, looked on favorably by certain members of the town council, is that all streets be made one-way to simplify traffic flow. Certain minimum requirements must be met, however. For example, it must remain possible to travel from any point in town to any other point along one-way streets. Is there a way of putting a direction on each street so that this requirement is met? In the language of graph theory, the one-way street problem asks, "Does a given connected graph have a strongly connected orientation?"

Remember that a digraph is strongly connected if it is possible to move from any vertex to any other vertex along arcs, in the proper direction. (See Section 11.2.) For example, the digraph shown on the right in Fig. 12.28 is strongly connected.

Figure 12.28 A graph and a solution to the One-Way Street Problem.

12.6.1 DEFINITIONS

Figure 12.29 A graph for which the One-Way Street Problem cannot be solved.

To *orient* or to *assign an orientation* to an edge in a graph is to assign a direction to that edge. To orient or assign an orientation to a graph is to orient every edge in the graph. A graph has a *strongly connected orientation* if it is possible to orient it in such a way that the resulting digraph is strongly connected. ❖

The graph on the left in Fig. 12.28 has a strongly connected orientation (shown beside it). On the other hand, Fig. 12.29 displays a graph that does not have a strongly connected orientation. The trouble is the middle edge; once this is given a direction, flow will only be permitted from one side of that edge to the other, but not in reverse. Such an edge is called a *bridge* or *cut edge*.

12.6.2 DEFINITION

An edge e of a connected graph G is called a *bridge* or a *cut edge* if the subgraph $G \setminus \{e\}$ is not connected. ❖

Let e be an edge that is not a bridge in a connected graph G. Show that e is part of a circuit. ∎

We shall show that the presence of a bridge in a connected graph G is exactly what prevents G from having a strongly connected orientation. First, however, we illustrate a technique that will be useful in our proof.

PROBLEM 6. Find a strongly connected orientation for the graph on the left of Fig. 12.30.

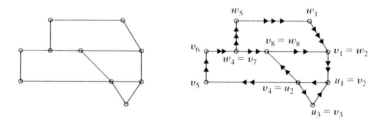

Figure 12.30 A graph and a strongly connected orientation for it.

Solution. We begin by finding a circuit, for example, $u_1 u_2 u_3 u_1$, and orienting the edges $u_1 \to u_2 \to u_3 \to u_1$ as shown (by single arrows) on the right of Fig. 12.30.

Next, we look for a vertex that is not in but that is adjacent to some vertex of this circuit; v_1 is adjacent to u_1, for instance. Now we look for a circuit containing $v_1 u_1$, say, $v_1 v_2 (= u_1) v_3 (= u_3) v_4 (= u_2) v_5 v_6 v_7 v_8 v_1$. We would like to orient the edges of this circuit $v_1 \to v_2 \to \cdots \to v_8 \to v_1$ as before, but we cannot because edges $v_2 v_3$ and $v_3 v_4$ have already been oriented (and in the opposite direction). So we do the best we can by orienting those edges of this circuit not already assigned directions; we orient $v_1 \to v_2$, $v_4 \to v_5$, $v_5 \to v_6$, $v_6 \to v_7$, $v_7 \to v_8$, $v_8 \to v_1$ (with double arrows). So far, our procedure has identified eight vertices and oriented all but one of the edges between pairs of these. We orient the omitted edge $v_8 u_2$ arbitrarily, say $u_2 \to v_8$. It is critical to observe (and we leave it for you to check) that, at this stage, the subgraph whose vertices are the u_i and v_j and whose edges are all edges of the given graph among these vertices is strongly connected; you can get from any u_i or v_j to any other of these vertices following edges in the direction of arrows.

Again, we next look for a vertex that is not in but that is adjacent to some vertex in this subgraph; w_1 is adjacent to v_1, for instance. We find a circuit that includes the edge $w_1 v_1$, for example, $w_1 w_2 (= v_1) w_3 (= v_8) w_4 (= v_7) w_5 w_1$, and orient the edges of this circuit that have not so far been oriented in the direction this sequence of vertices indicates. We orient $w_1 \to w_2$, $w_4 \to w_5$ and $w_5 \to w_1$ as shown (with triple arrows). You should check that a strongly connected orientation has now been assigned to the given graph.

12.6.3 THEOREM   A graph has a strongly connected orientation if and only if it is connected and has no bridges.

Proof   ($\longrightarrow$) If a graph $\mathcal{G}$ has a strongly connected orientation, then $\mathcal{G}$ is surely connected. Let e be an edge, say with end vertices u and v. If e is oriented in the direction $u \to v$ when $\mathcal{G}$ is assigned its strongly connected orientation, then in this strongly connected digraph there is a directed path from v to u. In particular, there is a path $\mathcal{P}$ in $\mathcal{G}$ from v to u that does not use e (definition of path). So any walk in $\mathcal{G}$ that involves e can be replaced by a walk that avoids e, simply by replacing e with $\mathcal{P}$. It follows that $\mathcal{G} \setminus \{e\}$ is connected, so e is not a bridge.

($\longleftarrow$) Conversely, suppose $\mathcal{G}$ is connected and has no bridges. We first remark that every edge of $\mathcal{G}$ must be part of a circuit. (See PAUSE 17.) Now we show that $\mathcal{G}$ can be assigned a strongly connected orientation by mimicking the approach we used to solve Problem 6. Let $\mathcal{C}: u_1 u_2 \cdots u_n u_1$ be a circuit in $\mathcal{G}$. (As noted, every edge is part of a circuit, so some such circuit certainly exists.) For $1 \leq i \leq n - 1$, assign edge $u_i u_{i+1}$ the orientation $u_i \to u_{i+1}$. Assign edge $u_n u_1$ the orientation $u_n \to u_1$. Then orient any other edges between vertices of $\mathcal{C}$ arbitrarily.

If $\mathcal{C}$ contains all the vertices of $\mathcal{G}$, then clearly we have an orientation of $\mathcal{G}$ that is strongly connected, since $\mathcal{C}$ was strongly connected. Suppose, on the other hand, that $\mathcal{C}$ does not contain all the vertices of $\mathcal{G}$. Since $\mathcal{G}$ is connected, there must exist a vertex v_1 not in $\mathcal{C}$ such that $v_1 u_j$ is an edge for some u_j. Since every edge in $\mathcal{G}$ is part of a circuit, $v_1 u_j$ is part of a circuit $v_1 u_j (= v_2) v_3 \cdots v_m v_1$. Assign $v_1 v_2$ the direction $v_1 \to v_2$ and $v_m v_1$ the direction $v_m \to v_1$. Leave unchanged the orientation of edges on the circuit that have already been oriented (that is, those that are part of $\mathcal{C}$), but orient any $v_i v_{i+1}$ not yet oriented in the direction $v_i \to v_{i+1}$. Finally, assign an arbitrary orientation to any remaining edges among vertices considered to this point. We have drawn two possibilities for the oriented subgraph whose vertices are $u_1, \ldots, u_n, v_1, \ldots, v_m$ in Fig. 12.31. The subgraph on the right in this figure is intended to serve as a caution that, in addition to v_2, some other of the vertices $v_3, \ldots, v_m$ may coincide with vertices u_j. For example, in the rightmost subgraph, if you wanted to get from v_{k+1} to v_k, you would have to go first to v_1, then to u_j and around $\mathcal{C}$ to v_k.

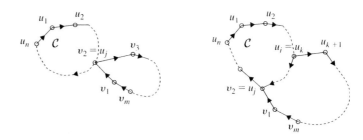

Figure 12.31

In PAUSE 18, we ask you to verify the following crucial **fact**: The subgraph of vertices and edges identified so far is strongly connected. Thus, if this subgraph is the entire graph, we are finished. Otherwise we find a vertex w_1 that is not part of but that is adjacent to some vertex in this subgraph, find a circuit containing this vertex, and orient edges as before. This procedure must terminate, and with a strongly connected orientation.

Pause 18 Establish the **fact** mentioned in the end of the preceding proof.

Since the identification of circuits in a graph is difficult without the advantage of sight, the following algorithm, based on depth-first search, is important.

12.6.4 AN ALGORITHM FOR A STRONGLY CONNECTED ORIENTATION

Suppose G is a connected graph.

Step 1. Carry out a depth-first search in G and let T be the spanning tree that this produces.

Step 2. For each edge e of G, consider the labels i and j of its ends. Suppose $i < j$.
If e is in T, orient it $i \rightarrow j$;
else orient it $j \rightarrow i$.

If G has no bridges, then the algorithm produces a strongly connected orientation.

We apply this algorithm to the graph in Fig. 12.30 and show in Fig. 12.32 the labels that a depth-first search might yield and, with heavy lines, the corresponding spanning tree as well. For each edge ij with $i < j$, the algorithm orients $i \rightarrow j$ if the edge is part of the tree and otherwise $j \rightarrow i$. Edge 45, for example, is in the tree, so it is oriented $4 \rightarrow 5$; on the other hand, edge 18 is not in the tree, so it is oriented $8 \rightarrow 1$.

Pause 19 Use Algorithm 12.6.4 to exhibit a strongly connected orientation for the graph in Fig. 12.24 based on the depth-first search shown in that figure.

Suppose G is a connected graph without bridges. To show that our algorithm actually works, it suffices to show that it orients the edges of G in such a way that there is a directed path between 1 and k (in each direction) for all k. For this, we use the strong form of mathematical induction on k.

The result is immediate if $k = 1$, so assume that $k > 1$ and that for all ℓ, $1 \le \ell < k$, there is a path from 1 to ℓ and from ℓ to 1 that respects the orientation of edges. We must show that such paths exist between 1 and k.

Vertex k acquired its label because it was adjacent to one that was already labeled, say ℓ. Since the depth-first search algorithm always chooses the smallest available label, we have $\ell < k$. By the induction hypothesis, there is a directed path from 1 to ℓ. Since edge ℓk is part of the depth-first search spanning tree and since $\ell < k$, the edge incident with ℓ and k is oriented $\ell \rightarrow k$; thus, there is a directed path from 1 to k. It is more difficult to show that there is also a directed path from k to 1.

Since every vertex is the terminal vertex of a backtracking [see Exercise 14(b)], eventually the algorithm will backtrack to ℓ from some vertex $k + s$, $s \ge 0$, any vertex adjacent to a vertex labeled $k + i$, $i \ge 0$, having a label of this type too. Note that there is a directed path from k to each vertex $k + i$, $0 \le i \le s$. (The argument is the same as the one we used earlier to establish the existence of a directed path from 1 to each labeled vertex.) Thus, if any vertex labeled $k + i$, $i \ge 0$, is adjacent to a vertex labeled t with $t < k$, the induction hypothesis makes it easy to establish the existence of a directed path from k to 1 (since the edge joining t and $k + i$ is not part of the depth-first search spanning tree).

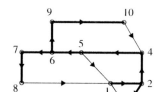

Figure 12.32 A depth-first search, a spanning tree, and a strongly connected orientation.

On the other hand, if ℓk is the only edge joining a vertex $k + i$, $i \geq 0$, to a vertex with a label $t < k$, then any path from $k + s$ to ℓ looks like

$$k + s, k + i_1, k + i_2, \ldots, k, \ell,$$

which implies that ℓk is a bridge, a contradiction that establishes the result.

As a concluding remark, we mention in passing that Algorithm 12.6.4 can be applied to give an orientation to any connected graph G although, if G has bridges, the result will not be strongly connected.

Answers to Pauses

17. Let u and v denote the end vertices of e. Since $G \setminus \{e\}$ is connected, there is a path in $G \setminus \{e\}$ from v to u. This path, followed by uv, is a circuit in G containing e.

18. We must show that it is possible to get from any u_i or v_j to any other u_i or v_j following edges in the assigned directions. We can get from any u_i to any other u_j along the circuit C. Next, we show that there is a directed path from each v_i to v_{i+1} and so, since $v_m v_1$ is oriented $v_m \to v_1$, there is a directed path from any v_i to any v_j. The orientation $v_1 \to v_2$ provides a directed path from v_1 to v_2 and, for any $i = 2, 3, \ldots, m - 1$, if the orientation is not $v_i \to v_{i+1}$, then both the vertices v_i and v_{i+1} are part of the circuit C, which we can use to find a directed path from v_i to v_{i+1}. In any case, there is always some directed path from each v_i to v_{i+1}, as asserted. This also shows that we can pass from C to any v_i via the directed edge $u_j(= v_2)v_3$. Since we can move in the other direction via $v_1 v_2 (= u_j)$, it follows that the subgraph is strongly connected.

19. For each edge ij with $i < j$, we orient $i \to j$ if the edge is in the spanning tree and otherwise $j \to i$.

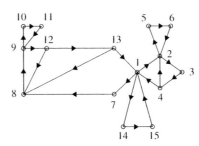

(Answers can be found in the back of the book.)

True/False Questions

1. The pictured digraph is strongly connected:  .

2. The pictured graph has a strongly connected orientation: .

3. The pictured graph has a strongly connected orientation: .

4. Every tree with $n \geq 2$ vertices contains a bridge.

5. In a tree with $n \geq 2$ vertices, every edge is a bridge.

6. If every edge in a connected graph G is a bridge, G is a tree.

7. If some edge in a connected graph G is a bridge, G must be a tree.

8. A graph has a strongly connected orientation if and only if it is connected and has no bridges.

9. A depth-first search has resulted in the following labeling: 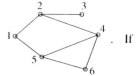 . If

   Step 2 of Algorithm 12.6.4 is carried out, edge 45 will be oriented $4 \to 5$.

10. In Question 9, edge 46 will be oriented $4 \to 6$.

Exercises

*The answers to exercises marked [BB] can be found in the **B**ack of the **B**ook.*

1. [BB; (a)] For each of the graphs in Exercise 1 of Section 12.5, assign an orientation based on your depth-first search and state whether this orientation is strongly connected.

2. Find strongly connected orientations of the graphs corresponding to the five *Platonic solids*: the cube, tetrahedron [BB], octahedron, icosahedron, and dodecahedron. (See pp. 313, 318, and 413.)

3. (a) [BB] Does there exist a strongly connected orientation for the Petersen graph? (See p. 312.) If so, find one.

   (b) Must a Hamiltonian graph have a strongly connected orientation? Explain.

   (c) What about the converse of (b)? Explain.

4. How many bridges does a tree with n vertices have? Explain.

5. [BB] Can an Eulerian graph have bridges? Explain.

6. [BB; ($\longrightarrow$)] Prove that an edge e in a connected graph G is a bridge if and only if there are vertices u and v in G such that every path from u to v requires the edge e.

7. (a) [BB] Show that any connected graph can be oriented so that the resulting digraph is **not** strongly connected.

   (b) Let G be a connected graph with all vertices of even degree. Can G be oriented so that the resulting digraph is strongly connected? Explain.

8. [BB] Let G be a graph with a strongly connected orientation assigned to it. Suppose that the direction of the arrow on each edge of G is reversed. Is the new digraph still strongly connected? Explain.

9. Answer true or false and explain your answers.

   (a) [BB] A graph has a strongly connected orientation if and only if every edge is part of a circuit.

   (b) A graph with a strongly connected orientation has no vertices of degree 1.

   (c) A connected graph with no odd vertices has a strongly connected orientation.

10. Let $e = uv$ be a bridge in a connected graph G. Let G_1 be the subgraph of $G \setminus \{e\}$ whose vertices are those from which there is a path to u and whose edges are all the edges of G among these vertices. Let G_2 be defined analogously, interchanging the roles of u and v.

    (a) [BB] Prove that there is no path between u and v in $G \setminus \{e\}$.

    (b) Prove that G_1 and G_2 have no vertices in common.

    (c) Prove that G_1 is a (connected) component of $G \setminus \{e\}$, that is, a maximal connected subgraph of $G \setminus \{e\}$.

    (In Fig. 12.29, G_1 and G_2 are the two triangles. This exercise shows that Fig. 12.29 shows what happens in general when there is a bridge in a graph.)

11. [BB] Faced with the undeniable fact that his town's street system does indeed have some bridges, Mayor Murphy decides that all bridges should remain two-way streets, but all other streets should be made one-way. Can this be done so as to allow (legal) travel from any intersection to any other?

12. Explain why the depth-first search algorithm can be used to find all bridges in a connected graph. Design a procedure to find all such bridges that is $\mathcal{O}(n^3)$ (where n is the number of vertices).

13. Let G be a graph with n vertices and m edges.

    (a) Assuming $m > \frac{(n-1)(n-2)}{2} + 1$, show that G can be given a strongly connected orientation. (You may assume that the condition implies that G is connected. See Exercise 24 of Section 10.1.)

    (b) Need G have a strongly connected orientation if $m > \frac{(n-1)(n-2)}{2}$?

14. (a) The depth-first search algorithm is applied to a connected graph G. Assume that a vertex receives label k from a vertex labeled ℓ, $1 \leq \ell < k$. Show that the edge ℓk is used exactly twice by the algorithm.

    (b) For every k, $1 \leq k < n$, show that there is a backtracking to k.

15. (a) [BB] Let $\mathcal{T}$ be an undirected tree, and let v be any vertex of $\mathcal{T}$. Show that it is possible to assign an orientation to $\mathcal{T}$ in such a way that v is the unique vertex of indegree 0.

(b) [BB] Using (a), if an undirected tree T is rooted in the sense of Definition 12.1.3, explain why T can be assigned an orientation such that digraph T is a rooted tree in the sense of Definition 12.4.4 (with the same root).

Key Terms & Ideas

Here are some technical words and phrases that were used in this chapter. Do you know the meaning of each? If you're not sure, check the glossary or index at the back of the book.

acyclic

bridge

canonical labeling

isomorphic labeled trees

leaf

minimum connector problem

minimum spanning tree

orient

root

rooted tree

spanning tree

strongly connected orientation

tree

Review Exercises for Chapter 12

1. Make a tree that displays all monotonically increasing subsequences of 4, 7, 3, 9, 5, 1, 8. How many are there?

2. Let G be a weighted graph with vertices $w_1, w_2, \ldots, w_6$ such that $w_j w_k$ is an edge if and only if $j + k$ is odd, in which case the weight of the edge $w_j w_k$ is $(\max\{j, k\})^2$.
   (a) Identify the unweighted graph described.
   (b) Using a tree, solve the Traveling Salesman's Problem for G.

3. (a) Is it possible for a tree to have nine vertices and degree sequence 4, 2, 2, 2, 2, 2, 2, 1, 1?
   (b) Is it possible for a tree to have nine vertices, two of which have degree 5?

4. Prove that the following conditions are equivalent for a tree T with $n \geq 2$ vertices.
   i. T has an Eulerian trail.
   ii. T has exactly two vertices of degree 1.
   iii. T has exactly $n - 2$ vertices of degree 2.

5. (a) Let G be a graph with the property that there is precisely one path between any pair of its vertices. Prove that G is a tree.
   (b) A tree has 33 vertices of degree 1, six of degree 3, and all other vertices of degree 7. Determine the number of vertices of degree 7.
   (c) Prove that it is impossible to have a tree with more than two vertices, two of which have degree 1 while all others have degree 3 or 5.

6. (a) Prove that up to isomorphism there is only one unlabeled tree on seven vertices with a vertex of degree 5 and another of degree 2. Draw a picture of this tree.
   (b) Label the tree obtained in (a) in two different ways so as to produce nonisomorphic labeled trees.

7. How many spanning trees has K_8? Why?

8. Use Kirchhoff's Theorem to find the number of spanning trees. Draw pictures of them all.

9. Is it possible for a graph to have exactly two spanning trees? Explain.

10. In Exercise 8 of Section 12.2, you proved that the number of spanning trees of the complete bipartite graph $K_{2,n}$ is $n2^{n-1}$. If e is an edge of $K_{2,n}$, how many of these spanning trees contain e? Explain.

11. Use Kruskal's algorithm to find a minimum spanning tree of the weighted graph shown. What is the weight of a minimum spanning tree?

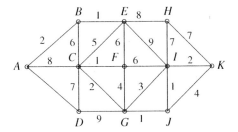

12. Repeat Exercise 11 using Prim's algorithm.

13. Let $v_1, v_2, \ldots, v_n$ denote the vertices of the complete graph K_n, $n \geq 3$, and give edge $v_i v_j$ weight $i + j$. Find a minimum spanning tree for this weighted graph and the weight of such a tree.

14. Determine whether each digraph shown is acyclic by finding a canonical labeling of vertices or exhibiting a cycle.

(a)

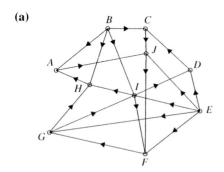

(b)

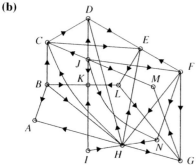

15. Change the direction of the arrows on JF and FG in each digraph of Exercise 14 and answer the questions again.

16. Can an acyclic digraph have two different canonical orderings of vertices? Explain.

17. Given that the digraph is acyclic, find a canonical ordering $v_0, v_1, \ldots$ of the vertices. Then find the lengths of shortest paths from the root to all other vertices, specifying the predecessor vertex (as defined in Bellman's algorithm) in each case when

   (a) the root is v_0,   **(b)** the root is v_2.

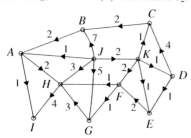

18. Repeat Exercise 17 using the digraph shown in Fig. 12.33 and root vertices v_0 and v_1.

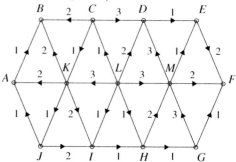

Figure 12.33 Graph for Exercise 18.

19. In each of the following graphs, a depth-first search has started and several vertices have been labeled. Finish each search, show all labels, list in order those used on the final backtracking, and show the resulting spanning tree.

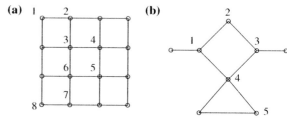

20. Assign an orientation to each of the graphs in Exercise 19 based on your depth-first search and state whether this orientation is strongly connected.

21. Let v be an arbitrary vertex and e an arbitrary edge of a connected graph $\mathcal{G}$. Show that it is always possible to carry out a depth-first search beginning at v that includes e as part of the resulting spanning tree.

22. Which graphs have the property that it is possible to start at some vertex v and carry out a depth-first search that labels all vertices without ever backtracking? Prove your answer.

23. If a connected graph $\mathcal{G}$ has a bridge e, show that every spanning tree of $\mathcal{G}$ must contain e.

24. Prove that a graph $\mathcal{G}$ is a tree if and only if $\mathcal{G}$ is connected and every edge of $\mathcal{G}$ is a bridge.

25. Is it possible for a Hamiltonian graph to contain a bridge? Explain.

26. (a) Is the orientation that appears in a tournament always strongly connected? Explain.

   (b) Is it possible to change the directions of some of the arrows in a tournament and achieve a strongly connected orientation? Explain. Assume the graph has at least three vertices.

13

Planar Graphs and Colorings

13.1 Planar Graphs

The Three Houses–Three Utilities Problem posed in Chapter 9 asks whether it is possible to draw the complete bipartite graph $\mathcal{K}_{3,3}$ without any crossovers of edges. (See Fig. 13.1.)

Figure 13.1 The graph $\mathcal{K}_{3,3}$, representing three houses and three utilities.

Thinking of the edges of this graph as pieces of string and the vertices as knots, the question is whether the *net* can be arranged without string crossovers. In the language of graph theory, the problem asks if $\mathcal{K}_{3,3}$ is *planar*.

13.1.1 DEFINITION A graph is *planar* if it can be drawn in the plane in such a way that no two edges cross. ❖

In this chapter (and abusing terminology) we find it convenient to refer to a picture of a graph in which there are no crossovers of edges as a *plane graph*. Thus, a planar graph is one that can be drawn as a plane graph. There are five places where edges in the graph $\mathcal{G}$ of Fig. 13.2(a) cross; nevertheless, $\mathcal{G}$ is planar because it can be drawn as a plane graph, as shown in Fig. 13.2(b).

Figure 13.2(c) shows $\mathcal{G}$ with all edges drawn as straight line segments. In fact, this is possible for any planar graph,[1] and so we lose no generality if planar graphs are drawn as plane graphs with straight edges.

A plane graph divides the plane into various connected regions, one of which is called the *exterior region*. Every region, including the exterior, is bounded by edges. The graph in Fig. 13.2(b) divides the plane into six regions, R_6 being the

---

[1]This result is due to I. Fary, "On Straight Line Representation of Planar Graphs," *Acta Scientiarum Mathematicarum (Szeged)* **11** (1948), 229–233. A proof also appears in *Combinatorial Problems and Exercises* by László Lovász, North-Holland (1979) (Problem 5.38).

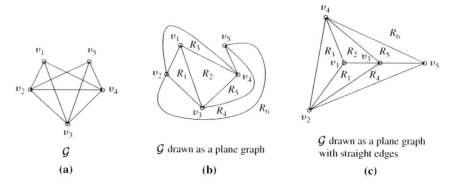

$\mathcal{G}$
(a)

$\mathcal{G}$ drawn as a plane graph
(b)

$\mathcal{G}$ drawn as a plane graph
with straight edges
(c)

Figure 13.2

exterior region. The boundary of R_2, for example, consists of the edges v_1v_3, v_3v_4, and v_4v_1. The boundary of R_6 is v_2v_4, v_4v_5, and v_5v_2. We require that every edge must be the boundary of some region. Thus, in Fig. 13.3(a), the edge labeled e is part of the boundary of region R, while in Fig. 13.3(b) it is part of the boundary of the exterior region.

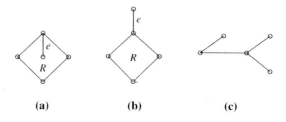

(a)   (b)   (c)

Figure 13.3

A tree determines just one region in the plane, the exterior region, and every edge of the tree is part of the boundary of this region. [See Fig. 13.3(c).]

Consider the plane graph shown on the left of Fig. 13.4.

(a) How many regions are there?
(b) List the edges that form the boundary of each region.
(c) Which region is exterior?

Answer these same questions for the graph on the right. ∎

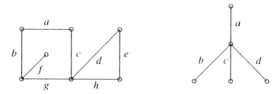

Figure 13.4

Planar graphs were first studied by Euler because of their connections with polyhedra. A *polyhedron* is a 3-dimensional solid whose surface consists of flat faces bounded by straight lines. It is *regular* if its faces are congruent regular polygons (corresponding sides and angles equal) and *convex* if a line joining any two points on its surface lies entirely within the solid. In all, there are just five regular convex polyhedra—the cube, the tetrahedron, the octahedron, the icosahedron, and the dodecahedron— and they are popularly known as the *Platonic solids* because they were regarded by Plato as symbolizing earth, fire, air, water, and the universe, respectively.

When we discussed Sir William Hamilton's World Tour in Section 10.2, we showed how to associate with the regular dodecahedron a planar graph whose edges and vertices correspond to the edges and vertices of the solid and whose regions correspond to the faces of the polyhedron. In the exercises of Section 10.2, we introduced planar graphs corresponding to the cube and the regular icosahedron. As we said at the time, we can obtain the planar graph associated with a particular polyhedron by imagining that the bottom face is stretched until the object collapses flat. Figure 13.5 shows the plane graphs associated with the tetrahedron, the cube, and the octahedron.

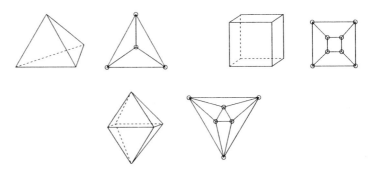

Figure 13.5 The tetrahedron, cube, and octahedron, and their corresponding planar graphs.

In 1752, Euler published the remarkable formula

$$V - E + F = 2,$$

which holds for any convex polyhedron with V vertices, E edges, and F faces.[2] For the cube, for instance, $V = 8$, $E = 12$, and $F = 6$; for the tetrahedron, $V = F = 4$ and $E = 6$. Euler's formula also works for any plane graph, with regions replacing faces. For example, the plane graph in Fig. 13.2 has $V = 5$, $E = 9$, and $R = 6$, so $V - E + R = 5 - 9 + 6 = 2$.

13.1.2 THEOREM   Let $\mathcal{G}$ be a connected plane graph with V vertices, E edges, and R regions. Then $V - E + R = 2$.

Proof   We use induction on E. If $E = 0$, then $V = R = 1$ (because $\mathcal{G}$ is connected) and the formula is true. Now assume the formula holds for connected plane graphs with $E - 1$ edges, where $E \geq 1$, and that $\mathcal{G}$ is a connected plane graph with E edges, V vertices, and R regions. We must show that $V - E + R = 2$. If $\mathcal{G}$ contains no cycles, then $\mathcal{G}$ is a tree, and so $E = V - 1$ by Theorem 12.1.6. Since $R = 1$, we have $V - E + R = V - (V - 1) + 1 = 2$, as desired. Suppose, on the other hand, that

[2]L. Euler, "Demonstratio nonnullarum insignium proprietatum quibus solida hedris planis inclusa sunt praedita," *Novi Commentarii Academiae Scientarium Petropolitanae* **4** (1752/53), 140–160.

$\mathcal{G}$ does contain a cycle C and that e is an edge of C. The subgraph $\mathcal{G} \setminus \{e\}$ is a plane graph and connected, and the region bounded by C disappears when e is removed. Thus $\mathcal{G} \setminus \{e\}$ contains $R - 1$ regions, all V vertices of $\mathcal{G}$, and $E - 1$ edges. By the induction hypothesis, $V - (E - 1) + (R - 1) = 2$; that is, $V - E + R = 2$. ◉

Show that this theorem is not necessarily true if "connected" is omitted from its statement. ▮

We are now ready to solve the Three Houses–Three Utilities problem. It turns out not to be possible to connect three houses to three utilities without crossovers of connection lines.

13.1.3 COROLLARY

$\mathcal{K}_{3,3}$ is not planar.

Proof

We provide a proof by contradiction. The graph $\mathcal{K}_{3,3}$ has six vertices and nine edges. If it is planar, it can be drawn as a plane graph with R regions. Since $V - E + R = 2$, we have $R = 5$. Now count the number of edges on the boundary of each region and sum over all regions. Suppose the sum is N. Since $\mathcal{K}_{3,3}$ is bipartite, it contains no triangles, so the boundary of each region contains at least four edges. Thus $N \geq 4R = 20$. On the other hand, in the calculation of N, each edge was counted at most twice, so $N \leq 2E = 18$. This contradiction establishes the corollary. ◉

Find the number N defined in this proof for the graph on the left of Fig. 13.4. Verify that $N \leq 2E$. Give an example of an edge that is counted just once. ▮

Intuitively, a graph with a lot of edges cannot be planar since it will be impossible to avoid crossovers when drawing it. Thus, we expect planar graphs to have relatively few edges. The next theorem makes this statement more precise.

13.1.4 THEOREM

Let $\mathcal{G}$ be a planar graph with $V \geq 3$ vertices and E edges. Then $E \leq 3V - 6$.

Proof

We give an argument for the case that $\mathcal{G}$ is connected and ask you to prove the general case in Exercise 19.

If $V = 3$, then $E \leq 3$ and the theorem holds. So we assume that $V > 3$. Thus, we may also assume that $E \geq 3$ (otherwise, the result is clearly true). Draw $\mathcal{G}$ as a plane graph with R regions. Then, as in the proof of Corollary 13.1.3, we count the number of edges on the boundary of each region, add these numbers, and denote the sum N. As before, $N \leq 2E$. Also, since each boundary contains at least three edges, $N \geq 3R$. Hence, $3R \leq 2E$. Theorem 13.1.2 says that $V - E + R = 2$. Therefore, $6 = 3V - 3E + 3R \leq 3V - 3E + 2E = 3V - E$ and the result follows. ◉

13.1.5 COROLLARY

$\mathcal{K}_5$ is not planar.

Proof

In $\mathcal{K}_5$, $V = 5$ and $E = \binom{5}{2} = 10$ (since every pair of vertices is joined by an edge). Since it is not true that $E \leq 3V - 6$, $\mathcal{K}_5$ cannot be planar. ◉

In a graph where the number of edges is not too large, it is reasonable to expect some restrictions on vertex degrees. In Exercise 20, we ask you to show that a planar graph with at least four vertices has at least four vertices of degree $d \leq 5$. For the present, we content ourselves with a weaker statement.

13.1.6 COROLLARY

Every planar graph contains at least one vertex of degree $d \le 5$.

Proof

Suppose $\deg v_i \ge 6$ for every vertex v_i. Since $\sum \deg v_i = 2E$, we would have $2E \ge 6V$, and hence $E \ge 3V > 3V - 6$. This contradicts $E \le 3V - 6$.

The Polish mathematician Kazimierz Kuratowski (1896–1980) discovered the crucial role played by $\mathcal{K}_{3,3}$ and $\mathcal{K}_5$ in determining whether a graph is planar. (The $\mathcal{K}$ in $\mathcal{K}_n$ and $\mathcal{K}_{m,n}$ is in Kuratowski's honor.) First, since these graphs are not planar, no graph that contains either of them as a subgraph can be planar. Second, any graph obtained from either $\mathcal{K}_{3,3}$ or $\mathcal{K}_5$ simply by adding more vertices to edges cannot be planar either.

13.1.7 DEFINITION

Two graphs are *homeomorphic* if and only if each can be obtained from the same graph by adding vertices (necessarily of degree 2) to edges.   ❖

EXAMPLE 1

The graphs $\mathcal{G}_1$ and $\mathcal{G}_2$ in Fig. 13.6 are homeomorphic since both are obtainable from the graph $\mathcal{G}$ in that figure by adding a vertex to one of its edges.

$\mathcal{G}_1$ $\quad\quad\quad$ $\mathcal{G}_2$ $\quad\quad\quad$ $\mathcal{G}$

Figure 13.6 Two homeomorphic graphs obtained from $\mathcal{G}$ by adding vertices to edges.

EXAMPLE 2

In Fig. 13.7, we show two homeomorphic graphs, each obtained from $\mathcal{K}_5$ by adding vertices to edges of $\mathcal{K}_5$. (In each case, the vertices of $\mathcal{K}_5$ are shown with solid dots.)

Figure 13.7 Two homeomorphic graphs obtained from $\mathcal{K}_5$.

 Pause 4

Any two cycles are homeomorphic. Why?   ∎

EXAMPLE 3

Two graphs are homeomorphic if one is simply obtained from the other by adding vertices to edges; that is, the third graph mentioned in Definition 13.1.7 may be one of the two given graphs. For instance, graphs $\mathcal{G}_1$ and $\mathcal{G}_2$ in Fig. 13.8 are homeomorphic because $\mathcal{G}_2$ is obtained by adding two vertices (the solid dots) to edges of $\mathcal{G}_1$.

When we say "adding vertices to edges," we do not include the possibility of adding a vertex where edges cross over each other, for this is achieved by adding a vertex to **each** edge and then joining these two vertices together. Joining vertices is not allowed. For example, graphs $\mathcal{G}_1$ and $\mathcal{G}_3$ of Fig. 13.8 are not homeomorphic.

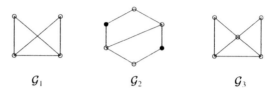

Figure 13.8 $\mathcal{G}_1$ is homeomorphic to $\mathcal{G}_2$, but not to $\mathcal{G}_3$.

The following theorem characterizes planar graphs in a remarkably simple way. The proof in one direction is straightforward and was given earlier: A graph that contains $\mathcal{K}_5$ or $\mathcal{K}_{3,3}$ cannot be made planar by adding vertices to edges. The proof of the converse is more complicated and will be omitted.

13.1.8 THEOREM   **(Kuratowski[3])** A graph is planar if and only if it has no subgraph homeomorphic to $\mathcal{K}_5$ or $\mathcal{K}_{3,3}$.

EXAMPLE 4   The graph $\mathcal{G}$ in Fig. 13.9 is not planar. By deleting two edges, we obtain a subgraph $\mathcal{S}$ that is $\mathcal{K}_{3,3}$ (the bipartition sets are the sets of hollow vertices and solid vertices) except for one vertex (the tiny one) added to an edge. Since $\mathcal{S}$ is homeomorphic to $\mathcal{K}_{3,3}$, $\mathcal{G}$ is not planar, by Kuratowski's Theorem.

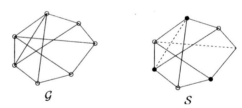

Figure 13.9   A nonplanar graph $\mathcal{G}$ and a subgraph $\mathcal{S}$ homeomorphic to $\mathcal{K}_{3,3}$.

EXAMPLE 5   The graph on the left in Fig. 13.10 is not planar because the subgraph shown on the right is homeomorphic to $\mathcal{K}_5$. Notice, for example, that A is adjacent to C and D, and, except for intermediate vertices of degree 2, also to B and E.

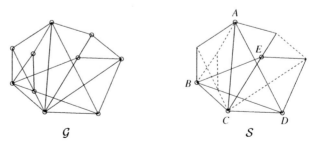

Figure 13.10   A nonplanar graph $\mathcal{G}$ and a subgraph $\mathcal{S}$ homeomorphic to $\mathcal{K}_5$.

---

[3]K. Kuratowski, "Sur le Problème des Courbes Gauches en Topologie," *Fundamenta Mathematicae* **15** (1930), 271–283.

Answers to Pauses

1. The graph on the left of Fig. 13.4 has three regions whose boundaries are $\{d, e, h\}$, $\{a, b, f, g, c\}$, and $\{a, b, g, c, d, e, h\}$; the last region is exterior. The graph on the right is a tree; it determines only one region, the exterior one, with boundary $\{a, b, c, d\}$.

2. In the graph shown, $V - E + R = 6 - 6 + 3 = 3.$

3. The boundaries of the regions are given in the answer to PAUSE 1: $N = 3 + 5 + 7 = 15 \leq 16 = 2E$. Edge f is counted only once.

4. Any cycle can be obtained from a 3-cycle by adding vertices to edges.

True/False Questions

(Answers can be found in the back of the book.)

1. The pictured graph has two edges crossing and so is not a planar graph: .

2. This is not the picture of a plane graph: [image] .

3. The pictured graph has two regions: [image] .

4. If $\mathcal{G}$ is a connected plane graph with V vertices, E edges, and R regions, then $V - E + R = 2$.

5. A tree with n vertices has n edges and two regions.

6. $\mathcal{K}_{3,7}$ is planar.

7. $\mathcal{K}_8$ is planar.

8. A graph with eight vertices and 19 edges is not planar.

9. The graphs shown here are homeomorphic: [image] .

10. A graph is planar if and only if it has no subgraph isomorphic to $\mathcal{K}_5$ or $\mathcal{K}_{3,3}$.

Exercises

The answers to exercises marked [BB] can be found in the Back of the Book.

1. **(a)** [BB] Show that the graph is planar by drawing an isomorphic plane graph with straight edges.

   (b) [BB] Label the regions defined by your plane graph and list the edges that form the boundary of each region.

   (c) [BB] Verify that $V - E + R = 2$, $N \leq 2E$, and $E \leq 3V - 6$ (where, as defined in the proof of Corollary 13.1.3, N is the sum of the numbers of edges on the boundaries of all regions).

2. Repeat Exercise 1 for the complete bipartite graph $\mathcal{K}_{2,5}$.

3. [BB] Verify Euler's formula $V - E + F = 2$ for each of the five Platonic solids.

4. One of the two graphs is planar; the other is not. Which is which? Explain. (Note that the graph on the right is the *Petersen Graph*, which was introduced in Section 10.2.)

5. Determine which of the graphs in Fig. 13.11 are planar. In each case, either draw a plane graph and a plane graph with straight edges isomorphic to the one presented or exhibit a subgraph homeomorphic to $\mathcal{K}_{3,3}$ or $\mathcal{K}_5$.

(a) [BB]

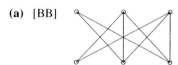

Note that this is just $\mathcal{K}_{3,3}$ less one edge.

(b)

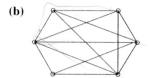

(c)

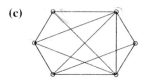

(d)

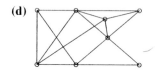

(e) [BB]

(f)

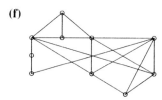

Figure 13.11 Graphs for Exercise 5.

6. Let $\mathcal{G}$ be a connected plane graph such that every region of $\mathcal{G}$ has at least five edges on its boundary. Prove that $3E \leq 5V - 10$.

7. [BB] If $\mathcal{G}$ is a connected plane graph with $V \geq 3$ vertices and R regions, show that $R \leq 2V - 4$.

8. (a) [BB] Give an example of a connected planar graph for which $E = 3V - 6$.

   (b) Let $\mathcal{G}$ be a connected plane graph for which $E = 3V - 6$. Show that every region of $\mathcal{G}$ is a triangle.

9. (a) If $\mathcal{G}$ is a connected plane graph with at least three vertices such that no boundary of a region is a triangle, prove that $E \leq 2V - 4$.

   (b) Let $\mathcal{G}$ be a connected planar bipartite graph with E edges and $V \geq 3$ vertices. Prove that $E \leq 2V - 4$.

10. (a) [BB] For which n is $\mathcal{K}_n$ planar?

    (b) For which m and n is $\mathcal{K}_{m,n}$ planar?

11. [BB] Show that $\mathcal{K}_{2,2}$ is homeomorphic to $\mathcal{K}_3$.

12. Show that any graph homeomorphic to $\mathcal{K}_5$ or to $\mathcal{K}_{3,3}$ is obtainable from $\mathcal{K}_5$ or $\mathcal{K}_{3,3}$, respectively, by addition of vertices to edges.

13. Suppose a graph $\mathcal{G}_1$ with V_1 vertices and E_1 edges is homeomorphic to a graph $\mathcal{G}_2$ with V_2 vertices and E_2 edges. Prove that $E_2 - V_2 = E_1 - V_1$.

14. (a) [BB] Let $\mathcal{G}$ be a connected graph with V_1 vertices and E_1 edges, and let $\mathcal{H}$ be a subgraph with V_2 vertices and E_2 edges. Show that $E_2 - V_2 \leq E_1 - V_1$.

    (b) Let $\mathcal{G}$ be a connected graph with V vertices, E edges, and $E \leq V + 2$. Show that $\mathcal{G}$ is planar.

    (c) Is (b) true if $E = V + 3$? Explain.

15. [BB] Let $\mathcal{G}$ be a graph and let $\mathcal{H}$ be obtained from $\mathcal{G}$ by adjoining a new vertex of degree 1 to some vertex of $\mathcal{G}$. Is it possible for $\mathcal{G}$ and $\mathcal{H}$ to be homeomorphic? Explain.

16. Discover what you can about Kazimierz Kuratowski and write a short biographical note about this famous Polish mathematician (in good, clear English, of course).

17. Answer true or false and explain.

    (a) If $\mathcal{G}$ is Eulerian and $\mathcal{H}$ is homeomorphic to $\mathcal{G}$, then $\mathcal{H}$ is Eulerian.

    (b) [BB] If $\mathcal{G}$ is Hamiltonian and $\mathcal{H}$ is homeomorphic to $\mathcal{G}$, then $\mathcal{H}$ is Hamiltonian.

18. (a) Show that any planar graph all of whose vertices have degree at least 5 must have at least 12 vertices. [*Hint*: It suffices to prove this result for **connected** planar graphs. Why?]

    (b) Find a planar graph each of whose vertices has degree at least 5.

19. (a) [BB] If $\mathcal{G}$ is a planar graph with n connected components, each component having at least three vertices, prove that $E \leq 3V - 6n$.

    (b) If $\mathcal{G}$ is a planar graph with n connected components, prove that $E \leq 3V - 3n$. Deduce that Theorem 13.1.4 holds for arbitrary planar graphs.

20. (a) [BB] Prove that every planar graph with $V \geq 2$ vertices has at least two vertices of degree $d \leq 5$.

    (b) Prove that every planar graph with $V \geq 3$ vertices has at least three vertices of degree $d \leq 5$.

    (c) Prove that every planar graph with $V \geq 4$ vertices has at least four vertices of degree $d \leq 5$.

21. (a) [BB] A connected planar graph $\mathcal{G}$ has 20 vertices. Prove that $\mathcal{G}$ has at most 54 edges.

    (b) A connected planar graph $\mathcal{G}$ has 20 vertices, seven of which have degree 1. Prove that $\mathcal{G}$ has at most 40 edges.

22. **(a)** [BB] Suppose G is a connected planar graph in which every vertex has degree at least 3. Prove that at least two regions of G have at most five edges on their boundaries.

    (b) Establish (a) for planar graphs that are not connected.

23. Suppose that a convex polygon with n vertices is *triangulated*, that is, partitioned into triangles, possibly by the introduction of new vertices. For example, two triangulations of a convex polygon with seven vertices are shown at the right; in the leftmost graph, four edges were required and, in the rightmost, 13. Show that the number of edges added to effect a triangulation is at least $n - 3$.

24. [BB] Find a formula for $V - E + R$ that applies to planar graphs that are not necessarily connected.

25. Prove that the Platonic solids are the only regular polyhedra. [*Hint*: In a regular polyhedron, every vertex has the same degree d and every face has the same number a of edges on its boundary. Try to solve $V - E + F = 2$ under such conditions.]

13.2 Coloring Graphs

One of the most exciting mathematical developments of the twentieth century was the proof, in 1976, of the Four-Color Theorem, which is easy to state and understand, but whose proof had remained unsolved since 1852 when it was first posed to his brother by Francis Guthrie. Guthrie had discovered that he could color a map of the counties of England with only four colors in such a way that each county had exactly one color and bordering counties had different colors. He guessed that it was possible to color the countries of **any** map with just four colors in such a way that bordering countries have different colors.[4] Both brothers had been students of Augustus De Morgan and so, unable to answer the question themselves, they asked their former teacher, one of the greatest mathematicians of the age. De Morgan was able to show that it is impossible to have five countries each adjacent to all of the others, but this result, while lending support to Francis Guthrie's guess, did not settle it.

It has long been known that five colors are enough, but for well over 100 years, whether one could make do with just four colors was not known. In 1879, the prestigious *American Journal of Mathematics* published a "proof" of the conjecture by one Alfred B. Kempe[5] (the final "e" is not pronounced), a London barrister, but 11 years later a fatal flaw was discovered. In fact, as pointed out by Percy Heawood,[6] Kempe's argument was a valid one for five colors, but not for four. It turns out that four colors are indeed enough, but the proof, by Kenneth Appel and Wolfgang Haken,[7] occupies almost 140 pages of the *Illinois Journal of Mathematics* and will not be presented here. The proof involved showing that any planar graph must contain a subgraph of a certain type. If this subgraph were deleted, one could 4-color the resulting reduced graph. With the assistance of J. Koch and 1200 hours of computer time, it was shown that any 4-coloring of the boundary of any of the subgraphs identified by Appel and Haken could be extended to a 4-coloring of the subgraph; thus, any planar graph could be 4-colored. The final settling of what had been the *Four-Color Conjecture* was considered such an achievement that for a period of time the postage meters at the University of Illinois bore the inscription "Four Col-

[4]Our use of the term *map* is not intended to limit us to those maps found between the covers of an atlas. In the context of map colorings, a map just means a plane (possibly pseudo-) graph in which the edges represent borders and vertices are points where borders meet.

[5]A. B. Kempe, "On the Geographical Problem of the Four Colors," *American Journal of Mathematics* **2** (1879), 193–200.

[6]P. J. Heawood, "Map-Color Theorem," *Quarterly Journal of Mathematics* **24** (1890), 332–339.

[7]K. Appel, W. Haken, and J. Koch, "Every Planar Map Is Four-Colorable," *Illinois Journal of Mathematics* **21** (1977), 429–567.

ors Suffice." Some readers might well be interested in an article by Robin Thomas, which, after a brief history of the Four-Color Problem, describes subsequent efforts to verify independently the proof, this being no small task.[8]

Our modest goal here is to show how graph theory can be used to attack a coloring problem and also to prove that any map can be 5-colored.

 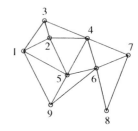

Figure 13.12 A map and an associated planar graph.

Our starting point is the observation that with any map we may associate a planar graph whose vertices correspond to countries and where an edge joins two vertices if the corresponding countries share a common border. There are nine countries in the map depicted in the left of Fig. 13.12, so the associated planar graph has nine vertices. Since countries 5 and 6 share a border, vertices 5 and 6 are joined by an edge, and so on. The point is that coloring the countries of the map so that countries with a common border receive different colors is equivalent to coloring the vertices of the associated graph so that adjacent vertices have different colors. For example, the following assignment of four colors to countries (or vertices) in Fig. 13.12 colors the map (and the graph) in the proper sense:

$$1 - \text{red}; \ 2 - \text{blue}; \ 3 - \text{green}; \ 4 - \text{red}; \ 5 - \text{green}; \ 6 - \text{blue};$$
$$7 - \text{green}; \ 8 - \text{red}; \ 9 - \text{yellow}.$$

Figure 13.13 shows a map of North America in which most provinces and states have been colored. Starting the coloring with the western states, it is soon apparent that three colors are not enough.

We formalize the notions we have been discussing.

13.2.1 DEFINITIONS

A *coloring* of a graph is an assignment of colors to the vertices so that adjacent vertices have different colors. An *n-coloring* is a coloring with n colors. The *chromatic number* of a graph G, denoted $\chi(G)$, is the minimum value of n for which an n-coloring of G exists. ❖

 Suppose $\chi(G) = 1$ for some graph G. What do you know about G? ∎

The graph on the left of Fig. 13.14 has been colored with three colors. Thus, its chromatic number is at most 3. Since it contains several triangles (the vertices of which must be colored differently), at least three colors are required: Its chromatic number is 3. The graph on the right has been colored with four colors, so for this graph G, $\chi(G) \leq 4$. Since G contains $\mathcal{K}_4$ as a subgraph (consider the subgraph determined by the vertices v_3, v_4, v_5, v_6) and since $\mathcal{K}_4$ requires four colors, G cannot be colored with less than four colors. For this graph then, $\chi(G) = 4$.

[8] Robin Thomas, "An Update on the Four-Color Theorem," *Notices of the American Mathematical Society* **45** (1998), no. 7, 848–859.

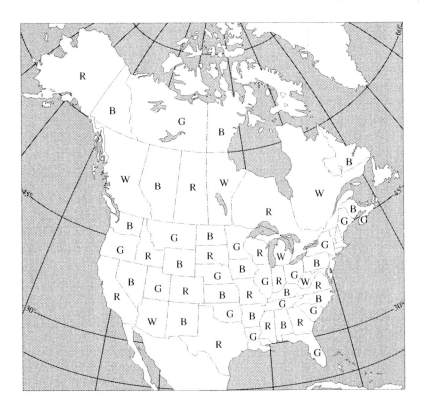

Figure 13.13 A partial 4-coloring of a map of North America.

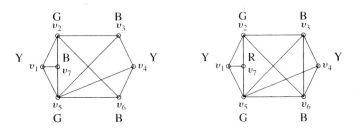

Figure 13.14 The graph on the left has chromatic number 3; the graph on the right has chromatic number 4.

What is the chromatic number of the graph in Fig. 13.12?   ∎

$\chi(\mathcal{K}_n) = n$, $\chi(\mathcal{K}_{m,n}) = 2$. Why?   ∎

13.2.2 THE FOUR-COLOR THEOREM

For any planar graph $\mathcal{G}$, $\chi(\mathcal{G}) \leq 4$.

Because of the Four-Color Theorem, a cartographer with at most four colors at her disposal is certain to be able to color the countries of any map with which she is confronted (so that countries with a common border have different colors) since an n-coloring of the associated (planar) graph with $n \leq 4$ translates into a coloring of the countries of the map.

How can $\chi(\mathcal{G})$ be determined in a specific situation? For a small graph, trial and error is likely the best method, though this approach would surely not be feasible for graphs with a large number of vertices and edges. Actually, it is unknown whether a "good" (polynomial time) algorithm exists for determining $\chi(\mathcal{G})$; like the Traveling Salesman's Problem, this problem is NP-complete.

One general result that applies to any graph links the chromatic number to the degrees of the vertices.

13.2.3 THEOREM

Let $\Delta(\mathcal{G})$ be the maximum of the degrees of the vertices of a graph $\mathcal{G}$. Then $\chi(\mathcal{G}) \leq 1 + \Delta(\mathcal{G})$.

Proof

The proof is by induction on V, the number of vertices of the graph. When $V = 1$, $\Delta(\mathcal{G}) = 0$ and $\chi(\mathcal{G}) = 1$, so the result clearly holds. Now let k be an integer, $k \geq 1$, and assume that the result holds for all graphs with $V = k$ vertices. Suppose $\mathcal{G}$ is a graph with $k + 1$ vertices. Let v be any vertex of $\mathcal{G}$, and let $\mathcal{G}_0 = \mathcal{G} \setminus \{v\}$ be the subgraph with v (and all edges incident with it) deleted. Note that $\Delta(\mathcal{G}_0) \leq \Delta(\mathcal{G})$. Now $\mathcal{G}_0$ can be colored with $\chi(\mathcal{G}_0)$ colors. Since $\mathcal{G}_0$ has k vertices, we can use the induction hypothesis to conclude that $\chi(\mathcal{G}_0) \leq 1 + \Delta(\mathcal{G}_0)$. Thus, $\chi(\mathcal{G}_0) \leq 1 + \Delta(\mathcal{G})$, so $\mathcal{G}_0$ can be colored with at most $1 + \Delta(\mathcal{G})$ colors. Since there are at most $\Delta(\mathcal{G})$ vertices adjacent to v, one of the available $1 + \Delta(\mathcal{G})$ colors remains for v. Thus, $\mathcal{G}$ can be colored with at most $1 + \Delta(\mathcal{G})$ colors.

The result of Theorem 13.2.3 is best possible as we see by considering the complete graph on n vertices. Since $\chi(\mathcal{K}_n) = n$ (PAUSE 7) and $\Delta(\mathcal{K}_n) = n - 1$, we have $\chi(\mathcal{K}_n) = 1 + \Delta(\mathcal{K}_n)$.

If $\mathcal{G}$ is an n-cycle, then $\Delta(\mathcal{G}) = 2$, and it is not hard to see that $\chi(\mathcal{G}) = 2$ or 3 according as n is even or odd. Thus, if $\mathcal{G}$ is a cycle with an odd number of vertices, we again have $\chi(\mathcal{G}) = 1 + \Delta(\mathcal{G})$. A theorem of R. L. Brooks[9] asserts that the only connected graphs $\mathcal{G}$ for which $\chi(\mathcal{G}) = 1 + \Delta(\mathcal{G})$ are $\mathcal{K}_n$ and cycles with an odd number of vertices. So for all other connected graphs, we have $\chi(\mathcal{G}) \leq \Delta(\mathcal{G})$.

For either graph $\mathcal{G}$ in Fig. 13.14, $\Delta(\mathcal{G}) = 5$, and so we can conclude from Theorem 13.2.3 that $\chi(\mathcal{G}) \leq 6$ or, from the result of Brooks, that $\chi(\mathcal{G}) \leq 5$. Neither observation tells us what is evident from the figure, that the actual chromatic numbers are 3 and 4. Nevertheless, Theorem 13.2.3 and its improvement due to Brooks do give us some information about the chromatic number of a graph and are, therefore, of interest since there is, in general, no easy way to find a chromatic number. Given a graph $\mathcal{G}$, we must simply apply ad hoc methods and hope to find $\chi(\mathcal{G})$ by trial and error.

While we cannot prove the Four-Color Theorem, we can prove the Five-Color Theorem without too much difficulty.

13.2.4 THEOREM

(Kempe, Heawood) If $\mathcal{G}$ is a planar graph, then $\chi(\mathcal{G}) \leq 5$.

Proof

We must prove that any planar graph with V vertices has a 5-coloring. Again we use induction on V and note that if $V = 1$ the result is clear. Let $k \geq 1$ be an integer and suppose that any planar graph with k vertices has a 5-coloring. Let $\mathcal{G}$ be a planar graph with $k + 1$ vertices and assume that $\mathcal{G}$ has been drawn as a plane graph with straight edges. We describe how to obtain a 5-coloring of $\mathcal{G}$.

---

[9]R. L. Brooks, "On Coloring the Nodes of a Network," *Proceedings of the Cambridge Philosophical Society* **37** (1941), 194–197.

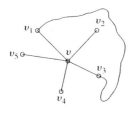

Figure 13.15

First, by Corollary 13.1.6, $\mathcal{G}$ contains a vertex v of degree at most 5. Let $\mathcal{G}_0 = \mathcal{G} \setminus \{v\}$ be the subgraph obtained by deleting v (and all edges with which it is incident). By the induction hypothesis, $\mathcal{G}_0$ has a 5-coloring. For convenience, label the five colors 1, 2, 3, 4, and 5. If one of these colors was not used to color the vertices adjacent to v, then it can be used for v, and $\mathcal{G}$ has been 5-colored. Thus, we assume that v has degree 5 and that each of the colors 1 through 5 appears on the vertices adjacent to v. In clockwise order, label these vertices $v_1, v_2, \ldots, v_5$ and assume that v_i is colored with color i. (See Fig. 13.15.)

We show how to recolor certain vertices of $\mathcal{G}_0$ so that a color becomes available for v. There are two possibilities.

Case 1: There is no path in $\mathcal{G}_0$ from v_1 to v_3 through vertices all of which are colored 1 or 3.

In this situation, let $\mathcal{H}$ be the subgraph of $\mathcal{G}$ consisting of the vertices and edges of all paths through vertices colored 1 or 3 that start at v_1. By assumption, v_3 is not in $\mathcal{H}$. Also, any vertex that is not in $\mathcal{H}$, but that is adjacent to a vertex of $\mathcal{H}$, is colored neither 1 nor 3. Therefore, interchanging colors 1 and 3 throughout $\mathcal{H}$ produces another 5-coloring of $\mathcal{G}_0$. In this new 5-coloring both v_1 and v_3 acquire color 3, so we are now free to give color 1 to v, thus obtaining a 5-coloring of $\mathcal{G}$.

Case 2: There is a path $\mathcal{P}$ in $\mathcal{G}_0$ from v_1 to v_3 through vertices all of which are colored 1 or 3.

In this case, the path $\mathcal{P}$, followed by v and v_1, gives a circuit in $\mathcal{G}$ that does not enclose both v_2 and v_4. Thus, any path from v_2 to v_4 must cross $\mathcal{P}$ and, since $\mathcal{G}$ is a plane graph, such a crossing can occur only at a vertex of $\mathcal{P}$. It follows that there is no path in $\mathcal{G}_0$ from v_2 to v_4 that uses just colors 2 and 4. Now we are in the situation described in Case 1, where we have already shown that a 5-coloring for $\mathcal{G}$ exists.

Readers may notice that vertex v_5 appears to play no role in this proof. Can our proof be adapted to prove the Four-Color Theorem? Recall that Alfred Kempe thought he had such a proof. See Exercise 18.

We conclude this section with an application of the idea of chromatic number to a problem familiar to most university registrars, the scheduling of exams. At a university of even moderate size, it is not unusual for 500 or 600 exams to be scheduled within a reasonably short period of time. The principal problem is always to minimize "conflicts," that is, to try to avoid situations where a student finds the exams in two of his or her courses scheduled for the same time period.

PROBLEM 6.   (Examination Scheduling) Suppose that in one particular semester there are students taking each of the following combinations of courses.

- Mathematics, English, Biology, Chemistry
- Mathematics, English, Computer Science, Geography
- Biology, Psychology, Geography, Spanish
- Biology, Computer Science, History, French
- English, Psychology, History, Computer Science
- Psychology, Chemistry, Computer Science, French
- Psychology, Geography, History, Spanish

What is the minimum number of examination periods required for exams in the ten courses specified so that students taking any of the given combinations of courses have no conflicts? Find a possible schedule that uses this minimum number of periods.

Solution. To picture the situation, we draw a graph (shown on the left of Fig. 13.16) with ten vertices labeled M, E, B, ... corresponding to Mathematics, English, Biology, and so on, and join two vertices with an edge if exams in the corresponding subjects must not be scheduled together.

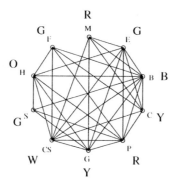

Period 1	Mathematics, Psychology
Period 2	English, Spanish, French
Period 3	Biology
Period 4	Chemistry, Geography
Period 5	Computer Science
Period 6	History

Figure 13.16

The minimal number of examination periods is evidently the chromatic number of this graph. What is this? Since the graph contains $\mathcal{K}_5$ (with vertices M, E, B, G, CS), at least five different colors are needed. (The exams in the subjects that these vertices represent must be scheduled at different times.) Five colors are not enough, however, since P and H are adjacent to each other and to each of E, B, G, and CS. The chromatic number of the graph is, in fact, 6. In Fig. 13.16, we show a 6-coloring and the corresponding exam schedule.

Answers to Pauses

5. If $\mathcal{G}$ has an edge, its end vertices must be colored differently, so $\chi(\mathcal{G}) \geq 2$. Thus, $\chi(\mathcal{G}) = 1$ if and only if $\mathcal{G}$ has no edges.

6. A way to 4-color the associated graph was given in the text. From this, we deduce that $\chi(\mathcal{G}) \leq 4$. To see that $\chi(\mathcal{G}) = 4$, we investigate the consequences of using fewer than four colors. Vertices 1, 2, 3 form a triangle, so three different colors are needed for these. Suppose we use red, blue, and green, respectively, as before. To avoid a fourth color, vertex 4 has to be colored red and vertex 5 green. Thus, vertex 6 has to be blue. Since vertex 9 is adjacent to vertices 1, 5, and 6 of colors red, green, and blue, respectively, vertex 9 requires a fourth color.

7. It takes n colors to color $\mathcal{K}_n$ because any two vertices of $\mathcal{K}_n$ are adjacent: $\chi(\mathcal{K}_n) = n$. On the other hand, $\chi(\mathcal{K}_{m,n}) = 2$; coloring the vertices of each bipartition set the same color produces a 2-coloring of $\mathcal{K}_{m,n}$.

True/False Questions

(Answers can be found in the back of the book.)

1. The Four-Color conjecture was settled in 1976 by Appel and Haken.

2. If $\mathcal{G}$ is a tree with at least two vertices, then $\chi(\mathcal{G}) = 2$.

3. If $\mathcal{G}$ is connected and $\chi(\mathcal{G}) = 2$, then $\mathcal{G}$ must be a tree.

4. If a graph $\mathcal{G}$ has an n-coloring, then $\chi(\mathcal{G}) = n$.

5. If $\chi(\mathcal{G}) = n$, then $\mathcal{G}$ has an n-coloring.

6. $\chi(\mathcal{K}_{m,n})$ is the minimum of m and n.

7. If $\chi(\mathcal{G}) \leq 4$, then $\mathcal{G}$ is planar.

8. If $\mathcal{G}$ is a planar graph, then $\chi(\mathcal{G}) \leq 4$.

9. If the maximum degree of a vertex in a graph $\mathcal{G}$ is 7, then $\chi(\mathcal{G}) \leq 7$.

10. In scheduling exams as illustrated in Problem 6, suppose it is discovered that the corresponding graph can be drawn with no edges crossing. Then at most four examination periods will be needed.

Exercises

Assume that all graphs in these Exercises are connected.

1. Name and describe two major mathematical accomplishments of the twentieth century.

2. (a) [BB] Draw a graph corresponding to the map shown and find a coloring that requires the least number of colors. What is the chromatic number of the graph?

   (b) [BB] Answer true or false and explain: The Four-Color Theorem says that the chromatic number of a planar graph is 4.

3. (a) [BB] When we discussed the coloring of maps at the beginning of this section, we assumed implicitly that *bordering* countries were countries that had some positive length of border in common. Suppose we deem countries to border if they merely have a point in common. Will four colors still suffice to color a map?

   (b) [BB] We also assumed that a country should consist of a single region. If we drop this restriction, will four colors still suffice to color a map?

4. Compute $\chi(\mathcal{G})$ for each of the graphs shown in Fig. 13.17. In each case, explain your answer and exhibit a $\chi(\mathcal{G})$-coloring.

5. Answer Exercise 4 for each of the graphs in Exercise 5, Section 13.1.

6. (a) [BB] Find the chromatic number of each of the graphs in Exercise 4 of Section 13.1.

   (b) [BB] State the converse of the Four-Color Theorem. Is it true?

7. (a) [BB] Is a tree planar? Explain.

   (b) Use (a) to prove that a tree with n vertices has $n - 1$ edges.

   (c) Suppose T is a tree with $n > 1$ vertices. Prove that $\chi(T) = 2$.

8. (a) [BB] Let $\mathcal{G}$ be a connected graph with n vertices and n edges. Prove that $\chi(\mathcal{G}) \leq 3$. [*Hint*: Note Exercise 7.]

   (b) Show that (a) remains true if $\mathcal{G}$ has $n + 1$ edges.

   (c) Does (a) remain true if $\mathcal{G}$ has $n + 2$ edges? Explain.

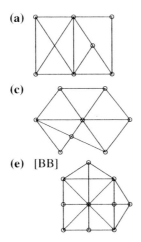

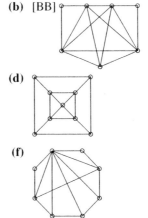

Figure 13.17 Graphs for Exercise 4.

9. Consider the graph shown below.
   (a) Is it planar? Either draw an isomorphic plane graph or explain why the graph is not planar.
   (b) Find its chromatic number and explain why this piece of information is consistent with the Four-Color Theorem.

10. [BB] Consider the graph shown above.
    (a) Find a subgraph homeomorphic to K_5.
    (b) Find a subgraph homeomorphic to $K_{3,3}$.
    (c) Is the graph planar? Explain.
    (d) What is the chromatic number of the graph?
    (e) Use this graph to comment on the converse of the Four-Color Theorem.

11. (a) [BB] What is $\chi(K_{14})$? What is $\chi(K_{5,14})$? Why?
    (b) Let G_1 and G_2 be cycles with 38 and 107 edges, respectively. What is $\chi(G_1)$? What is $\chi(G_2)$? Explain.

12. Answer true or false and explain:
    (a) [BB] If $\chi(G) = 3$, then G contains a triangle.
    (b) If $\chi(G) = 4$, then G contains K_4.

13. Let $n \geq 4$ be a natural number. Let G be the graph that consists of the union of K_{n-3} and a 5-cycle C, together with all possible edges between the vertices of these graphs. Show that $\chi(G) = n$, yet G does not have K_n as a subgraph.

14. Answer true or false and explain. If G is homeomorphic to H, then $\chi(G) = \chi(H)$.

15. Answer true or false and explain:
    (a) [BB] A Hamiltonian graph with chromatic number 2 must be planar.
    (b) A planar graph with chromatic number 2 must be Hamiltonian.
    (c) A graph that is both Hamiltonian and Eulerian and has chromatic number 2 must be planar.
    (d) [BB] A graph that is both Hamiltonian and Eulerian must have chromatic number less than 6.

16. [BB] The graph to the right arises in a certain problem of exam scheduling such as that described in Problem 6. Find the minimum number of exam periods required so that conflicts are avoided.

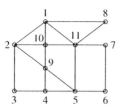

17. Suppose that in one particular semester there are students taking the following combinations of courses:
    - Math, Physics, French;
    - Math, English, German;
    - English, French, Physics;
    - Chemistry, Physics, French.

    What is the minimum number of examination periods required for examinations in the specified courses so that the students involved have no conflicts? Justify your answer.

18. Can our proof of the Five-Color Theorem be adapted to prove the Four-Color Theorem? Go through the proof presented in this section, assuming that only four colors are available, and find any possible flaw.

19. In addition to the combinations of courses described in Problem 6, suppose there are also students taking all of Geography, Computer Science, Spanish, and French. Does this force a change in the exam schedule? If it does, find a new examination schedule that avoids conflicts and uses the fewest number of periods.

20. [BB] Ten students, in the coming semester, will be taking the courses shown in the following table. How many time periods must be allowed for these students to take the courses they want without conflicts?

Arnold	Physics, Mathematics, English
Bill	Physics, Earth Science, Economics
Carol	Earth Science, Business
Calvin	Statistics, Economics
Eleanor	Mathematics, Business
Frederick	Physics, Earth Science
George	Business, Statistics
Huber	Mathematics, Earth Science
Ingrid	Physics, Water Skiing, Statistics
Jacquie	Physics, Economics, Water Skiing

21. [BB] The following semester, all the students in Exercise 20, except Calvin, plan to take second courses in the same subjects. Calvin decides not to take further courses in statistics. How many time periods will then be required?

22. Hubert Noseworthy loves snakes and keeps a dozen different varieties in his apartment (contrary to regulations). Since some varieties of snake attack other varieties, as shown in the following tables, Hubert needs several boxes in which to keep his snakes to separate antagonists. What is the minimum number of boxes he needs?

Variety	Attacks Variety
1	3,4,5,8,10, 12
2	1,3,6,7,10,11
3	4,9,12
4	5, 8, 9
5	6, 7, 10
6	9, 12
7	10, 12
8	7
9	8, 11
10	11
11	12

23. The local day care center has a problem because certain children do not get along with certain others. The table shows which of 15 children don't get along with whom. Finally, it is decided that children who do not get along with each other will have to be put into separate rooms. Find the minimum number of rooms required.

Child	Doesn't get along with
1	2, 6, 9, 10, 11, 13
2	1, 8, 10, 12, 13, 14, 15
3	4, 5, 7, 8, 12
4	3, 5, 6, 8, 11, 14
5	3, 4, 7, 8, 12, 13
6	1, 4, 7, 12, 15
7	3, 5, 6, 8, 11, 14
8	2, 3, 4, 5, 7, 9, 14
9	1, 8, 10, 12, 15
10	1, 2, 9, 11, 15
11	1, 4, 7, 10, 12
12	2, 3, 5, 6, 9, 11, 15
13	1, 2, 5, 14
14	2, 4, 7, 8, 13
15	2, 6, 9, 10, 12

24. Television channels are to be assigned to stations based in nine cities $A, B, \ldots, I$. Broadcasting regulations require that cities within 150 km of each other be assigned different channels. What is the least number of channels required if the distances between the cities are as given in the table?

	A	B	C	D	E	F	G	H
B	85							
C	137	165						
D	123	39	205					
E	164	132	117	171				
F	105	75	235	92	201			
G	134	191	252	223	298	177		
H	114	77	113	117	54	147	247	
I	132	174	22	213	138	237	245	120

25. Continuing the previous problem, city J is to acquire a television station too. Can it be assigned one of the existing channels or must it have a new one? Its distances from cities $A, \ldots, I$ are as follows.

	A	B	C	D	E	F	G	H	I
J	78	149	101	189	171	183	160	143	94

13.2.5 The Dual of a Planar Graph

In this section, we showed how to associate a planar graph with a map, by introducing a vertex for each country and connecting vertices if corresponding countries shared a border. By introducing one additional vertex corresponding to the exterior region and additional edges as before, we obtain a graph known as the *dual graph* of the map.

26. **(a)** [BB] Draw the dual graph of the cube (considered as a map) (Fig. 13.5) as a plane graph with straight edges. Identify this dual graph. [*Hint*: It's another of the Platonic solids.]

(b) Repeat (a) for the dodecahedron (Fig. 10.16).

27. [BB] Is it possible for a plane graph, considered as a map, to be its own dual?

13.3   Circuit Testing and Facilities Design

In this section, we present two interesting applications of the material in Sections 13.1 and 13.2. The first shows how knowledge of graph colorings can be used to assist in testing printed circuit boards for the existence of possible short circuits. In the second, we apply what we have learned about graph colorings, planarity, and Hamiltonian cycles to the design of floor plans for facilities such as hospitals or shopping malls to meet, so far as possible, various requirements of juxtaposition.

Circuit Testing

A printed circuit board can be represented by a finite rectangular grid composed of evenly spaced rows of evenly spaced grid points called *nodes*, which are connected by horizontal and vertical line segments called *grid segments*. On this board, certain vertices are connected via disjoint paths (called *nets*) along grid segments. For example, Fig. 13.18 shows a grid with 49 nodes and seven nets labeled $N_1, N_2, \ldots, N_7$.

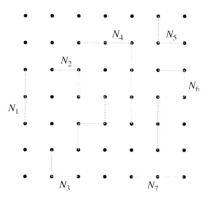

Figure 13.18 A grid of 49 nodes and 7 nets, comprising altogether 24 grid segments.

In general, the grid segments in a particular net pattern correspond to conductor paths in the circuit board. The problem of interest is to determine whether any extra conductor paths (short circuits) between nets have been introduced into the board during the manufacturing process. A short circuit need not begin or end at a node.

One definite way to determine whether or not there are short circuits is to take each pair of distinct nets, in turn, and to apply an electrical signal to one member of the pair. If this signal appears in the other net, then there must be a short. This procedure can be extremely time consuming; for instance, in Fig. 13.18, $\binom{7}{2} = 21$ comparisons would be required. Many of these comparisons may be unnecessary, however. As an example, the left-hand grid in Fig. 13.19 shows two nets, A and C, that cannot possibly have a short between them unless there is also a short between each of them and B. Hence, it suffices to test B against each of A and C.

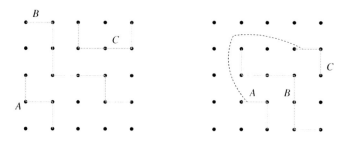

Figure 13.19

In the right-hand grid of Fig. 13.19, it is theoretically possible to have a short between A and C that does not touch B, as shown by the dotted line, but this seems unlikely. We shall assume henceforth that any short circuit between nets must be a single straight horizontal or vertical line (of arbitrary length) not touching any other net (but not necessarily through nodes).

An efficient way of testing either grid in Fig. 13.19 would be to combine nets A and C into a single set that could be tested against B. In general, a good procedure is to partition the set of nets into subsets such that, if two nets N_i, N_j are in the same subset, then N_i and N_j cannot have a short between them. Then we need only test these subsets against each other to determine whether a short circuit exists. For example, in Fig. 13.18, the subsets could be $\{N_1, N_3, N_6\}$, $\{N_2, N_5, N_7\}$, and $\{N_4\}$, and three tests would suffice (instead of 21). Note that N_1 and N_3 cannot have a short between them, nor can N_3 and N_6, nor N_1 and N_6. The other subsets are obtained by similar reasoning.

Find another partition of the net pattern in Fig. 13.18 into three appropriate subsets.

∎

PAUSE 8 illustrates an important point: The sorts of partitions we have been discussing are not necessarily unique. From an efficiency point of view, however, we do not care about this. What matters is that we find a partition into as few subsets as possible. Here is where graph theory helps.

Given a grid with a net pattern, we construct the graph that has a vertex corresponding to each net and where two vertices are joined by an edge if and only if there could be a short circuit between the corresponding nets. Figure 13.20 shows the graph corresponding to Fig. 13.18. Note that N_1 is joined to N_2, but to no other vertex because the only possible short involving N_1 must be between N_1 and N_2. Other edges are obtained by similar reasoning. Any graph that can be obtained by the procedure described will be called a *line-of-sight graph*.

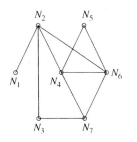

Figure 13.20

How would the line-of-sight graph change if net N_2 were not present in the net shown in Fig. 13.18? Draw the revised graph.

∎

Since two vertices in a line-of-sight graph are joined by an edge if and only if the corresponding nets could have a short between them, it is easy to see that any coloring of such a graph yields subsets of the type desired for the corresponding nets. For example, a 3-coloring of the graph in Fig. 13.20 could be obtained by coloring N_1, N_3, and N_6 blue; N_2, N_5, and N_7 red; and N_4 white. Placing like-colored nets in the same subset gives the partition described earlier.

Another possibility would be to color N_1 and N_6 blue; N_3 and N_4 red; and N_2, N_5, and N_7 white. This yields another suitable partition. Since the graph in Fig. 13.20 contains a triangle, we know that at least three colors are required and, hence, we cannot reduce further the number of partitions. In general, the minimum number of subsets obtainable in a suitable partition of nets is the chromatic number of the associated line-of-sight graph.

Find the chromatic number of the graph you obtained in PAUSE 9, and determine a corresponding partition of the nets.

∎

Is our approach to finding partitions of nets really useful? After all, chromatic numbers are notoriously hard to determine. Fortunately, only certain graphs are obtainable as line-of-sight graphs. Any planar graph is a line-of-sight graph, but $\mathcal{K}_9$, for example, is not. It is known that no matter how large the grid is or how many nets are involved, the corresponding graph $\mathcal{G}$ has $\chi(\mathcal{G}) \leq 12$. It follows that the nets can always be partitioned into at most 12 subsets and, hence, we never need to carry out more than $\binom{12}{2} = 66$ tests. Is 12 best possible? Perhaps nets can always be partitioned into at most 11 subsets, or at most 10. The answer is not known, but it is not less than 8 since there exists a line-of-sight graph $\mathcal{G}$ for which $\chi(\mathcal{G}) = 8$. (See Exercise 10.)

The preceding results, as well as many others, appear in a fundamental and very interesting paper by Garey, Johnson, and So.[10] There are still a number of intriguing open problems here, which we encourage you to investigate. For example, is it possible to characterize precisely the graphs that are line-of-sight graphs?

Facilities Design

Next, we are interested in the design and layout of physical facilities such as hospital floors. In such problems, there are a number of design areas (rooms perhaps), and it is often desirable (or critical) that certain of these areas be adjacent to each other. The planner of such a project will be presented with a list of relationships from which it must be determined whether it is possible to construct such a floor plan and, if so, how. If it is not possible, the question becomes how close can one come to meeting the requirements.

If it is possible to produce a layout satisfying all the given relationships of one area to another, then we say that the given relationships are *feasible*. If a set of relationships is not feasible, we would like to determine the smallest number of relationships whose omission produces a feasible set.

The first thing to do is to draw a graph (called the *relationship graph*) whose vertices represent design areas and in which an edge between vertices indicates that corresponding areas are to be adjacent. Thinking of a given layout of the design areas as a map whose associated graph (see Fig. 13.12) is the relationship graph, we see that a set of relationships will be feasible if and only if the relationship graph is planar.

Theoretically then, Kuratowski's Theorem (13.1.8) could be used to decide whether or not a given set of relationships is feasible. There are, however, two difficulties with this approach. First, Kuratowski's Theorem is difficult to apply, and most architects would prefer an easier algorithm. Second, and much more significant, if the relationship graph is not planar, Kuratowski's Theorem provides no indication of which relationships should be deleted to achieve planarity.

What we are looking for, therefore, is a simple test for planarity that will readily identify the edges that are causing a particular graph not to be planar. While this is too much to expect, progress has been made in the case of Hamiltonian graphs.[11] The procedure we outline determines, in a rather nice way, whether a Hamiltonian graph is planar. While it does not rigorously identify the edges that should be deleted in the case of nonplanarity, it does model the problem in such a way that it is generally not difficult to locate such edges. We demonstrate this procedure by working through a specific example.

EXAMPLE 7   Consider the relationship graph $\mathcal{G}$ shown on the left in Fig. 13.21. This graph has a Hamiltonian cycle, 1243561. We start by drawing a graph $\mathcal{G}_1$ isomorphic to $\mathcal{G}$ with the vertices of the Hamiltonian cycle in $\mathcal{G}$ appearing in order around the circumference of a circle. We then label arbitrarily those edges of $\mathcal{G}_1$ that are not on the cycle. Next, we draw a new graph $\mathcal{H}$ whose vertices correspond to the edges of $\mathcal{G}_1$ just labeled. Two vertices of $\mathcal{H}$ are joined by an edge if the corresponding edges cross inside the circle. The graph we obtain in this way is shown on the left in Fig. 13.22.

Now examine this new graph $\mathcal{H}$. We claim that the original graph $\mathcal{G}$ is planar if and only if $\chi(\mathcal{H}) \leq 2$, and here is why. If $\chi(\mathcal{H}) \leq 2$, then there is a coloring of

[10]Michael R. Garey, David Stifler Johnson, and Hing C. So, "An Application of Graph Coloring to Printed Circuit Testing," *IEEE Transactions on Circuits and Systems*, Vol. CAS-23, (1976), no. 10, 591–599.
[11]G. Demourcron, V. Malgrance, and R. Pertuiset, "Graphes Planaires: Reconnaissance et Construction de Representations Planaires Topologiques," *Recherche Operationelle*, **30** (1964), 33.

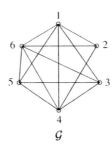
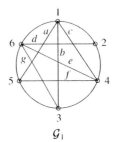

Figure 13.21

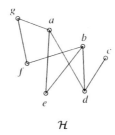
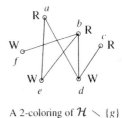

Figure 13.22

the vertices of $\mathcal{H}$ requiring at most two colors. Therefore, the interior edges of $\mathcal{G}_1$ could be colored with at most two colors in such a way that edges crossing inside the circle (if any) have different colors. By drawing all the edges of one color outside the circle and leaving alone all edges of the other color, we would then obtain a representation of $\mathcal{G}_1$ with no crossovers of edges; in other words, $\mathcal{G}$ would be drawn as a plane graph. Conversely, if $\mathcal{G}$ is planar and drawn as a plane graph, then coloring all edges inside the cycle with one color and all edges outside with another produces a coloring of the associated graph $\mathcal{H}$ that uses at most two colors.

We return to our example and note from Fig. 13.22 that $\chi(\mathcal{H}) \neq 2$ since $\mathcal{H}$ contains a 5-cycle, $adbfga$; hence, the original graph $\mathcal{G}$ is not planar. So we must now look for the smallest number of vertices that, when removed from $\mathcal{H}$, leave a graph whose chromatic number is 2. In our example, if we remove any of a, b, f, or g, we will achieve the desired result.

Suppose we remove g. We picture the resulting graph and a 2-coloring on the right in Fig. 13.22. This, in turn, provides a coloring of the interior edges of $\mathcal{G}_1 \setminus \{g\}$. In Fig. 13.23(a), we draw $\mathcal{G}_1 \setminus \{g\}$ as a plane graph with all edges of one of the two colors drawn outside the circle. To draw a layout with $\mathcal{G}_1 \setminus \{g\}$ as its relationship graph, it is helpful first to draw this plane graph with straight edges, as in Fig. 13.23(b). In Fig. 13.23(c), we show the corresponding layout. If this were, for example, the floor plan of a hospital, Fig. 13.23(c) shows a way that the rooms can be laid out so as to satisfy the aforementioned relationships. Strange-looking rooms, perhaps, but feasible!

Carry out the steps in the previous paragraph, assuming f is removed instead of g. ∎

13.3.1 CLOSING REMARKS

1. We proved in Section 13.1 that connected planar graphs with at least three vertices must satisfy $E \leq 3V - 6$ (Theorem 13.1.4). Thus, $3V - 6$ is an upper bound for the number of relationships that are theoretically possible in a facilities de-

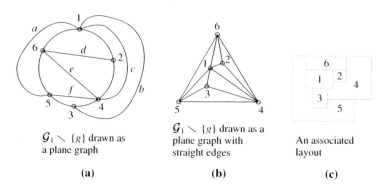

$\mathcal{G}_1 \smallsetminus \{g\}$ drawn as a plane graph

(a)

$\mathcal{G}_1 \smallsetminus \{g\}$ drawn as a plane graph with straight edges

(b)

An associated layout

(c)

Figure 13.23 A plane graph, then drawn with straight edges, and an associated layout of design areas.

sign having V rooms. Despite what the planner might want, it is impossible to do better!

2. In many practical problems, some relationships are more important than others. Certain ones, in fact, might be crucial (in a hospital, for example). The relative importance of relationships can be incorporated into the model by assigning weights to the edges of the relationship graph and then attempting to achieve planarity by removing the least important edges. Kruskal's algorithm, adapted to choose a maximal weight spanning tree (instead of a minimal one), has been applied to this case with some success.

3. The authors first read about this fascinating area in Roberts's book *Applied Combinatorics*.[12] Certainly, there is great potential here for further investigation. We refer the interested reader also to Chapter 8 of Chachra, Ghare, and Moore[13] for additional information.

Answers to Pauses

8. $\{N_1, N_6\}, \{N_2, N_5, N_7\}, \{N_3, N_4\}$.

9.

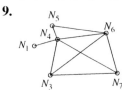

10. The chromatic number of the preceding graph is 4 since it contains $\mathcal{K}_4$ as a subgraph. One partition would be $\{N_1, N_3\}, \{N_4\}, \{N_6\}, \{N_5, N_7\}$.

11. A 2-coloring of $\mathcal{H} \setminus \{f\}$ is shown below. On the left in the graphs that follow is $\mathcal{G}_1 \setminus \{f\}$, drawn as a plane graph with all white edges drawn outside the circle. In the middle, it is redrawn with straight edges, and on the right there is a layout whose relationship graph is $\mathcal{G}_1 \setminus \{f\}$.

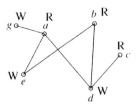

[12]Fred S. Roberts, *Applied Combinatorics*, Prentice Hall, Upper Saddle River, NJ, 1984.
[13]V. Chachra, P. M. Ghare, and J. M. Moore, *Applications of Graph Theory Algorithms*, Elsevier, North-Holland, New York, 1979.

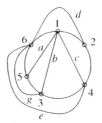
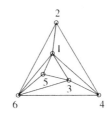
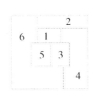

(Answers can be found in the back of the book.)

1. The grid segments on a printed circuit board are the horizontal and vertical line segments that connect nodes.

2. Nets are disjoint paths consisting of grid segments.

3. Short circuits are horizontal or vertical paths between two nets that do not meet any other net.

4. In a line-of-sight graph, the vertices represent nets and an edge is drawn between two vertices if and only if the corresponding nets could have a short circuit between them.

5. The chromatic number $\chi(\mathcal{G})$ of a line-of-sight graph is related to the minimum number of tests required to determine if short circuits exist in a printed circuit board.

6. Every graph is a line-of-sight graph.

7. In a relationship graph, vertices represent design areas and edges mean that corresponding design areas should be adjacent.

8. A set of relationships is feasible if and only if the corresponding relationship graph is planar.

9. If eight design areas are required and there are 19 desired relationships requiring areas to be adjacent, the set of relationships is not feasible.

10. In practice, architects always use Kuratowski's Theorem when planning physical layouts.

*The answers to exercises marked [BB] can be found in the **B**ack of the **B**ook.*

1. [BB] The following questions refer to the net pattern in Fig. 13.24.

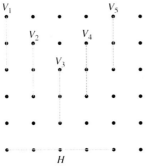

Figure 13.24

(a) Find the number of nodes, grid segments, and nets.

(b) Give an example of two nets that cannot have a vertical or horizontal short circuit between them unless there is a similar short circuit between one of them and another net.

(c) Draw the associated line-of-sight graph $\mathcal{G}$.

(d) Determine $\chi(\mathcal{G})$ and find a corresponding partition of the nets.

2. Repeat Exercise 1 if the nodes of the far right-hand column are all connected by a vertical line of grid segments, thus forming another net, V_6.

3. [BB] True or false? A line-of-sight graph is always connected.

4. (a) Draw the line of sight graph $\mathcal{G}$ associated with the given net pattern.

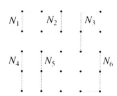

(b) Determine $\chi(\mathcal{G})$ and find a corresponding partition of nets.

(c) How many tests would need to be carried out on a printed circuit board with the given net pattern to determine if short circuits are present.

5. Let $\mathcal{N}$ be the set of nets in a given net pattern. Define a relation $\sim$ on $\mathcal{N}$ by $A \sim B$ if there could be a short circuit between A and B. Determine whether or not $\sim$ is

(a) [BB] reflexive,   (b) symmetric,

(c) antisymmetric,   (d) transitive.

6. Refer to the net pattern shown in Fig. 13.25.

(a) [BB] Draw the associated line-of-sight graph $\mathcal{G}$.

(b) Determine $\chi(\mathcal{G})$ and find a corresponding partition of the nets.

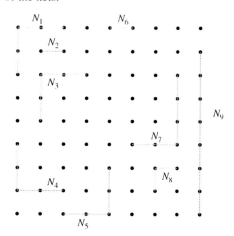

Figure 13.25

7. Repeat Exercise 6 if net N_3 is removed.

8. [BB] True or false? A line-of-sight graph is always planar.

9. (a) [BB] Assume that the only short circuits in a printed circuit board are **horizontal** straight lines; that is, vertical shorts are not possible. Prove that the associated line-of-sight graph $\mathcal{G}$ is then planar and conclude that $\chi(\mathcal{G}) \leq 4$.

(b) [BB] Let $\mathcal{V}$ and $\mathcal{E}$ be the vertices and edges, respectively, of a general line-of-sight graph $\mathcal{G}$. Show that $\mathcal{E}$ can be partitioned into subsets $\mathcal{E}_1, \mathcal{E}_2$ such that the graphs $\mathcal{G}(\mathcal{V}, \mathcal{E}_1), \mathcal{G}(\mathcal{V}, \mathcal{E}_2)$ are both planar.

(c) Using (a) and (b), show that $\chi(\mathcal{G}) \leq 16$ for any line-of-sight graph $\mathcal{G}$.

(d) Using (b), show that $\mathcal{K}_{11}$ is not a line-of-sight graph.

10. [BB] The net pattern shown has a line-of-sight graph $\mathcal{G}$ with $\chi(\mathcal{G}) = 8$. Why? (This example is due to M. R. Garey, D. S. Johnson, and H. C. So, cited in footnote 10.)

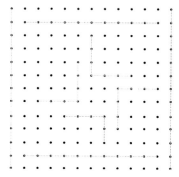

11. Find a best possible feasible relationship graph and draw the corresponding floor plan for $\mathcal{K}_5$ [BB], $\mathcal{K}_{3,3}$, and $\mathcal{K}_6$, each of these considered as a relationship graph.

12. For each of the following relationship graphs, find a best possible feasible relationship graph and draw the corresponding floor plan.

(a)

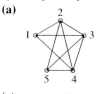

(b)

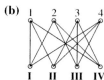

(c)

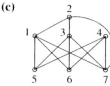

13. A contractor is building a single-story house for a newly married couple. The house is to consist of a living room, dining room, family room, kitchen, two bedrooms, bathroom, and hall. The couple insists that all rooms border on the hall. The kitchen is to share a wall with the dining room, family room, and bathroom. Both bedrooms should share a wall with the bathroom and the family room. The living room is to border the family room and the dining room. Is it possible for the contractor to meet the couple's demands? If not, how close could the contractor come to meeting all requirements? Justify your answer.

14. Jack is commissioned to build a nine-hole golf course that meets the following specifications.

- The first hole must return to the clubhouse and hence have a common border with the ninth hole.
- To satisfy thirsty patrons, the fifth hole also returns to the clubhouse; it must have a common border with the first hole, but not necessarily with the ninth.
- All even-numbered holes share a common water hazard and have some common border with each other.

- Each hole (after the first) has a common border with the one preceding it.

(a) [BB] Show that it is impossible for Jack to build a golf course meeting all these requirements.

(b) State three different ways in which Jack could sat-

isfy all but one of the requirements.

15. [BB] Apply Kuratowski's Theorem (Theorem 13.1.8), to the graph G in Fig. 13.21 to show that G is not planar.

16. [BB] Apply Brooks's Theorem (p. 422) to find the chromatic number of the graph H in Fig. 13.22.

Key Terms & Ideas

Here are some technical words and phrases that were used in this chapter. Do you know the meaning of each? If you're not sure, check the glossary or index at the back of the book.

chromatic number

coloring

homeomorphic

minimum connector problem

minimum spanning tree

n-coloring

orient

planar

root

rooted tree

spanning tree

strongly connected orientation

tree

Review Exercises for Chapter 13

1. **(a)** Show that the graph below is planar by drawing an isomorphic plane graph with straight edges.

(b) Label the regions defined by your plane graph and list the edges that form the boundary of each region.

(c) Verify that $V - E + R = 2$, $N \leq 2E$ and $E \leq 3V - 6$. (Recall that N is the sum of the numbers of edges on the boundaries of all regions.)

2. Determine whether each of the graphs is planar. In each case, either draw a plane graph with straight edges isomorphic to the one presented or exhibit a subgraph homeomorphic to $K_{3,3}$ or K_5.

(a) **(b)**

(c) **(d)**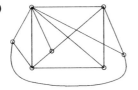

(e)

3. **(a)** Is the graph planar?

(b) What is the chromatic number of the graph? Explain your answers.

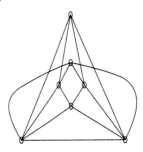

4. A *near-tree* is a connected graph that contains exactly one circuit.

(a) Explain why a near-tree must be planar.

(b) Find a relationship between the number of edges and the number of vertices in a near-tree. Justify your answer.

(c) Show that if a near-tree has a vertex of degree 3 then it also has a vertex of degree 1.

5. If G is a connected plane graph with $V \geq 3$ vertices and R regions, each with at least five edges on its boundary, prove that $3R \leq 2V - 4$. (You may use the result of Exercise 6 of Section 13.1, but first be sure you can prove it!)

6. (a) A connected planar graph G has 30 vertices. Prove that G has at most 84 edges.

   (b) A connected planar graph G has 30 vertices, 15 of which have degree 1. Prove that G has at most 54 edges.

7. Show that $K_{2,3}$ is homeomorphic to a subgraph of K_4.

8. True or false? If G is a tree and $\mathcal{H}$ is homeomorphic to G, then $\mathcal{H}$ is a tree. Explain your answer.

9. Compute $\chi(G)$, where G is the graph in Exercise 1. Explain your answer and exhibit a $\chi(G)$-coloring.

10. Compute $\chi(G)$ for the graphs of Exercise 2. Do your results say anything about the converse of the Four-Color Theorem?

11. Answer true or false and explain your answers.

    (a) A planar graph with chromatic number 3 must be Hamiltonian.

    (b) If G is a planar graph that contains K_4 as a subgraph, then $\chi(G) = 4$.

12. Let G be a connected graph with at least two vertices. Prove that $\chi(G) = 2$ if and only if G is bipartite with at least one edge.

13. (a) Give an example showing that the following theorem, which resembles Theorem 13.2.3, is false:

    Let $\Sigma(G)$ be the minimum of the degrees of the vertices of a graph G. Then $\chi(G) \geq 1 + \Sigma(G)$.

    (b) Is the "theorem" stated in 13(a) true if we restrict our attention to trees with at least two vertices?

14. Suppose that in one particular semester there are students taking the following combinations of courses:
    - Math, English, French;
    - Math, English, Chemistry;
    - Biology, French, Math;
    - Biology, Physics, Math;
    - Chemistry, Physics, Math.

    What is the minimum number of examination periods required for examinations in the specified courses so that students involved have no conflicts? Justify your answer.

15. A town jail contains four holding cells. On a particularly busy night, 12 people are arrested. Certain prisoners do not get along with certain others and must be put into separate cells, as shown in the following tables. If possible, find a way of putting the prisoners into the four cells in such a way as to avoid possible conflicts during the night.

Prisoner	Doesn't get along with
1	3, 5, 8, 9, 10, 11
2	3, 4, 6, 7, 9, 11
3	1, 2, 6, 8, 11, 12
4	2, 5, 6, 8, 10, 12
5	1, 4, 7, 9, 10
6	2, 3, 4, 7, 9, 11, 12
7	2, 5, 6, 8, 10
8	1, 3, 4, 7, 12
9	1, 2, 5, 6, 11
10	1, 4, 5, 7, 12
11	1, 2, 3, 6, 9
12	3, 4, 6, 8, 10

16. Draw the line-of-sight graph associated with the net pattern shown on the left in Fig. 13.26. Determine $\chi(G)$ and find a corresponding partition of the nets.

17. Repeat Exercise 16 for the net pattern shown on the right of Fig. 13.26.

18. Give an example of a net pattern whose line-of-sight graph is Eulerian, but not Hamiltonian.

19. Show that the complete bipartite graph $K_{7,7}$ is **not** a line-of-sight graph. [*Hint*: Use Exercise 9(b) of Section 13.3 and Exercise 9(a) of Section 13.1.]

20. Find a best possible feasible relationship graph and draw the corresponding floor plan for each of the graphs in Exercise 2.

21. A hospital board calls for the construction of a clinic consisting of seven rooms with a floor plan that corresponds to the graph shown.

    (a) Explain why the graph is not planar.

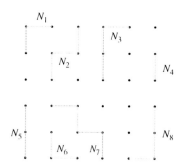 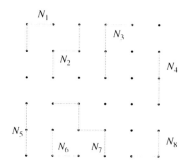

Figure 13.26 Net patterns for Exercises 16 and 17.

(b) Find a Hamiltonian cycle and use it to determine the extent to which the original plans can be met.

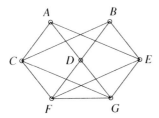

(c) Sketch a floor plan for the clinic that meets as many of the specifications as possible.

22. A contractor is building a single-story house for a newly married couple. The house is to consist of a living room, dining room, family room, kitchen, two bedrooms, bathroom and hall. The couple insists that all rooms border on the hall. The kitchen is to share a wall with the dining room, family room, and bathroom. Both bedrooms should share a wall with the bathroom and the family room. The living room is to border the family room and on the dining room. Is it possible for the contractor to meet the couple's demands? If not, how close could he come to meeting all requirements? Justify your answer, including a "best" floor plan.

23. The Central Newfoundland Hospital Board would like to build a medical complex with the relationship graph shown.

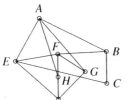

To determine the feasibility of the project, the contractor hires a student who recently completed a course in graph theory. The student writes a report that
- states Kuratowski's Theorem and uses it to prove that the above graph is not planar;
- finds two different Hamiltonian cycles in the graph; and
- uses each cycle to determine a different best possible approximation to the original demands.

Write such a report yourself and illustrate with diagrams.

24. A school board calls for the construction of a facility consisting of eight rooms with the relationship graph shown.

(a) State Kuratowski's Theorem and use it to prove that this graph is not planar.

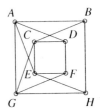

(b) Find a Hamiltonian cycle in the graph and use it to determine the extent to which the original plans can be met.

(c) Sketch a plane graph that is a best possible approximation to the plans. Label the vertices and specify the edge or edges that have not been preserved.

1. True   **2.** True   **3.** False   **4.** False   **5.** False (the $n = n_0$ case).

6. True   **7.** False   **8.** False   **9.** True   **10.** False

1. (a) $\sum_{i=1}^{5} i^2 = 1^2 + 2^2 + 3^2 + 4^2 + 5^2 = 55$ (b) $\sum_{i=1}^{4} 2^i = 2^1 + 2^2 + 2^3 + 2^4 = 30$

(c) $\sum_{t=1}^{1} \sin \pi t = \sin \pi(1) = \sin \pi = 0$

2. (a) The values of $\sum_{i=1}^{n} (-1)^i$ for $n = 0, 1, 2, 3$ are $1, 1 - 1 = 0, 1 - 1 + 1 = 1$, and $1 - 1 + 1 - 1 = 0$.
The answer is $0, 1$.

4. (a) If $n = 1$, $n^3 + 2n = 1^3 + 2 \cdot 1 = 3$, which is divisible by 3. Suppose $k \geq 1$ and the result is true for $n = k$; that is, $3 \mid (k^3 + 2k)$. We wish to prove that $3 \mid [(k + 1)^3 + 2(k + 1)]$. But $(k + 1)^3 + 2(k + 1) = k^3 + 3k^2 + 3k + 1 + 2k + 2 = (k^3 + 2k) + (3k^2 + 3k + 3)$. Since $3 \mid (k^3 + 2k)$ (by the induction hypothesis) and since $3 \mid (3k^2 + 3k + 3)$, we have the desired result. We conclude that $3 \mid (n^3 + 2n)$ for all $n \geq 1$, by the Principle of Mathematical Induction.

(c) If $n = 1$, $5^n - 1 = 5 - 1 = 4$ is divisible by 4. Suppose the result is true for $n = k \geq 1$; that is, $4 \mid (5^k - 1)$. Then $5^{k+1} - 1 = 5^k(5) - 1 = 5^k(4 + 1) - 1 = 5^k(4) + 5^k - 1$. Since $4 \mid (5^k - 1)$ and $4 \mid 5^k(4)$, we have $4 \mid (5^{k+1} - 1)$ as desired. By the Principle of Mathematical Induction, the result holds for all $n \geq 1$.

(f) If $n = 1$, $10^{n+1} + 10^n + 1 = 100 + 10 + 1 = 111$ is divisible by 3, because $111 = 3(37)$. Now suppose that $k \geq 1$ and the result is true for $n = k$; that is, suppose that $3 \mid (10^{k+1} + 10^k + 1)$. Then

$$10^{k+2} + 10^{k+1} + 1 = 10(10^{k+1} + 10^k) + 1$$
$$= 10(10^{k+1} + 10^k + 1 - 1) + 1$$
$$= 10(10^{k+1} + 10^k + 1) - 10 + 1$$
$$= 10(10^{k+1} + 10^k + 1) - 9.$$

Since the first term here is divisible by 3, by the induction hypothesis, and, since 9 is divisible by 3, $10^{k+2} + 10^{k+1} + 1$ is divisible by 3, as desired. By the Principle of Mathematical Induction, $10^{n+1} + 10^n + 1$ is divisible by 3 for all $n \geq 1$.

(j) For $n = 1$, $2! = 2$ is divisible by 2^1, so the result is true. Now assume that $k \geq 1$ and that $(2k)!$ is divisible by 2^k. We have $[2(k + 1)]! = (2k + 2)! = (2k + 2)(2k + 1)(2k)!$. Since $(2k)!$ is divisible by 2^k and $2k + 2$ is divisible by 2, $[2(k + 1)]!$ is divisible by 2^{k+1}, the desired result with $n = k + 1$. By the Principle of Mathematical Induction, we conclude that $(2n)!$ is divisible by 2^n for all $n \geq 1$.

5. (a) For $n = 1$, $1 + 2 + 3 \cdots + n$ is 1, by definition, and $\frac{n(n+1)}{2} = \frac{2}{2} = 1$ also. Thus, the result is true for $n = 1$. Now suppose that $k \geq 1$ and the result is true for k; that is, assume that $1 + 2 + 3 + \cdots + k = \frac{k(k+1)}{2}$. Then

$$1 + 2 + \cdots + (k + 1) = (1 + 2 + \cdots + k) + (k + 1)$$
$$= \frac{k(k + 1)}{2} + (k + 1) \quad \text{(by the induction hypothesis)}$$
$$= \frac{k(k + 1) + 2(k + 1)}{2} = \frac{(k + 1)(k + 2)}{2},$$

which is the given statement with $n = k + 1$. So, by the Principle of Mathematical Induction, we conclude that $1 + 2 + \cdots + n = \frac{1}{2}n(n + 1)$ for all $n \geq 1$.

6. (a) If $n = 1$, $1 + 2^1 + 2^2 + 2^3 + \cdots + 2^n = 1 + 2 = 3$, while $2^{1+1} - 1 = 4 - 1 = 3$, so the result is true if $n = 1$. Suppose the result is true for $n = k \geq 1$; that is, suppose $1 + 2 + 2^2 + 2^3 + \cdots + 2^k = 2^{k+1} - 1$. We wish to prove the result for $n = k + 1$; that is, we wish to prove that $1 + 2 + 2^2 + 2^3 + \cdots + 2^{k+1} = 2^{(k+1)+1} - 1$. Now $1 + 2 + 2^2 + 2^3 + \cdots + 2^{k+1} = (1 + 2 + 2^2 + 2^3 + \cdots + 2^k) + 2^{k+1} = (2^{k+1} - 1) + 2^{k+1}$ (by the induction hypothesis) $= 2 \cdot 2^{k+1} - 1 = 2^{k+2} - 1 = 2^{(k+1)+1} - 1$ as required. By the Principle of Mathematical Induction, we conclude that the given assertion is true for all $n \geq 1$.

(b) If $n = 1$, $1^2 - 2^2 + 3^2 - 4^2 + \cdots + (-1)^{n-1}n^2 = 1^2 = 1$, by definition, while $(-1)^{n-1}\frac{n(n+1)}{2} = (-1)^{1-1}\frac{1(1+1)}{2} = 1$, and so the result is true for $n = 1$. Now suppose that $k \geq 1$ and the result is true for $n = k$; that is, suppose that

$$1^2 - 2^2 + 3^2 - 4^2 + \cdots + (-1)^{k-1}k^2 = (-1)^{k-1}\frac{k(k + 1)}{2}.$$

We wish to prove that

$$1^2 - 2^2 + 3^2 - 4^2 + \cdots + (-1)^{(k+1)-1}(k + 1)^2 = (-1)^{(k+1)-1}\frac{(k + 1)[(k + 1) + 1]}{2}.$$

Now

$$1^2 - 2^2 + 3^2 - 4^2 + \cdots + (-1)^{(k+1)-1}(k+1)^2$$

$$= [1^2 - 2^2 + 3^2 - 4^2 + \cdots + (-1)^{k-1}k^2] + (-1)^{(k+1)-1}(k+1)^2$$

$$= (-1)^{k-1}\frac{k(k+1)}{2} + (-1)^k(k+1)^2 \qquad \text{(using the induction hypothesis)}$$

$$= (-1)^{k-1}\frac{k^2+k}{2} + (-1)^{k-1}(-1)(k^2+2k+1)$$

$$= (-1)^{k-1}\left(\frac{k^2+k}{2} - k^2 - 2k - 1\right)$$

$$= (-1)^{k-1}\frac{k^2+k-2k^2-4k-2}{2}$$

$$= (-1)^{k-1}\left(\frac{-k^2-3k-2}{2}\right) = (-1)^k\frac{(k+1)(k+2)}{2},$$

as desired. By the Principle of Mathematical Induction, the result is true for all $n \geq 1$.

(f) For $n = 1$, the left side is $\frac{2}{3} = 1 - \frac{1}{3^1}$, so the formula is correct. Now assume $k \geq 1$ and that the formula holds for $n = k$; that is, assume that

$$\frac{2}{3} + \frac{2}{9} + \frac{2}{27} + \cdots + \frac{2}{3^k} = 1 - \frac{1}{3^k}.$$

With $n = k + 1$, the left side of the sum in question is

$$\frac{2}{3} + \frac{2}{9} + \frac{2}{27} + \cdots + \frac{2}{3^{k+1}} = \left(1 - \frac{1}{3^k}\right) + \frac{2}{3^{k+1}}$$

$$= \frac{3^{k+1} - 3 + 2}{3^{k+1}} = \frac{3^{k+1} - 1}{3^{k+1}} = 1 - \frac{1}{3^{k+1}},$$

which is the desired formula. By the Principle of Mathematical Induction, the formula holds for all $n \geq 1$.

(g) When $n = 1$, the left side is $6 - 2 = 4$ and the right side is $1(4)$, so the formula holds. Now assume that $k \geq 1$ and that $4 + 10 + 16 + \cdots + (6k - 2) = k(3k + 1)$. We have

$$4 + 10 + 16 + \cdots + [6(k+1) - 2]$$

$$= 4 + 10 + 16 + \cdots + (6k + 4)$$

$$= \big(4 + 10 + 16 + \cdots + (6k - 2)\big) + (6k + 4)$$

$$= k(3k + 1) + (6k + 4) \qquad \text{using the induction hypothesis}$$

$$= 3k^2 + 7k + 4 = (k + 1)(3k + 4)$$

which is the given formula with $n = k + 1$. By the Principle of Mathematical Induction, we conclude that $4 + 10 + 16 + \cdots + (6n - 2) = n(3n + 1)$ for all $n \geq 1$.

7. (a) $\displaystyle\sum_{k=0}^{n} 2^k$

8. (a) For $n = 1$, $\displaystyle\sum_{i=1}^{1}(i + 1)2^i = 2(2^1) = 4$, while $n2^{n+1} = 1(2^2) = 4$. Thus, the formula is correct for $n = 1$. Now suppose that $k \geq 1$ and the formula is correct for $n = k$; thus, we suppose that $\displaystyle\sum_{i=1}^{k}(i + 1)2^i = k2^{k+1}$. We must prove that the formula is correct for $n = k + 1$; that is, we must prove that $\sum_{i=1}^{k+1}(i + 1)2^i = (k + 1)2^{k+2}$. Now

$$\sum_{i=1}^{k+1}(i+1)2^i = \sum_{i=1}^{k}(i+1)2^i + (k+2)2^{k+1}$$

$$= k2^{k+1} + (k+2)2^{k+1} \quad \text{(using the induction hypothesis)}$$

$$= (k + k + 2)2^{k+1} = (2k + 2)2^{k+1} = 2(k + 1)2^{k+1} = (k + 1)2^{k+2},$$

as required. By the Principle of Mathematical Induction, the given assertion is true for all $n \geq 1$.

9. (a) If $n = 5$, $2^5 = 32$, $5^2 = 25$. Since $32 > 25$, the result is true for $n = 5$. Now suppose that $k \geq 5$ and the result is true for $n = k$; that is, suppose that $2^k > k^2$. We must prove that the result is true for $n = k + 1$; that is, we must prove that $2^{k+1} > (k + 1)^2$. Now $2^{k+1} = 2 \cdot 2^k > 2k^2$ by the induction hypothesis, and $2k^2 = k^2 + k^2 \geq k^2 + 5k$ (since $k \geq 5$), and $k^2 + 5k = k^2 + 4k + k > k^2 + 2k + 1$ (since $k \geq 1$), and $k^2 + 2k + 1 = (k + 1)^2$. By the Principle of Mathematical Induction, the result is true for all $n \geq 5$.

(c) Since $6! = 720 > 216 = 6^3$, the inequality holds for $n = 6$. Now assume that $k \geq 6$ and that $k! > k^3$. We have

$$(k + 1)! = (k + 1)k!$$
$$> (k + 1)k^3 \qquad\qquad \text{using the induction hypothesis}$$
$$= k^4 + k^3$$
$$\geq 6k^3 + k^3 \qquad\qquad \text{since } k \geq 6$$
$$= k^3 + 3k^3 + 3k^3$$
$$\geq k^3 + 3k^2 + 3(36)k \qquad \text{since } k^2 \geq 36$$
$$\geq k^3 + 3k^2 + 3k + 1 = (k + 1)^3,$$

which is the desired inequality with $n = k + 1$. By the Principle of Mathematical Induction, we conclude that $n! > n^3$ for all $n \geq 6$.

(i) With $n = 2$, $2(2) - 1 = 3 \geq 2(2) - 2 = 2$, so the inequality holds. Now assume $k \geq 2$ and that $1(3)(5) \cdots (2k - 1) \geq 2(4)(6) \cdots (2k - 2)$. We have

$$1(3)(5) \cdots [2(k + 1) - 1] = 1(3)(5) \cdots (2k + 1)$$
$$= \big(1(3)(5) \cdots (2k - 1)\big)(2k + 1)$$
$$\geq \big(2(4)(6) \cdots (2k - 2)\big)(2k + 1),$$
$$\text{using the induction hypothesis,}$$
$$\geq 2(4)(6) \cdots (2k - 2)(2k),$$

which is the desired inequality with $n = k + 1$, since $2k = 2(k + 1) - 2$. By the Principle of Mathematical Induction, $1(3)(5) \cdots (2n - 1) \geq 2(4)(6) \cdots (2n - 2)$ for every integer $n \geq 2$.

10. (a) For $n = 1$, $\sum_{i=1}^{1}(x_i + y_i)$ is, by convention, just the single term $x_1 + y_1$. Since this equals $\sum_{i=1}^{1}x_1 + \sum_{i=1}^{1}y_1$ the formula holds for $n = 1$. Now suppose $k \geq 1$ and the formula holds for $n = k$. Then

$$\sum_{i=1}^{k+1}(x_i + y_i) = \left[\sum_{i=1}^{k}(x_i + y_i)\right] + (x_{k+1} + y_{k+1})$$

$$= \sum_{i=1}^{k}x_i + \sum_{i=1}^{k}y_i + (x_{k+1} + y_{k+1}) \quad \text{(by the induction hypothesis)}$$

$$= \left[\left(\sum_{i=1}^{k}x_i\right) + x_{k+1}\right] + \left[\left(\sum_{i=1}^{k}y_i\right) + y_{k+1}\right] = \sum_{i=1}^{k+1}x_i + \sum_{i=1}^{k+1}y_i,$$

which is the formula with $n = k + 1$. Thus, the result holds for all $n \geq 1$ by the Principle of Mathematical Induction.

11. The k to $k+1$ step does not apply to the case $k = 1$. When $k = 1$, $G = \{a_1, a_2\}$. Observe that the groups $\{a_1\}, \{a_2\}$ have no member in common.

12. The induction was not started properly. When $n = 1$, the left side is 1, while the right side is 9/8. The statement is not true when $n = 1$.

15. If a set A contains $n = 0$ elements, then $A = \emptyset$ and A has exactly 1 subset, $\emptyset$. Since $1 = 2^0$, the statement is true for $n = 0$. Now assume that a set of k elements has 2^k subsets. Let $A = \{a_1, a_2, \dots, a_{k+1}\}$ be a set of $k + 1$ elements. We show that A must have 2^{k+1} subsets. This follows because every subset of A either contains a_{k+1} or it doesn't. By the induction hypothesis, there are 2^k sets that do not contain a_{k+1}; but, by the induction hypothesis, there are also 2^k subsets that **do** contain a_{k+1}, since these are precisely those sets obtained by forming the union of a subset of $\{a_1, a_2, \dots, a_k\}$ and $\{a_{k+1}\}$. Altogether A has $2^k + 2^k = 2(2^k) = 2^{k+1}$ subsets. So, by the Principle of Mathematical Induction, we conclude that a set of n elements contains 2^n subsets.

16. Let S be a nonempty set of natural numbers. Let a be any element of S. Then the smallest element of S is the smallest element of the nonempty set $\{x \in S \mid 1 \le x \le a\}$ (which is finite).

18. For $n = 1$, $\bigcap_{i=1}^{n} B_i = B_1$, and so $A \cup \left(\bigcap_{i=1}^{n} B_i\right) = A \cup B_1 = \bigcap_{i=1}^{n}\left(A \cup B_i\right)$ and the result holds for $n = 1$. Now assume that $A \cup \left(\bigcap_{i=1}^{k} B_i\right) = \bigcap_{i=1}^{k}\left(A \cup B_i\right)$ for $k \ge 1$. Then, given a set A and $k + 1$ sets $B_1, B_2, \dots, B_{k+1}$, we have

$$
\begin{aligned}
A \cup \left(\bigcap_{i=1}^{k+1} B_i\right) &= A \cup \left[\left(\bigcap_{i=1}^{k} B_i\right) \cap B_{k+1} \right] \\
&= \left[A \cup \left(\bigcap_{i=1}^{k} B_i\right) \right] \cap \left(A \cup B_{k+1} \right) \quad \text{since } A \cup (B \cap C) = (A \cup B) \cap (A \cup C) \\
&= \left[\bigcap_{i=1}^{k}(A \cup B_i) \right] \cap (A \cup B_{k+1}) \quad \text{(by the induction hypothesis)} \\
&= \bigcap_{i=1}^{k+1}\left(A \cup B_i \right),
\end{aligned}
$$

giving the result for $k+1$. By the Principle of Mathematical Induction, we conclude that $A \cup \left(\bigcap_{i=1}^{n} B_i\right) = \bigcap_{i=1}^{n}\left(A \cup B_i \right)$, for all $n \ge 1$.

22. When $n = 2$, $\gcd(a_1, a_2) = s_1 a_1 + s_2 a_2$ by Theorem 4.2.9. Now suppose that $k \ge 2$ and the statement is true for $n = k$; that is, suppose that the gcd of any $k \ge 2$ integers is an integral linear combination of them. We have to show the statement is true for $n = k + 1$; that is, the gcd of $k + 1$ integers is an integral linear combination of them. Now $\gcd(a_1, a_2, \dots, a_{k+1}) = \gcd(a_1, \gcd(a_2, \dots, a_{k+1}))$. By the induction hypothesis, there are k integers $r_2, r_3, \dots, r_{k+1}$ such that $\gcd(a_2, \dots, a_{k+1}) = \sum_{i=2}^{k+1} r_i a_i$. Then Theorem 4.2.9 tells us that

$$
\gcd\left(a_1, \sum_{2}^{k+1} r_i a_i\right) = x a_1 + y\left(\sum r_i a_i\right) = x a_1 + (y r_2)a_2 + \cdots (y r_{k+1})a_{k+1},
$$

as desired ($s_1 = x$, $s_2 = y r_2$, $\dots$, $s_{k+1} = y r_{k+1}$). By the Principle of Mathematical Induction, the statement is true for all $n \ge 1$.

26. (a) i. $0 \in n\mathbf{Z}$ because $0 = 0(n)$ is a multiple of n.
    ii. If $a \in n\mathbf{Z}$, then $a = kn$ for some k, so $-a = (-k)n \in n\mathbf{Z}$ because it is also a multiple of n.
    iii. If $a, b \in n\mathbf{Z}$, then $a = k_1 n$ and $b = k_2 n$ for some integers k_1, k_2, so $a + b = (k_1 + k_2)n \in n\mathbf{Z}$ because it is also a multiple of n.

    (b) i. $0 \in A$ by definition of ideal, so if A contains just one element, the element must be 0, in which case $A = 0\mathbf{Z}$ is of the form $n\mathbf{Z}$.
    ii. If A contains more than element, it contains a nonzero element a. By definition of ideal, A contains both a and $-a$, one of which is positive.
    iii. The set of positive integers in A is not empty (by ii) and hence contains a smallest element by the Well-Ordering Principle (4.1.2).
    iv. First, $1n = n \in A$. Then, if $kn \in A$ for some $k > 0$, so also is $(k + 1)n \in A$, by definition, because $(k+1)n = kn+n$. By the Principle of Mathematical Induction, we conclude that $kn \in A$ for all $k > 0$. Since $(-k)n = -kn$ is the negative of kn, all negative multiples of n are in A. Finally, $0n = 0 \in A$, by definition of ideal. Thus, $kn \in A$ for any $k \in \mathbf{Z}$; that is, $n\mathbf{Z} \subseteq A$.
    v. Let $a \in A$ and write $a = kn + r$, $0 \le r < n$. Then $(-k)n \in A$ by iii, so $r = a + (-kn) \in A$, by definition of ideal. Since r is smaller than the smallest positive integer in A, it cannot be that $r > 0$. So $r = 0$ and $a = kn \in n\mathbf{Z}$. Therefore, $A \subseteq n\mathbf{Z}$, as desired.

27. When $n = 2$, we have two distinct points in the plane joined by exactly one line. Since $\frac{2(2-1)}{2} = 1$, the result holds in this case. Now suppose the result is true for $n = k \geq 2$; that is, suppose that the number of lines obtained by joining k distinct points in the plane, no three of which are collinear, is $\frac{1}{2}k(k-1)$. We must prove the result for $n = k + 1$; that is, we must prove that the number of lines obtained by joining $k + 1$ distinct points, no three of which are collinear, is $\frac{1}{2}(k+1)[(k+1) - 1] = \frac{1}{2}k(k+1)$. Let P be one of the $k + 1$ points. By the induction hypothesis, the remaining k points are joined by $\frac{1}{2}k(k-1)$ lines. On the other hand, P can be joined to each of the remaining k points, giving k additional lines. (Since no three of the $k + 1$ points are collinear, these additional lines are different from the lines determined by the other k points.) The total number of lines is

$$\frac{k(k-1)}{2} + k = \frac{k(k-1) + 2k}{2} = \frac{k^2 - k + 2k}{2} = \frac{k^2 + k}{2} = \frac{k(k+1)}{2}.$$

as desired. We conclude that the given assertion is true for all $n \geq 2$, by the Principle of Mathematical Induction.

30. (a) First set aside two coins; then separate the remaining six into two piles of three and compare weights. If the weights are equal, the only possible light coin is one of the two set aside, and this can be found in a second weighing. If one set of three is lighter than the other, then there is indeed a light coin and it is one of a known three. Remove one of these three and compare the weights of the remaining two coins (with a second weighing). Either one of these coins will be found to be lighter or the one set aside is the light one.

31. (a) False. If $n = 3$, $5^n + n + 1 = 129$ and $7 \nmid 129$.

35. $\displaystyle\lim_{x \to \pm 1} \frac{1 - x^{2^{r+1}}}{1 - x^2} = \lim_{x \to \pm 1} \prod_{r=1}^{n}(1 + x^{2^r})$ (using the result of Exercise 34)

$$= \prod_{r=1}^{n}(1 + (\pm 1)^{2^r}) = 2^n.$$

Section 5.2 True/False

1. True   **2.** False   **3.** True   **4.** False   **5.** True   **6.** False: You need $r \neq 1$.
7. True   **8.** False   **9.** True   **10.** True

Exercises 5.2

1. (a) $a_1 = 1$; $a_{k+1} = 5a_k$ for $k \geq 1$.   **2.** (a) $16, 8, 4, 2, 1, 1, 1$

4. When $n = 1$, the formula becomes $\frac{(1-1)(1+2)(1^2+1+2)}{4} = 0$, which is a_1. Now assume that the formula is correct when $n = k$. When $n = k + 1$,

$$a_{k+1} = (k + 1)^3 + a_k = (k + 1)^3 + \frac{(k - 1)(k + 2)(k^2 + k + 2)}{4}$$

$$= \frac{4k^3 + 12k^2 + 12k + 4 + k^4 + 2k^3 + k^2 - 4}{4}$$

$$= \frac{k^4 + 6k^3 + 13k^2 + 12k}{4}$$

$$= \frac{k(k + 3)(k^2 + 3k + 4)}{4} = \frac{k(k + 3)[(k + 1)^2 + (k + 1) + 2]}{4}.$$

as desired. By the Principle of Mathematical Induction, we conclude that the formula is correct for all $n \geq 1$.

6. The first six terms are $1, 3, 7, 15, 31, 63$. Our guess is that $a_n = 2^n - 1$. When $n = 1$, $2^1 - 1 = 1$, agreeing with a_1. Now assume that $k \geq 1$ and the result is true for $n = k$; that is, assume that $a_k = 2^k - 1$. We must prove the result is true for $n = k + 1$; that is, we must prove that $a_{k+1} = 2^{k+1} - 1$. Now $a_{k+1} = 2a_k + 1 = 2(2^k - 1) + 1$ (by the induction hypothesis) $= 2^{k+1} - 2 + 1 = 2^{k+1} - 1$, as required. By the Principle of Mathematical Induction, we conclude that the result is true for all $n \geq 1$.

8. (a) $a_2 = 1(a_1 + a_0) = 1(1 + 1) = 2$; $a_3 = 2(a_2 + a_1) = 2(2 + 1) = 2(3) = 6$;

$a_4 = 3(a_3 + a_2) = 3(6 + 2) = 3(8) = 24$; $a_5 = 4(a_4 + a_3) = 4(24 + 6) = 4(30) = 120$.

9. $a_1 = 1$, $a_2 = 2^2 - a_1 = 4 - 1 = 3$, $a_3 = 3^2 - a_2 = 9 - 3 = 6$. $a_4 = 4^2 - a_3 = 16 - 6 = 10$, $a_5 = 5^2 - a_4 = 25 - 10 = 15$, $a_6 = 6^2 - a_5 = 36 - 15 = 21$. Thus, the first six terms are 1, 3, 6, 10, 15, 21. We recognize these numbers as the six sums 1, $1 + 2$, $1 + 2 + 3$, $1 + 2 + 3 + 4$, $1 + 2 + 3 + 4 + 5$, and $1 + 2 + 3 + 4 + 5 + 6$ and so guess that $a_n = n(n + 1)/2$. [See Exercise 5a of Section 5.1.]

For $n = 1$, $n(n + 1)/2 = 1(2)/2 = 1$, which agrees with a_1. Now assume the formula holds for $n = k$; that is, assume $a_k = \frac{k(k+1)}{2}$. We must prove the formula holds for $n = k + 1$; that is, we must prove that $a_{k+1} = \frac{(k+1)(k+2)}{2}$. Now

$$a_{k+1} = (k + 1)^2 - a_k = (k + 1)^2 - \frac{k(k + 1)}{2} \quad \text{using the induction hypothesis}$$
$$= \frac{2(k + 1)^2 - k(k + 1)}{2} = \frac{(k + 1)[2(k + 1) - k]}{2} = \frac{(k + 1)(k + 2)}{2},$$

as required. By the Principle of Mathematical Induction, we conclude that the result is true for all $n \geq 1$.

11. The first few terms are 0, 1, 0, 4, 0, 16, ... Our guess is that

$$a_n = \begin{cases} 0 & \text{if } n \text{ is odd} \\ 4^{\frac{n}{2}-1} & \text{if } n \text{ is even.} \end{cases}$$

We will prove this using the strong form of mathematical induction. Note first that $a_1 = 0$ and $4^{\frac{2}{2}-1} = 4^0 = 1 = a_2$, so our guess is correct for a_1 and a_2. Now let $k > 2$ and assume the result is true for all n, $1 \leq n < k$. We must show that the result is true if $n = k$. If k is odd, then $a_k = 4a_{k-2} = 4(0) = 0$, since $a_{k-2} = 0$ by the induction hypothesis, $k - 2$ being odd. If k is even, then

$$a_k = 4a_{k-2} = 4(4^{\frac{k-2}{2}-1}) \text{ (using the induction hypothesis)} = 4^{\frac{k-2}{2}} = 4^{\frac{k}{2}-1},$$

as desired. By the Principle of Mathematical Induction, the result is true for all $n \geq 1$.

13. We use the strong form of mathematical induction. When $n = 1$, the formula gives $2^1(1 - 1/2) = 1$, agreeing with a_1. When $n = 2$, the formula gives $2^2(1 - 1) = 0$, agreeing with a_2. Now let $k > 2$ and assume the formula is correct for all $1 \leq n < k$. We must prove it is correct for $n = k$. Since $k > 2$, we have $a_k = 4a_{k-1} - 4a_{k-2}$. Applying the induction hypothesis to both $k - 1$ and $k - 2$, we have

$$a_k = 4\left[2^{k-1}(1 - \frac{k - 1}{2})\right] - 4\left[2^{k-2}(1 - \frac{k - 2}{2})\right]$$
$$= 2^{k+1}\left(1 - \frac{k - 1}{2}\right) - 2^k\left(1 - \frac{k - 2}{2}\right)$$
$$= 2^{k+1} - 2^k(k - 1) - 2^k + 2^{k-1}(k - 2)$$
$$= 2(2^k) - k2^k + 2^k - 2^k + k2^{k-1} - 2^k$$
$$= 2^k - k2^k + \frac{k}{2}2^k$$
$$= 2^k\left(1 - k + \frac{k}{2}\right) = 2^k\left(1 - \frac{k}{2}\right),$$

as desired. By the Principle of Mathematical Induction, we conclude that the formula is correct for all $n \geq 1$.

16. (b) $f^1(1) = f(1) = [4(1) - 1]/3 = 1$. $f^2(1) = f \circ f(1) = f(f(1)) = f(1) = 1$. This continues: $f^n(1) = 1$ for all n.

18. (a) The first ten terms are 2, 5, 8, 11, 14, 17, 20, 23, 26, 29. The 123rd term is $2 + 122(3) = 368$.

(b) We attempt to solve $752 = 2 + (n - 1)3$ and discover $n - 1 = 250$. So 752 does belong to the sequence; it is the 251st term.

(d) The sum of 75 terms is $\frac{75}{2}[2(2) + (74)3] = 8475$.

19. (a) $a_{17} = -1$; $a_{92} = -38\frac{1}{2}$ (b) $S = -\frac{171}{2}$

22. For $n = 1$, $a + (1 - 1)d = a$, which agrees with $a_1 = a$. Now assume that the formula is correct for the integer k; that is, $a_k = a + (k - 1)d$. Then $a_{k+1} = a_k + d = a + (k - 1)d + d = a + kd$ shows that the formula is true also for $k + 1$. So, by the Principle of Mathematical Induction, the formula is correct for all $n \geq 1$.

25. (a) The first ten terms are $59,049, -19,683, 6561, -2187, 729, -243, 81, -27, 9, -3$. The 33rd term is $59,049(-\frac{1}{3})^{32}) = \frac{3^{10}}{3^{32}} = (\frac{1}{3})^{22}$.

(b) The sum of the first 12 terms is

$$59,049\left[\frac{1 - (-\frac{1}{3})^{12}}{1 - (-\frac{1}{3})}\right] = (3^{10})\frac{3}{4}\left(1 - (\frac{1}{3})^{12}\right) = \frac{1}{4}(3^{11}) - \frac{1}{12} = \frac{3^{12} - 1}{12}.$$

28. (a) $a_{129} = (-.00001240)(-1.1)^{128} \approx -2.4643$.   (b) $S = \frac{-.00001240[1 - (-1.1)^{129}]}{2.1} \approx -1.2908$.

29. This is straightforward to prove by mathematical induction, but we give an alternative proof. Letting $S = a + ar + ar^2 + \cdots + ar^{n-1}$, we have $rS = ar + ar^2 + \cdots + ar^n$. Subtraction gives $(1 - r)S = S - rS = a - ar^n = a(1 - r^n)$, from which the formula follows.

31. (b) If $|r| < 1$, then $\lim_{n \to \infty} r^n = 0$. Hence, $\lim_{n \to \infty} a\frac{1 - r^n}{1 - r} = \frac{a}{1 - r}$.   (c) 6

33. (a) This is the sum of an arithmetic sequence with $a = 75$, $d = -4$. Solving $-61 = a + (n - 1)d = 75 + (n - 1)(-4)$, we obtain $n = 35$. So the sum is $\frac{35}{2}[2(75) + 34(-4)] = 245$.

(b) This is the sum of a geometric sequence with $a = 75$, $r = \frac{1}{5}$. Solving $\frac{3}{5^7} = ar^{n-1} = 75(\frac{1}{5})^{n-1}$, we get $n = 10$. So the sum is

$$75\frac{1 - \frac{1}{5^{10}}}{1 - \frac{1}{5}} = 3(5^2)\frac{5}{4}\left(1 - \frac{1}{5^{10}}\right) = \frac{3}{4}\left(5^3 - \frac{1}{5^7}\right) \approx 93.75.$$

34. (a) This is the sum of an arithmetic sequence with $a = 1004$ and $d = -3$. With $a_n = -397 = a + (n - 1)d$, we have $1004 - 3(n - 1) = -397$, so $3(n - 1) = 1401$, $n - 1 = 467$, so $n = 468$. The sum is $S = \frac{n}{2}[2a + (n - 1)d] = \frac{468}{2}[2008 + 467(-3)] = 234(607) = 142,038$.

35. Suppose the arithmetic sequence $a_0, a_0 + d, a_0 + 2d, \ldots$ is also the geometric sequence $a_1, a_1r, a_1r^2, \ldots$. Then $a_0 = a_1$. Let's call this number a. Note that one and only one possibility occurs when $a = 0$, namely $(0, 0, 0, \ldots)$, so assume henceforth that $a \neq 0$. Since the sequence is both arithmetic and geometric, it follows that all terms of this sequence are nonzero. We have $a + d = ar$ and $a + 2d = ar^2$, so

$$\frac{a + d}{a} = \frac{ar}{a} = r = \frac{a + 2d}{a + d}.$$

So $(a + d)^2 = a(a + 2d)$, giving $a^2 + 2ad + d^2 = a^2 + 2ad$ and hence $d = 0$. Since $ar = a + d = a$, $r = 1$. The only arithmetic sequences that are also geometric are constant, of the form $a, a, a, \ldots$ for some number a.

36. (a) We want b to be the $n + 2$nd term of an arithmetic sequence, so $b = a + (n + 1)d$. Thus $d = \frac{b - a}{n + 1}$ and $x_i = a + id = a + \frac{(b - a)i}{n + 1}$.

41. (a) $\$1000(1.15)^2 = \$1322.50$.

(b) We seek t such that $1000(1.15)^t = 2000$. Thus, $1.15^t = 2$, $t = \log 2 / \log 1.15 \approx 4.9595$ years.

46. Rewriting $f_{k+1} = f_k + f_{k-1}$ as $f_{k-1} = f_{k+1} - f_k$, we see that $f_0 = f_2 - f_1 = 1 - 1 = 0$. Similarly, $f_{-1} = 1$, $f_{-2} = -1$, $f_{-3} = 2$, $f_{-4} = -3$, $f_{-5} = 5$, $f_{-6} = -8$. In general, $f_{-n} = (-1)^{n+1}f_n$.

47. The Fibonacci sequence is the sequence $1, 1, 2, 3, 5, 8 \ldots$, each term after the first two being the sum of the two previous terms. For $n = 1$, $f_2f_1 = 1(1) = 1^1 = f_1^2$. So the assertion is correct for $n = 1$. Let $k \geq 1$ and assume the assertion is correct for $n = k$; that is, assume that $f_{k+1}f_k = \sum_{i=1}^k f_i^2$. We wish to prove the assertion is correct for $n = k + 1$; that is, we wish to prove that $f_{k+2}f_{k+1} = \sum_{i=1}^{k+1} f_i^2$. But $f_{k+2} = f_{k+1} + f_k$, so, $f_{k+2}f_{k+1} = (f_{k+1} + f_k)f_{k+1} = f_{k+1}^2 + f_{k+1}f_k = f_{k+1}^2 + \sum_{i=1}^k f_i^2$ (using the induction hypothesis) $= \sum_{i=1}^{k+1} f_i^2$ as desired. By the Principle of Mathematical Induction, we conclude that the assertion is correct for all $n \geq 1$.

51. The induction hypothesis is valid only for n in the interval $3 \leq n < k$, because all integers in this problem are at least as large as $n_0 = 3$. But the induction hypothesis is applied to the integer $k - 2$; this is not valid if $k = 4$.

53. (a) $a_1 = 1, a_2 = 2$ (2 and $1 + 1$), $a_3 = 4$, as given. We can write $4 = 4 = 3 + 1 = 1 + 3 = 2 + 1 + 1 = 1 + 2 + 1 = 1 + 1 + 2 = 2 + 2 = 1 + 1 + 1 + 1$, so $a_4 = 8$. Careful counting shows that $a_5 = 16$.

55. (a) $a_n = 2a_{n-1}$. The sequence is the sequence $2, 4, 8, \ldots$ of powers of 2.

Section 5.3 True/False

1. True   **2.** False   **3.** False   **4.** False   **5.** False

6. True   **7.** True   **8.** True   **9.** True   **10.** True

Exercises 5.3

1. $a_n = 3^n$ **3.** $a_n = -5(3^n) + 6n(3^n)$ **5.** $a_n = \frac{1}{2\sqrt{15}}(-4 + \sqrt{15})^n - \frac{1}{2\sqrt{15}}(-4 - \sqrt{15})^n$

7. $a_n = -2(-1)^n + 2(3^n) = 2[(-1)^{n+1} + 3^n]$

10. (a) $a_n = \frac{1}{2}(3^n) + \frac{1}{2}(-5)^n$ (b) $a_n = 2(3^n) + (-5)^n - 2$

12. (a) $a_n = 4^n$ (b) $a_n = 2(8^n) - 4^n$

     (c) For $n = 0, 2(8^0) - 4^0 = 2 - 1 = 1$, as required.

     Let $k \geq 0$ and assume that $a_k = 2(8^k) - 4^k$. We wish to prove that $a_{k+1} = 2(8^{k+1}) - 4^{k+1}$. Now

$$a_{k+1} = 4a_k + 8^{k+1} = 4[2(8^k) - 4^k] + 8^{k+1} \quad \text{(by the induction hypothesis)}$$
$$= 8^{k+1} - 4^{k+1} + 8^{k+1} = 2(8^{k+1}) - 4^{k+1}$$

     as desired. By the Principle of Mathematical Induction, the result is true for all $n \geq 0$.

15. (a) $a_n = 4^n + 3$ (b) $a_n = 10(4^n) - (3n + 6)2^n$

17. Try $p_n = a + bn + cn^2$. We obtain

$$a + bn + cn^2 = 5[a + b(n - 1) + c(n - 1)^2] - 2[a + b(n - 2) + c(n - 2)^2] + 3n^2$$
$$= 5[a - b + c + (b - 2c)n + cn^2] - 2[a - 2b + 4c + (b - 4c)n + cn^2] + 3n^2$$
$$= 3a - b - 3c + (3b - 2c)n + (3c + 3)n^2.$$

This gives the system

$$a = 3a - b - 3c; \quad b = 3b - 2c; \quad c = 3c + 3$$

with solution $a = -3, b = -\frac{3}{2}, c = -\frac{3}{2}$. Hence, a particular solution is $p_n = -3 - \frac{3}{2}n - \frac{3}{2}n^2$. The homogeneous recurrence $a_n = 5a_{n-1} - 2a_{n-2}$ has characteristic polynomial $x^2 - 5x + 2$ with characteristic roots $\frac{5 \pm \sqrt{17}}{2}$. Hence, $q_n = c_1(\frac{5-\sqrt{17}}{2})^n + c_2(\frac{5+\sqrt{17}}{2})^n$ and

$$p_n + q_n = -3 - \frac{3}{2}n - \frac{3}{2}n^2 + c_1\left(\frac{5-\sqrt{17}}{2}\right)^n + c_2\left(\frac{5+\sqrt{17}}{2}\right)^n.$$

The initial conditions give $-3 + c_1 + c_2 = 0$ and $-6 + c_1(\frac{5-\sqrt{17}}{2}) + c_2(\frac{5+\sqrt{17}}{2}) = 3$. This gives $c_1 = \frac{3}{2}(1 - \frac{1}{\sqrt{17}}), c_2 = \frac{3}{2}(1 + \frac{1}{\sqrt{17}})$ and hence

$$a_n = -3 - \frac{3}{2}n - \frac{3}{2}n^2 + \frac{3}{2}\left(1 - \frac{1}{\sqrt{17}}\right)\left(\frac{5-\sqrt{17}}{2}\right)^n + \frac{3}{2}\left(1 + \frac{1}{\sqrt{17}}\right)\left(\frac{5+\sqrt{17}}{2}\right)^n.$$

19. (a) $1, 1, 0, -1, -1, 0, 1, 1, 0, -1, -1, \ldots$. The corresponding characteristic polynomial is $x^2 - x + 1$ whose roots are $\frac{1}{2}(1 \pm \sqrt{3}i)$. By Theorem 5.3.1, the solution is $a_n = c_1(\frac{1+\sqrt{3}i}{2})^n + c_2(\frac{1-\sqrt{3}i}{2})^n$. The initial conditions give $a_0 = 1 = c_1 + c_2, a_1 = 1 = c_1(\frac{1+\sqrt{3}i}{2}) + c_2(\frac{1-\sqrt{3}i}{2})$, so $c_1 = \frac{1}{2} - \frac{i}{2\sqrt{3}}$, $c_2 = \frac{1}{2} + \frac{i}{2\sqrt{3}}$, and $a_n = (\frac{1}{2} - \frac{i}{2\sqrt{3}})(\frac{1+\sqrt{3}i}{2})^n + (\frac{1}{2} + \frac{i}{2\sqrt{3}})(\frac{1-\sqrt{3}i}{2})^n$.

21. The nth term of the Fibonacci sequence is $a_{n-1} = \frac{1}{\sqrt{5}}\left(\frac{1+\sqrt{5}}{2}\right)^n - \frac{1}{\sqrt{5}}\left(\frac{1-\sqrt{5}}{2}\right)^n$. Thus, $|a_{n-1} - \frac{1}{\sqrt{5}}\left(\frac{1+\sqrt{5}}{2}\right)^n| = |\frac{1}{\sqrt{5}}\left(\frac{1-\sqrt{5}}{2}\right)^n|$. Now $|\frac{1}{\sqrt{5}}\left(\frac{1-\sqrt{5}}{2}\right)^n| \le \frac{1}{\sqrt{5}} < \frac{1}{2}$ since $|\frac{1-\sqrt{5}}{2}| < 1$, so $|a_{n-1} - \frac{1}{\sqrt{5}}\left(\frac{1+\sqrt{5}}{2}\right)^n| < \frac{1}{2}$. Remembering that a_{n-1} is an integer, the result follows from the fact that there is precisely one integer within $\frac{1}{2}$ of any given real number.

25. (a) Since x is a root of the characteristic polynomial, $x^2 = rx + s$. Hence, $ra_{n-1} + sa_{n-2} = r(cx^{n-1}) + s(cx^{n-2}) = cx^{n-2}(rx + s) = cx^{n-2}(x^2) = cx^n = a_n$.

(b) We know that $p_n = rp_{n-1} + sp_{n-2}$ and $q_n = rq_{n-1} + sq_{n-2}$. Thus, $p_n + q_n = rp_{n-1} + sp_{n-2} + rq_{n-1} + sq_{n-2} = r(p_{n-1} + q_{n-1}) + s(p_{n-2} + q_{n-2})$.

(c) If x_1 and x_2 are the characteristic roots, part (a) tells us that $c_1 x_1^n$ and $c_2 x_2^n$ both satisfy the recurrence relation while part (b) says that $c_1 x_1^n + c_2 x_2^n$ is also a solution. Two initial conditions determine c_1 and c_2, for they determine two linear equations in the unknowns c_1, c_2, which, because $x_1 \ne x_2$, must have a unique solution.

26. (a) The characteristic polynomial is $x^2 - rx - s$ with characteristic roots $x = \frac{r \pm \sqrt{r^2 + 4s}}{2}$. Since there is only one root, we must have $r^2 = -4s$, in which case $x = r/2$. Hence, $r = 2x$ and $s = -r^2/4 = -4x^2/4 = -x^2$.

Section 5.4 True/False

1. False **2.** True **3.** True **4.** True **5.** True
6. False **7.** True **8.** True **9.** False **10.** True

Exercises 5.4

1. (a) $4, -12, 9, 0, 0, \ldots$ (c) $1, -6, 27, -108, \ldots, (n+1)(-3)^n, \ldots$

2. (a) $1 + 2x + 5x^2$ (f) $\dfrac{1}{1-x^2}$ **3.** $a_n = 2^n$ **5.** $a_n = -7(2^n) + 4(3^n)$

7. $a_n = 2^{n+1} + 3$ **9.** (a) $a_n = 2(-5)^n$ **11.** $a_n = -\frac{1}{2} + (-\frac{1}{6})(-1)^n + \frac{5}{3}(2^n)$

12. $a_n = \frac{1}{4}(2n+1) + \frac{7}{4}(-1)^n$

Section 6.1 True/False

1. False **2.** True **3.** True **4.** False **5.** True **6.** True
7. False. (The equation given is a special case of the general principle.)
8. True **9.** True **10.** True

Exercises 6.1

1. Let B be the set of connoisseurs of Canadian bacon, and A the set of those who like anchovies.
(a) $|B \cup A| = |B| + |A| - |B \cap A| = 10 + 7 - 6 = 11$
(b) $|B \setminus A| = |B| - |B \cap A| = 4$
(c) $|B \oplus A| = |B \cup A| - |B \cap A| = 5$ (d) $|U| - |B \cup A| = 4$

4. Let A be the set of people with undergraduate degrees in arts, S those with undergraduate degrees in science, and G those with graduate degrees.
(a) $|A \cup S \cup G| = 300$ (b) $|S \setminus (A \cup G)| = 35$

7. Let D be the set of delegates who voted to decrease the deficit, E be the set of delegates who voted in favor of the motion concerning environmental issues, and T be the set of delegates who voted in favor of not increasing taxes.
(a) $\left|(D \cup E \cup T)^c\right| = 200$ (b) $|T \setminus (D \cup E)| = 316$

9. Let O, A, G, and C denote the sets of people who bought orange juice, apple juice, grapefruit juice, and citrus punch, respectively.

(a) $|O \cap A \cap G \cap C| = 1$

10. (a) $75 - (4(28) - 6(12) + 4(5) - 1) = 75 - 59 = 16$

11. (a) Let A and B be the set of integers between 1 and 500 that are divisible by 3 and 5, respectively. The question asks for $|A \cup B|$. This number is $|A| + |B| - |A \cap B| = \lfloor \frac{500}{3} \rfloor = 233$.

(b) The question asks for $|A \setminus (B \cup C)| = 66$.

13. Let A, B, and C be the sets of integers between 1 and 250 that are divisible by 4, by 6, and by 15, respectively. We want $|A \cup B \cup C| = 91$.

14. (a) Let A, B, C, D be the sets of integers between 1 and 1000 (inclusive) that are divisible by 2, by 3, by 5, and by 7, respectively. We want $|A \cup B \cup C \cup D|^c = 1000 - 772 = 228$.

17. Let A, B, C, D, E, F be the sets of natural numbers between 1 and 200 (exclusive) that are not prime and are divisible by 2, 3, 5, 7, 11, and 13, respectively. Let A, B, C, D, E, F be the sets of natural numbers between 1 and 200 (exclusive) that are not prime and divisible by 2, 3, 5, 7, 11, and 13, respectively.

$|A \cup B \cup C \cup D \cup E \cup F| = 152$, so the number of primes less than 200 is $198 - 152 = 46$.

18. Write $a = qb + r$ with $0 \le r < b$. Then $\lfloor \frac{a}{b} \rfloor = q$. Clearly, the positive integers b, $2b$, ..., qb are all less than or equal to a and are all divisible by b. On the other hand, if $sb \le a$, then s must belong to the set $\{1, 2, \dots, q\}$. Hence, there are exactly q such natural numbers, as required.

20. Recall that $A \times B = \{(a, b) \mid a \in A, b \in B\}$. If $A = \{a_1, a_2, \dots, a_n\}$ and $B = \{b_1, b_2, \dots, b_m\}$, the ordered pairs of $A \times B$ can be enumerated with n rows of m elements each,

$$
\begin{array}{ccccc}
(a_1, b_1) & (a_1, b_2) & (a_1, b_3) & \dots & (a_1, b_m) \\
(a_2, b_1) & (a_2, b_2) & (a_2, b_3) & \dots & (a_2, b_m) \\
\vdots & \vdots & \vdots & & \vdots \\
(a_n, b_1) & (a_n, b_2) & (a_n, b_3) & \dots & (a_n, b_m)
\end{array}
$$

giving $nm = |A| \times |B|$ elements in all.

22. (a) $|(A \oplus B) \cap C| = \left|\left((A \setminus B) \cup (B \setminus A)\right) \cap C\right| = \left|\left((A \setminus B) \cap C\right) \cup \left((B \setminus A) \cap C\right)\right|$
$= |(A \cap C) \setminus B| + |(B \cap C) \setminus A| \quad \text{since } (A \setminus B) \cap (B \setminus A) = \emptyset$
$= |A \cap C| - |A \cap B \cap C| + |B \cap C| - |A \cap B \cap C|$
$= |A \cap C| + |B \cap C| - 2|A \cap B \cap C|$

Section 6.2 True/False

1. False   **2.** True   **3.** False   **4.** True   **5.** False

6. True   **7.** True   **8.** True   **9.** True   **10.** True

Exercises 6.2

1. (a) 12   (b) 7   **3.** $10 \times 9 \times 8 = 720$

5. (a) $9 \times 26 \times 26 \times 26 \times 10 \times 10 \times 10 = 158,184,000$

(b) $9 \times 26 \times 10^5 = 23,400,000$ (c) $158,184,000 + 23,400,000 = 181,584,000$

7. (a) $13 \times 6 \times 2 \times 4 = 624$ (b) $13 + 4 = 17$ (c) 25

9. (a) $4 \times 4 = 16$ (b) $4 \times 4 \times 4 = 64$ (c) $16 + 64 = 80$ **11.** $60 \times 60 \times 60 = 216,000$

13. $500 + (500)(499) + (500)(499)(498) = 1.24501 \times 10^8$ **16.** (a) $52 \times 3 \times 2 \times 1 = 312$

18.

Total	2	3	4	5	6	7	8	9	10	11	12
No. of ways	1	2	3	4	5	6	5	4	3	2	1

20. (a) HHHH, HHHT, HHTH, HTHH, THHH, HHTT, HTHT, HTTH, THHT, THTH, TTHH, HTTT, THTT, TTHT, TTTH, TTTT.

There are 16 possibilities in all.

22. (a) $26 \times 26 \times 26 \times 10 \times 9 \times 8 = 12,654,720$

25. (a) The easiest way to see that there are 2^n functions from A to B is to note that $\{a_i \mid (a_i, 0) \in f\} \leftrightarrow f$ is a one-to-one correspondence between the (2^n) subsets of A and the set of functions $f: A \to B$.

(b) Of the 2^n functions $A \to B$, precisely two are not onto,

$$\{(a_1, 0), (a_2, 0), \ldots, (a_n, 0)\} \quad \text{and} \quad \{(a_1, 1), (a_2, 1), \ldots, (a_n, 1)\}.$$

Thus, the number of onto functions is $2^n - 2$ as claimed.

Section 6.3 True/False

1. True **2.** False **3.** True **4.** False (leap year) **5.** True
6. False **7.** True **8.** False **9.** True **10.** False

Exercises 6.3

1. There are seven days of the week. Hence, we wish to put eight objects (people) into seven boxes (days). By the Pigeonhole Principle, some day must have at least two people corresponding to it.

4. $\lceil \frac{100}{12} \rceil = 9$

7. (a) Any given processor is connected to at least one of 19 other processors. There are 20 processors, so the Pigeonhole Principle assures us that at least two are connected to the same number.

(b) The result is still true, though for a somewhat more subtle reason. The number of processors to which a given processor is connected is in the range 0–19 (inclusive). On the other hand, if 0 occurs (that is, some processor is not connected to any other), then 19 cannot. So, as in part (a), there are at most 19 possibilities for the number of processors connected to a given processor. By the Pigeonhole Principle, at least two processors are connected to the same number.

10. Mimicking the solution to Problem 14, we let a_i be the number of sets Martina plays on day i. Then we have $1 \le a_1 < a_1 + a_2 < \cdots < a_1 + a_2 + \cdots + a_{77} \le 132$. Now it is not true that the only integer in the range 1–77 that is divisible by 21 is 21 itself. Thus, while two of these sums must leave the same remainder upon division by 21, we can conclude this time only that the difference of these sums is divisible by 21, **not** that the difference **is** 21.

11. Suppose Brad and his mother drive a_1 quarter-hours on day 1, a_2 quarter-hours on day two, and so on, a_{35} quarter-hours on day 35. The list

$$a_1, \ a_1 + a_2, \ a_1 + a_2 + a_3, \ \ldots, \ a_1 + a_2 + \cdots + a_{35}$$

consists of 35 natural numbers between 1 and $15 \times 4 = 60$ (15 hours = 60 quarter hours) and so, if any of them is divisible by 35 ($8\frac{3}{4}$ hr = 35 quarter hr), it is 35 and we are done. Otherwise, each of these numbers leaves a remainder between 1 and 34 upon division by 35, and so two leave the same remainder. Suppose

$$a_1 + a_2 + \cdots + a_s = 35q + r$$
$$a_1 + a_2 + \cdots + a_t = 35q' + r.$$

Then (assuming $s > t$) $a_{t+1} + a_{t+2} + \cdots + a_s$ is divisible by and hence equal to 35; that is, Brad drives $8\frac{3}{4}$ hours on days $t + 1, t + 2, \ldots, s$.

14. Let box 1 correspond to days 1, 2, and 3; box 2 to days 4, 5, and 6; box 3 to days 7, 8, and 9, and box 4 to days 10, 11, and 12. Putting each bill into the box corresponding to the day it was mailed, we see that one box must contain at least $\lceil \frac{195}{4} \rceil = 49$ bills, by the general form of the Pigeonhole Principle. This gives the desired result.

17. Divide the rectangle into 25 rectangles, each 3×4. By the Pigeonhole Principle, at least two points are within, or on the boundary of, one of these smaller rectangles. This gives the result since the maximum distance between two points of such a rectangle is $\sqrt{3^2 + 4^2} = 5$.

21. As suggested, we consider the sequence of natural numbers $M_1 = 3$, $M_2 = 33, \ldots, M_n = 33 \cdots 3$ (n 3's). If one of these is divisible by n, we have the desired result. Otherwise, at least two of these natural numbers leave the same (nonzero) remainder upon division by n; that is, for some $i \neq j$, $M_i = qn + r$, $M_j = q'n + r$ for the same r. Assuming, without loss of generality, that $i > j$, $M_i - M_j = (q - q')n$ is divisible by n and has only 3's and 0's in its base 10 representation.

23. After finitely many steps in the long-division process, we will be adjoining a 0 at each stage to the remainder from the division at the previous stage. Since only finitely many remainders are possible (each remainder is less than the divisor), two must be the same and, from the first repetition, all steps (and corresponding decimal places) will repeat.

25. (a) Suppose no two people have the same age so that there are at least 51 different ages in the room. Let box 1 correspond to integers 1 and 2, box 2 correspond to integers 3 and 4, ... , box 50 to 99 and 100. Assigning ages to boxes, by the Pigeonhole Principle, some box contains two ages. This says that ages of two people are consecutive integers, as required.

27. (a) Focus on one of the ten people, say Hilda. Suppose first that at least four of the remaining nine people are strangers to Hilda. If these four are mutual friends we are done; otherwise, two of these are strangers and hence, together with Hilda, we have three mutual strangers and again we are done. Thus, we suppose that less than four people are strangers to Hilda; so Hilda has at least six friends in the group. By Problem 17, this group of six contains either three mutual strangers (in which case we are done) or three mutual friends who, together with Hilda, give four mutual friends.

28. (a) The set $S = \{a_1, a_2, \ldots, a_{10}\}$ has $2^{10} = 1024$ subsets and the sum of the elements in each subset is between 0 and 1000, so the Pigeonhole Principle implies the existence of two subsets with the same sum.

Section 7.1 True/False

1. True   **2.** False   **3.** True   **4.** False   **5.** True

6. True   **7.** False   **8.** False   **9.** False   **10.** True

Exercises 7.1

1. $13 \cdot 12 \cdot 11 \cdots 6 = P(13, 8) = 51891840$ **3.** $10 \cdot 9 \cdot 8 \cdot 7 = P(10, 4) = 5040$

5. $3 \times 5! = 360$ **7.** (b) $10!4!2!$ **9.** (a) $3! \times 4! = 144$ (b) $P(4, 2) \times 4! = 288$

10. (a) $m!$

(b) If $m > n$, there are 0 injective functions $X \to Y$.

If $m \leq n$, the number is $\underbrace{n(n - 1)(n - 2) \cdots (n - m + 1)}_{m \text{ factors}} = P(n, m)$.

12. Let N be the set of lines in which the Noseworthys are beside each other and A the set of lines in which the Abbotts are beside each other.

(a) $|N| = 2 \times 3! = 12$ (b) $|N^c| = 24 - 12 = 12$ (c) $|N \cap A| = 2 \times 2 \times 2 = 8$

(d) 4   (e) $|N \cup A| = |N| + |A| - |N \cap A| = 12 + 12 - 8 = 16$

(f) $|N \oplus A| = |N| + |A| - 2|N \cap A| = 12 + 12 - 2(8) = 8$

14. (a) $2 \times 5! = 240$ **16.** (a) $9 \times 9 \times 8 \times 7 \times 6 \times 5 \times 4 = 9 \times P(9, 6) = 9 \times 60,480 = 544,320$

17. (b) $7 \times 6 \times P(7, 5) = 42 \times 2520 = 105840$ (d) $P(7, 7) = 5040$

Section 7.2 True/False

1. False   **2.** True   **3.** True   **4.** True   **5.** True   **6.** True   **7.** True   **8.** True   **9.** False

Exercises 7.2

1. (a) $\binom{6}{2}\binom{7}{2}\binom{8}{2} = 8820$ (b) $\binom{6}{3}\binom{7}{2}\binom{8}{2} + \binom{6}{2}\binom{7}{3}\binom{8}{2} + \binom{6}{2}\binom{7}{2}\binom{8}{3} = 44,100$

3. $\binom{12}{5} = \frac{12!}{7!5!} = 792$ **5.** (a) $\binom{15}{5}\binom{10}{5}$ (b) $\binom{15}{7}\binom{8}{4}$ (c) $3\binom{15}{7}\binom{8}{4}$

6. $\binom{10}{0} + \binom{10}{1} + \binom{10}{2} + \binom{10}{3} = 176$ **8.** (a) $4\binom{13}{5} = 5148$ **10.** (a) 2^{10} (b) $\binom{10}{4} = 210$

11. (a) $\binom{25}{5} = 53130$ (b) $\binom{15}{5} = 3003$ (c) $\binom{15}{3}\binom{10}{2} = 20475$

13. (a) $\binom{100}{20}$ (b) $\binom{100}{20}$ (c) $\binom{100}{20} \times \binom{100}{20}$

(d) The answer is $\binom{100}{5} \times \binom{95}{15} \times \binom{80}{15}$. This is also $\binom{100}{20}\binom{20}{5}\binom{80}{15}$. (Why?)

17. (a) $\binom{10}{8} = 45$ (c) $\binom{5}{3} + \binom{5}{4}\binom{5}{1} = 10 + 25 = 35$ **19.** (a) $\binom{10}{2} = 45$ **20.** (a) $\binom{12}{3} = 220$

21. (a) $\binom{8}{2} - 8 = 28 - 8 = 20$

23. The product of n consecutive natural numbers starting at m is

$$m(m + 1)(m + 2) \cdots (m + n - 1) = P(m + n - 1, n) = n!\binom{m+n-1}{n}.$$

So $\frac{m(m+1)(m+2)\cdots(m+n-1)}{n!}$ is the integer $\binom{m+n-1}{n}$.

24. (a) $\binom{n}{k}\binom{n-k}{\ell} = \frac{n!}{k!(n-k)!} \cdot \frac{(n-k)!}{\ell!(n-k-\ell)!} = \frac{n!}{k!\ell!(n-k-\ell)!}$; $\binom{n}{\ell}\binom{n-\ell}{k} = \frac{n!}{\ell!(n-\ell)!} \cdot \frac{(n-\ell)!}{k!(n-\ell-k)!} = \frac{n!}{\ell!k!(n-\ell-k)!}$

The two expressions are equal.

(b) To choose two teams as suggested, we may choose either team first. Choosing the team of size k first, the number of possibilities is $\binom{n}{k}\binom{n-k}{\ell}$; choosing the team of size ℓ first, the number is $\binom{n}{\ell}\binom{n-\ell}{k}$. Certainly, these numbers must be the same.

Section 7.3 True/False

1. False: It's $\frac{2}{36}$.   **2.** False   **3.** False: It's $\frac{2(5 \times 7)}{12 \times 11}$.   **4.** True   **5.** True

6. False: It's $\frac{\binom{5}{4}\binom{8}{2}}{\binom{13}{6}}$.   **7.** True   **8.** False   **9.** True   **10.** True

Exercises 7.3

1. (a) $\frac{1}{36}$ (b) $\frac{3}{36} = \frac{1}{12}$

(c) Since the possibilities are $(1, 2)$, $(2, 3)$, $(3, 4)$, $(4, 5)$, $(5, 6)$, and their reverses, the answer is $\frac{10}{36} = \frac{5}{18}$.

(d) There are $3 \times 3 = 9$ cases, when the odd number is first, and 9 more, when the even number is first. The answer is $\frac{18}{36} = \frac{1}{2}$.

5. (a) $\frac{1}{64}$ (b) $\frac{\binom{6}{2}}{64} = \frac{15}{64}$ (c) $\frac{1 + \binom{6}{1} + \binom{6}{2}}{64} = \frac{11}{32}$ (d) $1 - \frac{1}{64} = \frac{63}{64}$ (e) $\frac{\binom{6}{1} + \binom{6}{3} + \binom{6}{5}}{64} = \frac{1}{2}$

7. (a) There are $\binom{49}{6}$ outcomes in the sample space. For an outcome to be in the event described, we need to choose three from the six selected numbers and three from the 43 other numbers. The answer is $\frac{\binom{6}{3}\binom{43}{3}}{\binom{49}{6}} \approx 0.018$.

(b) $\frac{\binom{6}{3}\binom{43}{3} + \binom{6}{4}\binom{43}{2} + \binom{6}{5}\binom{43}{1} + 1}{\binom{49}{6}} \approx 0.019$ (c) $1 - \frac{1}{\binom{49}{6}} \approx 1.000$

9. (a) $\frac{4(4)}{12(12)} = \frac{1}{9}$ (b) $1 - \frac{1}{9} = \frac{8}{9}$ (c) $1 - \frac{8(8)}{12(12)} = \frac{5}{9}$ (d) $\frac{2(5)(4)}{12(12)} = \frac{5}{18}$

(e) We will use the formula given in part (3) of Theorem 7.3.2. Let A be the event "at least one white ball" and B be "exactly one red ball." We saw in (c) that $P(A) = \frac{5}{9}$. Also $P(B) = \frac{2(5)(7)}{12(12)} = \frac{35}{72}$. Since $A \cap B$ is the event described in (d), $P(A \cap B) = \frac{5}{18}$. The required probability is $P(A \cup B) = \frac{5}{9} + \frac{35}{72} - \frac{5}{18} = \frac{55}{72}$.

11. (a) $\frac{4(3)}{12(11)} = \frac{1}{11}$ (b) $1 - \frac{1}{11} = \frac{10}{11}$ (c) $1 - \frac{8(7)}{12(11)} = \frac{19}{33}$ (d) $\frac{2(5)(4)}{12(11)} = \frac{10}{33}$

(e) Let A be "at least one white ball" and B be "exactly one red ball." We saw in (c) that $P(A) = \frac{19}{33}$. Also, $P(B) = \frac{2(5)(7)}{12(11)} = \frac{35}{66}$. Since $A \cap B$ is the event "one white ball and one red ball," part (d) says $P(A \cap B) = \frac{10}{33}$. The required probability is $P(A \cup B) = \frac{19}{33} + \frac{35}{66} - \frac{10}{33} = \frac{53}{66}$.

13. (a) $\dfrac{\binom{5}{4}\binom{7}{2}}{\binom{12}{6}} = \dfrac{5}{44}$ (b) $\dfrac{\binom{7}{4}\binom{5}{2} + \binom{7}{5}\binom{5}{1} + \binom{7}{6}}{\binom{12}{6}} = \dfrac{1}{2}$ (c) $1 - \dfrac{\binom{7}{3}\binom{5}{3}}{\binom{12}{6}} = \dfrac{41}{66}$

    (d) Let A be "majority of Americans" and B be "exactly four Canadians." From (a) and (b), we know $P(A) = \frac{1}{2}$ and $P(B) = \frac{5}{44}$. Since $A \cap B = \emptyset$, A and B are mutually exclusive, so the answer is $P(A \cup B) = \frac{1}{2} + \frac{5}{44} = \frac{27}{44}$.

15. (a) $\frac{11}{15}$ (b) $\frac{4}{15}$ (c) $\frac{1}{3}$ (d) $\frac{4}{15}$ (e) $\frac{3}{5}$ **16.** (a) $\frac{233}{500}$ (b) $\frac{33}{250}$ (c) $\frac{17}{500}$ **19.** $\frac{720}{1000} = \frac{18}{25}$

23. The event mentioned has one choice for president, eight for treasurer, and then 8×7 choices for the other two positions. The answer is $\frac{8(8)(7)}{10(9)(8)(7)} = \frac{4}{45}$.

26. (a) $\dfrac{\binom{100}{20}\binom{20}{5}\binom{80}{15}}{\binom{100}{20}\binom{100}{20}} = \dfrac{\binom{20}{5}\binom{80}{15}}{\binom{100}{20}}$ (b) $\dfrac{\binom{100}{20}\binom{80}{20}}{\binom{100}{20}\binom{100}{20}} = \dfrac{\binom{80}{20}}{\binom{100}{20}}$

28. A and B are not mutually exclusive: The ordered pair $(2, 2)$ is in each.

    A and C are mutually exclusive: $(2, 2)$ is not in C because $4 \nmid 70$.

30. (a) $P(A) = P(A \cap B_1) + P(A \cap B_2) + \cdots + P(A \cap B_n)$. Note that, when $n = 2$, $B_1 \cap B_2 = \emptyset$ and $B_1 \cup B_2 = S$, so $B_2 = B_1^c$ and the identity here indeed generalizes that of Exercise 30.

31. (a) Using Proposition 6.1.1(c), we have

$$P(A \setminus B) = \frac{|A \setminus B|}{|S|} = \frac{|A| - |A \cap B|}{|S|} = \frac{|A|}{|S|} - \frac{|A \cap B|}{|S|} = P(A) - P(A \cap B).$$

    (d) From (c), $P(A \oplus B) = P(A) + P(B) - 2P(A \cap B)$
$$= P(A) + P(B) - 2(P(A) + P(B) - P(A \cup B))$$
$$= 2P(A \cup B) - P(A) - P(B).$$

    (e) $P(A \cap (B \cup C)) = P((A \cap B) \cup (A \cap C)) = P(A \cap B) + P(A \cap C) - P(A \cap B \cap C)$.

    (i) $P((A \oplus B) \cap C) = \dfrac{|(A \oplus B) \cap C|}{|S|}$

$$= \frac{|A \cap C| + |B \cap C| - 2|A \cap B \cap C|}{|S|}, \quad \text{using Exercise 22(a)}$$

$$= P(A \cap C) + P(B \cap C) - 2P(A \cap B \cap C).$$

Section 7.4 True/False

1. False   **2.** True   **3.** True   **4.** False (but this was true in Section 7.3).   **5.** False

6. False   **7.** True   **8.** True   **9.** True   **10.** False: $A_1, \ldots, A_n$ must be pairwise mutually exclusive.

Exercises 7.4

1. (a) $P(2) + P(4) + P(6) = \frac{1}{8} + \frac{1}{6} + \frac{5}{24} = \frac{1}{2}$ (b) $P(5) + P(6) = \frac{7}{24}$

2. (a) $P(2, 6) + P(3, 5) + P(4, 4) + P(5, 3) + P(6, 2) = 2(\frac{1}{8})(\frac{5}{24}) + 2(\frac{1}{6})(\frac{1}{12}) + (\frac{1}{6})(\frac{1}{6}) = \frac{31}{288}$.

    (d) $2(\frac{1}{4})(\frac{1}{12}) + 2(\frac{1}{8})(\frac{5}{24}) = \frac{3}{32}$.

3. We have $P(H) = 4P(T)$ and $P(H) + P(T) = 1$. So $5P(T) = 1$, giving $P(T) = \frac{1}{5}$ and $P(H) = \frac{4}{5}$.

5. We have $P(1) + 2P(1) + 3P(1) + 4P(1) + 5P(1) = 1$, so $15P(1) = 1$, $P(1) = \frac{1}{15}$, $P(2) = \frac{2}{15}$, $P(3) = \frac{1}{5}$, $P(4) = \frac{4}{15}$, and $P(5) = \frac{1}{3}$.

7. (a) $\binom{6}{4}(\frac{1}{4})^4(\frac{3}{4})^2 = \frac{135}{4096}$ (b) $\binom{6}{5}(\frac{1}{4})^5(\frac{3}{4}) + (\frac{1}{4})^6 = \frac{19}{4096}$ (c) $1 - (\frac{3}{4})^6 = \frac{3367}{4096}$

9. (a) $A \cap B$ is "three or four heads appear," so $P(A \cap B) = \left[\binom{5}{3} + \binom{5}{4}\right](\frac{1}{2})^5 = \frac{15}{32}$. Also, $P(A) = \left[\binom{5}{3} + \binom{5}{4} + 1\right](\frac{1}{2})^5 = \frac{1}{2}$ and $P(B) = 1 - (\frac{1}{2})^5 = \frac{31}{32}$. So $P(A \mid B) = \dfrac{P(A \cap B)}{P(B)} = \frac{15}{31}$.

    (b) $P(B \mid A) = \dfrac{P(B \cap A)}{P(A)} = \frac{15}{16}$.   (c) Since $A \cap C = \emptyset$, $P(A \cap C) = 0$, so $P(A \mid C) = 0$.

(d) $P(C \mid A) = \dfrac{P(C \cap A)}{P(A)} = 0.$ (e) Since $B \cap C = C$, $P(B \mid C) = \dfrac{P(B \cap C)}{P(C)} = 1.$

(f) $P(C \mid B) = \dfrac{P(C \cap B)}{P(B)} = \dfrac{P(C)}{P(B)} = \dfrac{\binom{5}{2}}{31} = \dfrac{10}{31}.$

11. $A \cap B$ is the event "a 6 appears." So $P(A \mid B) = \dfrac{P(A \cap B)}{P(B)} = \dfrac{\frac{5}{24}}{\frac{7}{24}} = \dfrac{5}{7}$, and $P(B \mid A) = \dfrac{\frac{5}{24}}{\frac{1}{2}} = \dfrac{5}{12}$. A

and B are not independent because $P(A)P(B) = \frac{1}{2}(\frac{7}{24}) = \frac{7}{48}$ while $P(A \cap B) = \frac{5}{24}$. A and B are not mutually exclusive because $A \cap B \neq \emptyset$.

13. Let A be the event "a 1 appears on the first die" and B the event "a 1 appears on the second die." A and B are not mutually exclusive because $(1, 1)$ belongs to $A \cap B$. However, $P(A) = \frac{1}{6} = P(B)$ and $P(A \cap B) = \frac{1}{36} = P(A)P(B)$, so A and B are independent.

15. (a) Here $P(A) = \frac{3}{4}$, $P(B) = \frac{1}{2}$, $P(A \cap B) = \frac{1}{2}$. So $P(A \cap B) \neq P(A)P(B)$.

(b) Here $P(A) = \frac{1}{2}$, $P(B) = \frac{3}{4}$, $P(A \cap B) = \frac{3}{8}$, so $P(A \cap B) = P(A)P(B)$.

17. $P(A^c)P(B^c) = (1 - P(A))(1 - P(B))$
$$= 1 - P(A) - P(B) + P(A)P(B)$$
$$= 1 - P(A) - P(B) + P(A \cap B) \quad \text{since } A \text{ and } B \text{ are independent}$$
$$= 1 - (P(A) + P(B) - P(A \cap B))$$
$$= 1 - P(A \cup B) = P((A \cup B)^c) = P(A^c \cap B^c).$$

20. We use induction on n, the strong form. For $n = 1$, the result is clear. If $n = 2$, $P(A_1 \cup A_2) = P(A_1) + P(A_2) - P(A_1 \cap A_2) \leq P(A_1) + P(A_2)$. Now assume $n > 2$ and the result holds for all integers k with $1 \leq k < n$. We have

$$P(A_1 \cup A_2 \cup \cdots \cup A_n) = P((A_1 \cup A_2 \cup \cdot \cup A_{n-1}) \cup A_n)$$
$$\leq P(A_1 \cup A_2 \cup \cdots \cup A_{n-1}) + P(A_n) \quad \text{using the } k = 2 \text{ case}$$
$$\leq (P(A_1) + P(A_2) + \cdots + P(A_{n-1}) + P(A_n) \quad \text{using the } k = n - 1 \text{ case.}$$

By the Principle of Mathematical Induction, the result follows.

24. (a) $_{50}P_{20} = (_{30}P_{20})(_{20}P_{50}) = .8(.7) = .56$ (b) $_{30}P_{40} = (_{10}P_{40})(_{20}P_{50}) = .9(.7) = .63$

(c) $(_{10}P_{40})(_{20}P_{20}) = (_{30}P_{20})$, so $_{20}P_{20} = \frac{.8}{.9} = 0.\dot{8}$

26. Since the lives are assumed independent, the first condition says $_{10}P_{20}(_{10}P_{30}) = .9$, that is, $_{20}P_{20} = .9$. We are also give that $_{15}P_{20} = .94$ and $_{60}P_{20} = .55$. We want $_5P_{35} - _{45}P_{35}$. Now $_5P_{35}(_{15}P_{20}) =_{20} P_{20}$, so $_5P_{35} = \frac{.9}{.94}$. Also, $_{45}P_{35}(_{15}P_{20}) =_{60} P_{20}$, so $_{45}P_{35} = \frac{.55}{.94}$. The answer is $\frac{.9-.55}{.94} = .372$.

29. Let A, B, C be the events of eating at Leonce's, Harold's, and Vegan Delights, respectively, and let D be the event a customer is satisfied. We are given that $P(A) = .4$, $P(B) = .35$, $P(C) = .25$, $P(D \mid A) = .85$, $P(D \mid B) = .9$, $P(D \mid C) = .95$.

(a) $P(D \cap C) = P(C)P(D \mid C) = .25(.95) = .2375$

(b) $P(B \cap D^c) = P(B) - P(B \cap D) = P(B) - P(B)P(D \mid B) = .35(1 - .9) = .035$

(c) $P(D) = P(A)P(D \mid A) + P(B)P(D \mid B) + P(C)P(D \mid C) = .4(.85) + .35(.9) + .25(.95) = .8925$

(d) $P(A \mid D) = \dfrac{P(A)P(D \mid A)}{P(D)} = \dfrac{.4(.85)}{.8925} = .381$, using (c)

(e) $P(D^c \mid C^c) = \dfrac{P(D^c \cap C^c)}{P(C^c)} = \dfrac{P((D \cup C)^c)}{1 - P(C)} = \dfrac{1 - P(D \cup C)}{1 - P(C)}$
$$= \dfrac{1 - (P(D) + P(C) - P(D \cap C))}{1 - P(C)}$$
$$= \dfrac{1 - (.8925 + .25 - .2375)}{.75} = .127, \quad \text{using (a) and (c).}$$

Section 7.5 True/False

1. True **2.** True: $\binom{18}{10} = \binom{18}{8}$. **3.** True **4.** False: It is 11^8. **5.** False: It is $\binom{16}{5}$.

6. True **7.** True **8.** False: It is $P(12, 5)$. **9.** True **10.** False: It is $\dfrac{11!}{2!2!2!2!}$.

Exercises 7.5

1. $\binom{30+7-1}{30} = \binom{36}{30}$ **3.** $\binom{6+5-1}{5} = \binom{10}{5} = 252$ **4.** $\binom{10+4-1}{10} = \binom{13}{10} = 286$ **6. (a)** $\binom{27}{8} = 2220075$

7. (c) $\frac{12!}{3!} = 79833600$ **11. (a)** $\binom{60}{10}\binom{50}{10}\binom{40}{10} = \frac{60!}{10!10!10!30!}$ **13.** $\binom{13}{1}\binom{12}{2}\binom{10}{5} = \frac{13!}{1!2!5!5!} = 216216$

14. (a) $\frac{10!}{2!3!} = 302400$ **15.** $\frac{30!}{10!5!7!8!}$

18. (a) Given any solution (x_1, x_2, x_3, x_4) of (*) with $x_1 \geq 8$, then $(x_1 - 8, x_2, x_3, x_4)$ is a solution of (**) with $x_1 - 8, x_2, x_3, x_4$ nonnegative integers. Conversely, given a solution (x_1, x_2, x_3, x_4) of (**) in nonnegative integers, then $(x_1 + 8, x_2, x_3, x_4)$ is a solution to (*) with $x_1 + 8 \geq 8$. The number of solutions to (**) in nonnegative integers corresponds to the number of ways to put 13 identical marbles into four boxes labeled x_1, x_2, x_3, x_4. This number is $\binom{16}{13} = 560$.

Section 7.6 True/False

1. False **2.** True **3.** False **4.** True **5.** False

6. True **7.** False: e is irrational. **8.** True **9.** True **10.** False

Exercises 7.6

1. $D_6 = 265$; $D_7 = 1854$; $D_8 = 14{,}833$ **3.** $D_{11} = 11!\left(1 - \frac{1}{1!} + \frac{1}{2!} - \frac{1}{3!} + \cdots - \frac{1}{11!}\right)$

5. (b) $7! - D_7$ **6. (c)** $20D_{19}$ **7. (a)** $9! - [5(8!) - 10(7!) + 10(6!) - 5(5!) + 4!] = 205{,}056$

10. (a) Using Proposition 7.6.2,

$$D_n = n! - n! + \left[n(n-1)(n-2)\cdots 3\right] - \left[n(n-1)(n-2)\cdots 4\right] + \cdots + (-1)^{n-1}n + (-1)^n$$
$$= n[\,(n-1)(n-2)\cdots 3 - (n-1)(n-2)\cdots 4 + \cdots + (-1)^{n-1}(n-1)\,] + (-1)^n$$
$$\equiv (-1)^n \pmod{n}.$$

(b) This follows immediately from part (a).

11. (a) $(n-1)(D_{n-1} + D_{n-2}) = (n-1)\left\{ (n-1)!\left[1 - \frac{1}{1!} + \frac{1}{2!} - \cdots + (-1)^{n-1}\frac{1}{(n-1)!}\right] \right.$
$$\left. +(n-2)!\left[1 - \frac{1}{1!} + \frac{1}{2!} - \cdots + (-1)^{n-2}\frac{1}{(n-2)!}\right] \right\}$$
$$= n(n-1)!\left[1 - \frac{1}{1!} + \frac{1}{2!} - \cdots + (-1)^{n-1}\frac{1}{(n-1)!}\right]$$
$$-(n-1)!\left[1 - \frac{1}{1!} + \frac{1}{2!} - \cdots + (-1)^{n-1}\frac{1}{(n-1)!}\right]$$
$$+(n-1)!\left[1 - \frac{1}{1!} + \frac{1}{2!} - \cdots + (-1)^{n-2}\frac{1}{(n-2)!}\right]$$
$$= n!\left(1 - \frac{1}{1!} + \frac{1}{2!} - \cdots + (-1)^n\frac{1}{n!}\right) - n!(-1)^n\frac{1}{n!}$$
$$-(n-1)!(-1)^{n-1}\frac{1}{(n-1)!}$$
$$= D_n - (-1)^n - (-1)^{n-1} = D_n$$

Section 7.7 True/False

1. True **2.** False **3.** True **4.** False: The formula is correct with $k < n$.

5. False: This symbol starts the ninth row. **6.** True **7.** True **8.** True **9.** True **10.** False

Exercises 7.7

1. (a) $(x + y)^6 = x^6 + 6x^5y + 15x^4y^2 + 20x^3y^3 + 15x^2y^4 + 6xy^5 + y^6$

(b) $(2x + 3y)^6 = 64x^6 + 576x^5y + 2160x^4y^2 + 4320x^3y^3 + 4860x^2y^4 + 2916xy^5 + 729y^6$

3. (b) $(2x^3 - x^2)^8 = 256x^{24} - 1024x^{23} + 1792x^{22} - 1792x^{21} + 1120x^{20} - 448x^{19} + 112x^{18} - 16x^{17} + x^{16}$

4. $\binom{12}{3}(x^3)^9(-2y^2)^3 = -1760x^{27}y^6$

5. (c) The seventh term is $\binom{20}{6}x^{14}y^6 = 38{,}760x^{14}y^6$. The fifteenth term is $\binom{20}{14}x^6y^{14} = 38{,}760x^6y^{14}$.

6. (a) 17 terms

(b) There is a middle term (since 16 is even). This term is $\binom{16}{8}(2x)^8(-y)^8 = 3{,}294{,}720x^8y^8$.

8. The required term is $\binom{10}{7}(4x)^3(5y)^7 = 120(64x^3)(78125y^7)$. The coefficient is 600,000,000.

9. The term in question is $\binom{17}{4}x^{13}(3y^2)^4 = 2380x^{13}(81y^8)$. The coefficient is $2380(81) = 192{,}780$.

11. The general term is $\binom{18}{k}\left(\dfrac{3}{x}\right)^{18-k}(x^2)^k = \binom{18}{k}3^{18-k}x^{3k-18}$. We want $3k - 18 = 27$, so $k = 15$ and the coefficient is $\binom{18}{15}3^3 = (816)(27) = 22{,}032$.

14. (a) If $n = 0$, $(1 + \sqrt{2})^0 = 1 = 1 + 0\sqrt{2}$, so $x_0 = 1$, $y_0 = 0$.
If $n = 1$, $(1 + \sqrt{2})^1 = 1 + \sqrt{2}$, so $x_1 = 1$, $y_1 = 1$.
If $n = 2$, $(1 + \sqrt{2})^2 = 1 + 2\sqrt{2} + 2 = 3 + 2\sqrt{2}$ so $x_2 = 3$, $y_2 = 2$.
If $n = 5$, $(1 + \sqrt{2})^5 = 1 + 5\sqrt{2} + 10(\sqrt{2})^2 + 10(\sqrt{2})^3 + 5(\sqrt{2})^4 + (\sqrt{2})^5$
$$= 1 + 5\sqrt{2} + 20 + 20\sqrt{2} + 20 + 4\sqrt{2} = 41 + 29\sqrt{2}$$
and so $x_5 = 41$, $y_5 = 29$.

16. With the given interpretation, row n of Pascal's triangle becomes the single number

$$10^n\binom{n}{0} + 10^{n-1}\binom{n}{1} + \cdots + 10\binom{n}{n-1} + 1 = \sum_{r=0}^{n}10^{n-r}\binom{n}{r}.$$

So we are trying to prove that $\sum_{r=0}^{n}10^{n-r}\binom{n}{r} = 11^n$. This follows immediately from the Binomial Theorem since $11^n = (10 + 1)^n = \sum_{r=0}^{n}\binom{n}{r}(10)^{n-r}(1)^r$.

20. Consider $(x - y)^n = \sum_{k=0}^{n}\binom{n}{k}x^{n-k}(-y)^k = \sum_{k=0}^{n}\binom{n}{k}x^{n-k}(-1)^ky^k$.
Setting $x = y = 1$, we obtain

$$0 = (1 - 1)^n = \sum_{k=0}^{n}\binom{n}{k}1^{n-k}(-1)^k1^k = \sum_{k=0}^{n}\binom{n}{k}(-1)^k = \binom{n}{0} - \binom{n}{1} + \binom{n}{2} - \cdots + (-1)^n.$$

22. (a) $\sum_{k=1}^{n}k\binom{n}{k} = \binom{n}{1} + 2\binom{n}{2} + 3\binom{n}{3} + 4\binom{n}{4} + \cdots + (n-1)\binom{n}{n-1} + n$

$$= n + n(n-1) + \frac{n(n-1)(n-2)}{2} + \frac{n(n-1)(n-2)(n-3)}{3!} + \cdots + n(n-1) + n$$

$$= n\left[1 + (n-1) + \frac{(n-1)(n-2)}{2} + \frac{(n-1)(n-2)(n-3)}{3!} + \cdots + n - 1 + 1\right]$$

$$= n\left[1 + \binom{n-1}{1} + \binom{n-1}{2} + \binom{n-1}{3} + \cdots + 1\right] = n2^{n-1},$$

using the result of Problem 34 in the last step.

Section 8.1 True/False

1. False **2.** True **3.** True **4.** True **5.** True **6.** False **7.** True **8.** False

9. False **10.** False: The average is $\frac{9+10+15}{3} = \frac{34}{3}$.

Exercises 8.1

1. To find the midpoint of a line segment AB, choose a radius r (for example, $r = |AB|$) such that the arcs with centers A and B and radius r meet at two distinct points, P and Q. The point of intersection, M, of AB and PQ is the required midpoint.

To see why this works, consider the diagram to the right, in which the labels are given as before and line segments AP, BP, AQ, BQ are joined. Note that $\angle PAB = \angle PBA$ since $\triangle APB$ is isosceles. Since $\triangle BPQ$ is congruent to $\triangle APQ$ (three pairs of sides of equal length), $\angle BPQ = \angle APQ$. Thus, triangles PAM and PBM are congruent (two equal pairs of sides and equal contained angles), so $|AM| = |BM|$, as required.

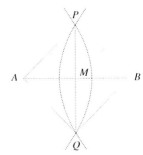

3. (a) Let A be any point on ℓ and let $r = |AP|$. Draw the circle with center P and radius r. If this meets ℓ in only the single point A, then PA is the desired perpendicular to ℓ. Otherwise, the circle meets ℓ in two points, A and B. Draw arcs with centers A and B and radius r meeting in P and Q. Then PQ is the desired perpendicular to ℓ.

To see this, consider the diagram at the right, with M the point of intersection of PQ and ℓ. Since triangles PAQ and PBQ are congruent, $\angle APM = \angle BPM$. Then it follows that $\triangle APM \equiv \triangle BPM$, and thus $\angle AMP = \angle BMP$. Since these angles have sum $180°$, each is a right angle.

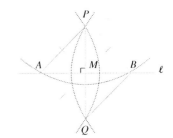

4. (a)

~~168~~ $\times$	~~413~~
~~84~~	~~826~~
~~42~~	~~1,652~~
21	3,304
~~10~~	~~6,608~~
5	13,216
~~2~~	~~26,432~~
1	52,864
	69,384

5. The basic idea behind this is the simple fact that $xy = (\frac{x}{2})(2y)$.

When x is even, the product xy can be equally well determined as the product of $x/2$ and $2y$. This explains why one crosses out a line where the first term is even: The product of the two numbers in a crossed-out line equals the product of the numbers in the line below.

When x is odd, however, the entry below x is $\frac{x-1}{2}$, while the entry below y is $2y$. Their product is $(\frac{x-1}{2})(2y) = xy - y$, so the product xy is the product of the numbers in the line below, **plus** y. Note that y is the number in the right column corresponding to the odd x on the left. Thus, we do not cross out lines where x is odd; the y terms must be added at the end to give the correct product.

7. $\sqrt{3} \approx 1.7321$ as shown.

```
                    1.    7     3     2     0     5
              ┌──────────────────────────────────────
              │ 3.  0   0 | 0   0 | 0   0 | 0   0 | 0   0
        1     │ 1
       27     │ 2   0   0
              │ 1   8   9
      343     │     1   1   0   0
              │     1   0   2   9
     3462     │             7   1   0   0
              │             6   9   2   4
    34640     │                 1   7   6   0   0
              │                             0
   346405     │                 1   7   6   0   0   0   0
              │                 1   7   3   2   0   2   5
              │                 ───────────────────────
              │                     2   7   9   8   5
```

8. We find the sum of the numbers and divide by n. Thus, to find the average of n numbers $a_1, a_2, \ldots, a_n$,

Step 1: set $S = 0$;

Step 2: for $i = 1$ to n, replace S by $S + a_i$;

Step 3: output $\frac{S}{n}$.

9. To find the maximum of n numbers $a_1, a_2, \ldots, a_n$,

Step 1: let $M = a_1$;

Step 2: for $i = 2$ to n, if $a_i > M$, replace M by a_i;

Step 3: output M.

The value of M output in Step 3 is the maximum of the a_i.

12. If $x \le a_1$, we wish to output $x, a_1, a_2, \ldots, a_n$. If $a_1 < x \le a_2$, we wish to output $a_1, x, a_2, \ldots, a_n$, and so on. If $x \ge a_n$, we wish to output $a_1, a_2, \ldots, a_n, x$. Here is one suitable algorithm.

To insert x into its correct position in the ordered list $a_1 \le a_2 \le \cdots \le a_n$,

Step 1: set $F = 0$;

Step 2: for $i = 1$ to n,

    if $x \le a_i$ and $F = 0$, output x and set $F = 1$;

    output a_i.

Step 3: if $F = 0$, output x.

The variable F introduced here is a *flag*, whose purpose is to tell us whether x has been output. At the end of the loop in Step 2, if x has not been output (that is, x is larger than all the a_i's), then we will know this, because F will not have changed from its initial value of 0; hence, we must output x as the final element. Note that the "and" in Step 2 is the logical "and" introduced in Section 0.1. We output x and set $F = 1$ only if both $x \le a_i$ and $F = 0$ are true.

14. Here's the idea. Divide a by 2, thereby obtaining $a = 2q_1 + a_1, 0 \le a_1 < 2$. Then divide q_1 by 3, obtaining $q_1 = 3q_2 + a_2, 0 \le a_2 < 3$. Note that, at this point, we have $a = 2(3q_2 + a_2) + a_1 = 3!q_2 + 2!a_2 + a_1$. Next, divide q_2 by 4, obtaining $q_2 = 4q_3 + a_3$ and $a = 4!q_3 + 3!a_3 + 2!a_2 + a_1$. Eventually, we have

$$a = n!q_{n-1} + a_{n-1}(n-1)! + \cdots + a_2 2! + a_1,$$

which, with $a_n = q_{n-1}$, is the required expression. (Note that if at some stage $q_{k-1} = 0$ we have $a_n = a_{n-1} = \cdots = a_k = 0$, but the procedure is still valid.)

    Here is the algorithm for writing $a = a_n n! + a_{n-1}(n-1)! + \cdots + a_2 2! + a_1$.

Step 1: Let $q_0 = a$.

Step 2: For $i = 1$ to $n - 1$, write $q_{i-1} = (i+1)q_i + a_i$ with $0 \le a_i < i + 1$.

Step 3: Let $a_n = q_{n-1}$.

16. A number between 0 and $2^n - 1$, when expressed in base 2, is a string of at most n 0's and 1's. By "padding" with initial 0's, if necessary, we can assume that all such strings have length exactly n. Then such a string, $\epsilon_1 \epsilon_2 \cdots \epsilon_n$, each $\epsilon_i = 0$ or 1, determines the subset A of $\{a_1, a_2, \ldots, a_n\}$ as follows: $a_i \in A \leftrightarrow \epsilon_i = 1$. Thus, the string $00 \ldots 0$ of n 0's corresponds to the empty set, the string $11 \ldots 1$

of n 1's to the entire set $\{a_1, a_2, \ldots, a_n\}$, the string $11010 \ldots 0$ to the subset $\{a_1, a_2, a_4\}$, and so on. Enumerating the subsets of $\{a_1, \ldots, a_n\}$ now simply amounts to listing the integers between 0 and $2^n - 1$ in base 2. Here is an algorithm.

Step 1: Let $M = 0$. Output the words "empty set."
Step 2: for $i = 1$ to $2^n - 1$

- replace M by $M + 1$;
- write $M = \epsilon_1 \epsilon_2 \cdots \epsilon_n$ as an n-digit number in base 2;
- for $k = 1$ to n, if $\epsilon_k = 1$, output a_k.

Each value of i in Step 2 yields one subset of $\{a_1, \ldots, a_n\}$ and, when Step 2 is complete, all subsets have been output.

17. (a) i. $S = 1$; $S = 1 + (-3)(2) = -5$; $S = -5 + 2(2^2) = -5 + 8 = 3$.
    ii. $S = 2$; $S = -3 + 2(2) = 1$; $S = 1 + 1(2) = 3$.

18. The first value of S is $S = a_n$.

With $i = 1$ in Step 2, the value of S is $a_{n-1} + Sx = a_{n-1} + a_n x$.

With $i = 2$ in Step 2, the value of S is $a_{n-2} + Sx = a_{n-2} + (a_{n-1} + a_n x)x = a_{n-2} + a_{n-1}x + a_n x^2$.

With $i = 3$ in Step 2, the value of S is $a_{n-3} + Sx = a_{n-3} + a_{n-2}x + a_{n-1}x^2 + a_n x^3$.

With $i = n$, the value of S is $a_{n-n} + a_{n-(n-1)}x + a_{n-(n-2)}x^2 + \cdots + a_n x^n = a_0 + a_1 x + a_2 x^2 + \cdots + a_n x^n$, as desired.

Section 8.2 True/False

1. False   **2.** False   **3.** False: $n^2 = \mathcal{O}(n^3)$, but $n^3 \neq \mathcal{O}(n^2)$.   **4.** True
5. False: $n^2 = \mathcal{O}(n^3)$, but $(n^2)(n^2) = n^4 \neq \mathcal{O}(n^3)$.   **6.** True   **7.** True   **8.** True
9. True: $\log_a n = \log_a b \log_b n$.   **10.** False

Exercises 8.2

1. $f(n) = n + 2n + n - 1 + 20 = 4n + 19$

3. Consider the division of a number a, which has at most two digits, by a single-digit number b, where $a < 10b$.

$$b \,\overline{\left) \begin{array}{c} q \\ a \\ qb \\ \hline a - qb \end{array}\right.}$$

Since the quotient q has just one digit, the division counts as one operation, the product qb counts as another, and, since $a - qb < b$, the difference $a - qb$ has just a single digit, so the subtraction requires a third operation. In the division of an n-digit number by a single-digit number, this process is repeated at most $n - 1$ or n times, depending on whether b is greater than the first digit of a. So at most $3n$ operations are required.

5. The number of multiplications required by Algorithm $\mathcal{A}$ is the number of times Step 2 is executed, which is 2^n. On the other hand, Algorithm $\mathcal{B}$ requires just n multiplications. Algorithm $\mathcal{B}$ is more efficient because $n \prec 2^n$.

6. (a) With reference to Horner's algorithm as described in (8.1.1), each iteration of Step 2 requires two operations. Since Step 2 is repeated n times, this method requires $2n$ operations. This is fewer operations than are needed by the obvious method of polynomial evaluation, as we now show.

Assuming i multiplications to compute $a_i x^i$, $1 + 2 + \cdots + n = \frac{1}{2}n(n + 1)$ multiplications are involved in the evaluation of $a_0 + a_1 x + \cdots + a_n x^n$. As well, n additions are required, for a total of $\frac{n(n + 1)}{2} + n = \frac{n^2 + 3n}{2}$ operations. This estimate can be improved. Problem 18 shows that x^i can be computed with approximately $\log i$ multiplications. So $1 + \log i$ multiplications are required for $a_i x^i$ and

$$1 + (1 + \log 2) + (1 + \log 3) + \cdots + (1 + \log n) = n + \log n!$$

for the polynomial. Including additions, approximately $2n + \log n!$ operations are required.

7. (a) Since $5n \leq n^3$ for all $n \geq 3$, we can take $c = 1, n_0 = 3$, or $c = 5, n_0 = 1$.

(c) For $n \geq 1$, we have $8n^3 + 4n^2 + 5n + 1 \leq 9n^4 + 18n^2 + 24n + 6 = 3(3n^4 + 6n^2 + 8n + 2)$, so we can take $c = 3, n_0 = 1$.

8. (a) By Proposition 8.2.7, for instance, $5n \asymp n$, and by Proposition 8.2.8, $n \prec n^3$. Thus, $5n \prec n^3$.

(c) By Proposition 8.2.7, $f(n) \asymp n^3$ and $g(n) \asymp n^4$. By Proposition 8.2.8, $n^3 \prec n^4$, so $f \prec g$.

10. (c) Suppose $f \prec g$ and $g \prec h$. We must prove $f \prec h$. By part (a), $f = \mathcal{O}(h)$, so it remains only to prove that $h \neq \mathcal{O}(f)$. Assume to the contrary that $h = \mathcal{O}(f)$. Then, since $f = \mathcal{O}(g)$, using part (a) again, we would have that $h = \mathcal{O}(g)$, contradicting $g \prec h$.

11. If $f \asymp g$, then $f = \mathcal{O}(g)$. Since $g \prec h$, $g = \mathcal{O}(h)$ and so, by Exercise 10(a), $f = \mathcal{O}(h)$. To obtain $f \prec h$, we have now to prove that h is not $\mathcal{O}(f)$. But if $h = \mathcal{O}(f)$, then, because $f = \mathcal{O}(g)$, we would have that $h = \mathcal{O}(g)$, contradicting $g \prec h$.

12. We have $a^n < b^n$ for $n \geq 1$ since $a < b$, so $a^n = \mathcal{O}(b^n)$. We must prove $b^n \neq \mathcal{O}(a^n)$. If $b^n = \mathcal{O}(a^n)$, then there would exist a constant c such that $b^n \leq ca^n$ for all sufficiently large n. Dividing by a, we obtain $(\frac{b}{a})^n \leq c$, for all sufficiently large n, but this is not true because $\frac{b}{a} > 1$ implies that $(\frac{b}{a})^n$ grows without bound as n increases.

13. (a) We established $2^n < n!$ for $n \geq 4$ in Problem 6 of Chapter 5. Thus, $2^n = \mathcal{O}(n!)$ ($c = 1, n_0 = 4$). On the other hand, $n! \neq \mathcal{O}(2^n)$, for consider

$$\frac{n!}{2^n} = \frac{1}{2}\frac{2}{2}\frac{3}{2}\frac{4}{2} \cdots \frac{n}{2}.$$

The product of the first three factors on the right is $\frac{3}{4}$, and each of the remaining $n - 3$ terms is bigger than 2. So $\frac{n!}{2^n} > \frac{3}{4}(2^{n-3})$ for $n > 3$. If $n! = \mathcal{O}(2^n)$, then $n! < c2^n$ for some constant c and all sufficiently large n and so $\frac{n!}{2^n} < c$. We have shown this is not possible. Since $2^n = \mathcal{O}(n!)$ but $n! \neq \mathcal{O}(2^n)$, we have $2^n \prec n!$, as required.

15. For any $n \geq 1$, $|kf(n)| = |k||f(n)|$. Taking $n_0 = 1$ and $c = |k|$ in Definition 8.2.1, we see that kf is $\mathcal{O}(f)$. Also, $|f(n)| = \frac{1}{|k|}|k(f(n))|$ says that $f = \mathcal{O}(kf)$, and so $f \asymp kf$.

17. Reflexivity: For all $n \geq 1$, $|f(n)| \leq |f(n)|$, so with $c = 1, n_0 = 1$ in Definition 8.2.1 we see that f is $\mathcal{O}(f)$ and hence $f \asymp f$.

Symmetry: If $f \asymp g$, then $f = \mathcal{O}(g)$ and $g = \mathcal{O}(f)$. Hence, $g = \mathcal{O}(f)$ and $f = \mathcal{O}(g)$, so $g \asymp f$.

Transitivity: If $f \asymp g$ and $g \asymp h$, then $f = \mathcal{O}(g)$ and $g = \mathcal{O}(h)$. Therefore, $f = \mathcal{O}(h)$ by Exercise 10(a). Since $h = \mathcal{O}(g)$ and $g = \mathcal{O}(f)$, an argument identical to the one just given yields that $h = \mathcal{O}(f)$ as well. Thus, $f \asymp h$.

18. Since $\log_2 n = \mathcal{O}(n)$ by Proposition 8.2.9 and $n = \mathcal{O}(n)$, we have $n \log_2 n = \mathcal{O}(n^2)$ by Proposition 8.2.3. Thus, it remains only to show that $n^2 \neq \mathcal{O}(n \log_2 n)$. Assume to the contrary that for some positive constant c we have $n^2 \leq cn \log_2 n$ for all sufficiently large n. Then, for large n, we would have $n \leq c \log_2 n$. This says $n = \mathcal{O}(\log_2 n)$, contradicting Proposition 8.2.9.

19. (b) $f \asymp n^2$

(e) Note first that $3n! - 17n^4 < 3n!$, so $3n! - 17n^4 = \mathcal{O}(n!)$ using $c = 3, n_0 = 1$. For the converse, recall (see just before Proposition 8.2.9) that $n^4 < 2^n$ for large enough n (here, $n \geq 17$), so that $n! - 17n^4 > n! - 17(2^n)$ for $n \geq 17$. However, for such values of n, it is clear that $n! - 17(2^n) > 0$, so $3n! - 17n^4 > n!$. Thus, $n!$ is $\mathcal{O}(3n! - 17n^4)$, taking $c = 1, n_0 = 17$.

20. (a) n^5 (e) Since $2 + 4 + 6 + \cdots + 2n = n^2 + n$, the answer is n^2.

21. Since $\log_a n = (\log_a b)(\log_b n)$, we have $|\log_a n| = |\log_a b||\log_b n|$ for all $n \geq 1$. With $c = \log_a b$ and $n_0 = 1$ in Definition 8.2.1, we see that $\log_a n$ is $\mathcal{O}(\log_b n)$. By symmetry, $\log_b n = \mathcal{O}(\log_a n)$; hence, $\log_a n \asymp \log_b n$.

24. Since $n! = n(n-1)(n-2) \cdots 3 \cdot 2 \cdot 1 < n^n$, $\log n! \leq n \log n$. With $c = 1, n_0 = 1$ in Definition 8.2.1, we see that $\log n! = \mathcal{O}(n \log n)$, as required.

Section 8.3 True/False

1. False: The final value of i is 8. **2.** True **3.** True **4.** True **5.** False **6.** True

7. True **8.** False: $F = 1$ at the end. **9.** True **10.** False: It's $\frac{4+5}{2} = 4.5$.

Exercises 8.3

1. (a) Since $n = 9 \neq 1$, we set $m = \lfloor \frac{9}{2} \rfloor = 4$. Since $2 = x \leq a_4 = 4$, we set $n = m = 4$ and change the list to 1, 2, 3, 4.

Since $4 = n \neq 1$, we set $m = \lfloor \frac{4}{2} \rfloor = 2$. Since $2 = x \leq a_2 = 2$ we set $n = m = 2$ and change the list to 1, 2.

Since $2 = n \neq 1$, we set $m = \lceil \frac{2}{2} \rceil = 1$. Since $2 = x > a_1 = 1$, we replace n by $n - m = 1$ and change the list to 2.

Since $n = 1$ and $x = a_1$, we output "true" and stop.

This search required four comparisons of x with an element in the list; a linear search would have used two.

6. (a) To find the complement of $A = \{a_1, a_2, \dots, a_k\}$ with respect to $U = \{1, 2, \dots, 100\}$,

Step 1: For $i = 1$ to 100, search A for i, and if i is not found, output i.

The output numbers are the elements of A^c.

7.

$\mathcal{L}_1$	$\mathcal{L}_2$	$\mathcal{L}_3$
1, 2, 3, 4, 5	2, 4, 6, 8, 10	
2, 3, 4, 5	2, 4, 6, 8, 10	1
3, 4, 5	2, 4, 6, 8, 10	1, 2
3, 4, 5	4, 6, 8, 10	1, 2, 2
4, 5	4, 6, 8, 10	1, 2, 2, 3
5	4, 6, 8, 10	1, 2, 2, 3, 4
5	6, 8, 10	1, 2, 2, 3, 4, 4
		1, 2, 2, 3, 4, 4, 5, 6, 8, 10

The algorithm required seven comparisons.

10. (a) The lists 1 and 2, 3, 4 can be merged with one comparison.

$\mathcal{L}_1$	$\mathcal{L}_2$	$\mathcal{L}_3$
1	2, 3, 4	
		1, 2, 3, 4

(b) The lists 5 and 2, 3, 4 can be merged with three comparisons.

$\mathcal{L}_1$	$\mathcal{L}_2$	$\mathcal{L}_3$
5	2, 3, 4	
5	3, 4	2
5	4	2, 3
		2, 3, 4, 5

(c) The lists 1, 3, 5 and 2, 4, 6 can be merged with $3 + 3 - 1 = 5$ comparisons.

$\mathcal{L}_1$	$\mathcal{L}_2$	$\mathcal{L}_3$
1, 3, 5	2, 4, 6	
3, 5	2, 4, 6	1
3, 5	4, 6	1, 2
5	4, 6	1, 2, 3
5	6	1, 2, 3, 4
		1, 2, 3, 4, 5, 6

13. (a) Here's the bubble sort:

$k = 5$:   3, 1, 7, 2, 5, 4 → 1, 3, 7, 2, 5, 4 → 1, 3, 7, 2, 5, 4 → 1, 3, 2, 7, 5, 4 → 1, 3, 2, 5, 7, 4

$k = 4$:   1, 3, 2, 5, 4, 7 → 1, 3, 2, 5, 4, 7 → 1, 2, 3, 5, 4, 7 → 1, 2, 3, 5, 4, 7

$k = 3$:   1, 2, 3, 4, 5, 7 → 1, 2, 3, 4, 5, 7 → 1, 2, 3, 4, 5, 7

$k = 2$:   1, 2, 3, 4, 5, 7 → 1, 2, 3, 4, 5, 7

$k = 1$:   1, 2, 3, 4, 5, 7 → 1, 2, 3, 4, 5, 7

This required a total of $5 + 4 + 3 + 2 + 1 = 15$ comparisons.

(b) Here's the merge sort.

Step 2:   1;   3;   2;   7;   4;   5

Step 3: 1, 3; 2, 7; 4, 5

Step 3: 1, 2, 3, 7; 4, 5

Step 3: 1, 2, 3, 4, 5, 7

Merging two lists of length 1 to one of length 2 requires $1 + 1 - 1 = 1$ comparison. Thus, the initial merging of six lists of length 1 to three lists of length 2 requires $1 + 1 + 1 = 3$ comparisons. Merging three lists of length 2 to one of length 4 and one of length 2 required $2 + 2 - 1 = 3$ comparisons. The final merging of lists of lengths 4 and 2 requires $4 + 2 - 1 = 5$ comparisons, for a total of $3 + 3 + 5 = 11$ comparisons.

16. Sort the list into increasing order $a_1 \leq a_2 \leq \cdots \leq a_n$. If $n = 2m + 1$ is odd, the median is a_m; if $n = 2m$ is even, the median is $\frac{1}{2}(a_m + a_{m+1})$. Since determining the parity of n adds only another operation, the complexity of this algorithm is the complexity of the sort, at best $\mathcal{O}(n \log n)$.

17. (a) Here's the bubble sort.

$k = 7$: $\underline{a,b},c,d,u,v,w,x \to a,\underline{b,c},d,u,v,w,x \to a,c,\underline{b,d},u,v,w,x$
$\to a,c,d,\underline{b,u},v,w,x \to a,c,d,u,\underline{b,v},w,x$
$\to a,c,d,u,b,\underline{v,w},x \to a,c,d,u,b,v,\underline{w,x}$

$k = 6$: $\underline{a,c},d,u,b,v,x,w \to a,\underline{c,d},u,b,v,x,w \to a,d,\underline{c,u},b,v,x,w$
$\to a,d,u,\underline{c,b},v,x,w \to a,d,u,c,\underline{b,v},x,w \to a,d,u,c,b,\underline{v,x},w$

$k = 5$: $\underline{a,d},u,c,b,x,v,w \to d,\underline{a,u},c,b,x,v,w \to d,a,\underline{u,c},b,x,v,w$
$\to d,a,u,\underline{c,b},x,v,w \to d,a,u,c,\underline{b,x},v,w$

$k = 4$: $\underline{d,a},u,c,x,b,v,w \to d,\underline{a,u},c,x,b,v,w \to d,a,\underline{u,c},x,b,v,w$
$\to d,a,u,\underline{c,x},b,v,w$

$k = 3$: $\underline{d,a},u,c,x,b,v,w \to d,\underline{a,u},c,x,b,v,w \to d,a,\underline{u,c},x,b,v,w$

$k = 2$: $\underline{d,a},u,c,x,b,v,w \to d,\underline{a,u},c,x,b,v,w$

$k = 1$: $\underline{d,a},u,c,x,b,v,w \to d,a,u,c,x,b,v,w$

A total of $7 + 6 + 5 + 4 + 3 + 2 + 1 = 28$ comparisons is needed.

18. (a) $\underline{c,a},e,b,d \to a,\underline{c,e},b,d \to a,c,\underline{e,b},d \to a,c,b,\underline{e,d}$
$\underline{a,c},b,d,e \to a,\underline{c,b},d,e \to a,b,\underline{c,d},e$
$\underline{a,b},c,d,e \to a,\underline{b,c},d,e$
$\underline{a,b},c,d,e \to a,b,c,d,e$

21. The answer is $\min\{s, t\}$. It is impossible to have fewer than this number of comparisons since, until $\min\{s, t\}$ of comparisons have been made, elements remain in each list. To see that $\min\{s, t\}$ can be achieved, consider ordered lists $a_1, a_2, \ldots, a_s$ and $b_1, b_2, \ldots, b_t$ where $s < t$ and $a_s < b_1$. After s comparisons, the first list is empty.

23. Using the efficient binary search, $\mathcal{O}(\log k)$ comparisons are needed to search the predecessors of a_k. In all, the number of comparisons is $\mathcal{O}(\log 1 + \log 2 + \cdots + \log n)$. Since $\log a + \log b = \log ab$, we have $\log 1 + \log 2 + \cdots + \log n = \log n!$. The result follows.

25. This is less efficient. A merge sort is $\mathcal{O}(n \log n)$ and a binary search is $\mathcal{O}(\log n)$. Since $n + n \log n \asymp n \log n$, the suggested procedure is $\mathcal{O}(n \log n)$, while a linear search is $\mathcal{O}(n)$, which is better.

Section 8.4 True/False

1. True **2.** True **3.** False: It's 152436. **4.** True

5. False: There is no permutation following 654321. **6.** True: $6! = 720$. **7.** False

8. False: It's 123578. **9.** False: It's 123457. **10.** True

Exercises 8.4

1. (a)

t	Perm(t)	j	m	S
1	$\begin{array}{cccc} 1 & 2 & 3 & 4 \\ \pi_1 & \pi_2 & \pi_3 & \pi_4 \end{array}$	3	4	$\{1, 2, 4\}^c = \{3\}$
2	$\begin{array}{cccc} 1 & 2 & 4 & 3 \\ \pi_1 & \pi_2 & \pi_3 & \pi_4 \end{array}$	2	3	$\{1, 3\}^c = \{2, 4\}$
3	$\begin{array}{cccc} 1 & 3 & 2 & 4 \\ \pi_1 & \pi_2 & \pi_3 & \pi_4 \end{array}$	3	4	$\{1, 3, 4\}^c = \{2\}$
4	$\begin{array}{cccc} 1 & 3 & 4 & 2 \\ \pi_1 & \pi_2 & \pi_3 & \pi_4 \end{array}$	2	4	$\{1, 4\}^c = \{2, 3\}$
5	$\begin{array}{cccc} 1 & 4 & 2 & 3 \\ \pi_1 & \pi_2 & \pi_3 & \pi_4 \end{array}$	3	3	$\{1, 4, 3\}^c = \{2\}$
6	$\begin{array}{cccc} 1 & 4 & 3 & 2 \\ \pi_1 & \pi_2 & \pi_3 & \pi_4 \end{array}$	1	2	$\{2\}^c = \{1, 3, 4\}$
7	$\begin{array}{cccc} 2 & 1 & 3 & 4 \\ \pi_1 & \pi_2 & \pi_3 & \pi_4 \end{array}$	3	4	$\{2, 1, 4\}^c = \{3\}$
8	2143			

2. (b) 42531, 43125, 43152, 43215, 43251

3. (a) We consider each part of Step 2. Finding the largest j such that $\pi_j < \pi_{j+1}$ requires at most n comparisons. At most another n comparisons are needed to find the minimum of $\{\pi_i \mid i < j, \pi_i > \pi_j\}$. To find the complement of a subset A of $\{1, 2, \ldots, n\}$ requires searching A for each of the elements $1, 2, \ldots, n$ and noting those that are not in A. Using the efficient binary search, each search is $\mathcal{O}(\log_2 n)$, adding another $n \log_2 n$ comparisons. An efficient merge sort adds another $n \log_2 n$ comparisons, so each pass through Step 2 requires at most $n+n+n \log_2 n+n \log_2 n = 2(n+n \log_2 n)$ comparisons. Since this step is executed $n! - 1$ times and $n + n \log_2 n \sim n \log_2 n$, the algorithm is $\mathcal{O}(n!n \log_2 n)$.

5. (a)

1234	1235	1236	1245	1246
1256	1345	1346	1356	1456
2345	2346	2356	2456	3456

6. (a) 23459, 23467, 23468 precede; 23478, 23479, 23489 follow.

7. (b) First list the combinations of $1, 2, \ldots, n$ taken r at a time by the method of Proposition 8.4.3. Then, for each of these combinations, enumerate all permutations of its elements using Algorithm 8.4.2.

8. (a)

123456	123457	123458	123467	123468	123478	123567
123568	123578	123678	124567	124568	124578	124678
125678	134567	134568	134578	134678	135678	145678
234567	234568	234578	234678	235678	245678	345678

9. If $a_1 a_2 \ldots a_r$ is one of the combinations of $1, 2, \ldots, n$ taken r at a time, a_1 cannot be less than 1, a_2 cannot be less than 2, and, in general, a_i cannot be less than i. Thus, $123 \ldots r$ is the smallest combination.

Now let π be a combination and π' the combination determined by π as in the proposition. We show that π' is the immediate successor of π with respect to lexicographic order. First, since all numbers to the left of $k - 1$ are the same in both combinations, while $k - 1$ is increased to k, we conclude that $\pi \prec \pi'$. Now suppose that $\pi \prec \sigma \preceq \pi'$ for some combination σ. All integers to the left of $k - 1$ (in π) are the same in π' as well, and hence also in σ. If $k - 1$ were also the same in σ, then we would have $\sigma = \pi$ since no number to the right of $k - 1$ can be increased in π. Thus, in σ, $k - 1$ must be increased to k (and no more, since $\sigma \prec \pi'$). It then follows that $\sigma = \pi'$ since π' is the smallest sequence whose initial segment (up to k) consists of the integers of π'.

10. (a) $n; n - r + 1; n - r + j$ (b) It must be $123 \ldots r$.   (c) It must be $(n - r + 1)(n - r + 2) \ldots n$.

11. Given $n \geq r > 0$, to enumerate the $\binom{n}{r}$ combinations of $1, 2, \ldots, n$ taken r at a time, proceed as follows.

Step 1: Set $t = 1$. Output Comb$(1) = 123 \ldots r$. If $r = n$, stop.

Step 2: For $t = 1$ to $\binom{n}{r} - 1$, given combination $\mathrm{Comb}(t) = a_1 a_2 \dots a_r$, determine the next combination $\mathrm{Comb}(t + 1)$ as follows.
  (i) Find the largest j such that $a_j < n - r + j$.
  (ii) Output $\mathrm{Comb}(t + 1) = a_1 \, a_2 \, \dots \, a_{j-1} \, a_j + 1 \, a_j + 2 \, \dots \, a_j + r - j + 1$.

Section 9.1 True/False

1. True   **2.** False: Euler is.   **3.** True   **4.** False: It will have 16 edges.   **5.** True
6. False   **7.** False: The graph has four edges.   **8.** True   **9.** True   **10.** True

Exercises 9.1

1. 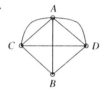   **2.**

4. (a) We present the graph that corresponds to the cubes and two edge-disjoint subgraphs.

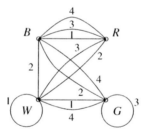   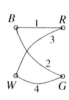

Here is the solution indicated.

	F	B	R	L
Cube 4	B	G	W	G
Cube 3	R	B	R	W
Cube 2	W	R	G	B
Cube 1	G	W	B	R

(e) Here are the graphs corresponding to the cubes and two edge-disjoint subgraphs.

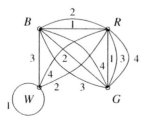

Here is the solution indicated.

	F	B	R	L
Cube 4	G	B	W	R
Cube 3	R	G	B	W
Cube 2	B	R	G	B
Cube 1	W	W	R	G

5. (a) Beta index $= \frac{7}{6}$ **6.**

9. If there are four or more vertices of one color, say red, then there are at least $\binom{4}{3} = 4$ red triangles. Otherwise, there are three red and three white vertices, hence, one triangle of each color.

Section 9.2 True/False

1. True   **2.** False: This statement defines **adjacent** vertices.   **3.** True   **4.** False

5. False: The second one does not represent a graph.   **6.** False: It has six edges.

7. True   **8.** True   **9.** True   **10.** True

Exercises 9.2

1. Here is one possibility.   **3.**

5. 10 edges. This is $\mathcal{K}_5$, the complete graph on five vertices.

9. (a)   i.

	v_1	v_2	v_3	v_4	v_5	v_6
v_1	0	1	2	2	2	1
v_2	1	0	1	2	3	2
v_3	2	1	0	1	2	1
v_4	2	2	1	0	2	1
v_5	2	3	2	2	0	1
v_6	1	2	1	1	1	0

ii.

Vertex	v_1	v_2	v_3	v_4	v_5	v_6
column total	8	9	7	8	10	6
vertex degree	2	2	3	2	1	4
accessibility index	4	4.5	2.$\dot{3}$	4	10	1.5

City v_6 has the lowest accessibility index; it is the most accessible. City v_5 is least accessible.

iii. Joining v_1 and v_3 gives now eight edges, with still six vertices.
New beta index $= \frac{8}{6} = 1.\dot{3}$.
New accessibility indexes are 2.$\dot{3}$, 4.5, 1.5, 4, 10, 1.5.
Cities v_6 and v_3 are now tied for most accessible; v_5 is least accessible.

iv. Joining v_2 and v_6 gives eight edges and still six vertices.
New beta index $= \frac{8}{6} = 1.\dot{3}$.
New accessibility indexes are 4, 2.$\dot{3}$, 2.$\dot{3}$, 4, 9, 1.
City v_6 is most accessible; v_5 is least accessible.

10. $\mathcal{K}_n$ has $\binom{n}{2} = \frac{n(n-1)}{2}$ edges. Each of the n vertices has degree $n - 1$, so the sum of the degrees is $n(n - 1)$. This is twice the number of edges, as asserted by Proposition 9.2.5. If n is even there are n odd vertices; if n is odd, there are 0 odd vertices. In either case the number of odd vertices is even, in accordance with Corollary 9.2.6. The beta index is $\frac{n(n-1)/2}{n} = \frac{n-1}{2}$.

12. (a) Suppose $\mathcal{G}$ has a vertices of degree 3 and b vertices of degree 4. Then $\sum \deg v_i = 3a + 4b = 56 = 2|\mathcal{E}|$ and $a + b = 12$. These equations imply $a < 0$, which cannot be. No such $\mathcal{G}$ exists.

13. Consider the graph in which the vertices correspond to the people at the party and an edge between vertices indicates that the corresponding people shook hands. The degree of a vertex in this graph is the number of hands that person shook. Thus, the result is an immediate consequence of Corollary 9.2.6.

15. (a) Yes, as indicated.

16. (a)

$\mathcal{G} \smallsetminus \{e\}$ $\mathcal{G} \smallsetminus \{v\}$ $\mathcal{G} \smallsetminus \{u\}$

17. (a) Degree of v_1 is 1; degree of v_2 is 3; degree of v_3 is 4; degree of v_4 is 2.

   (b) No. The maximum degree of a vertex in a graph with four vertices is 3. (Loops are not allowed in graphs.)

18. (a) No such graph exists. The sum of the degrees of the vertices is an odd number, 17, which is impossible.

   (c) Impossible. A vertex of degree 5 in a graph with six vertices must be adjacent to all other vertices. Two vertices of degree 5 means all other vertices have degree at least 2, but the given degree sequence contains a 1.

20. (a) 12

21. (a) This is not bipartite because it contains a triangle.

   (c) This is bipartite with bipartition sets indicated R and W.

22. (a) At least two of the three vertices must lie in one of the bipartition sets. Since these two are joined by an edge, the graph cannot be bipartite.

24. Let x be the number of vertices in one of the bipartition sets. Then $n - x$ is the number of vertices in the other. The largest number of edges occurs when all x vertices in one set are joined to all $n - x$ vertices in the other; so the number of edges is at most $x(n - x)$. The function $f(x) = x(n - x)$ (whose graph is a parabola) has a unique maximum at $(\frac{n}{2}, \frac{n^2}{4})$, so $x(n - x) \le \frac{n^2}{4}$ for all x, and the result follows.

26. (a) $2^{\binom{n}{2}}$ (c) $\binom{n}{3} 2^{\binom{n}{2} - 3}$ **28.** 23

30. $\sum \deg v_i = k|\mathcal{V}|$. But also, $\sum \deg v_i = 2|\mathcal{E}|$. Therefore, $2|\mathcal{E}| = k|\mathcal{V}|$, and so k divides $2|\mathcal{E}|$. But k is odd, so $k \mid |\mathcal{E}|$.

32. There are n vertices and n possible degrees for the vertices; $0, 1, 2, \ldots, n - 1$. If, however, we have a vertex of degree 0, then it is not possible to have another vertex of degree $n - 1$. Hence, there are really only $n - 1$ possible "holes" into which the n vertices can fit. Hence, some vertex degree is repeated.

Section 9.3 True/False

1. False   **2.** True   **3.** True   **4.** False   **5.** False   **6.** True   **7.** True   **8.** True   **9.** False

10. True: All graphs in this text are finite, so a one-to-one function from $\mathcal{V}_1$ to $\mathcal{V}_2$ must be onto.

1. (i) and (ii) are not isomorphic because (i) has five edges and (ii) has four. (i) and (iii) are isomorphic, as shown by the labeling.

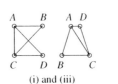

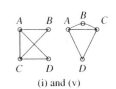

(i) and (iii)   (i) and (v)

(i) and (iv) are not isomorphic because (iv) has a vertex of degree 1 and (i) does not. Also, (iv) has only four edges.

(i) and (v) are isomorphic, as shown by the labeling.

(ii) and (iii) are not isomorphic because (ii) has four edges and (iii) has five edges.

(ii) and (iv) are not isomorphic because (iv) has a vertex of degree 1 and (ii) does not.

(ii) and (v) are not isomorphic because (v) has five edges and (ii) has four edges.

(iii) and (iv) are not isomorphic because (iv) has a vertex of degree 1 and (iii) does not.

(iii) and (v) are isomorphic, as shown by the labeling to the right.

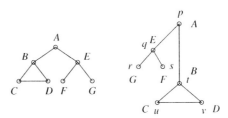

(iv) and (v) are not isomorphic because (iv) has a vertex of degree 1, or because (v) has five edges.

3. (a)

○   ○

○   ○   ○——○   ○——○   △

0, 0, 0   1, 1, 0   2, 1, 1   2, 2, 2

4. (b) These graphs are isomorphic. One possible isomorphism is given by

$$\varphi(A) = p, \quad \varphi(B) = t, \quad \varphi(C) = u, \quad \varphi(D) = v,$$
$$\varphi(E) = Q, \quad \varphi(F) = s, \quad \varphi(G) = r$$

as illustrated.

5. (a) No; it has a vertex of degree 5.

7. Any graph $\mathcal{G}$ with n vertices is a subgraph of $\mathcal{K}_n$, as is easily seen by joining any pair of vertices of $\mathcal{G}$ where there is not already an edge.

8. (a) Suppose that $\mathcal{G}$ and $\mathcal{H}$ are isomorphic graphs and $\varphi \colon \mathcal{V}(\mathcal{G}) \to \mathcal{V}(\mathcal{H})$ is the isomorphism of vertex sets given by Definition 9.3.1. Label the edges of $\mathcal{G}$ arbitrarily, $g_1, g_2, \ldots, g_m$, and then use φ to label the edges of $\mathcal{H}$ as $h_1, h_2, \ldots, h_m$; that is, if edge g_1 has end vertices v and w in $\mathcal{G}$, let h_1 be the edge joining $\varphi(v)$ and $\varphi(w)$ in $\mathcal{H}$. Repeat to obtain $h_2, \ldots, h_m$. Now a triangle in $\mathcal{G}$ is a set of three edges $\{g_i, g_j, g_k\}$ each two of which are adjacent. It follows from the way we labeled the edges of $\mathcal{H}$ that $\{g_i, g_j, g_k\}$ is a triangle in $\mathcal{G}$ if and only if $\{h_i, h_j, h_k\}$ is a triangle in $\mathcal{H}$. Thus, the number of triangles in each graph is the same.

9. (a) Each graph has seven vertices and 14 edges. The degree sequence of $\mathcal{G}_1$ is 4, 4, 4, 4, 4, 4, 4; the degree sequences of $\mathcal{G}_2$ and $\mathcal{G}_3$ are 5, 4, 4, 4, 4, 4, 3. The numbers of triangles in $\mathcal{G}_1, \mathcal{G}_2, \mathcal{G}_3$ are 7, 8, 8, respectively; specifically,

$$\begin{aligned}
\mathcal{G}_1 &: \quad ABC, ABG, AFG, BCD, CDE, DEF, EFG \\
\mathcal{G}_2 &: \quad abc, abd, acd, adg, bcd, bcf, deg, efg \\
\mathcal{G}_3 &: \quad 125, 126, 156, 167, 236, 256, 347, 367
\end{aligned}$$

11. (a) No.

Section 10.1 True/False

1. False   **2.** True   **3.** False   **4.** True   **5.** True   **6.** False: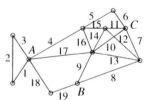

7. False   **8.** True   **9.** False   **10.** False   **11.** True   **12.** True   **13.** True

Exercises 10.1

1. (a) ○————○

2. Since the graph describing the Königsberg Bridge Problem (Fig. 9.2) has several odd vertices, it is not Eulerian. It is not possible to walk over the bridges of Königsberg exactly once and return to the starting position.

3. (a) The graph is Eulerian because it is connected and each vertex has even degree 4. Piecing the circuits $ABCDEFGA$ and $ACFBDGEA$ together at A gives the Eulerian circuit $ABCDEFGACFBD$ GEA.

4. (a)

5. This definition does not work. In the graph to the right, the sequence $e_1e_2e_3$ of edges fits Gerard's criteria, but does not define a walk.

7. (a) Yes, there is, because A and B are the only vertices of odd degree.

8. (a) No. In the graph representing the modified Königsberg Bridge Problem, there are two vertices of odd degree.

(b) This question asks about the possibility of an Eulerian trail and there is one, between the two vertices A and B of odd degree. One possibility is $ACBDADCAB$.

10. Yes. In this case, both $\mathcal{G}$ and $\mathcal{H}$ must be cycles.

12. (a) $\mathcal{K}_n$ is Eulerian $\leftrightarrow n$ is odd.

(b) $\mathcal{K}_n$ has an Eulerian trail if and only if $n = 2$. For $n = 2$, certainly ○—○ has an Eulerian trail. For $n > 2$, if two vertices have odd degree, then there are other vertices of odd degree, so no Eulerian trail can exist.

15. Suppose the vertices of the circuit are $v_0, v_1, \ldots, v_n, v_0$. Consider all subcircuits of the form $v_i, v_{i+1}, v_{i+2}, \ldots, v_i$. (There is at least one such, taking $i = 0$.) The subcircuit $v_i, v_{i+1}, v_{i+2}, \ldots, v_i$ that uses the fewest number of vertices is a cycle. If the original circuit was not a cycle, then those vertices not on the first chosen subcircuit $v_i, v_{i+1}, v_{i+2}, \ldots, v_i$, together with v_i, form another subcircuit, and the same argument as before shows that this contains a second cycle.

16. False. In the graph shown, $v_1 v_2 v_3 v_2 v_1$ is a closed walk that does not contain a cycle.

$$v_1 \qquad v_2 \qquad v_3$$

18. By definition, $u \sim u$, so $\sim$ is reflexive. If $u \sim v$, then there is a walk $u = u_0, u_1, \ldots, u_k = v$ from u to v. But then $v = u_k, u_{k-1}, \ldots, u_1, u_0 = u$ is a walk from v to u, so $v \sim u$ and $\sim$ is symmetric. Finally, if $u \sim v$ and $v \sim w$, then there is a walk $u = u_0, u_1, \ldots, u_k = v$ from u to v and a walk $v = v_0, v_1, \ldots, v_\ell = w$ from v to w. But then $u = u_0, u_1, \ldots, u_k = v = v_0, v_1, \ldots, v_\ell = w$ is a walk from u to w, proving $u \sim w$ and establishing transitivity.

22. We must show that there is a walk between any two vertices x and y of $\mathcal{G}$. We show that there is, in fact, a walk of length at most 2 between x and y. If xy is an edge, then obviously there is a walk from x to y, so suppose that xy is not an edge. Let $\mathcal{S}$ be the set of vertices adjacent to x and $\mathcal{T}$ be the set of vertices adjacent to y. Thus $x \notin \mathcal{S} \cup \mathcal{T}$ and $y \notin \mathcal{S} \cup \mathcal{T}$, so the number of vertices in $\mathcal{G}$ is $20 \geq |\mathcal{S} \cup \mathcal{T}| + 2$. Using the Principle of Inclusion-Exclusion, $20 \geq |\mathcal{S}| + |\mathcal{T}| - |\mathcal{S} \cap \mathcal{T}| + 2 = \deg x + \deg y - |\mathcal{S} \cap \mathcal{T}| + 2 \geq 21 - |\mathcal{S} \cap \mathcal{T}|$. It follows that $\mathcal{S} \cap \mathcal{T} \neq \emptyset$, so there is a vertex u in both $\mathcal{S}$ and $\mathcal{T}$ and thus a walk xuy from x to y.

23. (a) Since $\mathcal{G}$ is connected and $n > 1$, no vertices have degree zero. Therefore, if there are no vertices of degree 1, every vertex of $\mathcal{G}$ has degree at least 2. Using $\mathcal{E}$ to denote the set of edges of $\mathcal{G}$, it follows that $2|\mathcal{E}| = \sum \deg v_i \geq 2n$ (by Proposition 9.2.5), and the number of edges $|\mathcal{E}| \geq n$, as required.

27. Suppose that $\mathcal{G}_1$ has n_1 components and that $\mathcal{G}_2$ has $n_2 < n_1$ components. Let $v_1, \ldots, v_{n_1}$ be vertices of $\mathcal{G}_1$ each in a different component. Then there is no walk between any pair of these vertices. On the other hand, if $w_1, \ldots, w_{n_1}$ are any n_1 vertices of $\mathcal{G}_2$, at least two of these must lie in the same component (by the Pigeonhole Principle), and hence there is a walk between these two. Thus, the vertices v_i in $\mathcal{G}_1$ do not correspond to any n_1 vertices of $\mathcal{G}_2$, so these graphs cannot be isomorphic.

Section 10.2 True/False

1. True   **2.** True   **3.** False   **4.** True   **5.** False   **6.** True   **7.** True
8. False   **9.** False (unfortunately)   **10.** False: "At most" should be "at least."

Exercises 10.2

1. This graph is not Hamiltonian. To see this, suppose $\mathcal{H}$ were a Hamiltonian cycle. Since vertices A and B have degree 2, the two edges incident with each of these vertices would be in $\mathcal{H}$. Thus, $\mathcal{H}$ would contain the cycle $ACBDA$, which cannot be the case since this does not contain all vertices of the graph. The graph is not Eulerian because it contains vertices of odd degree.

2. (b) This is not Hamiltonian, since it isn't connected.   (d)

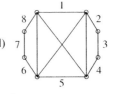

5. (a) Yes, it is Hamiltonian: $ABDCEA$ is a Hamiltonian cycle.

(c) The graph is not Eulerian. Vertices A and E have odd degree.

9. In the graph to the right, vertices correspond to rooms and edges to doorways.

(a) No, because the graph is not Hamiltonian. Since vertices A, C, D, and E have degree 2, the edges labeled 3, 4, 5, 6, 1, and 2 would have to be part of any Hamiltonian cycle. These edges, however, define a proper cycle, which is not allowed.

10. The result is obvious if $n = 1$, since in this case there are just two people who are friends. So we assume that $n > 1$. Consider the graph whose vertices correspond to people and where an edge between vertices v and u signifies that v and u are friends. The question asks us to prove that this graph is Hamiltonian. This is an immediate consequence of Dirac's Theorem, since the graph in question has $2n \geq 3$ vertices each of degree $d \geq n = \frac{2n}{2}$.

11. (a) n edges   (c) K_n has $\frac{n(n-1)}{2}$ edges, so the maximum is $\frac{n-1}{2}$ edge-disjoint cycles.

12. The cube is indeed Hamiltonian; the labels $1, \ldots, 8$ on the vertices exhibit a Hamiltonian cycle.

15. (a) As suggested, add an extra vertex v to $\mathcal{G}$ and join it to all other vertices. Then $\deg v = n \geq \frac{n+1}{2}$, and $\deg w \geq \frac{n-1}{2} + 1 = \frac{n+1}{2}$ for all other vertices. By Theorem 10.2.4, this new graph with $n + 1$ vertices has a Hamiltonian cycle. Deleting v and all the new edges incident with v leads to a Hamiltonian path in our original graph.

(e) ∘—∘ is an example!

16. As in the proof of Dirac's Theorem, all vertices adjacent to v_1 are in $\mathcal{P}$.

(a) If v_1 and v_t are adjacent, $\mathcal{C}_1$: $v_1 v_2 \cdots v_t v_1$ is a cycle. If $t < n$, then there exists a vertex w not in $\mathcal{C}_1$. As noted, w is not adjacent to v_1, hence the hypothesis tells us that $\deg v_1 + \deg w \geq n$. It follows that there exists some vertex u that is adjacent to both v_1 and w; otherwise, the graph has at least $n + 2$ vertices, counting v_1 and w and the disjoint sets of vertices adjacent to v_1 and to w. Since u is adjacent to v_1, $u = v_i$ for some i. Now $w v_i v_{i+1} \cdots v_t v_1 \cdots v_{i-1}$ is a path longer than $\mathcal{P}$, a contradiction. Thus $t = n$, so $\mathcal{C}_1$ is a Hamiltonian cycle and we are done.

18. Add a new vertex adjacent to all existing vertices and apply the result of Exercise 16.

20. By Dirac's Theorem, we know that $\mathcal{G}$ contains a Hamiltonian cycle $v_1, v_2, \ldots, v_n$.

First assume that v_1 and v_2 are not the vertices of a triangle, equivalently, that v_1 and v_2 are not adjacent to a common vertex. Then v_1 must be adjacent to exactly half of $v_3, \ldots, v_n$ while v_2 is adjacent to the other half. Since v_2 and v_3 are adjacent, there exists a minimal $i > 3$ such that v_2 is not adjacent to v_i. But then v_1 is adjacent to v_i, and v_2 is adjacent to v_{i-1}, so $v_1 v_2 v_{i-1} v_i$ is a 4-cycle.

Next assume that v_1 and v_2 are adjacent to two common vertices v_i and v_j. Then $v_1 v_i v_2 v_j$ is a 4-cycle.

Finally, we reach the case that v_1 and v_2 are adjacent to precisely one vertex v_j. We may also assume that $n \geq 6$, since if $n = 4$, the Hamiltonian cycle is a 4-cycle and, if $n = 5$, any edge added to the Hamiltonian cycle produces a 4-cycle. As before, choose the least $i > 3$ such that v_2 is not adjacent to v_i. If v_1 and v_i are adjacent, the previous argument still holds, so assume this is not the case. But then, for any $k \neq i, j$, $k \geq 3$, exactly one of v_1, v_2 must be adjacent to v_k. We finish the proof by considering a number of cases.

i. If $i > 4$ and $j = 3$, then $v_1 v_2 v_4 v_3$ is a 4-cycle.

ii. If $i > j > 3$, then $v_1 v_2 v_{j-1} v_j$ is a 4-cycle.

iii. If $i = 4$ and $j = 3$, then v_1 is adjacent to exactly half of $v_5, \ldots, v_n$, while v_2 is adjacent to the other half. If v_2 is adjacent to v_5, choosing $k > 5$ minimal with v_2 not adjacent to v_k, we have the 4-cycle $v_1 v_2 v_{k-1} v_k$. If v_1 is adjacent to v_5, choose $k > 5$ minimal with v_1 and v_k not adjacent. Then $v_1 v_2 v_k v_{k-1}$ is a 4-cycle.

iv. If $j = n$ and v_1 is adjacent to v_{n-1}, then $v_1 v_2 v_n v_{n-1}$ is a 4-cycle.

v. If $j = n$ and v_2 is adjacent to v_{n-1}, then $v_1 v_2 v_{n-1} v_n$ is a 4-cycle.
   We note that the case $j = n$, $i = n - 1$ is not possible.

vi. If $n > j > i$ and v_1 is adjacent to v_{j+1}, then $v_1 v_2 v_j v_{j+1}$ is a 4-cycle.

vii. If $n > j > i$ and v_2 is adjacent to v_{j+1}, then $v_1 v_2 v_{j+1} v_j$ is a 4-cycle.

21. (c) False. ⧖ is Eulerian but not Hamiltonian.

22. (a) Yes! Since there is a path between any two vertices, the graph is connected. Thus, there exists an edge e in the graph joining, say, vertices v and w. Now let $\mathcal{P}$ be a Hamiltonian path from v to w. Then starting at v following $\mathcal{P}$ to w and then e to v produces a Hamiltonian cycle from v to v.

Section 10.3 True/False

1. False   **2.** False   **3.** True   **4.** True   **5.** True   **6.** False

7. True   **8.** False: It's 3.   **9.** False   **10.** False

Exercises 10.3

1. $A = \begin{bmatrix} 0 & 1 & 0 & 1 & 0 & 0 \\ 1 & 0 & 1 & 1 & 0 & 0 \\ 0 & 1 & 0 & 1 & 1 & 1 \\ 1 & 1 & 1 & 0 & 0 & 0 \\ 0 & 0 & 1 & 0 & 0 & 1 \\ 0 & 0 & 1 & 0 & 1 & 0 \end{bmatrix}$ **3.** (a) The $(3, 5)$ entry of A^3 is 5. The $(2, 2)$ entry of A^3 is 2.

4. Each 1 represents an edge. Each edge $v_i v_j$ contributes two 1's to the matrix, in positions (i, j) and (j, i). The number of 1's is twice the number of edges.

6. (a) The (i, j) entry in A^2 is the number of walks of length 2 from i to j. Hence, the sum of all such entries is the total number of walks of length 2.

8. (a) $A_1 = \begin{bmatrix} 0 & 1 & 0 & 1 & 1 \\ 1 & 0 & 1 & 0 & 0 \\ 0 & 1 & 0 & 0 & 1 \\ 1 & 0 & 0 & 0 & 0 \\ 1 & 0 & 1 & 0 & 0 \end{bmatrix}$, $A_2 = \begin{bmatrix} 0 & 1 & 0 & 0 & 1 \\ 1 & 0 & 0 & 1 & 0 \\ 0 & 0 & 0 & 1 & 0 \\ 0 & 1 & 1 & 0 & 1 \\ 1 & 0 & 0 & 1 & 0 \end{bmatrix}$

(b) The function φ is an isomorphism because, if the vertices of $\mathcal{G}_1$ are relabeled, v_i being replaced by $\varphi(v_i) = u_i$, then the adjacency matrix of $\mathcal{G}_1$ relative to the u_i's is A_2. (See Theorem 10.3.3.)

(c) $P = \begin{bmatrix} 0 & 0 & 1 & 0 & 0 \\ 0 & 0 & 0 & 0 & 1 \\ 0 & 0 & 0 & 1 & 0 \\ 1 & 0 & 0 & 0 & 0 \\ 0 & 1 & 0 & 0 & 0 \end{bmatrix}$

11. (a) $PA = \begin{bmatrix} p & q & r \\ x & y & z \\ a & b & c \end{bmatrix}$ is A, but with rows written in the order 2, 3, 1, the order in which the rows of I were rearranged to give P.

13. (a) The matrices are the adjacency matrices of graphs $\mathcal{G}_1$, $\mathcal{G}_2$, respectively. Since $\mathcal{G}_2$ has three vertices of degree 1, while $\mathcal{G}_1$ has only one, the graphs are not isomorphic, so no such P exists, by Theorem 10.3.4.

14. The ith entry on the diagonal of A^{37} is the number of walks of length 37 from v_i to itself. But in a bipartite graph, you can only get from v_i back to itself in an even number of steps. Hence, the entry is 0.

15. (a) A^2 is an adjacency matrix $\leftrightarrow A$ is the 0 matrix.

Proof. For A^2 to be an adjacency matrix, it must have all diagonal entries equal to 0. But the ith diagonal entry of A^2 is the number of walks of length 2 from v_i to itself. Now, if $v_i v_j$ is an edge of $\mathcal{G}$, then $v_i v_j v_i$ is a walk of length 2 from v_i to itself, and the ith diagonal entry would not be 0. We conclude that $\mathcal{G}$ cannot have any edges; that is, A is the zero matrix. On the other hand, if A is the zero matrix, certainly $A^2 = A$ is an adjacency matrix.

18. We could store the *incidence matrix*, whose columns correspond to edges and rows to vertices. The (i, j) entry is 1 if vertex i is incident with edge j, and otherwise 0. We could also simply store the edges as a linear list, perhaps of numbers: Assuming less than 100 edges, we could store the edge ij as $100i + j$ and recover i as $\lfloor \frac{100i+j}{100} \rfloor$ and j as $(100i + j) - 100i$.

Section 10.4 True/False

1. True **2.** False **3.** True **4.** False **5.** True **6.** True **7.** True **8.** False

9. False: Vertices are not assigned labels in this algorithm.

10. False: The improved algorithm of Dijkstra is $\mathcal{O}(n^2)$.

Exercises 10.4

2.

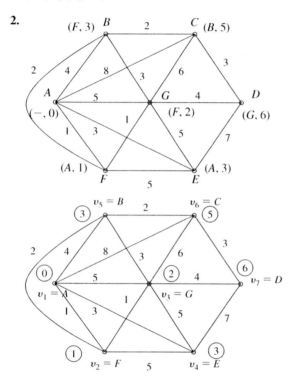

4. (a) The final labeling starting at A is shown to the right. The shortest path from A to E is $ABCJIGFKE$ and has length 13.

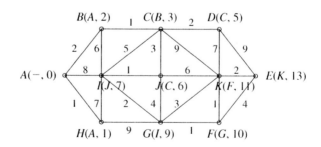

5. If we start at A, permanent labels will be assigned in the order A, H, B, C, D, J, I, G, F, K, E.

7. A shortest path has length 11. One way in which permanent labels might be assigned is in the order A, B, D, C, S, J, I, H, E, L, G, F, K, M, O, P, N, Q, R.

10. The shortest path has length 13, as shown.

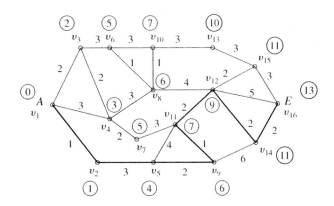

12. In each case the answer is yes, if A and E were in different components of a graph that was not connected.

15. (a) Assign each edge a weight of 1.

16. As explained in the text, the complexity function for determining the shortest distance from a given vertex to each of the others is $\mathcal{O}(n^2)$; that is, for sufficiently large n and some constant c, the algorithm requires at most cn^2 comparisons. Applying the algorithm to each of the n vertices (after which all shortest distances are known) requires at most $n(cn^2) = cn^3$ comparisons. This process is $\mathcal{O}(n^3)$.

17. (a) The final values are the shortest distances from A to itself and to the other vertices. From Fig. 10.23, we deduce these to be 0, 7, 15, 20, 21, 15, 8, 5, 10, and 17.

(b) After $k = 4$, the value of $d(1, 5)$ is the length of a shortest path from A to E via the vertices A, B, C, D. The only such path is $ABCDE$ of length 27: $d(1, 5) = 27$.

The value of $d(1, 6)$ is the length of a shortest path from A to F via A, B, C, D. There is no such path, so $d(1, 6)$ is still ∞.

The value of $d(3, 4)$ is 8.

The value of $d(8, 5)$ is the length of a shortest path from H to E via A, B, C, D. The shortest such path is $HBCDE$: $d(8, 5) = 24$.

(c) The initial value of $d(2, 5)$ is ∞ since BE is not an edge. After $k = 1, 2, \ldots, 10$, the values of $d(2, 5)$ are $\infty, \infty, \infty, 20, 20, 20, 20, 20, 18, 17$.

20. It is indeed necessary to continue. An identical set of $d(i, j)$ for $k = r$ and $k = r + 1$ simply indicates that the shortest path from each v_i to each v_j passing through $v_1, \ldots, v_r$ has the same length as the shortest path through $v_1, \ldots, v_{r+1}$. In the graph shown to the right, for instance, the values of $d(i, j)$ do not change until $k = 3$ since the shortest path between pairs of vertices cannot be reduced until vertex v_3 is used.

Section 11.1 True/False

1. False: This is true for Eulerian graphs.   **2.** True   **3.** False   **4.** True   **5.** False: Into groups of two.

6. True   **7.** False   **8.** False   **9.** True   **10.** False: No edge need be repeated.

Exercises 11.1

1. (a)

2. K_5 is Eulerian, so no additional edges are needed.

3. Here is the unique solution.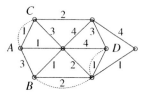

4. We show one of several solutions in each case.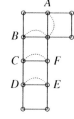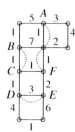

6. The shortest route from X to X is a circuit (perhaps in a pseudograph) passing through Y. Hence, it can also be viewed as a circuit from Y to Y. Any other route from Y to Y could also be viewed as a route from X to X. So there cannot be any shorter route from Y to Y.

9. It certainly is possible, and this is illustrated by the graph shown (all of whose vertices are odd).

10. Each odd vertex in $\mathcal{G}$ is the end vertex of precisely one new path constructed by the algorithm, or an intermediate vertex on a path between odd vertices, so it is even in $\mathcal{G}'$. Each even vertex in $\mathcal{G}$ either has unchanged degree in $\mathcal{G}'$ or, as an intermediate point on one or more paths between odd vertices, has its degree increased by a multiple of 2, and so remains even in $\mathcal{G}'$.

Section 11.2 True/False

1. False: Consider ⊶⟶⟶⊸ .   **2.** False   **3.** False: It equals the number of arcs.   **4.** False

5. False   **6.** True   **7.** True   **8.** True   **9.** True   **10.** False

Exercises 11.2

1. (a) These digraphs are not isomorphic because one has six vertices, while the other has five.

3. Every arc comes out of one vertex and goes into another and, hence, adds one to the sum of all indegrees and one to the sum of all outdegrees.

5. The answer is yes. Since $\mathcal{G}$ is an Eulerian graph, there exists an Eulerian circuit. Now just orient the edges of this circuit in the direction of a walk along it.

8. (a) $A = \begin{bmatrix} 0 & 1 & 1 & 0 \\ 1 & 0 & 1 & 0 \\ 0 & 1 & 0 & 1 \\ 1 & 1 & 1 & 0 \end{bmatrix}$

(b) The $(3, 3)$ entry of A^2 is 2 because there are two directed walks of length 2 from vertex 3 to vertex 3: 323 and 343. The $(1, 4)$ entry of A^2 is 1 because the only directed walk of length 2 from vertex 1 to vertex 4 is 134.

(c) The $(4, 2)$ entry of A^3 is 4 because there are four directed walks of length 3 from vertex 4 to vertex 2: 4212, 4232, 4132, and 4342. The $(1, 3)$ entry of A^4 is 6. There are six walks of length 4 from vertex 1 to vertex 3: 13423, 13413, 13213, 12123, 12323, and 12343.

(d) The digraph is strongly connected; 12341 is a directed circuit that permits travel in the right direction between any two vertices.

(e) The digraph is not Eulerian. Vertices 2, 3, and 4 have different indegree and outdegree; vertex 3, for instance, has indegree 3 and outdegree 2.

11. A digraph has an Eulerian trail between vertices u and v if and only if

- one of these vertices, say u, has outdegree one more than its indegree, the other vertex, v, has indegree one more than its outdegree,
- the indegrees and outdegrees of every vertex except u and v are equal, and
- for every pair of vertices x, y there is a (directed) path from x to y or from y to x.

Proof. If there is an Eulerian trail from u to v, it is clear that the three given conditions are necessary. On the other hand, suppose the three conditions hold in a digraph G. We show that G has an Eulerian trail. The result is obvious if u and v are the only vertices of G, so we may assume G has at least three vertices.

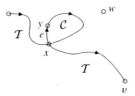

By hypothesis, there is an arc ux. If $x \neq v$, there is an arc xy, and so on. By hypothesis, this process can be continued without repeating an arc. It must eventually terminate, however, and only at v, at which point we have a directed trail T from u to v. Since G has at least three vertices, we may assume that T contains at least three vertices. If T contains every vertex and every arc, it is an Eulerian trail. Otherwise, there is a vertex x not in T and a vertex y in T, $y \neq u$, $y \neq x$. By hypothesis, there is a directed path from x to y or from y to x. In the former case, the existence of a terminal arc zy implies another arc yw. In either event, there is an arc yw not in T. Continue along a trail beginning yw and note that every time we reach a vertex different from y it is possible to leave on a new arc. Thus this trail can only terminate at y, with a circuit C. Now $uyCyv$ is a trail longer than T. If it contains every vertex and every edge, it is Eulerian. Otherwise, continue and eventually an Eulerian trail is achieved. ✹

13. (a) With the graphs labeled as shown, the adjacency matrices are

$$A_1 = \begin{bmatrix} 0 & 1 & 0 & 0 & 0 & 0 \\ 0 & 0 & 1 & 0 & 0 & 0 \\ 0 & 0 & 0 & 1 & 0 & 0 \\ 0 & 0 & 0 & 0 & 1 & 0 \\ 0 & 0 & 0 & 0 & 0 & 1 \\ 1 & 0 & 0 & 0 & 0 & 0 \end{bmatrix} \quad \text{and} \quad A_2 = \begin{bmatrix} 0 & 0 & 0 & 0 & 1 \\ 1 & 0 & 0 & 0 & 0 \\ 0 & 1 & 0 & 0 & 0 \\ 0 & 0 & 1 & 0 & 0 \\ 0 & 0 & 0 & 1 & 0 \end{bmatrix}.$$

14. (a) $A_1 = \begin{bmatrix} 0 & 1 & 0 & 1 \\ 0 & 0 & 1 & 0 \\ 0 & 0 & 0 & 1 \\ 1 & 1 & 0 & 0 \end{bmatrix} \quad \text{and} \quad A_2 = \begin{bmatrix} 0 & 0 & 0 & 1 \\ 1 & 0 & 1 & 0 \\ 1 & 1 & 0 & 0 \\ 0 & 0 & 1 & 0 \end{bmatrix}.$

(b) With the vertices of G_1 relabeled according to φ, its adjacency matrix becomes that of G_2.

(c) $P = \begin{bmatrix} 0 & 1 & 0 & 0 \\ 1 & 0 & 0 & 0 \\ 0 & 0 & 0 & 1 \\ 0 & 0 & 1 & 0 \end{bmatrix}$

(d) The digraphs are strongly connected: In G_1, for instance, $v_1 v_2 v_3 v_4 v_1$ is a circuit that respects arrows, and G_2 is isomorphic to G_1, hence, also strongly connected.

(e) The digraphs are not Eulerian. In G_1, for instance, vertex v_2 has indegree 2, but outdegree 1.

17. (a) Each of these graphs is strongly connected; each is a cycle.

18. (a) There are just two possibilities for the outdegree sequence; 1, 1, 1 and 2, 1, 0. The corresponding graphs are shown at the right.

19. No. $\mathcal{K}_3$ is connected, but  is not strongly connected.

20. True. Let v be a vertex. Since $\mathcal{G}$ has at least two vertices and $\mathcal{G}$ is strongly connected, there is some arc of the form vw. Since $\mathcal{G}$ is strongly connected, there is a path from w to v. This path does not use arc vw since all vertices of a path are distinct. For the same reason, all arcs on this (or any) path are distinct. Thus, arc vw followed by the path from w to v gives the desired circuit.

22. (a)

			Max. no. of arcs			
	1	2	3	4	5	6
v_2	$1, v_1$	$1, v_1$	$1, v_1$	$1, v_1$	$1, v_1$	$1, v_1$
v_3	$8, v_1$	$2, v_2$	$2, v_2$	$2, v_2$	$2, v_2$	$2, v_2$
v_4	∞	$11, v_3$	$5, v_3$	$4, v_5$	$4, v_5$	$4, v_5$
v_5	∞	$4, v_2$	$3, v_3$	$3, v_3$	$3, v_3$	$3, v_3$
v_6	$7, v_1$	$7, v_1$	$7, v_1$	$6, v_5$	$6, v_5$	$6, v_5$

23. Bellman–Ford works fine on undirected graphs without negative edges. It wouldn't make sense to apply Bellman–Ford to an undirected graph with a negative edge weight, since any walk could be shortened by passing up and down that edge as often as desired.

24. (a) Dijkstra incorrectly determines that the length of a shortest path to v_2 is 1. Dijkstra does not always work when applied to digraphs that have arcs of negative weight.

(b) No shortest path algorithm will work. There is a negative weight cycle, hence no shortest distance to v_2, for example.

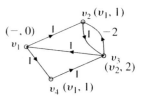

27. As described in the text, the second last vertex on a shortest path is $p(j)$. Since a shortest path to v_j makes use of a shortest path to $p(j)$ following by edge $p(j)v_j$, the third last vertex on a shortest path to v_j is $p(p(j))$, this being the second last vertex on a shortest path to $p(j)$. So the vertices of a shortest path to v_j, in reverse order, are $v_j, p(j), p(p(j)), p(p(p(j))), \dots, v_1$.

29. (a) As Step 2 of the algorithm shows, for each j, the values $d_i(j)$ depend only on the values $d_{i-1}(k)$ and the arc weights. It follows that, if the values $d_{i-1}(j) = d_i(j)$ are identical, then $d_{i-1}(j) = d_i(j) = d_{i+1}(j) = \cdots = d_{n-1}(j)$.

Section 11.3 True/False

1. False   **2.** True   **3.** False: 4!   **4.** True   **5.** False   **6.** False   **7.** False

8. False: If the abnormal fragment does not split, the Eulerian trail or circuit ends with a vertex labeled the abnormal fragment.

9. True: See the last sentence of this section.

Exercises 11.3

1. (a) Since the chain ends UC, the given G-fragments arise from any of $3! = 6$ chains. The given U,C-fragments arise from any of $5!/2! = 60$ chains. The better estimate is 6. The abnormal fragment is UC, and this ends the chain. There is one Eulerian circuit ending in UC, so the only answer is CAAGCUGGUC.

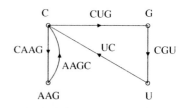

(e) Since the chain ends CC, the G-fragments arise from any of $4! = 24$ chains. The U,C-fragments arise from any of $6!/2! = 360$ chains. The better estimate is 24. We can find two Eulerian trails ending with CC, beginning at G. There are two answers: GUGAUGACCAGCC and GAUGUGACCAGCC.

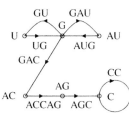

2. (a) The last letter in the chain is U, C, G, or A. If it is U or C, the last G-fragment will be abnormal. If it is G, the last U,C-fragment will be abnormal. If it is A, the last G and the last U,C-fragments will each be abnormal.

   (b) There are two abnormal fragments if and only if the chain ends with A.

3. The chains GGUGU and GUGGU have the same G- and U,C-fragments. We leave it to you to check that no shorter chains exist.

4. (a) An abnormal fragment must have arisen from the use of either a G-enzyme or a U,C-enzyme. But a G-enzyme cuts after each G, so an **abnormal** fragment containing a G must have come from a U,C-enzyme. But this enzyme cuts after each U or C, so the **abnormal** fragment cannot contain either of these.

   A similar argument holds if the abnormal fragment contains a U or a C.

Section 11.4 True/False

1. False   2. False: Use nonincreasing order.   3. False   4. True   5. True
6. False: There are $\binom{4}{2} = 6$ arcs and $4 \nmid 6$.   7. True   8. True: Reverse all arrows.
9. False: Hamiltonian path.   10. False

Exercises 11.4

1. (a) See Exercise 18(a) of Section 11.2. The score sequences (left to right) are 1, 1, 1 and 2, 1, 0. The tournament on the left is not transitive; the one on the right is.

2. Since for each pair of (distinct) vertices v_i, v_j precisely one of $v_i v_j$, $v_j v_i$ is an arc, in the adjacency matrix A, for each $i \neq j$, precisely one of a_{ij}, a_{ji} is 1. Thus, $A + A^T$ has 0's on the diagonal and 1's in every off-diagonal position.

5. (a) The sum of the scores is the number of arcs, by Proposition 11.2.2; thus, $\sum_{i=1}^{n} s_i = \binom{n}{2} = \frac{1}{2}n(n-1)$. Since $\sum_{i=1}^{n}(n-1-s_i) = \sum_{i=1}^{n}(n-1) - \sum_{i=1}^{n} s_i = n(n-1) - \frac{1}{2}n(n-1) = \frac{1}{2}n(n-1)$, we have the desired result. In a tournament with n players, each player plays $n-1$ games; so if a player wins s_i games, he loses $n-1-s_i$ games. The result says that the sum of the numbers of wins equals the sum of the numbers of losses.

6. Let w be any other vertex. If v beats w, there is a path of length 1 from v to w and we are fine. Hence, assume that w beats v, that is, $w \longrightarrow v$. Among those vertices that v beats, there must be one, say x, that beats w, since otherwise $s(w) \geq s(v) + 1$ (recall that w beats v), contradicting the maximum score of v.

   Hence, for some x, we have   (figure)   but then there is a path of length 2 from v to w.

7. (a) No. The sum of the scores, $\sum s(v)$, is the number of arcs. Here $1 + 1 + 2 + 3 = 7$, but the number of arcs is $\binom{4}{2} = 6$.

11. Suppose $\mathcal{T}$ is a transitive tournament that contains the cycle $v_1 v_2 \ldots v_n v_1$. Since $\mathcal{T}$ contains no 3-cycle, upon considering the vertices v_1, v_2 and v_3, we see that $v_1 v_3$ must be an arc. Then, considering v_1, v_3, v_4, we see that $v_1 v_4$ is an arc. Continuing, we eventually have an arc $v_1 v_n$, contradicting the fact that $v_n v_1$ is an arc. (In a tournament, for any pair u, v of vertices, precisely one of uv, vu is an arc.)

Section 11.5 True/False

1. False: Integer weights are needed.   2. False: The reverse is true.   3. True   4. False   5. True

6. True   **7.** True   **8.** True   **9.** False   **10.** True

Exercises 11.5

1. With reference to Fig. 11.24, the arc BD now has weight 4. This does not change any of the labels shown, but it does eliminate the possibility of a second shortest path. Now the only shortest path is $SADFT$, requiring 11 units of time as before.

2. (a) Since the times required for the tasks depend on which other tasks have already been completed and since tasks cannot take place at the same time, this is a Type I scheduling problem.

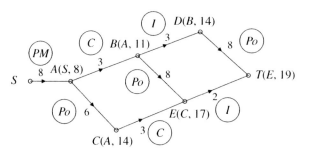

(b) The critical path is $SACET$; that is, pour the mold, polish, calibrate, inspect. The shortest time for the project is the length of this path: 19 units of time.

5. The new digraph is shown. The project now requires 18 units of time. The critical path is $SFEWPaDVCT$. The slack in Pl is now 1; the slack in the installation of kitchen cabinets is 3. All other tasks have slack 0 since they lie on the critical path.

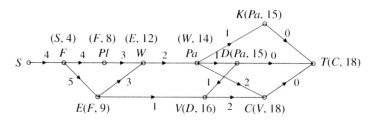

7. Since the time required for a task does not depend on which other tasks have been completed and since some tasks can occur simultaneously, this a Type II scheduling problem.

(a)

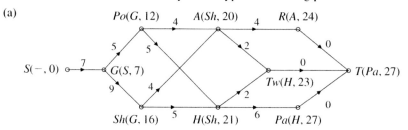

(b) The only critical path is $SGShHPaT$, taking a total of 27 months.

(c) The slack of Po is 4. This job could take as much as 9 units of time without affecting the time (21) by which the task H, subsequent to Po and on the critical path, would be accomplished. There is no slack in Sh. It is on the critical path. The slack in A is 3. If this task took 7 units of time, its label would be $(Sh, 23)$ and the label on R would become $(A, 27)$. There would be another critical path, $SGShART$, but the time for the job would be unaffected. The slack in Tw is 4. Twisting could take as long as 6 units of time and the project would still be completed in 27 units. The slack in R is 3.

(d) No, the project will not be delayed. Delaying Po by three months changes Po's label to $(G, 15)$, but this does not affect any other labels on the digraph. Delaying A by three months changes A's label to $(Sh, 23)$, but does not affect the critical path, or its length.

11. (a) This type I scheduling problem is described by the following digraph:

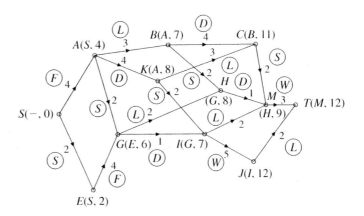

(b) The shortest time is 12 units.

(c) One of several ways in which this time can be achieved is to first conduct the library search, then do the fieldwork, then the laboratory analysis, then create the database and finally do the write-up.

14. (a) Since this is clearly a one-man project (!), it is of type I. The appropriate directed network is shown.

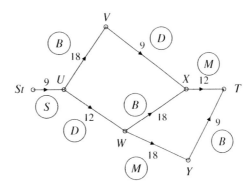

Section 12.1 True/False

1. False: $\mathcal{H}$ may not be connected.　**2.** False　**3.** False: Consider 　**4.** True

5. False: $\mathcal{G}$ might not be connected.　**6.** True　**7.** False: The graph must also be connected.

8. False: "At most" should be "at least." Consider ○——●——○ .

9. False: Paraffins have the form $C_k H_{2k+2}$.　**10.** True

Exercises 12.1

1.

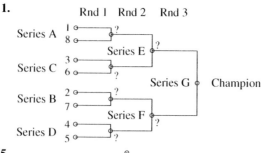

5.

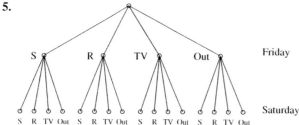

7.

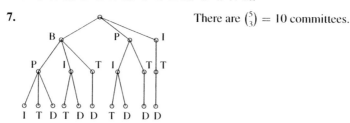

There are $\binom{5}{3} = 10$ committees.

12. We think of a path as a sequence of vertices. There are at least two vertices of P_2 that are also in P_1 (v and w, for example). Let $u \neq w$ be the first vertex of P_1 that is encountered on the reversed path P_2 from w back to v. (It is possible that u might equal v.) It follows that the path from u to w along P_1 followed by the path back to u along P_2 in reverse from w is a cycle.

13. (a)

(b) Since each tree with five vertices has all vertices of degree at most 4, there is one isomer for each such tree, the C atoms corresponding to the vertices. There are three isomers of C_5H_{12}.

15. A beta index less than 1 says that there are fewer edges than vertices. One possibility is that the graph is not connected; in other words, there exist two cities such that it is impossible to fly from one city to the other. If the graph is connected, then it must be a tree by Theorem 12.1.6. This means there is a unique way of flying from any city to any other city.

17. ($\longrightarrow$) A tree with n vertices has $n - 1$ edges by Theorem 12.1.6 and no cycles by Proposition 12.1.2.

($\longleftarrow$) Suppose $\mathcal{G}$ is an acyclic graph with n vertices and $n - 1$ edges. Since $\mathcal{G}$ has no cycles, Proposition 12.1.2 shows that we have only to prove that $\mathcal{G}$ is connected. Then let $C_1, C_2, \ldots, C_k$ be the connected components of $\mathcal{G}$ and suppose that C_i has n_i vertices. (Thus, $\sum n_i = n$.) Since $\mathcal{G}$ has no cycles, there are no cycles within each C_i. It follows that each C_i is a tree with $n_i - 1$ edges. The number of edges in $\mathcal{G}$ is, therefore, $\sum_1^k (n_i - 1) = (\sum_1^k n_i) - k = n - k$. So $n - k = n - 1$, $k = 1$, and $\mathcal{G}$ has only one component; that is, $\mathcal{G}$ is connected.

19. (a) $\mathcal{T}$ has n vertices and $n - 1$ edges. Hence $\mathcal{T} \setminus \{e\}$ has n vertices and $n - 2$ edges; $\mathcal{T} \setminus \{e\}$ has no circuits. Hence $\mathcal{T}$ cannot be connected or it would be a tree (with the wrong number of edges).

21. There are no circuits in the subgraph since there are no circuits in C_kH_{2k+2}. Also, given any two C vertices, there is a path between them in C_kH_{2k+2} (because C_kH_{2k+2} is connected). Any H vertex on this path would have degree 2. Thus, there is none; the path consists entirely of C vertices and hence lies within the subgraph. The subgraph is connected and hence a tree.

25. A tree is a complete bipartite graph if and only if it is $\mathcal{K}_{1,n}$ for some n.

   Proof. Certainly $\mathcal{K}_{1,n}$ is a tree. Conversely, if a tree is complete bipartite, then it is $\mathcal{K}_{m,n}$ for some m and n. But such a graph has no vertices of degree 1 unless m or n is 1. The result follows.

26. (a) Remember that component means maximal connected subgraph. Also, any graph is the disjoint union of its components. If a graph has no cycles, neither does any component, so each component is a tree.

27. (a) Using Corollary 12.1.7, we have $\sum \deg(v_i) \geq 8$, so the tree has at least four edges and hence at least five vertices. If the result is not true, then there are at most three vertices of degree 1 while the rest have degree at least 2. Then

$$\sum \deg v_i \geq 2(3) + 3(1) + (n-5)2 = 2n - 1,$$

   contradicting the fact that $\sum \deg v_i = 2(n-1)$.

Section 12.2 True/False

1. True   **2.** True   **3.** True   **4.** True   **5.** True

6. False: Omit "nonisomorphic" and the statement is true.

7. False: There is a missing $-$ sign in front of the determinant.

8. True   **9.** False: It's 6^4.

Exercises 12.2

1. We show T and two other spanning trees found by adding a and then successively deleting f and g.

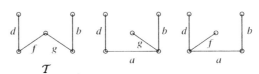

2. (a) Here is one possible answer. The second and third trees are isomorphic, but neither is isomorphic to the first.

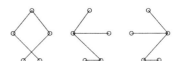

   Kirchhoff's matrix is

$$M = \begin{bmatrix} 2 & -1 & -1 & 0 & 0 \\ -1 & 3 & -1 & 0 & -1 \\ -1 & -1 & 3 & -1 & 0 \\ 0 & 0 & -1 & 2 & -1 \\ 0 & -1 & 0 & -1 & 2 \end{bmatrix}.$$

   The value of the $(5, 1)$ cofactor is

$$\begin{vmatrix} -1 & -1 & 0 & 0 \\ 3 & -1 & 0 & -1 \\ -1 & 3 & -1 & 0 \\ 0 & -1 & 2 & -1 \end{vmatrix} = - \begin{vmatrix} -1 & 0 & -1 \\ 3 & -1 & 0 \\ -1 & 2 & -1 \end{vmatrix} + \begin{vmatrix} 3 & 0 & -1 \\ -1 & -1 & 0 \\ 0 & 2 & -1 \end{vmatrix}$$

$$= -[(-1)(1) + (-1)(5)] + [3(1) - 1(-2)] = 11.$$

   We conclude that there are 11 spanning trees.

4. By Theorem 12.2.3, the numbers are $1^{-1} = 1$, $2^0 = 1$, $3^1 = 3$, $4^2 = 16$, $5^3 = 125$, and $6^4 = 1296$.

5.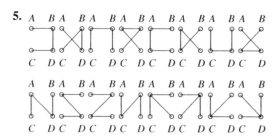

7. (a) $K_{2,2}$ has four spanning trees (obtained by deleting each edge in succession). They are all isomorphic to ○—○—○—○

9. The edge in question is a *bridge* (see Definition 12.6.2); that is, its removal disconnects the graph. To see why, call the edge e. If $\mathcal{G} \setminus \{e\}$ were connected, it would have a spanning tree. However, since $\mathcal{G} \setminus \{e\}$ contains all the vertices of $\mathcal{G}$, any spanning tree for it is also a spanning tree for $\mathcal{G}$. We have a contradiction.

12. (a) Say the edge is e and $\mathcal{T}$ is any spanning tree. If e is not in $\mathcal{T}$, then $\mathcal{T} \cup \{e\}$ must contain a circuit. Deleting any edge of this circuit other than e gives another spanning tree that includes e.

(c) No. If the three edges form a circuit, no spanning tree can contain them.

14. (a) The subgraph $\mathcal{T}_0 \cup \{e\}$ is connected because $\mathcal{T}_0$ is. Since it has the same number of vertices and edges, it cannot be a tree; therefore, it contains a circuit. Let f be an edge on this circuit such that $f \notin \mathcal{T}$. (Since $\mathcal{T}$ does not contain a circuit, this is possible.) Then $(\mathcal{T}_0 \cup \{e\}) \setminus \{f\}$ is still connected (you can go either way around a circuit), and it has n vertices and $n - 1$ edges, so it's a spanning tree.

16. There are $\binom{n}{2}$ possible edges from which we choose $n - 1$. The number of graphs is therefore $\binom{\binom{n}{2}}{n-1}$. The number of trees on n labeled vertices is n^{n-2}. For $n \le 6$, the table shows the numbers of trees as compared to the numbers of graphs.

n	No. of trees	No. of graphs
2	1	1
3	3	3
4	16	20
5	125	210
6	1296	3003

Section 12.3 True/False

1. True **2.** True **3.** True **4.** False **5.** True **6.** True

7. False: It depends on the choice of the starting vertex v. **8.** True **9.** True **10.** True

Exercises 12.3

1. (a) We want five edges (since there are six vertices). Choose BC and then AD, FE, and DE. We would like next to choose AE, but this would complete a circuit with AD and DE, so we choose AC and obtain the spanning tree shown, of weight 13.

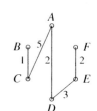

2. (a) The edge of least weight incident with E is EF. The least weight of those edges adjacent to EF is 3; we choose one of them, say AE (in an effort to obtain a different tree from before). There is just one edge of least weight that, together with EF and AE, forms a tree: AD. Now those edges that together with EF, AE, and AD form a tree have weights 5 and 6. We choose one of least weight, say CF. Finally, we choose BC, obtaining the tree of weight 13 shown to the right.

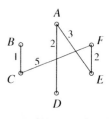

3. We need five edges because there are six vertices in the graph. We use Kruskal's algorithm. First select BC of weight 5, then DF of weight 6. Next we select BF and AB, both of weight 7. We would like to select AF next, but cannot since it completes the circuit $ABFA$, so we select EF of weight 9 next. The five edges we have selected comprise a minimum spanning tree. The smallest length of pavement required is $5 + 6 + 7 + 7 + 9 = 34$.

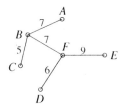

4. (b) i. Choose BD, BE, and CE each of weight 6. The remaining edge, CD, of maximum weight (6) cannot be chosen because it would complete the circuit $BDCEB$ with the previously chosen edges. So we choose DF and then AB, obtaining the spanning tree shown at the right of maximum weight 28.

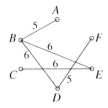

6. Assign all edges of the graph a weight of 1. Then carry out the algorithm.

8. (a) If the graph is unweighted, put a weight of 1 on edge e and 2 on every other edge. If the graph is weighted, ensure (by temporarily changing weights if necessary) that the weights of the edges different from e are all larger than the weight of e. In either case, Kruskal's algorithm will select e first.

10. Let d be the lowest weight among the edges incident with vertex v. The first time that an edge incident with v is considered for selection (because it has least weight among remaining edges), no edge incident with v will complete a circuit with edges previously selected. Always seeking edges of lowest weight, the algorithm must select an edge of weight d.

11. (b) If the weights of a graph with n vertices are distinct, then Kruskal's algorithm selects at each stage a unique edge of lowest weight. Since Kruskal's algorithm yields only one tree, the graph has only one minimum spanning tree, by (a).

12. (b) Each time a vertex is relabeled, the component to which it belongs contains at least twice as many vertices as before. Thus, if the label on a vertex changes t times, $2^t \le n$; so $t \le \log_2 n$ as required.

   (c) Since the initial sorting of edges requires $\mathcal{O}(N \log N)$ comparisons, we have only to show that the relabeling process described in (a) and (b) can also be accomplished within this bound. By (b), the total number of vertex relabelings is $\mathcal{O}(n \log n)$. If $n \le N$, we are done. If $n = N + 1$, then $n \log n \le (2N) \log N^2 = 4N \log N$ and again we are done, except when $n = 1$ or 2 when no steps are needed. Finally, if $N \le n - 2$, no spanning tree is possible and a check for this could be included at the beginning of the algorithm.

15. (a) The graph is complete, so an obvious approach is to try to choose the lowest weight available edge at each vertex. Such a cycle is $ADEFBCA$, which has weight $2 + 3 + 2 + 5 + 1 + 5 = 18$.

   (b) As shown on the left, the minimum weight of a spanning tree after A is removed is 11. The two edges of least weight at A have weights 2 and 3, so we obtain an estimate of $11 + 2 + 3 = 16$ as a lower bound for the weight of any Hamiltonian cycle.

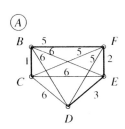
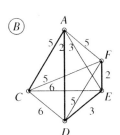

   (c) As shown on the right, the minimum weight of a spanning tree after B is removed is 12. The two least edges at B have weights 1 and 5, so we obtain $12 + 1 + 5 = 18$ as a lower bound.

Section 12.4 True/False

1. True **2.** True **3.** False: Consider the digraph in Question 1. **4.** False: $v_4 v_3$ is an arc.

5. False: Look at Questions 1 and 4. **6.** False: It has two vertices of indegree 0. **7.** True

8. False: "Indegree" 1. **9.** True **10.** True

Exercises 12.4

1. (a) This is acyclic: F, B, D, H, A, E, C, G is a canonical labeling.

3. Let G be a digraph with n vertices and let A be the adjacency matrix of G. The indegree of vertex i is the sum of the entries in column i. This requires $n - 1$ two-number additions. Repeating for n vertices involves $n(n - 1) = \mathcal{O}(n^2)$ additions.

5. (a) We use the notation and ideas of the proof of Theorem 12.4.3. If G has a cycle, then we can construct a (possibly empty) set of vertices $\{v_0, v_1, \ldots, v_k\}$ such that some $S = V \setminus \{v_0, v_1, v_2, \ldots, v_k\}$ is nonempty and has the property that $S_v \neq \emptyset$ for all $v \in S$; that is, for every $v \in S$, there exists an arc of the form xv with $x \in S$. Let $u_0 \in S$ be arbitrary and choose $u_1 \in S$ such that $u_1 u_0$ is an arc. Choose $u_2 \in S$ such that $u_2 u_1$ is an arc. If $u_2 = u_0$, then $u_2 u_1 u_0$ is a cycle. Otherwise, choose $u_3 \in S$ so that $u_3 u_2$ is an arc. In general, having chosen distinct vertices $u_0, u_1, \ldots, u_k \in S$ such that $u_{i+1} u_i$ is an arc for $i = 0, 1, \ldots k - 1$, choose $u_{k+1} \in S$ such that $u_{k+1} u_k$ is an arc. Since S is finite, there exists k such that $u_{k+1} = u_\ell$ with $\ell < k$. Then $u_{k+1} u_k u_{k-1} \cdots u_\ell$ is a cycle.

7. Since the undirected graph is a tree with n vertices, T has $n - 1$ arcs, by Theorem 12.1.6.

9. (a) Here are the distances d_t and the corresponding values of p_t.

t	0	1	2	3	4	5	6	7
d_t	0	5	7	4	5	7	6	6
p_t	-1	0	0	0	0	4	4	3

11. The arc $v_{p_t} v_t$ is the last on a shortest path that the algorithm has found from v_0 to v_t. Let G be the digraph that consists of precisely those arcs (and their end vertices). Vertex v_0 has indegree 0 since there is no arc $v_i v_0$ with $i > 0$. Every other vertex in G has indegree 1 since it is the last on a shortest directed path. Suppose G has r vertices. Then it has $r - 1$ edges, one for each of its vertices other than v_0. By Theorem 12.1.6, it suffices to show that G is connected. This will certainly be the case if we show that every vertex of G is connected to v_0 by some path in G. Suppose this is not the case, and let t be minimal with the property that there is no directed path from v_0 to v_t. Clearly $t > 0$. Then G contains an arc $v_{p_t} v_t$, the last on a directed path to v_t. Since $p_t < t$, there is a directed path from v_0 to v_{p_t}, and the arc $v_{p_t} v_t$ is directed $v_{p_t} \to v_t$. Thus there is a path from v_0 to v_t.

13. It is sufficient simply to modify Step 1 by setting $d_k = 0$ and $d_i = \infty$ for $i < k$. (We could also modify Step 2 by starting the for loop at $t = k + 1$, but there is little change in efficiency unless k is roughly the size of n.)

14. (a) i. Here are the distances d_t from v_1 and the corresponding values of p_t.

t	0	1	2	3	4	5	6	7
d_t	∞	0	∞	∞	∞	6	4	2
p_t	-1	-1	-1	-1	-1	1	1	1

ii. Here are the distances d_t from v_2 and the corresponding values of p_t.

t	0	1	2	3	4	5	6	7
d_t	∞	∞	0	∞	∞	3	2	7
p_t	-1	-1	-1	-1	-1	2	2	5

Section 12.5 True/False

1. True **2.** False **3.** True **4.** True **5.** True **6.** False: See Questions 2 and 3.

7. False: You must get ○—○—○ ⋯ ○—○ . **8.** True **9.** True

10. False: Breadth-first search only produces spanning trees that look like .

1. (a) The final backtracking is 7, 2, 1.

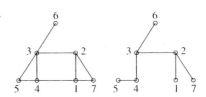

2. (a)

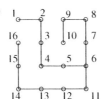

The final backtracking is 16, 15, 14, 13, 12, 11, 6, 5, 4, 3, 2, 1.

4. (a) Consider the status of the algorithm at the time that v is labeled. If there are no unlabeled vertices adjacent to v at this stage, we have nothing to prove. So we assume that there are some. Let $\mathcal{G}'$ denote the subgraph of $\mathcal{G}$ consisting of those vertices as yet unlabeled that are connected to v via a path of unlabeled vertices and all the edges among these vertices. After v is labeled, the algorithm moves to an unlabeled vertex adjacent to v and hence into the subgraph $\mathcal{G}'$. It then either returns to v or moves to another vertex in $\mathcal{G}'$ and gives it a label.

Now the depth-first search algorithm covers any edge at most twice, once when it labels a vertex and once when it backtracks. Since there are only finitely many edges in $\mathcal{G}'$, the algorithm must eventually backtrack to v. If there remain any adjacent unlabeled vertices, the algorithm chooses one to label and moves again into $\mathcal{G}'$. As before, it must eventually backtrack to v. The process continues until all vertices adjacent to v are labeled.

6. If $\mathcal{G}$ is ⊠ , one spanning tree, ⟋ , is not obtainable by depth-first search.

7. (a) Each time the procedure terminates, start it again with an unlabeled vertex. The number of connected components is equal to the number of times the procedure terminates.

9. No. For instance, you can get from $(7, 1, 0)$ to $(3, 5, 0)$ in one step, but not back.

10. Breadth-first search is another way of systematically moving through all the vertices of a graph. Suppose a graph has n vertices. The procedure assigns to these vertices labels from the set $\{1, 2, \ldots, n\}$. Assign label 1 to any vertex. Then label **all** vertices adjacent to vertex 1 with consecutive labels starting at 2. Then pass to vertex 2 and label **all** vertices adjacent to 2 that have not yet been labeled with consecutive labels from the unused members of $\{1, 2, \ldots, n\}$, always using the smallest available integer first. Then pass to vertex 3 and so on, at each stage moving to the next highest labeled vertex and labeling all adjacent vertices not yet labeled with the unused members of $\{1, 2, \ldots, n\}$, smallest unused integer first. Continue until some vertex acquires label n or all vertices adjacent to the vertex with the highest label are already labeled.

11. (a)

1. False **2.** True **3.** False **4.** True **5.** True **6.** True **7.** False: See Question 3.

8. True **9.** True **10.** False

1. (a) Not strongly connected; edge 36 is a bridge.

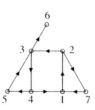

2.

3. (a) A strongly connected orientation for the Petersen graph is shown above on the right.

5. No, it cannot. Every edge of an Eulerian graph is part of a circuit; the removal of an edge of a circuit certainly does not disconnect a graph.

6. If e is a bridge, we can let u and v be its ends. If there were a path from u to v that did not require e, together with e, we would have a circuit containing e. Since the deletion of an edge that is part of a circuit cannot disconnect a graph, we have a contradiction.

7. (a) Choose a vertex v. For each vertex u adjacent to v, orient the edge uv in the direction $u \to v$.

8. Yes. To get from a to b in the new orientation, just find the path from b to a in the old orientation and follow it in reverse.

9. (a) False. The graph shown at the right cannot be given a strongly connected orientation, yet every edge is part of a circuit.

10. (a) If there were a path $\mathcal{P}$ between u and v in $\mathcal{G} \setminus \{e\}$, then $\mathcal{P} \cup \{e\}$ would be a circuit, contradicting the fact that e is a bridge.

11. Yes it can. Cutting all the bridges divides the city into connected components without bridges. Each component, therefore, has a strongly connected orientation (by Theorem 12.6.3), so it is possible to assign directions to the streets of each component that allow the possibility of (legal) travel between any two points. Now note that making each bridge a two-way street allows arbitrary travel between components.

15. (a) Orient the depth first search spanning tree as in 12.6.4.   (b) This follows from the definitions.

1. False: It can be drawn without edges crossing.   **2.** True   **3.** False: It has three regions.   **4.** True
5. False: It has $n - 1$ edges and one region.   **6.** False: It has $\mathcal{K}_{3,3}$ as a subgraph.
7. False: It has $\mathcal{K}_5$ as a subgraph.   **8.** True: It does not satisfy the condition $E \leq 3V - 6$.
9. True   **10.** False: "Isomorphic" should be "homeomorphic."

1. (a) We draw the graph quickly as a planar and then, after some thinking, as a plane graph with straight edges.

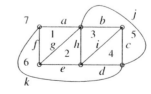

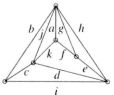

(b) There are seven regions, numbered $1, 2, \ldots, 7$, with boundaries afg, ghe, hbi, icd, bjc, $fedk$, and ajk, respectively.

(c) $E = 11$, $V = 6$, $R = 7$, $N = 22$; so $V - E + R = 6 - 11 + 7 = 2$; $N = 22 \leq 22 = 2E$ and $E = 11 \leq 12 = 3V - 6$.

3.

Solid	V	E	F	$V - E + F$
tetrahedron	4	6	4	2
cube	8	12	6	2
octahedron	6	12	8	2
dodecahedron	20	30	12	2
icosahedron	12	30	20	2

5. (a) This is planar. Here it is drawn as a plane graph (with straight edges).

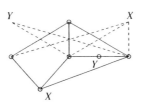

(e) This is not planar. There is a subgraph homeomorphic to $\mathcal{K}_{3,3}$ as shown.

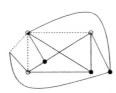

7. We know from Theorem 13.1.4 that $E \leq 3V - 6$. Substituting in $E = V + R - 2$, we obtain $V + R - 2 \leq 3V - 6$, or $R \leq 2V - 4$, as required.

8. (a) $E = 3 = 3(3) - 6 = 3V - 6.$ **10.** (a) $\mathcal{K}_n$ is planar if and only if $n \leq 4$.

11.

14. (a) Assume the result is not true. Then there is some counterexample $\mathcal{G}$ and subgraph $\mathcal{H}$; that is, for these graphs, $E_1 - V_1 < E_2 - V_2$. (In particular, $V_1 \neq V_2$.) Choose $\mathcal{H}$ such that $V_1 - V_2$ is as small as possible. Since $\mathcal{G}$ is connected, we can find a vertex v that is in $\mathcal{G}$, but not $\mathcal{H}$, that is joined to some vertex in $\mathcal{H}$. Let $\mathcal{K}$ be that subgraph of $\mathcal{G}$ consisting of $\mathcal{H}$, v and all edges joining v to vertices in $\mathcal{H}$. Letting V_3 and E_3 denote the numbers of vertices and edges, respectively, in $\mathcal{K}$, we have $V_3 = V_2 + 1$, while $E_3 \geq E_2 + 1$. Hence, $E_2 - V_2 \leq E_3 - V_3$ and so $E_1 - V_1 < E_3 - V_3$. Thus, $\mathcal{G}$ and its subgraph $\mathcal{K}$ provide another counterexample, but this contradicts the minimality of $V_1 - V_2$ since $V_1 - V_3 < V_1 - V_2$.

15. Yes. An example is shown to the right.

The graphs are homeomorphic since the one on the right is obtainable from the other by adding a vertex of degree 2.

17. (b) False, as shown by the homeomorphic graphs below. The graph on the left is Hamiltonian, but the one on the right is not.

19. (a) Let $\mathcal{G}_1, \mathcal{G}_2, \ldots, \mathcal{G}_n$ be the connected components of $\mathcal{G}$. Since $\mathcal{G}_i$ has at least three vertices, we have $E_{\mathcal{G}_i} \leq 3V_{\mathcal{G}_i} - 6$. Hence, $\sum E_{\mathcal{G}_i} \leq 3 \sum V_{\mathcal{G}_i} - 6n$, so $E \leq 3V - 6n$ as required.

20. (a) We may assume that $\mathcal{G}$ is connected. Say there is only one vertex of degree at most 5. Then $\sum \deg v_i \geq 6(V - 1) = 6V - 6$, contradicting $\sum \deg v_i = 2E \leq 6V - 12$.

21. (a) By Theorem 13.1.4, $E \leq 3V - 6$, so $E \leq 3(20) - 6 = 54$.

22. (a) Say at most one region has at most five edges on its boundary. Then, with N as in the proof of Corollary 13.1.3, $N \geq 6(R-1)$. But $N \leq 2E$, so $2E \geq 6R-6$, $3R \leq E+3$. Since $V-E+R=2$, $6 = 3V-3E+3R \leq 3V-2E+3$; that is, $2E \leq 3V-3$. But $2E = \sum \deg v_i \geq 3V$ by assumption, and this is a contradiction.

24. Letting x denote the number of connected components of $\mathcal{G}$, we have $V-E+R = 1+x$.

Proof. For each component C, $V_C - E_C + R_C = 2$. Adding, we get $\sum V_C - \sum E_C + \sum R_C = 2x$. We have $\sum V_C = V$ and $\sum E_C = E$, but $\sum R_C = R + (x-1)$ since the exterior region is common to all components. Thus, $V-E+R+x-1 = 2x$, $V-E+R = x+1$. ◈

Section 13.2 True/False

1. True   **2.** True   **3.** False: Consider [ ].   **4.** False   **5.** True

6. False: $\chi(\mathcal{K}_{m,n}) = 2$.   **7.** False: $\chi(K_{3,3}) = 2$.   **8.** True   **9.** False: $\chi(K_8) = 8$.   **10.** True

Exercises 13.2

2. (a) We show the graph superimposed over the given map. Since this graph contains triangles, at least three colors are necessary. A 3-coloring is shown, so the chromatic number is 3.

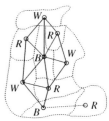

(b) False! The Four-Color Theorem says that the chromatic number of a planar graph is **at most** 4. The planar graph in (a) has chromatic number 3.

3. In neither case, will four colors necessarily suffice, as the pictures to the right demonstrate.

4. (b) A 5-coloring is shown; hence, $\chi(\mathcal{G}) \leq 5$. Since $\mathcal{K}_5$ is a subgraph, $\chi(\mathcal{G}) = 5$.

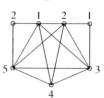

(e) A 4-coloring is shown; hence, $\chi(\mathcal{G}) \leq 4$. Since $\mathcal{G}$ contains $\mathcal{K}_4$ as a subgraph, $\chi(\mathcal{G}) = 4$.

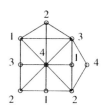

6. (a) The graph $\mathcal{G}_1$ on the left has a 3-coloring, as shown. Since it contains a triangle, $\chi(\mathcal{G}_1) = 3$. The graph $\mathcal{G}_2$ on the right has a 3-coloring, as shown. By trying to label alternately the vertices of the outer pentagon, we see that two colors will not suffice, so $\chi(\mathcal{G}_2) = 3$ too.

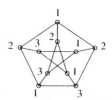

(b) The converse of the Four-Color Theorem states that, if the chromatic number of a graph is at most 4, the graph is planar. This result is false. The Petersen graph is not planar (Exercise 4 of Section 13.1), but, as we saw in part (a), $\chi = 3$.

7. (a) Yes, a tree is planar and we can prove this by induction on n, the number of vertices. Certainly, a tree with one vertex is planar. Then, given a tree with n vertices, removing a vertex of degree 1 (and the edge with which it is incident) leaves a tree with $n-1$ vertices that is planar by the induction hypothesis. The deleted vertex and edge can now be reinserted without destroying planarity.

8. (a) We assume $\mathcal{G}$ has more than three vertices for otherwise there is nothing to prove. Let $\mathcal{T}$ be a spanning tree for $\mathcal{G}$. By Exercise 7(c), we know that $\chi(\mathcal{T}) = 2$. Since $\mathcal{G}$ has n vertices, $\mathcal{G} = \mathcal{T} \cup \{e\}$ for some edge e. If the ends of e have different colors in $\mathcal{T}$, then $\chi(\mathcal{G}) = 2$; otherwise, one of these ends must be given a third color and $\chi(\mathcal{G}) = 3$. In either case, $\chi(\mathcal{G}) \leq 3$, as required.

10. (a)   (b)

(c) The graph isn't planar, by Kuratowski's Theorem, as the results of (a) and (b) each illustrate.

(d) A 3-coloring is shown. Since the graph contains triangles, fewer than three colors will not suffice. The chromatic number is 3.

(e) The converse of the Four-Color Theorem says that a graph with $\chi \leq 4$ is planar. This is not true, as this graph illustrates: The chromatic number is 3, but the graph is not planar.

11. (a) By PAUSE 7, for any n, $\chi(\mathcal{K}_n) = n$, and for any m, n, $\chi(\mathcal{K}_{m,n}) = 2$. Thus, $\chi(\mathcal{K}_{14}) = 14$ and $\chi(\mathcal{K}_{5,14}) = 2$.

12. (a) False. If $\mathcal{G}$ is a 5-cycle, then $\chi(\mathcal{G}) = 3$ since 5 is odd but $\mathcal{G}$ contains no triangle.

15. (a) False. $\mathcal{K}_{3,3}$ is Hamiltonian and has chromatic number 2 (by PAUSE 7), but it is not planar.

(d) False. $\mathcal{K}_7$ is Eulerian (since the degree of every vertex is 6) and Hamiltonian (since every complete graph is Hamiltonian), yet $\chi(\mathcal{K}_7) = 7$.

16. Three exam periods are required since this is the chromatic number of the graph.

20. We draw a graph $\mathcal{G}$. The vertices are courses, and two vertices are joined if somebody is taking both courses. Since $\chi(\mathcal{G}) = 4$, four time periods are required.

21. This means we can delete the edge joining "Econ" to "Stat," so "Stat" can be colored 3, $\chi(\mathcal{G}) = 3$, and three time periods now suffice.

26. (a) The dual of the cube is the octahedron whose graph appears in Fig. 13.5.

27. Yes, it is. Both the tetrahedron and its dual are $\mathcal{K}_4$.

Section 13.3 True/False

1. True   **2.** True   **3.** True   **4.** True   **5.** True   **6.** False

7. True   **8.** True   **9.** True: Recall that $E \leq 3V - 6$.   **10.** False

Exercises 13.3

1. (a) 36 nodes, 14 grid segments, 6 nets.   (b) V_1 and V_3, for example.   (c)

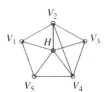

(d) We know $\chi(\mathcal{G}) \geq 4$ since $\mathcal{G}$ contains $\mathcal{K}_4$ (vertices H, V_2, V_3, V_4). On the other hand, a 4-coloring is given by $\{V_1, V_3\}$, $\{V_2, V_5\}$, $\{V_4\}$, $\{H\}$. Hence, $\chi(\mathcal{G}) = 4$. The above 4-coloring is also a partition of the nets.

3. False. An example is the net pattern ![net pattern] for which the line-of-sight graph is o   o.

5. (a) $\sim$ need not be reflexive. Consider ![pattern].

6. (a)

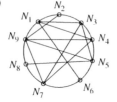

8. False. The graph in Exercise 6 is not planar. The subgraph with vertices N_1, N_3, N_4, N_5, N_6, N_7 and with edge N_3N_4 removed is isomorphic to $\mathcal{K}_{3,3}$.

9. (a) Imagine the possible shorts between nets as the edges in a graph: They will not cross since they are all parallel. Now compress each net to a point, and we have a plane graph. By the Four-Color Theorem, $\chi(\mathcal{G}) \leq 4$.

(b) Draw separate graphs $\mathcal{G}(V, \mathcal{E}_1)$, $\mathcal{G}(V, \mathcal{E}_2)$ for horizontal lines of sight, as in (a), and vertical lines of sight. These graphs have the same vertex set, so combine them. If an edge is repeated (that is, both horizontal and vertical lines exist between nets), then omit one of the original occurrences of it.

10. It is possible for a short to exist between any pair of nets here. Hence, $\mathcal{G} \cong \mathcal{K}_8$ and $\chi(\mathcal{G}) = 8$, as required.

11. $\mathcal{K}_5$:

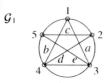   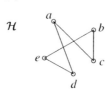

$\mathcal{H}$ cannot be 2-colored since it is a cycle of odd length. If we delete any vertex, however, the resulting graph can be 2-colored. If we delete e, for example, we obtain the graph at the right. Shown are $\mathcal{G}'$ and a corresponding floor plan.

14. (a) We can immediately draw $\mathcal{G}_1$ for this problem (using the obvious Hamiltonian cycle that a golfer must follow). Both $\mathcal{G}_1$ and $\mathcal{H}$ are shown.

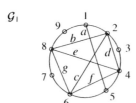   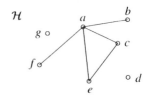

Since $\mathcal{H}$ contains a triangle, $\chi(\mathcal{H}) = 3$, so such a course is impossible.

15. Deleting vertex 2 (and the three edges incident with 2) leaves $\mathcal{K}_5$.

16. Since the graph is not $\mathcal{K}_n$ for any n, nor an odd cycle, Brooks's Theorem says $\chi(\mathcal{G}) \leq \Delta(\mathcal{G})$. Here $\Delta(\mathcal{G}) = 3$, so we have $\chi(\mathcal{G}) \leq 3$. But this graph contains cycles of odd length, so $\chi(\mathcal{G}) \geq 3$. We conclude that $\chi(\mathcal{G}) = 3$.

Appendix

Notation

Here, and on the last two end papers, is a list of the symbols and other notation used in this book grouped, as best as possible, by subject. Page numbers give the location of first appearance.

Page	Symbol	Meaning
Miscellaneous		
4	/	used to express the negation of any symbol over which it is written; for example, $\notin$ means "does not belong to"
76	$\lvert x \rvert$	the absolute value of x
90	$\aleph_0$	pronounced "aleph naught," this is the cardinality of the natural numbers
120	$\approx$	approximately
149	$\sum$	sum
159	$\prod$	product
Logical		
3	$\rightarrow$	implies
4	$\leftrightarrow$	if and only if
4	$\neg$	negation
7	$\forall$	for all
7	$\exists$	there exists
19	$\wedge$	and
19	$\vee$	or
24	$\Longleftrightarrow$	denotes logical equivalence
24	**0**	contradiction
24	**1**	tautology

Page	Symbol	Meaning
Common Sets		
38	**Z** or $\mathbb{Z}$	the integers
38	**N** or $\mathbb{N}$	the natural numbers
39	**Q** or $\mathbb{Q}$	the rational numbers
39	**R** or $\mathbb{R}$	the real numbers
39	**C** or $\mathbb{C}$	the complex numbers
81	$\mathbf{R}^+$	the positive real numbers
Set Theoretical		
39	$\in$	belongs to, is an element of
40	$\emptyset$	the empty set
40	$\subseteq$	is a subset of
40	$\subsetneq$	is a proper subset of
40	$\supseteq$	is a superset of, contains
41	$\mathcal{P}(A)$	the power set (the set of all subsets) of A
43	$\cup$	union
43	$\cap$	intersection
45	$\backslash$	set difference
45	A^c	the complement of A
46	$[a, b]$	$\{x \in \mathbf{R} \mid a \leq x \leq b\}$, where $a, b \in \mathbf{R}$
46	$(a, b]$	$\{x \in \mathbf{R} \mid a < x \leq b\}$, where $a, b \in \mathbf{R}$
46	$(-\infty, b]$	$\{x \in \mathbf{R} \mid x \leq b\}$, where $b \in \mathbf{R}$
46	(a, ∞)	$\{x \in \mathbf{R} \mid x > a\}$, where $a \in \mathbf{R}$
46	$\oplus$	symmetric difference
47	$\times$	Cartesian (or direct) product
88	$|A|$	the cardinality of A (if A is finite, this is just the number of elements in A)

Page	Symbol	Meaning

Equivalence Relations

| 59 | $A/\sim$ | quotient set of A (the set of equivalence classes of the equivalence relation $\sim$ on a set A) |
| 59, 126 | $\bar{a}$ | equivalence class of a; also used to denote the congruence class of an integer a (mod n) |

Partially Ordered Sets

64	$\preceq$	a partial order
67	$\vee$	least upper bound
67	$\wedge$	greatest lower bound

Functions

73	$f: A \to B$	f is a function from A to B
74	1–1	one-to-one
75	ι	the identity function
75	ι_A	the identity function on the set A
80	f^{-1}	inverse of the function f
82	$\circ$	composition (of functions)

Complexity/Order of Functions

254	$\mathcal{O}$	Big Oh
255	$f \prec g$	f has smaller order than g
255	$f \asymp g$	functions f and g have the same order

Number Theory

59	$n\mathbb{Z}$	the set of multiples of the integer n
59	$n\mathbb{Z} + r$	the set of integers of the form $na + r$, equivalently, the set of integers congruent to r (mod n)
77	$\lceil x \rceil$	ceiling of x, least integer $\geq x$
77	$\lfloor x \rfloor$	floor of x, greatest integer $\leq x$
105	$\mid$	divides
120	$\pi(x)$	number of primes $p \leq x$
125	$a \equiv b \pmod{n}$	a is congruent to b mod n, i.e., $n \mid (a-b)$

Page	Symbol	Meaning
	Combinatorial	
152	$n!$	n factorial
205	$P(n, r)$	the number of permutations of n objects taken r at a time
211	$\binom{n}{r}$	a binomial coefficient; read "n choose r," it equals the number of combinations of n objects taken r at a time; i.e., the number of ways to choose r objects from n
236	D_n	number of derangements of n symbols
	Graph Theoretical	
289	$\mathcal{G}(\mathcal{V},\mathcal{E})$	$\mathcal{G}$ is a graph with vertex set $\mathcal{V}$ and edge set $\mathcal{E}$
289	$\deg v$	the degree of vertex v
290	$\mathcal{G} \setminus \{e\}$	the graph whose vertices are those of $\mathcal{G}$ and whose edges consist of those of $\mathcal{G}$ except for e
290	$\mathcal{G} \setminus \{v\}$	the graph whose vertices are those of $\mathcal{G}$ except for v and whose edges are those edges of $\mathcal{G}$ not incident with v
290	$\mathcal{K}_n$	complete graph on n vertices
291	$\mathcal{K}_{m,n}$	complete bipartite graph on vertex sets of m and n elements
297	$\cong$	isomorphic
326	$w(e)$	weight of edge e
356	$s(v)$	score of vertex v in a tournament
420	$\chi(\mathcal{G})$	chromatic number of the graph $\mathcal{G}$

PART II
LINEAR PROGRAMMING

Notes prepared for:

MATH 2602 Linear and Discrete Mathematics

Fall 2000

Georgia Institute of Technology

Table of Contents

LINEAR PROGRAMMING

1 Background

In this document, we will look at a class of optimization problems that are quite well-solved in the sense that especially powerful mathematical and computational machinery exists for dealing with them. Before we begin, however, let us examine what we mean by a *mathematical optimization problem* in general. We can state this in the following way:

For a given function $z(x_1, x_2, \ldots, x_n)$ find values for the variables $x_1, x_2, \ldots, x_n$ such that z is maximized (minimized) and where the determined values satisfy all of a given (possibly empty) set of constraints.
□

Put more formally we have:

$$P: \quad \max(\min) \; z(x_1, x_2, \ldots, x_n)$$

$$\text{subject to: } g_i(x_1, x_2, \ldots, x_n) \leq b_i, \text{ for } i = 1, 2, \ldots, m.$$

In P, the function z is referred to as the *objective function* and the *constraints* are given by the functions g_i. An example is given below:

$$\min z = (x_1 - x_2^2)^3 + x_1 x_2 x_3 + x_3^{\frac{3}{2}}$$

$$\text{s.t.} \quad x_1 x_2 x_3 \leq 10$$

$$x_1 + x_2^2 + \tfrac{x_3}{2} \leq 12.$$

Another example might require *integrality* restrictions on some or all of the variables:

$$\max z = x_1^3 + x_2 x_3 x_4 + x_2^2 - x_3(x_2 - x_4)^2$$

$$\text{s.t.} \qquad x_1 + x_2 + x_3 + x_4 = 7$$

$$x_1, x_3 \geq 0 \text{ and } x_2, x_4 \text{ nonnegative integers.}$$

Of course, these are just randomly generated mathematical expressions that demonstrate the complexion of an optimization formulation. For any of this to have practical relevance, the idea would obviously be to examine some realistic setting and from same, build or create its mathematical representation. This is rather like what is done in your first algebra class with those dreaded "story problems." The entire exercise of creating and solving these mathematical models of real-world settings is, by and large, what constitutes the field of *operations research*.

2   Introduction to Linear Programming

2.1   Basic Forms

If all of the functions in our problem are linear and if all of the variables are continuous, we have a *linear programming* (LP) problem. Stating this in a formal way produces the following model. Note that for simplicity, we will adopt only the "maximize" format:

$$P_C: \qquad \max z = c_1 x_1 + c_2 x_2 + \ldots + c_n x_n$$

$$\text{s.t.} \quad a_{11} x_1 + a_{12} x_2 + \ldots + a_{1n} x_n \leq b_1$$

$$a_{21} x_1 + a_{22} x_2 + \ldots + a_{2n} x_n \leq b_2$$

$$\vdots$$

$$a_{m1} x_1 + a_{m2} + \ldots + a_{mn} x_n \leq b_m$$

$$x_1, x_2, \ldots, x_n \geq 0.$$

The last, *nonnegativity constraints* require that all variables take on values no less than 0; the c_j, a_{ij}, and b_j parameters are problem *coefficients*. Often the b_j values are called the *right-hand-sides* of the formulation. Note also that the model indicated by P_C is referred to as *canonical form*, *i.e.*, objective function of "maximize" form, less-than-or-equal inequalities, and nonnegativity restrictions on all of the variables. Readers may want to take time to convince themselves that every linear program can be expressed in canonical form.

Often, it is convenient to consider an LP problem in compact form. For P_C, we can write:

$$\max z = \mathbf{cx}$$

$$\text{s.t. } \mathbf{Ax} \le \mathbf{b}$$

$$\mathbf{x} \ge \mathbf{0}$$

Here, $\mathbf{c}$ is a $1 \times n$ vector $(c_1, c_2, \ldots, c_n)$; $\mathbf{A}$ is an $m \times n$ matrix (a_{ij}) where $1 \le i \le m$ and $1 \le j \le n$; $\mathbf{b}$ is an $m \times 1$ vector of right-hand-side values; and of course, $\mathbf{x}$ is an $n \times 1$ vector of the variables, $(x_1, x_2, \ldots, x_n)$.

Now, an alternative way to express LP's, and one that we will employ extensively in this treatise, is in *standard form*:

$$P_S : \qquad \max (\min) z = \mathbf{cx}$$

$$\text{s.t. } \mathbf{Ax} = \mathbf{b}$$

$$\mathbf{x} \ge \mathbf{0}.$$

Required now are: (i) equality constraints, (ii) nonegative right-hand-side values, and (iii) nonnegativity restrictions on all variables.

Conversions between canonical and standard forms are easy. For example, a constraint of the form $ax \le b$ can be converted to an equality by simply adding a nonnegative *slack* variable s in order to produce $ax + s = b$. Alternately, an equation of the form $ax = b$ can obviously be replaced by a pair of inequalities given by $ax \le b$ and $ax \ge b$. If variables x_j in a "real" problem are allowed to be unrestricted or *free* (*i.e.*, not required to be nonegative), then we can replace x_j everywhere by the difference between two new variables x_j' and x_j'' where the latter are required to be nonnegative. A useful exercise is to work through a few conversions between these two forms.

2.2 Modeling

As indicated earlier, the basic trick in operations research is to grapple with a physical problem setting or system description and create ultimately, a formulation or mathematical model that captures the requirements of the real setting. Especially helpful, is to create a model that qualifies as a linear program for as we will see subsequently, this constitutes a major step in the direction of ultimately solving the problem. Following, we go through some easy illustrations of the model-building activity.

Example 1: An oil refinery can buy two types of oil: light crude and heavy crude. The cost per barrel is 11 and 9 dollars respectively. The portion of gasoline, kerosene, and jet fuel produced per barrel of each type of crude is given below:

	Gasoline	Kerosene	Jet Fuel
Light	0.40	0.20	0.35
Heavy	0.32	0.40	0.20

Observe that the proportions do not add to 1.00 because there is some loss in the refining process itself, *i.e.*, 5 % in the case of light crude oil and 8 % for heavy. Now, the refinery must deliver 1,000,000 barrels of gasoline, 400,000 barrels of kerosene, and 250,000 barrels of jet fuel. How can they meet this production requirement at least total cost?

Solution: Our approach begins with a specification of the *decision variables* (unknowns) for the problem. Accordingly, let us define x_L to be the number of barrels of light crude to purchase and let x_H to be the relevant number of barrels of heavy crude. Obviously, for any assignment of values to x_L and x_H, our total cost is $z = 11x_L + 9x_H$. Now, what are the constraints that we have to be mindful of relative to fixing values for the variables? Obviously, we have to produce certain minimum amounts of gasoline, kerosene, and jet fuel and we know how much of each, relatively speaking, we can extract from each type of crude through the refining process. For example, if we consider the production of gasoline, then we know that whatever our amount of light and heavy crude oil, the amount of gasoline possible upon refinement will be $0.4x_L + 0.32x_H$ and this total must be at least 1,000,000 barrels, $i.e.$, $0.4x_L + 0.32x_H \geq 1,000,000$. The other constraints (relative to kerosene and jet fuel) are handled in the same fashion. Finally, it makes no sense to purchase a negative amount of crude oil which suggests nonnegativity restrictions on the variables and we are thus led to an LP model of the stated problem:

$$\min z = 11x_L + 9x_H$$

$$\text{s.t.} \quad 0.40x_L + 0.32x_H \geq 1,000,000$$

$$0.20x_L + 0.40x_H \geq 400,000$$

$$0.35x_L + 0.20x_H \geq 250,000$$

$$x_L, x_H \geq 0.$$

□

Example 2: A company in South America processes beans into coffee at its m different production facilities. The coffee is then shipped to n warehouses for retail distribution and exportation. A unit shipping cost ($i.e.$, cost per ton) from plant i to warehouse j is specified by c_{ij}. The production capacity at plant i is a_i and the demand called for at warehouse j is denoted by b_j. What is the least total cost production-shipping strategy for the company in order that production capacity not be exceeded while satisfying the demands at all of the warehouses?

Solution: This is an example of what is commonly known as a *transportation problem*. Let x_{ij} be a decision variable denoting the amount of coffee shipped from plant i to warehouse j. Now, for a given i, the total amount shipped from the relevant plant cannot exceed the plant's capacity given by a_i. Similarly, the total amount demanded at a warehouse j, shipped from any source, needs to be at least b_j. Finally, the total cost of a shipping decision x_{ij} is obviously $c_{ij}x_{ij}$. Combining all of this produces the following formulation:

$$\min z = c_{11}x_{11} + c_{12}x_{12} + \ldots + c_{mn}x_{mn}$$

$$\text{s.t} \qquad x_{11} + x_{12} + \ldots + x_{1n} \leq a_1$$

$$x_{21} + x_{22} + \ldots + x_{2n} \leq a_2$$

$$\vdots$$

$$x_{m1} + x_{m2} + \ldots + x_{mn} \leq a_m$$

$$x_{11} + x_{21} + \ldots + x_{m1} \geq b_1$$

$$x_{12} + x_{22} + \ldots + x_{m2} \geq b_2$$

$$\vdots$$

$$x_{1n} + x_{2n} + \ldots + x_{mn} \geq b_n$$

$$x_{ij} \geq 0 \text{ for all } i \text{ and } j.$$

$\square$

Example 3: Find the largest integer in the list $a_1, a_2, \ldots, a_n$.

Solution: This is not an interesting example in any practical sense; clearly, there are better ways to sort through a list of values and select the largest (or smallest). Rather, we employ the illustration simply to exhibit th the modeling exercise even in somewhat nonstandard contexts. In this regard, let z be a largest integer value. Then it should be clear that solving the following LP formulation will produce the value of the largest integer in our list:

$$\min z$$

$$\text{s.t.} \quad z \geq a_1$$
$$z \geq a_2$$
$$\vdots$$
$$z \geq a_n.$$

$\square$

In fact, there is little "science" involved in modeling optimization problems, including linear programming formulations; there are no algorithms that specify a precise step-by-step receipt. That said, one usually gains much from experience; very often apparently diverse problem settings in the real world can be modeled correctly by exploiting similar tricks that have proven successful in other recognizable settings. Indeed, effective modeling is a bit of an art. Still, a reasonable general tactic to pursue when beginning, is to reflect on what the problem is asking. In doing this, one usually is able to specify the variables in the problem. Next, ask what it is in the problem that restricts or *constrains* values that are assignable to the variables. In progressing through this exercise, one is often very close to being able to quantify the functional contraints in the formulation. To reiterate, there is no magic key to formulating what can be very complicated *story problems* but by progressing deliberately through the execise indicated, beginning students are often surprised at how close they can get to creating complete and valid formulations.

3   Solving Linear Programs

The basic notions that provide the underpinning for the actual solution of linear programs is not so complicated to appreciate. To be sure, there are some details that require arguments that are, in fact, quite delicate and some of the proofs that are needed to assure correctness are hard; however, the fundamental machinery that makes linear programs among the most *well-solved* of optimization problems is fairly easy to understand. In fact, we can motivate a great deal by simple geometric means.

3.1 Geometry and Basic Notions

Let us consider a simple LP instance:

$$\max z = 3x_1 + 2x_2$$

$$\text{s.t.} \quad 2x_1 + 3x_2 \leq 6 \qquad\qquad (1)$$

$$4x_1 + 2x_2 \leq 8 \qquad\qquad (2)$$

$$x_1, x_2 \geq 0. \qquad\qquad (3), (4)$$

Note that we have numbered the constraints for purposes of subsequent reference. Now, since our problem possesses only two variables, we are afforded the luxury of creating a graphical depiction. To this end, consider Figure 1. Obviously, the nonnegativity constraints ((3) and (4)) require that our search be restricted to the first orthant of the 2-dimensional space indicated. Similarly, we can plot the other two constraints given by inequalities (1) and (2) as shown. Obviously, if there is any nonempty space contained in the intersection of the *half-spaces* described by these four inequalities then we have at least one feasible solution for our problem. This solution set is referred to as the *feasible region*; in Figure 1, it it is indicated by the shaded area. The good news is that for the example used, we have a nonempty feasible solution set. The bad news is that there are infinitely many feasible solutions present; how then do we locate an optimal one?

Here's an idea. Suppose we examine the objective function: $z = 3x_1 + 2x_2$. This is just a line with slope $-\frac{3}{2}$ and intercept $\frac{z}{2}$. Now, for some fixed value of z, there are in infinite number of possibilities for x_1 and x_2, *i.e.*, every point on the line. So if we vary values for z, this has the effect, graphically speaking, of simply moving the line parallel to itself. Decreasing the value for z moves the line towards the origin; larger values move it away. Since large values for z are good (we are maximizing), we would want z to be as large as possible so long as there were values for x_1 and x_2 that remained feasible, *i.e.*, that intersected with the feasible region. But this means that we need only shift (through the setting for z) the objective function line in the direction of the *gradient* $\nabla z = (3, 2)$, continuing until we reach the edge of the feasible region. Since we have assumed all functions to be linear, there will be no

8

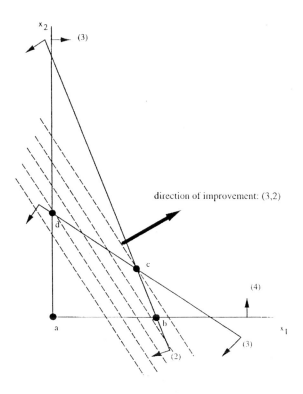

Figure 1: Graphical depiction of an LP solution space

"surprises" in proclaiming the last point or points that are touched to be optimal. In Figure 1, this movement is indicated by the dotted lines and accordingly, the last "point of contact" with the feasible region is the single point c corresponding to the values $x_1 = \frac{3}{2}$ and $x_2 = 1$. We thus claim this is the unique optimal solution; its *value* is $z = 6.5$. It is perhaps instructive to exhibit the 3-dimensional representation of this sample problem by including the axis corresponding to z. This is shown in Figure 2.

Now, our claim is that the simple approach made graphical by this elementary illustration, is enough, *i.e.*, that it is extendable to the solution of general linear programs. That is, we will simply pass the objective function plane (*i.e.*, hyperplane in arbitrary dimensions) through the feasible region generated by the problem constraints, and observe the last admissible point (or points) that intersect(s) with the plane accordingly. Of course, this is not something that can be done graphically but if we can make the process algebraic then we might (if our claim is true) be close to producing an algorithm for solving LPs.

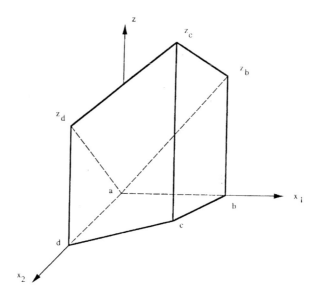

Figure 2: 3-Dimensional depiction of sample problem

3.1.1 The Feasible Region of Linear Programs

Consider the LP in standard form again; in fact, let us state it in the following, rather formal way:

$$\max(\min) \ \{\mathbf{cx} \mid \mathbf{x} \in S\}$$

where $S = \{\mathbf{x} \mid \mathbf{Ax} = \mathbf{b}, \mathbf{x} \geq \mathbf{0}\}$. Now, let us examine the structure of the contraint set. In general, a set C is *convex* if given any two points in C say $\mathbf{x}^1$ and $\mathbf{x}^2$, then any point $\mathbf{x}^3 = \lambda\mathbf{x}^1 + (1 - \lambda)\mathbf{x}^2$ is also in C where λ is a scaler bounded by 0 and 1, *i.e.*, $0 \leq \lambda \leq 1$. Sometimes we say that $\mathbf{x}^3$ is expressed as a *linear combination* of $\mathbf{x}^1$ and $\mathbf{x}^2$. Some convex and nonconvex sets are displayed in Figure 3.

Now, we claim that the set S formed as per the standard form above is a convex set (which is an important property if true). But it turns out that this claim is easy to justify. To see this, simply pick any two points in S, say $\mathbf{x}^1$ and $\mathbf{x}^2$ and then for an arbitrary value of λ in the interval $0 \leq \lambda \leq 1$, form $\mathbf{x}^3 = \lambda\mathbf{x}^1 + (1 - \lambda)\mathbf{x}^2$. Then multiplying both sides by the LP constraint matrix $\mathbf{A}$ yields $\mathbf{Ax}^3 = \lambda\mathbf{Ax}^1 + (1 - \lambda)\mathbf{Ax}^2 = \lambda\mathbf{b} + (1 - \lambda)\mathbf{b} = \mathbf{b}$. Also, it

10

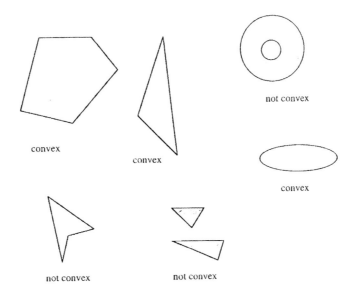

Figure 3: Convex and nonconvex sets

must be that $\mathbf{x}^3 \geq \mathbf{0}$ since λ is nonegative and bounded by 1 and hence we have arrived at the desired outcome that $\mathbf{x}^3 \in S$ and thus the set S is convex. Of course, we have assumed that the set S is nonempty and as we will see later, for cases where in fact, there is no feasible solution to a problem, *i.e.*, where $S = \emptyset$, we will need an unambiguous way to decide this.

3.1.2 Extreme Points

A point $\mathbf{x}$ is called an *extreme point* of the feasible region of an LP if $\mathbf{x}$ cannot be represented as a strict linear combination of two distinct points in the region. We can illustrate the notion by considering various points in the set shown in Figure 4. Note that in our example, there are four extreme points: a, b, c and d. But in fact, that we had any extreme points at all is guaranteed following a particularly modest requirement:

Property 1: If the convex set $S = \{\mathbf{x} \mid \mathbf{Ax} = \mathbf{b}, \mathbf{x} \geq \mathbf{0}\}$ is nonempty, it has at least one extreme point.
□

But why are extreme points relevant? The next property provides some insight:

11

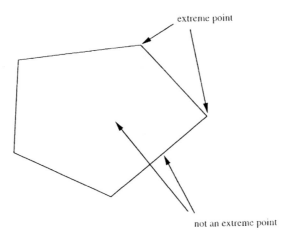

extreme point

not an extreme point

Figure 4: Extreme points and nonextreme points

Property 2: If a finite optima exists for an LP, then there is an optimal extreme point.

□

Of course, there may be optimal solutions to an LP that are not extreme points, but Property 2 indicates that if this is the case, then there has to also be an optimal solution that does, in fact, correspond to an extreme point. So then, in searching for an optimal solution, it is the case that we need only search among the extreme points of feasible region. Of course, there could exist more than one optimal extreme point but in this case, we know that our LP would have an entire family of optimal solutions:

Property 3: If an LP has at least two distinct optimal extreme points then there exists an infinite number of optimal solutions.

□

This property is also easy to justify. For a distinct pair of optimal extreme points, say $\mathbf{x}^1$ and $\mathbf{x}^2$ then any point $\mathbf{x}^3$ formed as $\mathbf{x}^3 = \lambda \mathbf{x}^1 + (1 - \lambda)\mathbf{x}^2$ is also optimal where $\lambda \in (0, 1)$. That is, any point on the line connecting $\mathbf{x}^1$ and $\mathbf{x}^2$ is optimal and, of course, there are infinitely many of these.

What this means geometrically is that the last portion of the feasible region to be "cut off" by the progression of the objective hyperplane through the region, is not a single (extreme) point but is rather, a *face* of the region. In our 2-dimensional example problem earlier, had our objective function

12

been parallel to say constraint 2, then the last part of the feasible region shown that would have been touched by the objective function would be the line segment between and including points b and c. Any of the infinitely many points on this line segment would have been optimal.

3.1.3 Basic Solutions

Let $\mathbf{A}$ be the constraint matrix of the LP in standard form; assume $\mathbf{A}$ to be of dimension $m \times n$, *i.e.*, m rows and n columns. Each column of $\mathbf{A}$ corresponds to a variable in the LP, including any which have been added to convert the LP to standard form. Now, let $\mathbf{B}$ be any $m \times m$ submatrix of $\mathbf{A}$ that consists of m *linearly independent* columns. Accordingly, $\mathbf{B}$ is an $m \times m$ invertible submatrix of $\mathbf{A}$. We will denote the variables that are identified with the columns of $\mathbf{B}$ by $\mathbf{x_B}$; the columns in $\mathbf{B}$ are said to form a *basis*.

Now, suppose we solve the system $\mathbf{Bx_B} = \mathbf{b}$. Then, the solution $\mathbf{x_B} = \mathbf{B^{-1}b}$ is called a *basic solution* of the system $\mathbf{Ax} = \mathbf{b}$; if $\mathbf{x_B} \geq 0$, the solution is a *basic feasible solution* and the corresponding variables are said to be *basic*. If any variable in $\mathbf{x_B}$ has value 0, the basic solution is called *degenerate* (nondegenerate otherwise). Variables not in $\mathbf{x_B}$ are called *nonbasic* and automatically have their value set to 0. As we shall see later, degeneracy can cause some computational problems in the solution of linear programs but fortunately, there are ways to guard against these.

Example 4: Suppose we consider the small two-variable LP used earlier. In this regard, let us convert the original model to standard form. Adding nonnegative slack varibales to each inequality produces the pair of equations given below:

$$2x_1 + 3x_2 + S_1 = 6$$

$$4x_1 + 2x_2 + S_2 = 8$$

$$x_1, x_2, S_1, S_2 \geq 0.$$

Observe that slack variables for each constraint are denoted by S_1 and S_2 respectively. Now, relative to the matrix representation of this standard form construction, the matrix $\mathbf{A}$ appears as

$$\begin{array}{cccc} x_1 & x_2 & S_1 & S_2 \end{array}$$
$$\mathbf{A} = \begin{pmatrix} 2 & 3 & 1 & 0 \\ 4 & 2 & 0 & 1 \end{pmatrix}.$$

We have indicated, across the top of the array, the variables identified with the corresponding columns. The vector representing the right-hand sides of the system is given by $\mathbf{b} = \begin{pmatrix} 6 \\ 8 \end{pmatrix}$. Now, suppose we consider the submatrix of $\mathbf{A}$ formed by the columns corresponding to variables x_1 and x_2. Calling this $\mathbf{B_1}$ we have:

$$\begin{array}{cc} x_1 & x_2 \end{array}$$
$$\mathbf{B_1} = \begin{pmatrix} 2 & 3 \\ 4 & 2 \end{pmatrix}.$$

The basic variables are given by $\mathbf{x_B} = (x_1, x_2)$ which then implies that the nonbasic variables (all of the others) result as $\mathbf{x_N} = (S_1, S_2)$. By definition then, we have $S_1 = S_2 = 0$. Now, matrix $\mathbf{B_1}$ is invertible and we obtain accordingly:

$$\mathbf{B_1^{-1}} = \begin{pmatrix} -\frac{1}{4} & \frac{3}{8} \\ \frac{1}{2} & -\frac{1}{4} \end{pmatrix}$$

whereupon we can solve for $\mathbf{x_B}$ as $\mathbf{B_1^{-1}b} = \begin{pmatrix} \frac{3}{2} \\ 1 \end{pmatrix}$. That is, $x_1 = \frac{3}{2}$ and $x_2 = 1$. Since all of the variables (including the slack variables) are nonnegative, we have produced a basic feasible solution. Suppose we repeat this process by forming another submatrix say $\mathbf{B_2}$ defined by the variables x_1 and S_1, i.e.,

$$\begin{array}{cc} x_1 & S_2 \end{array}$$
$$\mathbf{B_2} = \begin{pmatrix} 2 & 1 \\ 4 & 0 \end{pmatrix}.$$

Of course, what we are trying to do is solve the system given by

$$2x_1 + S_1 = 6$$

$$4x_1 = 8.$$

Again, we could form $\mathbf{B_2}^{-1}$ and post-multiply this by $\mathbf{b}$ to obtain the solution for variables in $\mathbf{x_B} = (x_1, S_1)$; however, the simplicity of the system allows us to find a solution directly. Accordingly, we find that $x_1 = 2$ and $S_1 = 2$. The nonbasic variables are x_2 and S_2 and they (by virtue of their nonbasic status) are set to 0. Again, since all four variables are nonegative, we have another basic feasible solution.

We could proceed with this; there are four more combinations of pairs of columns from $\mathbf{A}$ that are linearly independent and hence form bases. We will not take space nor time to create and actually solve all of these but below, we list the basic variable sets followed by the values that result upon solution, including those for the nonbasic variables which are of course known once the basic variables are indicated.

Basis	$\mathbf{x_B}$	(x_1, x_2, S_1, S_2)
$\mathbf{B_3}$	(x_1, S_2)	$(3, 0, 0, -4)$
$\mathbf{B_4}$	(x_2, S_1)	$(0, 4, -6, 0)$
$\mathbf{B_5}$	(x_2, S_2)	$(0, 2, 0, 4)$
$\mathbf{B_6}$	(S_1, S_2)	$(0, 0, 6, 8)$

The first two of these (given by $\mathbf{B_3}$ and $\mathbf{B_4}$) are not basic feasible solutions since at least one of the variables takes on a negative value. Of course some readers may wonder why this is relevant if the offending variables are only slack variables. The answer is easy and is evident by simply examining what the corresponding solution represents geometrically. Indeed, in Figure 5, we indicate precisely what each basis $\mathbf{B_i}$ corresponds to in the graphical depiction of this sample problem instance. In the cases of $\mathbf{B_3}$ and $\mathbf{B_4}$, what we have actually located are solutions that correspond to the intersection of certain problem constraints but unfortunately, not ones that define an extreme point of the problem's feasible region.

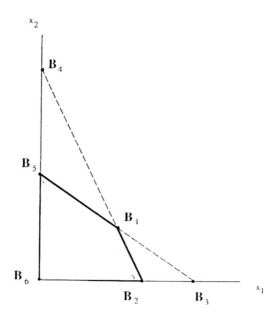

Figure 5: Basic feasible solutions and extreme points

So, the four basic feasible solutions identified by $\mathbf{B_1}, \mathbf{B_2}, \mathbf{B_5}$ and $\mathbf{B_6}$ correspond to the four points of the feasible region indicated. Of these, we know that $\mathbf{B_1}$ is optimal. Of course, how we would decide this algebraically is critical and subsequently, we will formulate a method. Important at this point, however, is to observe that the correspondence between the four extreme points indicated and the four basic feasible solutions in this case is more than a casual outcome. We have:

Property 4: The collection of extreme points of a linear program corresponds to the collection of basic feasible solutions.

□

In fact, the establishment of this "equivalence" property is one of the fundamental underpinnings in the theory of linear programming; the previous properties that were stated actually derive as corollaries of Property 4.

Since we saw that basic solutions were determined by forming invertible $m \times m$ submatrices of the constraint matrix $\mathbf{A}$, it follows that the total number of basic feasible solutions for an n-variable problem is bounded from above by $\binom{n}{m}$. Observe that n and m are defined by the LP stated in standard form. In addition, the implied inequality follows since many candidate $m \times m$ submatrices will not contain linearly independent columns and in addition, many that do, will not produce basic feasible solutions.

So, in theory we could solve an LP by simply examining its finitely many basic feasible solutions and then pick the best. Unfortunately, such a strategy would be tedious at best since for even small instances (*e.g.*, $n = 100, m = 25$), this enumeration would be very time-consuming. But beyond this, there are other, not so subtle, matters with which to be concerned. What if an LP has *no* solution space? What if its solution space is not bounded? What about multiple solutions? And what are those degenerate solutions that were defined previously; can they be an issue? Clearly, we need some formal way of addressing these matters.

3.2 The Simplex Algorithm

Assume that we are given an initial basic feasible solution (corresponding to a starting extreme point). Then suppose we were able to replace this solution with another one that was better (or at least no worse), repeating the process until we reached a point whereupon we could establsh that an optimal solution had been found. That is, suppose we could start at some extreme point of our feasible region, move succesively through alternative ones that, if not strictly improving in terms of the objective function value, are at least no worse, stopping at a final extreme point with a proof that our search was finished, *i.e.*, that we had found an optimum. Happily, it is exactly this sort of "controlled search" through extreme points, *vis-a-vis* the algebraic manipulation of basic feasible solutions, that constitutes the fundamental machinery of the *simplex algorithm*. Developed by George Dantzig during the second world war, work leading to the ultimate development of the simplex algorithm stands as one of the celebrated success stories in operations research (George Dantzig is often referred to as the father of linear programming).

In concept, the simplex algorithm is essentially a bookkeeping strategy for basic solution manipulation which, in turn, guides our search through a sequence of *adjacent* extreme points of an LP's feasible region. We need three things:

- a starting basic feasible solution

- a stopping criterion

- a method for moving from one extreme point to another

Rather than state the simplex algorithm in a formal way (which we will do later), it should be instructive to motivate the basic notions called for above. To this end, let us continue with the sample problem that has been used thus far. For ease, the original (standard form) system is presented again below:

$$z = 3x_1 + 2x_2$$

$$2x_1 + 3x_2 + S_1 = 6$$

$$4x_1 + 2x_2 + S_2 = 8$$

Observe that the slack variables take on coefficients of 0 and hence do not appear in the objective function equation. Although not stated as such, readers should be clear that all variables are required to be nonnegative in the system shown. Now, let us take as an initial basis the submatrix corresponding to variables $\mathbf{x_B} = (S_1, S_2)$. For obvious reasons this is called the "all-slack" basis. Certainly, this may not yield a very good initial solution but at least it is feasible. Accordingly, let us solve for the slack variables in their respective equations as follows:

$$S_1 = 6 - 2x_1 - 3x_2 = 6$$

18

$$S_2 = 8 - 4x_1 - 2x_2 = 8$$

.

Now, since x_1 and x_2 are nonbasic, they are set to 0 and we produce the solution $S_1 = 6$ and $S_2 = 8$ which we (trivially) expected; its value is $z = 0$. Obviously, the all slack solution corresponds to the origin (point a) in our 2-dimensional depiction of the feasible region.

Now, we observe that if the value of either x_1 or x_2 is elevated above 0, we will improve upon the current (all slack) solution value. Since $c_1 = 3 > 2 = c_2$, let us select variable x_1 to make basic. Acting in a "greedy" fashion, we would want to make x_1 as large as is feasibly possible. But this is easy to decide by simply evaluating the limit on how large x_1 can be by examining the two current constraint equations above. From the first of these, we see that x_1 can be no greater than 3 while from the second equation, x_1 is bounded from above by 2. The smaller of these values defines the maximum value that the variable can take on and still satisfy all contraints. So, let our new basis consist of variables x_1 and S_1, *i.e.*, variable x_1 has replaced slack variable S_2 from the previous basis. Solving for x_1 in the second equation yields:

$$x_1 = 2 - \frac{x_2}{2} - \frac{S_2}{4},$$

and substituting x_1 into the first equation, produces

$$2x_2 - \frac{S_2}{2} + S_1 = 2.$$

Obviously since variables x_2 and S_2 are now nonbasic and hence take on value 0, the new basic variables x_1 and S_1 both solve with value 2 accordingly. Geometrically, this means that we have moved from the basis associated with the origin along the x_1 axis, stopping at the extreme point b. Finally, if we also substitute for x_1 into our objective function, we obtain:

$$z = 6 + \frac{x_2}{2} - \frac{3}{4}S_2$$

This is also consistent; that is, setting nonbasic variables x_2 and S_2 to 0 yields $z = 6$. In any event, we can now replace our original, standard form representation of the problem by the following, equivalent system:

$$z = 6 + \frac{x_2}{2} - \frac{3}{4}S_2$$

$$2x_2 - \frac{S_2}{2} + S_1 = 2$$

$$x_1 + \frac{x_2}{2} + \frac{S_2}{4} = 2.$$

This new system is identical to the original one since all that has occurred is a manipulation of equations, *i.e.*, solutions feasible for one system are preserved in the creation of the new system.

Now, in lookng at this new extreme point and the algebraic representation given above, we can see that the corresponding basis can be improved since a current nonbasic variable (x_2) possesses a positive coefficient in the updated objective function; the modified value of c_2 is now $\frac{1}{2}$.

So, our intent is to bring into the basis, the improving variable x_2. Note that had more than one nonbasic variable had a positive coefficient, we could have used the previous rule-of-thumb selection policy of picking the variable having the greatest such value. In any event, and owing to linearity, we would seek to make x_2 as large as possible and this means examining both of the current constraint equations. Accordingly, from the first, we see that the value of x_2 can be no larger than 1 and from the second, no larger than 4. We are again bound by the smaller of these quantities and this results from the solution in the first equation. That is, x_2 will replace S_1 from the previous basis and solving as before yields:

$$x_2 = 1 + \frac{S_2}{4} - \frac{S_1}{2}.$$

Substituing this expression into the current objective and second constraint equations produces the new, equivalent system shown below:

$$z = 6\frac{1}{2} - \frac{S_1}{4} - \frac{5}{8}S_2$$

$$x_2 + \frac{S_1}{2} - \frac{S_2}{4} = 1$$

$$x_1 - \frac{S_1}{4} + \frac{3}{8}S_2 = \frac{3}{2}.$$

It is comforting to see, since S_1 and S_2 by virtue of their nonbasic status and hence, assignment of value 0, that we have produced the basic feasible solution $x_1 = \frac{3}{2}$ and $x_2 = 1$ with $z = 6\frac{1}{2}$.

This new basis corresponds to extreme point c. Moreover, the current solution is optimal since we need only examine our equivalent system whereupon we see that the modified objective row coefficients for nonbasic variables (the only ones that could improve our current solution value) are nonpositive, *i.e.*, their introduction into a basis at any feasible, positive value could only reduce the objective function value in hand. Therefore, we are prepared to conclude that our sequence of moves from the initial extreme point (the origin in this case) to the current one can stop with a claim that we have found an optimal solution.

Now, the simplex algorithm (stated crudely of course) simply performs the calculations just demonstrated in an organized way making use of tabular representations. Hence, the *initial simplex tableau* would appear as follows:

$$
\begin{array}{c}
\\
\\
S_1 \\
S_2
\end{array}
\begin{array}{cccc}
x_1 & x_2 & S_1 & S_2 \\
\end{array}
\left(
\begin{array}{ccccc}
-3 & - & 0 & 0 & 0 \\
2 & 3 & 1 & 0 & 6 \\
4 & 2 & 0 & 1 & 8
\end{array}
\right).
$$

The columns of the tableau are labeled by the variables; these labels never change. The rows relate to the objective function (treated as an equation beginning as $z - \mathbf{cx} = 0$) and the constraints. The constraint rows are labeled by the current basic variables, one per equation. As the initial tableau above indicates, the starting basis consists of slack variables S_1 and S_2, *i.e.*, in any basic tableau, the columns corresponding to the basic variables will be unit vectors.

Now, we saw earlier that an improvement of our current (initial) solution could be achieved by bringing into our basis the variable x_1 as a replacement for S_2. We solved for x_1 in the second constraint equation and substituted the outcome into the other constraint and the objective function. But this is equivalent to performing elementary row operations on the original system (first tableau) whereby a unit vector is created with the value 1 in the tableau cell corresponding to the intersection of the entering and departing variables respectively. This cell is referred to as the *pivot cell* of the tableau and the algebraic manipulation is referred to as *pivoting*. If we do this, we obtain the second tableau shown below:

$$
\begin{array}{c}
\begin{array}{ccccc} x_1 & x_2 & S_1 & S_2 & \end{array} \\
\begin{array}{c} \\ S_1 \\ x_1 \end{array}
\left(
\begin{array}{ccccc}
0 & -1/2 & 0 & 3/4 & 6 \\
0 & 2 & 1 & -1/2 & 2 \\
1 & 1/2 & 0 & 1/4 & 2
\end{array}
\right).
\end{array}
$$

The anxious reader may want to examine this tableau and compare the information captured accordingly, with that derived in the previous system of equations after the first basis exchange. Obviously, the value of this basic feasible solution is 6; the value is always read in the upper right-hand cell of each tableau.

Upon examining the second tableau, the analogous test of optimality relative to potential improvement of our current objective function value would now have us examining the objective function row and in particular, those (updated) row coefficients of nonbasic variables to see if any existed at a negative value. If so, then bringing one of these into a basis and throwing something out would possibly produce another basis and if so, one that was strictly better than our prevous one. Do not forget: looking for negative objective coefficients here corresponds to our search for positive ones earlier since in our tabular format, we have rewritten the objective function. In any event, we observe that the coefficient of nonbasic x_2 is -1/2 and so we will bring it into the basis. The decision of which variable it will replace, is determined by a *ratio test* that, as we observed, simply allows us to make the new variable as large as possible while satisfying the problem constraints. This is a check that asks only that we examine the ratio of a tableau's current right-hand-side value to the entering variable row coefficient and pick the smallest (negative values are not considered). In this case, our comparison is between the ratios $\frac{2}{2}$ and $\frac{2}{1/2}$ suggesting that x_2 will replace S_1 in the first constraint equation. We pivot on the relevant cell of the last tableau creating the third one as displayed below:

$$
\begin{array}{c}
\begin{array}{ccccc} x_1 & x_2 & S_1 & S_2 & \end{array}\\
\begin{array}{c} \\ x_2 \\ x_1 \end{array}
\left(\begin{array}{ccccc}
0 & 0 & 1/4 & 5/8 & 6\frac{1}{2}\\
0 & 1 & 1/2 & -1/4 & 1\\
1 & 0 & -1/4 & 3/8 & 3/2
\end{array}\right).
\end{array}
$$

All of the coefficients in the modified objective function row are now nonnegative which is our stopping signal. The solution in this last tableau corresponds to the basis consisting of x_1 and x_2 with values $3/2$ and 1 respectively which is consistent with our expectation given both our graphical and algebraic solutions provided earlier. Again, skeptical readers might derive some comfort in examining the final tableau above and verifying for themselves that the coefficients in the tableau are exactly those in the final set of equations produced previously. Indeed, any interim simplex tableau simply reflects the system of equations that would have been derived had our manipulation proceeded in the routine fashion demonstrated initially.....no more, no less.

Of course, we are not ready to claim, in a precise sense, that we can solve *all* linear programs. To be sure, there are a host of issues that have been left rather vague to this point, *i.e.,* how to determine if an LP has no solution, has no finite solution value, *etc.*. Naturally, we will look at how one responds to these issues; however, we have at least exposed the key notions that will provide the underpinning for the resolution of *any* linear program and prior to proceeding, we provide a high level statement of the fundamental process.

A Basic Summary of the Simplex Algorithm

Step 0: Start with *any* basic feasible solution.

Step 1: Determine an entering variable as one having a most negative coefficient in the objective row of the current tableau (if the original objective is of the "minimization" form, then look for a most positive coefficient). If all such coefficients are nonnegative (resp., nonpositive for minimization), stop; the current tableau represents an optimal solution.

Step 2: Let x_{j^*} denote the selected, entering variable selected in **Step 1**. Determine (if possible) a departing variable say x_{i^*} such that $\frac{b_{i^*}}{a_{i^*j^*}} \le \frac{b_i}{a_{ij^*}}$ for

all i for which $a_{ij^*} > 0$. Pivot on cell $(i^* j^*)$ and return to **Step 1**.
□

We emphasize again that the statement above, while sufficient to expose the basic computation of the simplex algorithm, leaves rather substantial gaps in how one might deal with what are practical, indeed very real-world, requirements for negotiating general linear programming problems. Among these are the following questions:

- Will the algorithm converge, *i.e.*, will it always stop?

- What if there is no departing variable, *i.e.*, what if the **Step 2** test is not satisfied?

- What if **Step 0** cannot be implemented, *i.e.*, what if the solution space is empty?

- Can ties in the minimum ratio test lead to problems?

- How can we detect when a problem has no finite optima; when it has multiple optima?

In the following section, we will provide machinery that allows us to respond to these questions.

4   Generalizations

Our approach will continue to be an informal one, relying largely on illustrations. In this regard, readers are advised to create their own instances and to replicate the phenomena captured in the following examples. Accordingly, it will be instructive to employ the graphical context afforded by small instances in order to fully appreciate the relationships between the algebraic and geometric interpretations of the various outcomes. First, we have to add a final piece to our basic methodology: the notion of *artificial variables*.

4.1 Artificial Variables

Suppose we were given the problem instance below:

$$\max z = 2x_1 + 3x_2 - 5x_3$$

$$\text{s.t.} \quad x_1 + x_2 + x_3 = 7$$

$$2x_1 - 5x_2 + x_3 \geq 10$$

$$x_1, x_2, x_3 \geq 0.$$

In standard form, the constraints would be written as follows:

$$x_1 + x_2 + x_3 = 7$$

$$2x_1 - 5x_2 + x_3 - S_1 = 10$$

$$x_1, x_2, x_3, S_1 \geq 0.$$

The first constraint in the original formulation is an equation and is therefore already in standard form format. The second, an inequality of the greater-than-or-equal-to variety, requires the subtraction of a nonnegative *surplus* variable.

Now, it is apparent that there is no "readily available" starting (feasible) basis; certainly, there is no so-called, all-slack basis as before. Of course, we could search for some combination of columns in the constraint matrix that provided a feasible basis but this exercise would take too long (to appreciate this, the reader should think in terms of a general problem having many rows (constraints) and columns (variables)). More importantly, however, it is conceivable that such a search could be exhaustive in that the problem instance at hand might not have feasible solutions at all. There must be a better way to deal with the matter.

Suppose we add to each equation above, an *artificial* variable. The use of the adjective, "artificial", follows since these variables are indeed "fake" in the sense that they are not part of the real problem formulation. Still, their role will be one of facilitation; that is, these artificial variables will allow us to create a quick, albeit synthetic, starting basis without the overhead of any computational effort. Denoting these variables as R_1 and R_2, and requiring these to also be nonnegative, the new system of constraints becomes:

$$\text{s.t.} \qquad x_1 + x_2 + x_3 + R_1 = 7$$

$$2x_1 - 5x_2 + x_3 - S_1 + R_2 = 10$$

$$x_1, x_2, x_3, S_1, R_1, R_2 \geq 0.$$

Now, in this new system we have an obvious starting basis consisting of R_1 and R_2 (obviously this is not feasible per the original instance). The artificial constraint matrix, say $\overline{\mathbf{A}}$ is given by

$$\overline{\mathbf{A}} = \begin{pmatrix} \overset{x_1}{1} & \overset{x_2}{1} & \overset{x_3}{1} & \overset{S_1}{0} & \overset{R_1}{1} & \overset{R_2}{0} \\ 2 & -5 & 1 & -1 & 0 & 1 \end{pmatrix}$$

Then, the scheme is to simply apply the simplex algorithm and hope that upon its application, we will ultimately eliminate the artificial variables since they are, by definition, not really part of the true formulation. There are two well-known approaches for dealing with artificial variables:

- big-M method;

- two-phase method.

4.1.1 Big-M

The big-M method of handling instances with artificial variables is the "common-sense" approach. Essentially, the notion is to make the artificial variables, through their coefficients in the objective function, so costly or unprofitable that *any* feasible solution to the real problem would be preferred....unless the original instance possessed no feasible solutions at all. But this means that we need to assign, in the objective function, coefficients to the artificial variables that are either very small (maximization problem) or very large (minimization problem); whatever this value, let us call it *big M*. In fact, this notion is an old trick in optimization in general; we simply associate a *penalty value* with variables that we do not want to be part of an ultimate solution (unless such an outcome is unavoidable). Indeed, the penalty is so costly that unless any of the respective variables' inclusion are warranted algorithmically, such variables will never be part of any feasible solution.

So, the objective function for this example, upon the addition of the artificial variables, would appear as follows:

$$\max z = 2x_1 + 3x_2 - 5x_3 - MR_1 - MR_2.$$

Obviously, any nonzero (recall that all variables are required to be nonnegative) value for R_1 or R_2 would occur in a final solution if and only if there were no alternatives involving the other, real variables.

Now, placing the formulation in tableau form, and employing only artificial variables in the starting basis, we have:

$$
\begin{array}{c}
\begin{array}{ccccccc}
x_1 & x_2 & x_3 & S_1 & R_1 & R_2 &
\end{array} \\
\begin{array}{c}
\\ R_1 \\ R_2
\end{array}
\left(
\begin{array}{ccccccc}
-2 & -3 & 5 & 0 & M & M & 0 \\
1 & 1 & 1 & 0 & 1 & 0 & 7 \\
2 & -5 & 1 & -1 & 0 & 1 & 10
\end{array}
\right).
\end{array}
$$

Making this tableau "basic" produces (remember that we need unit vectors under the R_1 and R_2 columns):

$$
\begin{array}{c}
\begin{array}{cccccc}
x_1 \qquad\quad & x_2 \qquad & x_3 & S_1 & R_1 & R_2
\end{array} \\
\begin{array}{c}
\\ R_1 \\ R_2
\end{array}
\left(
\begin{array}{cccccc}
-2-3M & -3+4M & 5-2M & M & 0 & 0 & -17M \\
1 & 1 & 1 & 0 & 1 & 0 & 7 \\
2 & -5 & 1 & -1 & 0 & 1 & 10
\end{array}
\right).
\end{array}
$$

At this point we know what to do. Applying the simplex algorithm, we can bring into the basis, variable x_1 and drive out (per the ratio check) artificial variable R_2 yielding:

$$
\begin{array}{c}
 \\
R_1 \\
x_1
\end{array}
\begin{array}{cc}
\begin{array}{cccccc}
x_1 & x_2 & x_3 & S_1 & R_1 & R_2
\end{array} \\
\left(
\begin{array}{cccccc}
0 & -8 - \frac{7}{2}M & 6 - \frac{1}{2}M & -1 - \frac{1}{2}M & 0 & 1 + \frac{3}{2}M & 10 - 2M \\
0 & \frac{7}{2} & \frac{1}{2} & \frac{1}{2} & 1 & -\frac{1}{2} & 2 \\
1 & -\frac{5}{2} & \frac{1}{2} & -\frac{1}{2} & 0 & \frac{1}{2} & 5
\end{array}
\right).
\end{array}
$$

Pivoting in x_2 next and removing R_1 produces:

$$
\begin{array}{c}
 \\
x_2 \\
x_1
\end{array}
\begin{array}{cc}
\begin{array}{cccccc}
x_1 & x_2 & x_3 & S_1 & R_1 & R_2
\end{array} \\
\left(
\begin{array}{cccccc}
0 & 0 & \frac{50}{7} & \frac{1}{7} & \frac{16}{7} + M & -\frac{1}{7} + M & \frac{102}{7} \\
0 & 1 & \frac{1}{7} & \frac{1}{7} & \frac{2}{7} & -\frac{1}{7} & \frac{4}{7} \\
1 & 0 & \frac{6}{7} & -\frac{1}{7} & \frac{5}{7} & \frac{1}{7} & \frac{45}{7}
\end{array}
\right).
\end{array}
$$

Now, at this point there are no nonpositive coefficients in the objective row of the current tableau (remember that M is a very large value) which is our sign that we are done. The final and hence optimal solution is $x_1 = \frac{45}{7}$ and $x_2 = \frac{4}{7}$. All other variables, by virtue of their being nonbasis, take on value 0. Particularly meaningful ("nonbasic-ness" aside), is that the artificial variables have now disappeared. As we intimated earlier, if we are to solve the real problem, this disappearance is not just important; in fact, it is essential.

4.1.2 Two-phase method

The *two-phase method* derives its name in an obvious way. Essentially, the notion is to formulate a problem instance with an objective function that seeks to minimize a sum of only artificial variables. The simplex algorithm is applied in the standard way with the intent that at stopping, the artificial variables will have value zero (and hence so will the objective function). That is, at the end of so-called phase-I, the artificial variables will have been removed; if this is not the case, then the original problem instance, as we shall see in the next section, must possess no feasible solution space. For the present, however, let us assume the former outcome. Then, we would remove the artificial variable columns from the final tableau of phase-I and enter *phase-II* with an admissible basis (the one produced at the end of phase-I). We then reapply the simplex at this point and continue in the normal fashion. An illustration should make the approach plain.

Consider the previous instance with the new objective function, consisting of only artificial variables, as indicated. That is, our phase-I instance would be:

$$\min z = R_1 + R_2$$

$$\text{s.t.} \qquad x_1 + x_2 + x_3 + R_1 = 7$$

$$2x_1 - 5x_2 + x_3 - S_1 + R_2 = 10$$

$$x_1, x_2, x_3, S_1, R_1, R_2 \geq 0.$$

Now, the initial tableau for phase-I (after having been made basic) appears as follows:

$$
\begin{array}{c}
\\
R_1 \\
R_2
\end{array}
\begin{array}{cccccc}
x_1 & x_2 & x_3 & S_1 & R_1 & R_2 \\
\end{array}
\left(
\begin{array}{cccccc|c}
3 & -4 & 2 & -1 & 0 & 0 & 17 \\
1 & 1 & 1 & 0 & 1 & 0 & 7 \\
2 & -5 & 1 & -1 & 0 & 1 & 10
\end{array}
\right).
$$

The first pivot brings in x_1 and replaces R_2 producing the following:

$$
\begin{array}{c}
\\
R_1 \\
x_1
\end{array}
\begin{array}{cccccc}
x_1 & x_2 & x_3 & S_1 & R_1 & R_2 \\
\end{array}
\left(
\begin{array}{cccccc|c}
0 & \frac{7}{2} & \frac{1}{2} & \frac{1}{2} & 0 & -\frac{3}{2} & 2 \\
0 & \frac{7}{2} & \frac{1}{2} & \frac{1}{2} & 1 & -\frac{1}{2} & 2 \\
1 & -\frac{5}{2} & \frac{1}{2} & -\frac{1}{2} & 0 & \frac{1}{2} & 5
\end{array}
\right).
$$

Next, we pivot in x_2 and R_1 departs. We have:

$$
\begin{array}{c}
\quad\;\; x_1 \quad x_2 \quad x_3 \quad S_1 \quad R_1 \quad R_2 \\
\begin{array}{c} \\ x_2 \\ x_1 \end{array}
\left(
\begin{array}{cccccccc}
0 & 0 & 0 & 0 & -1 & -1 & 0 \\
0 & 1 & \frac{1}{7} & \frac{1}{7} & \frac{2}{7} & -\frac{1}{7} & \frac{4}{7} \\
1 & 0 & \frac{6}{7} & -\frac{1}{7} & \frac{5}{7} & \frac{1}{7} & \frac{45}{7}
\end{array}
\right).
\end{array}
$$

But this is a final tableau (nonpositive objective row coefficients for minimization) and so we have concluded phase-I. More importantly, we have driven out the artificial variables (observe that the tableau objective function row value of 0 is consistent with this outcome). So, we can proceed to phase-II where operationally, we extract the relevant part of the above (phase-I final) tableau and strip off the first row replacing it with the original objective function, yielding the following:

$$
\begin{array}{c}
\quad\;\; x_1 \quad x_2 \quad x_3 \quad S_1 \\
\begin{array}{c} \\ x_2 \\ x_1 \end{array}
\left(
\begin{array}{ccccc}
-2 & -3 & 5 & 0 & 0 \\
0 & 1 & \frac{1}{7} & \frac{1}{7} & \frac{4}{7} \\
1 & 0 & \frac{6}{7} & -\frac{1}{7} & \frac{45}{7}
\end{array}
\right).
\end{array}
$$

Updating the first row in order to create a basic tableau produces

$$
\begin{array}{c}
\quad\;\; x_1 \quad x_2 \quad x_3 \quad S_1 \\
\begin{array}{c} \\ x_2 \\ x_1 \end{array}
\left(
\begin{array}{ccccc}
0 & 0 & \frac{50}{7} & \frac{1}{7} & \frac{102}{7} \\
0 & 1 & \frac{1}{7} & \frac{1}{7} & \frac{4}{7} \\
1 & 0 & \frac{6}{7} & -\frac{1}{7} & \frac{45}{7}
\end{array}
\right).
\end{array}
$$

which is the starting tableau for phase-II. Interestingly, however, this tableau is optimal. Of course, readers should be clear that for real instances this phenomenon will not typically occur; further pivoting will be required on the initial phase-II tableau. In any event, it is instructive to examine the phase-II tableau above and compare it with the corresponding "subtableau"

30

produced earlier by the big-M method; as we would expect, they are the same.

Obviously, appending artificial variables to a problem is only a "trick" that serves to allow the simplex calculations to at least commence. From the simplex algorithm's perspective, its application is routine; in the real problem context, however, we are pivoting through artificial bases with the intended effect of ultimately "hooking up" with real bases (extreme points for the oiginal problem) if possible. Geometrically, the process is captured in Figure 6.

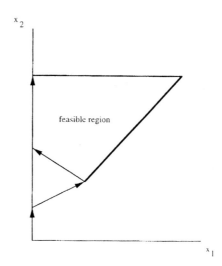

Figure 6: Pivoting through artificial bases

4.2   Empty Solution Space

A linear program may be constrained in such a way that there are no points at all that are admissible. Unfortunately, for real problem instances, this condition is not something that is easy to recognize by inspection and so an algebraic method is needed. Suppose we have the formulation below:

$$\max z = 2x_1 + x_2$$

31

s.t. $\qquad x_1 + x_2 \leq 3$

$$2x_1 + 3x_2 \geq 12$$

$$x_1, x_2 \geq 0.$$

Employing the big-M approach, the standard form representation is given by

$$\max z = 2x_1 + x_2 - MR_1$$

s.t. $\qquad x_1 + x_2 + S_1 = 3$

$$2x_1 + 3x_2 - S_2 + R_1 = 12$$

$$x_1, x_2, S_1, S_2, R_1 \geq 0.$$

Now, beginning with an initial basis that includes S_1 and R_1, we would proceed until stopping occurs with the tableau below (the computation is left as an exercise for the reader):

$$
\begin{array}{c}
\begin{array}{cccccc}
x_1 & x_2 & S_1 & S_2 & R_1 &
\end{array} \\
\begin{array}{c} \\ x_2 \\ R_1 \end{array}
\left(
\begin{array}{cccccc}
-1+M & 0 & 1+3M & M & 0 & 3-3M \\
1 & 1 & 1 & 0 & 0 & 3 \\
-1 & 0 & -3 & -1 & 1 & 3
\end{array}
\right).
\end{array}
$$

Unfortunately the final solution exhibits an artificial variable at a strictly positive value. But this must mean that there is no admissible solution to the original, "real" problem instance for otherwise, it would necessarily have been preferred to the one found above; if we have applied the simplex algorithm correctly, any better (*i.e.*, feasible) solution would have been produced.

Now, if "seeing is believing," it might be comforting to examine the graphical depiction of the original example. Shown in Figure 7, it is clear that there is no nonempty intersection of all constraints and hence there is no feasible solution space for the stated problem instance. On a side note, interested readers are encouraged to apply the two-phase method to this problem in order to see if the outcome of phase-I's feasibility test is consistent with the conclusion drawn above.

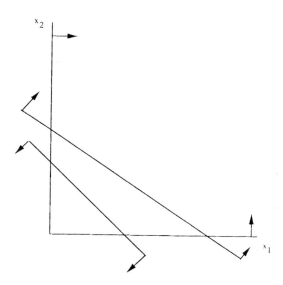

Figure 7: Graphical depiction of instance with empty solution space

4.3 Alternative Optima

Consider the following linear program:

$$\max z = 2x_1 + 3x_2$$

$$\text{s.t.} \quad 4x_1 + 6x_2 \leq 12$$

$$x_1 + 2x_2 \leq 6$$

$$x_1, x_2 \geq 0.$$

The instance is plotted in Figure 8; obviously, there is a nonempty solution space. Now, adopting our elementary, graphical approach of moving the objective function through this space, in the improving direction, it is evident that the last point of contact is the line segment indicated in bold. Thus, every point on this line segment is an optimal solution. But this occurs since the objective function is parallel to the first constraint in the instance where the latter is *binding* in the sense that it defines a portion of the feasible region specifying an optimal extreme point (obviously, the second constraint in the original instance is redundant).

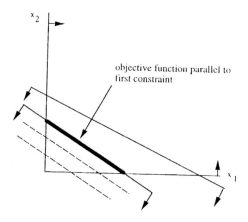

Figure 8: Graphical depiction of instance with multiple optima

But since we don't solve real-world linear programs graphically, what then is the "signal" *vis-a-vis* simplex computations, that would indicate multiple optima? Following is the final tableau that results upon a correct application of the simplex algorithm to this example:

$$
\begin{array}{c c c c c}
& x_1 & x_2 & S_1 & S_2 \\
& \begin{pmatrix} 0 & 0 & \frac{1}{2} & 0 & 6 \\ \frac{2}{3} & 1 & \frac{1}{6} & 0 & 2 \\ -\frac{1}{3} & 0 & -\frac{1}{3} & 1 & 2 \end{pmatrix}
\end{array}
$$

with row labels x_2 and S_2 on the second and third rows.

The basic variables are x_2 and S_2 which corresponds to the actual point $x_1 = 0$ and $x_2 = 2$. But observe that there is an objective row coefficient of 0 under the *nonbasic* variable x_1 (in the final tableau) . This indicates that there may be another optimal basis. Indeed, if we pivot in variable x_1 (on this tableau) to replace x_2, another basis, consisting of variables x_1 and S_2, results with values of 3 and 0 respectively. The latter corresponds to the extreme point given (graphically) by $x_1 = 3$ and $x_2 = 0$. But this is to be expected because we just argued that the line segment between these two extreme points of the feasible region (say $\mathbf{x}^1$ and $\mathbf{x}^2$) defined an entire family of optimal solutions for the given instance, *i.e.*, any point on this line segment is optimal. Put more formally, every solution $\mathbf{x}' = \lambda\mathbf{x}^1 + (1 - \lambda)\mathbf{x}^2$ for all $0 \leq \lambda \leq 1$ is an optimal solution to the indicated instance. The reader is invited to test this claim by picking any such λ value and checking if the outcome for $\mathbf{x}'$ yields a value for z of 6. Of course, for any $\lambda \in (0, 1)$, the resulting $\mathbf{x}'$ is a nonbasic solution.

4.4 Unbounded Solutions Spaces

In some crude sense, the opposite notion of that arising in the case of empty solution spaces, is the phenomenon of unbounded optima. Note that this is not synonomous with the concept of an unbounded solution space. The latter would occur if say our feasible region was the first orthant (*i.e.*, the only constraints were the nonnegativity restrictions) and we sought to minimize a linear function with all variables having strictly positive coefficients; obviously, the origin would be the optimal extreme point. That is, the space over which we are searching is unbounded but we still have a *bounded optima*, *i.e.*, the direction of unboundedness is irrelevant. Returning, nonetheless, to our case of unbounded optima, suppose we have the instance below:

$$\max z = 3x_1 + 2x_2$$

$$\text{s.t.} \quad x_1 - 2x_2 \leq 10$$

$$2x_1 - x_2 \leq 10$$

$$x_1, x_2 \geq 0.$$

Starting with the all-slack basis, we would ultimately reach the following tableau:

$$
\begin{array}{c}
\begin{array}{cccc}
x_1 & x_2 & S_1 & S_2
\end{array}\\
\begin{array}{c}
\\
S_1\\
x_1
\end{array}
\left(
\begin{array}{ccccc}
0 & -\frac{1}{2} & 0 & \frac{3}{2} & 15\\
0 & -\frac{3}{2} & 1 & -\frac{1}{2} & 5\\
1 & -\frac{1}{2} & 0 & \frac{1}{2} & 5
\end{array}
\right).
\end{array}
$$

From this tableau, we observe that there is an entering variable, x_2. However, in scanning the corresponding column, all coefficients are nonpositive which means that nothing can depart the current basis. But this is precisely what signals an unbounded optima. In fact, what this suggests in the specific instance shown, is that variable x_2 can be increased without bound while still maintaining problem feasibility. Geometrically, this effect is depicted in Figure 9.

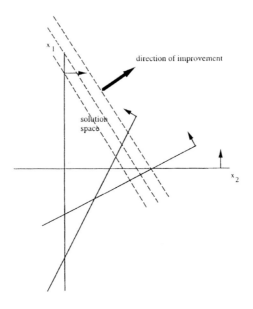

Figure 9: Graphical depiction of instance with unbounded optima

4.5 Degeneracy

Our final property relates to degeneracy. Recall that a degenerate basis is one in which at least one basic variable has value 0. Essentially, degeneracy is a "non-issue" in solving practical linear programs, but *only* if certain safeguards are in place; absent such safeguards, degeneracy can be a substantial problem. Consider the following instance:

$$\max z = 2x_1 + x_2$$

$$\text{s.t.} \quad x_1 + x_2 \leq 10$$

$$x_1 + 3x_2 \leq 10$$

$$x_1, x_2 \geq 0.$$

Starting with the all-slack initial basis, the first tableau appears as follows:

$$
\begin{array}{c}
 \\
S_1 \\
S_2
\end{array}
\begin{array}{cccc}
x_1 & x_2 & S_1 & S_2 \\
\end{array}
\left(
\begin{array}{ccccc}
-2 & -1 & 0 & 0 & 0 \\
1 & 1 & 1 & 0 & 10 \\
1 & 3 & 0 & 1 & 10
\end{array}
\right).
$$

Now, we can pivot in variable x_1 to replace either S_1 or S_2; let us arbitrarily choose S_1. The new tableau then appears as follows:

$$
\begin{array}{c}
 \\
x_1 \\
S_2
\end{array}
\begin{array}{cccc}
x_1 & x_2 & S_1 & S_2 \\
\end{array}
\left(
\begin{array}{ccccc}
0 & 1 & 2 & 0 & 20 \\
1 & 1 & 1 & 0 & 10 \\
0 & 2 & -1 & 1 & 0
\end{array}
\right).
$$

This is a final tableau; the optimal solution is given by the final basis consisting of x_1 and S_2 accordingly. But the final basis is degenerate since a basic variable exists at a value of 0. What does this mean graphically? Essentially, what a degenerate solution implies is that an extreme point is "over-specified." That is, the extreme point is represented by more than one basis. Figure 10 helps to make the point clear. Here, the final extreme point is represented by the intersection of three constraints when two would suffice.

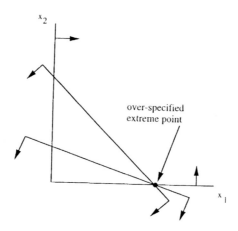

Figure 10: Graphical depiction of degeneracy

So what is the issue with degeneracy? Well, suppose we consider another instance:

$$\min z = -\tfrac{3}{4}x_4 + 20x_5 - \tfrac{1}{2}x_6 + 6x_7$$

$$\text{s.t.} \quad x_1 + \tfrac{1}{4}x_4 - 8x_5 - x_6 + 9x_7 = 0$$

$$x_2 + \tfrac{1}{2}x_4 - 12x_5 - \tfrac{1}{2}x_6 + 3x_7 = 0$$

$$x_3 + x_6 = 1$$

$$x_1, x_2, x_3, x_4, x_5, x_6, x_7 \geq 0.$$

If we start with (or at least reach) basis $\mathbf{B_1} = (x_1, x_2, x_3) = (0, 0, 1)$ with z-value of 0, then it is possible that a legal sequence of simplex pivots will produce the following succession of bases (after $\mathbf{B_1}$):

$$\mathbf{B_2} = (x_4, x_2, x_3) \text{ with } z = 0$$

$$\mathbf{B_3} = (x_4, x_5, x_3) \text{ with } z = 0$$

$$\mathbf{B_4} = (x_6, x_5, x_3) \text{ with } z = 0$$

$$\mathbf{B_5} = (x_6, x_7, x_3) \text{ with } z = 0$$

$$\mathbf{B_6} = (x_1, x_7, x_3) \text{ with } z = 0$$

$$\mathbf{B_7} = (x_1, x_2, x_3) \text{ with } z = 0$$

But $\mathbf{B_7} = \mathbf{B_1}$ and we have *cycled*. That is, any automatic continuation of the simplex algorithm will simply not converge. Indeed, for this example, the optimum solution is given by the tuple $(\frac{3}{4}, 0, 0, 1, 0, 1, 0)$ having value $z = -1.25$.

Now, it is a true state of affairs in linear programming that many real-world instances do give rise to degenerate bases which in turn suggests that cycling could be a fairly legitimate issue about which to be concerned. Happily, however, the cycling problem that is possible under degeneracy can be dealt with, indeed avoided by various *anti-cycling* techniques. In fact, these procedures are routinely included in commercial linear programming codes. In any event, we will not take these up here since the procedures involve details that are well beyond the scope of our treatise.

5   Final Comments

In concluding this basic coverage of linear programming, it is worth remarking that what we have presented here is but an introduction to what amounts to a most powerful and exceptionally rich optimization procedure. As we indicated at the outset, the methodology of linear programming represents a very important tool in the problem-solving arsenal of engineers and applied mathematicians who are charged with dealing with critical problems that arise on a daily basis in the world of business and industry.

Still, much of the richness, indeed, much of what is to be appreciated in linear programming must remain beyond the scope of this presentation. For example, the entire theory of linear programming *duality* represents an elegant development in its own right but more importantly, provides the basis for much of what constitutes the real power in the application of linear programming to real-world problems. The related concepts of *post-optimality* and *sensitivity analysis* are enormously powerful notions that derive from duality theory.

In addition, we do not have space to take up the cases of so-called *special LP structures*. These are linear programs that exhibit characteristics in their model formulations that allow shortcuts or stream-lined approaches. Interestingly, the arguments that are used to justify the correctness of these shortcuts also often stem from notions in duality. In any event, readers interested in these and other topics are directed to the various sources in the reference list where a number of excellent, full treatises of linear programming are cited.

6 Exercises

1. Place each of the formulations below in standard form.

(a)

$$\min z = 4x_1 + 2x_2 - 33x_3$$

$$\text{s.t.} \quad x_1 - 4x_2 + x_3 \leq 12$$

$$9x_1 + 6x_3 = 15$$

$$-5x_1 + 9x_2 \geq 3$$

$$x_1, x_2, x_3 \geq 0.$$

(b)

$$\max z = 45x_1 + 15x_3$$

$$\text{s.t.} \quad 4x_1 - 2x_2 + 9x_3 = 22$$

$$-2x_1 + 5x_2 - x_3 \geq 1$$

$$x_1 - x_2 \leq 3$$

$$x_1, x_2, x_3 \geq 0.$$

(c)

$$\min z = 2x_1 + x_2 - 4x_3$$

$$\text{s.t.} \quad x_1 - x_2 - 5x_3 \leq 10$$

$$3x_2 + 9x_1 = -6$$

$$x_1 \geq 0, x_3 \leq 0, x_2 \text{ unrestricted in sign.}$$

(d)

$$\min z = 3x_1 - 3x_2 + 7x3$$

s.t. $\quad x_1 + x_2 + 3x_3 \le 40$

$$x_1 + 9x_2 - 7x_3 \ge 50$$

$$|\, 5x_2 + 8x_3 \,| \le 70$$

$$x_1, x_2 \ge 0, x_3 \text{ unrestricted in sign.}$$

2. Solve the following problem graphically.

$$\max z = 2x_1 + 7x_2$$

s.t. $\quad x_1 + x_2 \le 4$

$$4x_1 + 3x_2 \le 12$$

$$-x_1 + x_2 \ge 1$$

$$x_1, x_2 \ge 0.$$

3. Solve graphically:

$$\max z = min\{3x_1 - 10, -5x_1 + 5\}$$

s.t. $\quad 0 \le x_1 \le 5.$

4. Consider the following instance:

$$\max z = 2x_1 - 4x_2 + 5x_3 - 6x_4$$

s.t.
$$x_1 + 4x_2 - 2x_3 + 8x_4 \leq 2$$

$$-x_1 + 2x_2 + 3x_3 + 4x_4 \leq 1$$

$$x_1, x_2, x_3, x_4 \geq 0.$$

Determine:

(a) the maximum number of possible basic solutions;
(b) the feasible extreme points;
(c) the optimal basic feasible solution.

5. Solve the following linear program using the simplex algorithm.

$$\max z = 2x_1 + x_2 - 3x_3 + 5x_4$$

s.t.
$$x_1 + 7x_2 + 3x_3 + 7x_4 \leq 46$$

$$3x_1 - x_2 + x_3 + 2x_4 \leq 8$$

$$2x_1 + 3x_2 - x_3 + x_4 \leq 10$$

$$x_1, x_2, x_3, x_4 \geq 0.$$

6. Solve the following minimization problem using the simplex algorithm.

$$\min z = x_1 - 3x_2 - 2x_3$$

s.t. $\quad 3x_1 - x_2 + 2x_3 \le 7$

$$-2x_1 + 4x_2 \le 12$$

$$-4x_1 + 3x_2 + 8x_3 \le 10$$

$$x_1, x_2, x_3 \ge 0.$$

7. Solve the following instance with the simplex; start with variables x_4, x_5, and x_6 in the initial basis.

$$\max z = 3x_1 + x_2 + 2x_3$$

s.t. $\quad 12x_1 + 3x_2 + 6x_4 = 9$

$$8x_1 + x_2 - 4x_3 + 2x_5 = 10$$

$$3x_1 - x_6 = 0$$

$$x_1, x_2, x_3, x_4, x_5, x_6 \ge 0.$$

8. Solve the following problem by employing both the big-M and the two-phase methods.

$$\max z = 2x_1 + 3x_2 - 5x_3$$

s.t. $\quad x_1 + x_2 + x + 3 = 7$

$$2x_1 - 5x_2 + x_3 \ge 10$$

$$x_1, x_2, x_3 \ge 0.$$

9. Find all of the alternative optimal basic solutions to the following instance and then write a general expression for all of the *nonbasic* solutions.

$$\max z = x_1 + 2x_2 + 3x_3$$

$$\text{s.t.} \quad x_1 + 2x_2 + 3x_3 \leq 10$$

$$x_1 + x_2 \leq 5$$

$$x_1 \leq 1$$

$$x_1, x_2, x_3 \geq 0.$$

10. Solve the following linear program by inspection and then justify the outcome in terms of the simplex algorithm.

$$\max z = 5x_1 - 6x_2 + 3x_3 - 5x_4 + 12x_5$$

$$\text{s.t.} \quad x_1 + 3x_2 + 5x_3 + 6x_4 + 3x_5 \leq 90$$

$$x_1, x_2, x_3, x_4, x_5 \geq 0.$$

11. Solve the following problem, showing that the optimal solution is degenerate and that there exist alternative solutions that are all nonbasic.

$$\max z = 3x_1 + x_2$$

$$\text{s.t.} \quad x_1 + 2x_2 \leq 5$$

$$x_1 + x_2 - x_3 \leq 2$$

$$7x_1 + 3x_2 - 5x_3 \leq 20$$

$$x_1, x_2, x_3 \geq 0.$$

12. In which direction is the solution space for the problem instance below unbounded?

$$\max z = 20x_1 + 10x_2 + x_3$$

$$\text{s.t.} \quad 3x_1 - 3x_2 + 5x_3 \leq 50$$

$$x_1 + x_3 \leq 10$$

$$x_1 - x_2 + 4x_3 \leq 20$$

$$x_1, x_2, x_3 \geq 0.$$

13. Apply the big-M method to the formulation below and conclude, accordingly, that there are no feasible solutions.

$$\max z = 3x_1 + 2x_2 + 3x_3$$

$$\text{s.t.} \quad 2x_1 + x_2 + x_3 \leq 2$$

$$3x_1 + 4x_2 + 2x_3 \geq 8$$

$$x_1, x_2, x_3 \geq 0.$$

14. Repeat exercise 13 using the two-phase method for artificial variables.

15. Suppose that at the end of phase-I, there is an artificial variable in the basis at a value of 0. Is this a problem? What would you do?

7 References

There have been many books written on the subject of linear programming. These range from ones at an exceptionally high level (*i.e.,* research monographs), to others that are quite basic and elementary. Following, we give a very short list of references that should be instructive to students pursuing technical degrees in fields such as engineering, mathematics, computer science and the like. Ones marked by bold reference numbers tend to be more advanced.

1. Bazaraa, M, J. Jarvis, and H. Sherali (1990), *Linear Programming and Network Flows*, Wiley, New York.

2. Chvatal, V. (1983), *Linear Programming*, W.H. Freeman, San Fransisco.

3. Rardin, R. L. (1998), *Optmization in Operations Research*, Prentice-Hall, Upper Saddle River, New jersey.

4. Taha, H. A. (1976), *Operations Research*, Macmillan, New York.

5. Winston, W. L. (1995), *Introduction to Mathematical Programming: Applications and Algorithms*, Duxbury Press, Belmont, California.

PART III

Taken from:

Elementary Linear Algebra with Applications, Ninth Edition
by Bernard Kolman and David R. Hill

CHAPTER

2

Solving Linear Systems

2.1 Echelon Form of a Matrix

In Section 1.1 we discussed the method of elimination for solving linear systems, which you studied in high school, and in Section 1.3 we introduced the coefficient matrix and augmented matrix associated with a linear system. In this section we discuss operations on a matrix, which when applied to an augmented matrix can greatly simplify the steps needed to determine the solution of the associated linear system. The operations discussed in this section apply to any matrix, whether or not it is an augmented matrix. In Section 2.2 we apply the constructions developed in this section to the solution of linear systems.

DEFINITION 2.1

An $m \times n$ matrix A is said to be in **reduced row echelon form** if it satisfies the following properties:

(a) All zero rows, if there are any, appear at the bottom of the matrix.

(b) The first nonzero entry from the left of a nonzero row is a 1. This entry is called a **leading one** of its row.

(c) For each nonzero row, the leading one appears to the right and below any leading ones in preceding rows.

(d) If a column contains a leading one, then all other entries in that column are zero.

A matrix in reduced row echelon form appears as a staircase ("echelon") pattern of leading ones descending from the upper left corner of the matrix.

An $m \times n$ matrix satisfying properties (a), (b), and (c) is said to be in **row echelon form**. In Definition 2.1, there may be no zero rows.

A similar definition can be formulated in the obvious manner for **reduced column echelon form** and **column echelon form**.

86

EXAMPLE 1   The following are matrices in reduced row echelon form, since they satisfy properties (a), (b), (c), and (d):

$$A = \begin{bmatrix} 1 & 0 & 0 & 0 \\ 0 & 1 & 0 & 0 \\ 0 & 0 & 1 & 0 \\ 0 & 0 & 0 & 1 \end{bmatrix}, \quad B = \begin{bmatrix} 1 & 0 & 0 & 0 & -2 & 4 \\ 0 & 1 & 0 & 0 & 4 & 8 \\ 0 & 0 & 0 & 1 & 7 & -2 \\ 0 & 0 & 0 & 0 & 0 & 0 \\ 0 & 0 & 0 & 0 & 0 & 0 \end{bmatrix},$$

and

$$C = \begin{bmatrix} 1 & 2 & 0 & 0 & 1 \\ 0 & 0 & 1 & 2 & 3 \\ 0 & 0 & 0 & 0 & 0 \end{bmatrix}.$$

The matrices that follow are not in reduced row echelon form. (Why not?)

$$D = \begin{bmatrix} 1 & 2 & 0 & 4 \\ 0 & 0 & 0 & 0 \\ 0 & 0 & 1 & -3 \end{bmatrix}, \quad E = \begin{bmatrix} 1 & 0 & 3 & 4 \\ 0 & 2 & -2 & 5 \\ 0 & 0 & 1 & 2 \end{bmatrix},$$

$$F = \begin{bmatrix} 1 & 0 & 3 & 4 \\ 0 & 1 & -2 & 5 \\ 0 & 1 & 2 & 2 \\ 0 & 0 & 0 & 0 \end{bmatrix}, \quad G = \begin{bmatrix} 1 & 2 & 3 & 4 \\ 0 & 1 & -2 & 5 \\ 0 & 0 & 1 & 2 \\ 0 & 0 & 0 & 0 \end{bmatrix}.$$ ∎

EXAMPLE 2   The following are matrices in row echelon form:

$$H = \begin{bmatrix} 1 & 5 & 0 & 2 & -2 & 4 \\ 0 & 1 & 0 & 3 & 4 & 8 \\ 0 & 0 & 0 & 1 & 7 & -2 \\ 0 & 0 & 0 & 0 & 0 & 0 \\ 0 & 0 & 0 & 0 & 0 & 0 \end{bmatrix}, \quad I = \begin{bmatrix} 1 & 0 & 0 & 0 \\ 0 & 1 & 0 & 0 \\ 0 & 0 & 1 & 0 \\ 0 & 0 & 0 & 1 \end{bmatrix},$$

$$J = \begin{bmatrix} 0 & 0 & 1 & 3 & 5 & 7 & 9 \\ 0 & 0 & 0 & 0 & 1 & -2 & 3 \\ 0 & 0 & 0 & 0 & 0 & 1 & 2 \\ 0 & 0 & 0 & 0 & 0 & 0 & 1 \\ 0 & 0 & 0 & 0 & 0 & 0 & 0 \end{bmatrix}.$$ ∎

A useful property of matrices in reduced row echelon form (see Exercise 9) is that if A is an $n \times n$ matrix in reduced row echelon form $\neq I_n$, then A has a row consisting entirely of zeros.

We shall now show that every matrix can be put into row (column) echelon form, or into reduced row (column) echelon form, by means of certain row (column) operations.

DEFINITION 2.2   An **elementary row (column) operation** on a matrix A is any one of the following operations:

(a) **Type I:** Interchange any two rows (columns).

(b) **Type II:** Multiply a row (column) by a nonzero number.

(c) **Type III:** Add a multiple of one row (column) to another.

We now introduce the following notation for elementary row and elementary column operations on matrices:

- Interchange rows (columns) i and j, Type I:

$$\mathbf{r}_i \leftrightarrow \mathbf{r}_j \quad (\mathbf{c}_i \leftrightarrow \mathbf{c}_j).$$

- Replace row (column) i by k times row (column) i, Type II:

$$k\mathbf{r}_i \to \mathbf{r}_i \quad (k\mathbf{c}_i \to \mathbf{c}_i).$$

- Replace row (column) j by k times row (column) i + row (column) j, Type III:

$$k\mathbf{r}_i + \mathbf{r}_j \to \mathbf{r}_j \quad (k\mathbf{c}_i + \mathbf{c}_j \to \mathbf{c}_j).$$

Using this notation, it is easy to keep track of the elementary row and column operations performed on a matrix. For example, we indicate that we have interchanged the ith and jth rows of A as $A_{\mathbf{r}_i \leftrightarrow \mathbf{r}_j}$. We proceed similarly for column operations.

Observe that when a matrix is viewed as the augmented matrix of a linear system, the elementary row operations are equivalent, respectively, to interchanging two equations, multiplying an equation by a nonzero constant, and adding a multiple of one equation to another equation.

EXAMPLE 3

Let

$$A = \begin{bmatrix} 0 & 0 & 1 & 2 \\ 2 & 3 & 0 & -2 \\ 3 & 3 & 6 & -9 \end{bmatrix}.$$

Interchanging rows 1 and 3 of A, we obtain

$$B = A_{\mathbf{r}_1 \leftrightarrow \mathbf{r}_3} = \begin{bmatrix} 3 & 3 & 6 & -9 \\ 2 & 3 & 0 & -2 \\ 0 & 0 & 1 & 2 \end{bmatrix}.$$

Multiplying the third row of A by $\frac{1}{3}$, we obtain

$$C = A_{\frac{1}{3}\mathbf{r}_3 \to \mathbf{r}_3} = \begin{bmatrix} 0 & 0 & 1 & 2 \\ 2 & 3 & 0 & -2 \\ 1 & 1 & 2 & -3 \end{bmatrix}.$$

Adding (-2) times row 2 of A to row 3 of A, we obtain

$$D = A_{-2\mathbf{r}_2 + \mathbf{r}_3 \to \mathbf{r}_3} = \begin{bmatrix} 0 & 0 & 1 & 2 \\ 2 & 3 & 0 & -2 \\ -1 & -3 & 6 & -5 \end{bmatrix}.$$

Observe that in obtaining D from A, row 2 of A *did not change*. ■

DEFINITION 2.3

An $m \times n$ matrix B is said to be **row (column) equivalent** to an $m \times n$ matrix A if B can be produced by applying a finite sequence of elementary row (column) operations to A.

EXAMPLE 4

Let
$$A = \begin{bmatrix} 1 & 2 & 4 & 3 \\ 2 & 1 & 3 & 2 \\ 1 & -2 & 2 & 3 \end{bmatrix}.$$

If we add 2 times row 3 of A to its second row, we obtain
$$B = A_{2\mathbf{r}_3+\mathbf{r}_2 \to \mathbf{r}_2} = \begin{bmatrix} 1 & 2 & 4 & 3 \\ 4 & -3 & 7 & 8 \\ 1 & -2 & 2 & 3 \end{bmatrix},$$

so B is row equivalent to A.

Interchanging rows 2 and 3 of B, we obtain
$$C = B_{\mathbf{r}_2 \leftrightarrow \mathbf{r}_3} = \begin{bmatrix} 1 & 2 & 4 & 3 \\ 1 & -2 & 2 & 3 \\ 4 & -3 & 7 & 8 \end{bmatrix},$$

so C is row equivalent to B.

Multiplying row 1 of C by 2, we obtain
$$D = C_{2\mathbf{r}_1 \to \mathbf{r}_1} = \begin{bmatrix} 2 & 4 & 8 & 6 \\ 1 & -1 & 2 & 3 \\ 4 & -3 & 7 & 8 \end{bmatrix},$$

so D is row equivalent to C. It then follows that D is row equivalent to A, since we obtained D by applying three successive elementary row operations to A. Using the notation for elementary row operations, we have
$$D = A_{\substack{2\mathbf{r}_3 + \mathbf{r}_2 \to \mathbf{r}_2 \\ \mathbf{r}_2 \leftrightarrow \mathbf{r}_3 \\ 2\mathbf{r}_1 \to \mathbf{r}_1}}.$$

We adopt the convention that the row operations are applied in the order listed. ■

We can readily show (see Exercise 10) that (a) every matrix is row equivalent to itself; (b) if B is row equivalent to A, then A is row equivalent to B; and (c) if C is row equivalent to B and B is row equivalent to A, then C is row equivalent to A. In view of (b), both statements "B is row equivalent to A" and "A is row equivalent to B" can be replaced by "A and B are row equivalent." A similar statement holds for column equivalence.

Theorem 2.1

Every nonzero $m \times n$ matrix $A = \begin{bmatrix} a_{ij} \end{bmatrix}$ is row (column) equivalent to a matrix in row (column) echelon form.

Proof

We shall prove that A is row equivalent to a matrix in row echelon form. That is, by using only elementary row operations, we can transform A into a matrix in row echelon form. A completely analogous proof by elementary column operations establishes the result for column equivalence.

We start by looking in matrix A for the first column with a nonzero entry. This column is called the **pivot column**; the first nonzero entry in the pivot column is called the **pivot**. Suppose the pivot column is column j and the pivot occurs in row i. Now interchange, if necessary, rows 1 and i, getting matrix $B = \begin{bmatrix} b_{ij} \end{bmatrix}$. Thus the pivot b_{1j} is $\neq 0$. Multiply the first row of B by the reciprocal of the pivot, that is, by $1/b_{1j}$, obtaining matrix $C = \begin{bmatrix} c_{ij} \end{bmatrix}$. Note that $c_{1j} = 1$. Now if c_{hj}, $2 \leq h \leq m$, is not zero, then to row h of C we add $-c_{hj}$ times row 1; we do this for each value of h. It follows that the elements in column j, in rows 2, 3, ..., m of C, are zero. Denote the resulting matrix by D.

Next, consider the $(m - 1) \times n$ submatrix A_1 of D obtained by deleting the first row of D. We now repeat this procedure with matrix A_1 instead of matrix A. Continuing this way, we obtain a matrix in row echelon form that is row equivalent to A.   ▨

EXAMPLE 5   Let

$$A = \begin{bmatrix} 0 & 2 & 3 & -4 & 1 \\ 0 & 0 & 2 & 3 & 4 \\ ② & 2 & -5 & 2 & 4 \\ 2 & 0 & -6 & 9 & 7 \end{bmatrix}.$$

Pivot column ────────┘   ╲ Pivot

Column 1 is the first (counting from left to right) column in A with a nonzero entry, so column 1 is the pivot column of A. The first (counting from top to bottom) nonzero entry in the pivot column occurs in the third row, so the pivot is $a_{31} = 2$. We interchange the first and third rows of A, obtaining

$$B = A_{\mathbf{r}_1 \leftrightarrow \mathbf{r}_3} = \begin{bmatrix} ② & 2 & -5 & 2 & 4 \\ 0 & 0 & 2 & 3 & 4 \\ 0 & 2 & 3 & -4 & 1 \\ 2 & 0 & -6 & 9 & 7 \end{bmatrix}.$$

Multiply the first row of B by the reciprocal of the pivot, that is, by $\dfrac{1}{b_{11}} = \dfrac{1}{2}$, to obtain

$$C = B_{\frac{1}{2}\mathbf{r}_1 \to \mathbf{r}_1} = \begin{bmatrix} 1 & 1 & -\frac{5}{2} & 1 & 2 \\ 0 & 0 & 2 & 3 & 4 \\ 0 & 2 & 3 & -4 & 1 \\ 2 & 0 & -6 & 9 & 7 \end{bmatrix}.$$

Add (-2) times the first row of C to the fourth row of C to produce a matrix D in which the only nonzero entry in the pivot column is $d_{11} = 1$:

$$D = C_{-2r_1+r_4 \to r_4} = \begin{bmatrix} 1 & 1 & -\frac{5}{2} & 1 & 2 \\ 0 & 0 & 2 & 3 & 4 \\ 0 & 2 & 3 & -4 & 1 \\ 0 & -2 & -1 & 7 & 3 \end{bmatrix}.$$

Identify A_1 as the submatrix of D obtained by deleting the first row of D: Do not erase the first row of D. Repeat the preceding steps with A_1 instead of A.

$$A_1 = \begin{matrix} 1 & 1 & -\frac{5}{2} & 1 & 2 \\ \begin{bmatrix} 0 & 0 & 2 & 3 & 4 \\ 0 & ② & 3 & -4 & 1 \\ 0 & -2 & -1 & 7 & 3 \end{bmatrix} \end{matrix}.$$

Pivot — Pivot column

Do $(A_1)_{r_1 \leftrightarrow r_1}$ to obtain B_1.

$$B_1 = \begin{matrix} 1 & 1 & -\frac{5}{2} & 1 & 2 \\ \begin{bmatrix} 0 & 2 & 3 & -4 & 1 \\ 0 & 0 & 2 & 3 & 4 \\ 0 & -2 & -1 & 7 & 3 \end{bmatrix} \end{matrix}.$$

Do $(B_1)_{\frac{1}{2}r_1 \to r_1}$ to obtain C_1.

$$C_1 = \begin{matrix} 1 & 1 & -\frac{5}{2} & 1 & 2 \\ \begin{bmatrix} 0 & 1 & \frac{3}{2} & -2 & \frac{1}{2} \\ 0 & 0 & 2 & 3 & 4 \\ 0 & -2 & -1 & 7 & 3 \end{bmatrix} \end{matrix}.$$

Do $(C_1)_{2r_1+r_3 \to r_3}$ to obtain D_1

$$D_1 = \begin{matrix} 1 & 1 & -\frac{5}{2} & 1 & 2 \\ \begin{bmatrix} 0 & 1 & \frac{3}{2} & -2 & \frac{1}{2} \\ 0 & 0 & 2 & 3 & 4 \\ 0 & 0 & 2 & 3 & 4 \end{bmatrix} \end{matrix}.$$

Deleting the first row of D_1 yields the matrix A_2. We repeat the procedure with A_2 instead of A. No rows of A_2 have to be interchanged.

$$A_2 = \begin{bmatrix} 1 & 1 & -\frac{5}{2} & 1 & 2 \\ 0 & 1 & \frac{3}{2} & -2 & \frac{1}{2} \\ 0 & 0 & ② & 3 & 4 \\ 0 & 0 & 2 & 3 & 4 \end{bmatrix} = B_2.$$

Pivot   Pivot column of A_2

Do $(B_2)_{\frac{1}{2}r_1 \to r_1}$ to obtain C_2.

$$C_2 = \begin{bmatrix} 1 & 1 & -\frac{5}{2} & 1 & 2 \\ 0 & 1 & \frac{3}{2} & -2 & \frac{1}{2} \\ 0 & 0 & 1 & \frac{3}{2} & 2 \\ 0 & 0 & 2 & 3 & 4 \end{bmatrix}.$$

Finally, do $(C_2)_{-2r_1 + r_2 \to r_2}$ to obtain D_2.

$$D_2 = \begin{bmatrix} 1 & 1 & -\frac{5}{2} & 1 & 2 \\ 0 & 1 & \frac{3}{2} & -2 & \frac{1}{2} \\ 0 & 0 & 1 & \frac{3}{2} & 2 \\ 0 & 0 & 0 & 0 & 0 \end{bmatrix}.$$

The matrix

$$H = \begin{bmatrix} 1 & 1 & -\frac{5}{2} & 1 & 2 \\ 0 & 1 & \frac{3}{2} & -2 & \frac{1}{2} \\ 0 & 0 & 1 & \frac{3}{2} & 2 \\ 0 & 0 & 0 & 0 & 0 \end{bmatrix}$$

is in row echelon form and is row equivalent to A.   ∎

When doing hand computations, it is sometimes possible to avoid fractions by suitably modifying the steps in the procedure.

Theorem 2.2   Every nonzero $m \times n$ matrix $A = \begin{bmatrix} a_{ij} \end{bmatrix}$ is row (column) equivalent to a unique matrix in reduced row (column) echelon form.

Proof

We proceed as in Theorem 2.1, obtaining matrix H in row echelon form that is row equivalent to A. Suppose that rows $1, 2, \ldots, r$ of H are nonzero and that the leading ones in these rows occur in columns $c_1, c_2, \ldots, c_r$. Then $c_1 < c_2 < \cdots < c_r$. Starting with the last nonzero row of H, we add suitable multiples of this row to all rows above it to make all entries in column c_r above the leading one in row r equal to zero. We repeat this process with rows $r-1, r-2, \ldots,$ and 2, making all entries above a leading one equal to zero. The result is a matrix K in reduced row echelon form that has been derived from H by elementary row operations and is thus row equivalent to H. Since A is row equivalent to H, and H is row equivalent to K, then A is row equivalent to K. An analogous proof can be given to show that A is column equivalent to a matrix in reduced column echelon form. It can be shown, with some difficulty, that there is only one matrix in reduced row echelon form that is row equivalent to a given matrix. For a proof, see K. Hoffman and R. Kunze, *Linear Algebra*, 2d ed. (Englewood Cliffs, N.J.: Prentice-Hall, 1971).

Remark It should be noted that a row echelon form of a matrix is not unique.

EXAMPLE 6   Find a matrix in reduced row echelon form that is row equivalent to the matrix A of Example 5.

Solution

We start with the matrix H obtained in Example 5 in row echelon form that is row equivalent to A. We add suitable multiples of each nonzero row of H to zero out all entries above a leading 1. Thus, we start by adding $\left(-\frac{3}{2}\right)$ times the third row of H to its second row:

$$J_1 = H_{-\frac{3}{2}r_3+r_2 \to r_2} = \begin{bmatrix} 1 & 1 & -\frac{5}{2} & 1 & 2 \\ 0 & 1 & 0 & -\frac{17}{4} & -\frac{5}{2} \\ 0 & 0 & 1 & \frac{3}{2} & 2 \\ 0 & 0 & 0 & 0 & 0 \end{bmatrix}.$$

Next, we add $\frac{5}{2}$ times the third row of J_1 to its first row:

$$J_2 = (J_1)_{\frac{5}{2}r_3+r_1 \to r_1} = \begin{bmatrix} 1 & 1 & 0 & \frac{19}{4} & 7 \\ 0 & 1 & 0 & -\frac{17}{4} & -\frac{5}{2} \\ 0 & 0 & 1 & \frac{3}{2} & 2 \\ 0 & 0 & 0 & 0 & 0 \end{bmatrix}.$$

Finally, we add (-1) times the second row of J_2 to its first row:

$$K = (J_2)_{-1r_2+r_1 \to r_1} = \begin{bmatrix} 1 & 0 & 0 & 9 & \frac{19}{2} \\ 0 & 1 & 0 & -\frac{17}{4} & -\frac{5}{2} \\ 0 & 0 & 1 & \frac{3}{2} & 2 \\ 0 & 0 & 0 & 0 & 0 \end{bmatrix}.$$

This is in reduced row echelon form and is row equivalent to A. Alternatively, we can express the reduced row echelon form of A as

$$H_{\substack{-\frac{3}{2}r_3 + r_2 \to r_2 \\ \frac{5}{2}r_3 + r_1 \to r_1 \\ -1r_2 + r_1 \to r_1}}.$$

■

Remark The procedure given here for finding a matrix K in reduced row echelon form that is row equivalent to a given matrix A is not the only one possible. For example, instead of first obtaining a matrix H in row echelon form that is row equivalent to A and then transforming H to reduced row echelon form, we could proceed as follows. First, zero out the entries below a leading 1 and then immediately zero out the entries above the leading 1. This procedure is not as efficient as the procedure given in Example 6.

Key Terms

Elimination method
Reduced row echelon form
Leading one

Row echelon form
Elementary row (column) operation
Row (column) equivalent

Pivot column
Pivot

2.1 Exercises

1. Find a row echelon form of each of the given matrices. Record the row operations you perform, using the notation for elementary row operations.

(a) $A = \begin{bmatrix} -1 & 2 & -5 \\ 2 & -1 & 6 \\ 2 & -2 & 7 \end{bmatrix}$

(b) $A = \begin{bmatrix} 1 & 1 & -1 \\ 3 & 4 & -1 \\ 5 & 6 & -3 \\ -2 & -2 & 2 \end{bmatrix}$

2. Find a row echelon form of each of the given matrices. Record the row operations you perform, using the notation for elementary row operations.

(a) $A = \begin{bmatrix} -1 & 1 & -1 & 0 & 3 \\ -3 & 4 & 1 & 1 & 10 \\ 4 & -6 & -4 & -2 & -14 \end{bmatrix}$

(b) $A = \begin{bmatrix} 1 & 1 & -4 \\ -2 & -1 & 10 \\ 4 & 3 & -12 \end{bmatrix}$

3. Each of the given matrices is in row echelon form. Determine its reduced row echelon form. Record the row operations you perform, using the notation for elementary row operations.

(a) $A = \begin{bmatrix} 1 & 2 & 4 \\ 0 & 1 & -2 \\ 0 & 0 & 1 \end{bmatrix}$

(b) $A = \begin{bmatrix} 1 & 4 & 3 & 5 \\ 0 & 0 & 1 & -4 \\ 0 & 0 & 0 & 1 \\ 0 & 0 & 0 & 0 \end{bmatrix}$

4. Each of the given matrices is in row echelon form. De-

termine its reduced row echelon form. Record the row operations you perform, using the notation for elementary row operations.

(a) $A = \begin{bmatrix} 1 & 0 & -3 & 2 \\ 0 & 1 & 1 & 1 \\ 0 & 0 & 1 & 2 \\ 0 & 0 & 0 & 0 \end{bmatrix}$

(b) $A = \begin{bmatrix} 1 & 3 & 0 & 2 & 4 \\ 0 & 1 & 0 & 1 & 0 \\ 0 & 0 & 1 & -1 & 0 \end{bmatrix}$

5. Find the reduced row echelon form of each of the given matrices. Record the row operations you perform, using the notation for elementary row operations.

(a) $A = \begin{bmatrix} 1 & 0 & -2 \\ -2 & 1 & 9 \\ 3 & 2 & 4 \end{bmatrix}$

(b) $A = \begin{bmatrix} 1 & 0 & 1 \\ -1 & 2 & -2 \\ 0 & 1 & 0 \\ -2 & 7 & -5 \end{bmatrix}$

6. Find the reduced row echelon form of each of the given matrices. Record the row operations you perform, using the notation for elementary row operations.

(a) $A = \begin{bmatrix} -1 & 2 & -5 \\ 2 & -1 & 6 \\ 2 & -2 & 7 \end{bmatrix}$

(b) $A = \begin{bmatrix} 1 & 1 & -1 \\ 3 & 4 & -1 \\ 5 & 6 & -3 \\ -2 & -2 & 2 \end{bmatrix}$

7. Let x, y, z, and w be nonzero real numbers. Label each of

the following matrices REF if it is in row echelon form, RREF if it is in reduced row echelon form, or N if it is not REF and not RREF:

(a) $\begin{bmatrix} 1 & x & y & 0 \\ 0 & 1 & 0 & z \\ 0 & 0 & w & 1 \end{bmatrix}$ **(b)** $\begin{bmatrix} 1 & x & y & z \\ 0 & 1 & 0 & 0 \\ 0 & 0 & 1 & 0 \\ 0 & 0 & 0 & 1 \end{bmatrix}$

(c) $\begin{bmatrix} 1 & 0 & 0 & x & 0 & 0 \\ 0 & 1 & w & y & 0 & 0 \\ 0 & 0 & 0 & 0 & 1 & 0 \\ 0 & 0 & 0 & 0 & 0 & 1 \end{bmatrix}$

8. Let x, y, z, and w be nonzero real numbers. Label each of the following matrices REF if it is in row echelon form, RREF if it is in reduced row echelon form, or N if it is not REF and not RREF:

(a) $\begin{bmatrix} 1 & 0 & x \\ 0 & 1 & y \\ 0 & 0 & 1 \end{bmatrix}$ **(b)** $\begin{bmatrix} 1 & x & 0 & 0 \\ 0 & 0 & 1 & 0 \\ 0 & 0 & 0 & 1 \\ 0 & 0 & 0 & 0 \end{bmatrix}$

(c) $\begin{bmatrix} 0 & y & 0 \\ 1 & 1 & 0 \\ 0 & 0 & 1 \end{bmatrix}$

9. Let A be an $n \times n$ matrix in reduced row echelon form. Prove that if $A \neq I_n$, then A has a row consisting entirely of zeros.

10. Prove:
  (a) Every matrix is row equivalent to itself.
  (b) If B is row equivalent to A, then A is row equivalent to B.
  (c) If C is row equivalent to B and B is row equivalent to A, then C is row equivalent to A.

11. Let
$$A = \begin{bmatrix} 1 & 2 & -3 & 1 \\ -1 & 0 & 3 & 4 \\ 0 & 1 & 2 & -1 \\ 2 & 3 & 0 & -3 \end{bmatrix}.$$
  (a) Find a matrix in column echelon form that is column equivalent to A.
  (b) Find a matrix in reduced column echelon form that is column equivalent to A.

12. Repeat Exercise 11 for the matrix
$$\begin{bmatrix} 1 & 2 & 3 & 4 & 5 \\ 2 & 1 & 3 & -1 & 2 \\ 3 & 1 & 2 & 4 & 1 \end{bmatrix}.$$

13. Determine the reduced row echelon form of
$$A = \begin{bmatrix} \cos\theta & \sin\theta \\ -\sin\theta & \cos\theta \end{bmatrix}.$$

2.2 Solving Linear Systems

In this section we use the echelon forms developed in Section 2.1 to more efficiently determine the solution of a linear system compared with the elimination method of Section 1.1. Using the augmented matrix of a linear system together with an echelon form, we develop two methods for solving a system of m linear equations in n unknowns. These methods take the augmented matrix of the linear system, perform elementary row operations on it, and obtain a new matrix that represents an equivalent linear system (i.e., a system that has the same solutions as the original linear system). The important point is that the latter linear system can be solved more easily.

To see how a linear system whose augmented matrix has a particular form can be readily solved, suppose that

$$\begin{bmatrix} 1 & 2 & 0 & \vdots & 3 \\ 0 & 1 & 1 & \vdots & 2 \\ 0 & 0 & 1 & \vdots & -1 \end{bmatrix}$$

represents the augmented matrix of a linear system. Then the solution is quickly found from the corresponding equations

$$\begin{aligned} x_1 + 2x_2 \quad\quad &= \quad 3 \\ x_2 + x_3 &= \quad 2 \\ x_3 &= -1 \end{aligned}$$

as

$$\begin{aligned} x_3 &= -1 \\ x_2 &= 2 - x_3 = 2 + 1 = 3 \\ x_1 &= 3 - 2x_2 = 3 - 6 = -3. \end{aligned}$$

The task of this section is to manipulate the augmented matrix representing a given linear system into a form from which the solution can be found more easily.

We now apply row operations to the solution of linear systems.

Theorem 2.3   Let $A\mathbf{x} = \mathbf{b}$ and $C\mathbf{x} = \mathbf{d}$ be two linear systems, each of m equations in n unknowns. If the augmented matrices $\begin{bmatrix} A \mid \mathbf{b} \end{bmatrix}$ and $\begin{bmatrix} C \mid \mathbf{d} \end{bmatrix}$ are row equivalent, then the linear systems are equivalent; that is, they have exactly the same solutions.

Proof

This follows from the definition of row equivalence and from the fact that the three elementary row operations on the augmented matrix are the three manipulations on linear systems, discussed in Section 1.1, which yield equivalent linear systems. We also note that if one system has no solution, then the other system has no solution. ■

Recall from Section 1.1 that the linear system of the form

$$\begin{aligned} a_{11}x_1 + a_{12}x_2 + \cdots + a_{1n}x_n &= 0 \\ a_{21}x_1 + a_{22}x_2 + \cdots + a_{2n}x_n &= 0 \\ \vdots \qquad \vdots \qquad\qquad \vdots \qquad \vdots \\ a_{m1}x_1 + a_{m2}x_2 + \cdots + a_{mn}x_n &= 0 \end{aligned} \tag{1}$$

is called a homogeneous system. We can also write (1) in matrix form as

$$A\mathbf{x} = \mathbf{0}. \tag{2}$$

Corollary 2.1   If A and C are row equivalent $m \times n$ matrices, then the homogeneous systems $A\mathbf{x} = \mathbf{0}$ and $C\mathbf{x} = \mathbf{0}$ are equivalent.

Proof

Exercise. ■

We observe that we have developed the essential features of two very straightforward methods for solving linear systems. The idea consists of starting with the linear system $A\mathbf{x} = \mathbf{b}$, then obtaining a partitioned matrix $\begin{bmatrix} C \mid \mathbf{d} \end{bmatrix}$ in either row echelon form or reduced row echelon form that is row equivalent to the augmented matrix $\begin{bmatrix} A \mid \mathbf{b} \end{bmatrix}$. Now $\begin{bmatrix} C \mid \mathbf{d} \end{bmatrix}$ represents the linear system $C\mathbf{x} = \mathbf{d}$, which is quite simple to solve because of the structure of $\left[\,C\mid \mathbf{d}\,\right]$, and the set of solutions to this system gives precisely the set of solutions to $A\mathbf{x} = \mathbf{b}$; that is, the linear systems $A\mathbf{x} = \mathbf{b}$ and $C\mathbf{x} = \mathbf{d}$ are equivalent. (See Section 1.1.) The method where $\left[\,C\mid \mathbf{d}\,\right]$ is in row echelon form is called **Gaussian elimination**; the method where $\left[\,C\mid \mathbf{d}\,\right]$ is in reduced row echelon form is called **Gauss*–Jordan^{+} reduction**. Strictly speaking, the original Gauss–Jordan reduction was more along the lines described in the preceding Remark. The version presented in this book is more efficient. In actual practice, neither Gaussian elimination nor Gauss–Jordan reduction is used as much as the method involving the LU-factorization of A that is discussed in Section 2.5. However, Gaussian elimination and Gauss–Jordan reduction are fine for small problems, and we use the latter heavily in this book.

Gaussian elimination consists of two steps:

Step 1. The transformation of the augmented matrix $\left[\,A\mid \mathbf{b}\,\right]$ to the matrix $\left[\,C\mid \mathbf{d}\,\right]$ in row echelon form using elementary row operations

Step 2. Solution of the linear system corresponding to the augmented matrix $\left[\,C\mid \mathbf{d}\,\right]$ using **back substitution**

For the case in which A is $n \times n$, and the linear system $A\mathbf{x} = \mathbf{b}$ has a unique solution, the matrix $\left[\,C\mid \mathbf{d}\,\right]$ has the following form:

CARL FRIEDRICH GAUSS

WILHELM JORDAN

---

*Carl Friedrich Gauss (1777–1855) was born into a poor working-class family in Brunswick, Germany, and died in Göttingen, Germany, the most famous mathematician in the world. He was a child prodigy with a genius that did not impress his father, who called him a "star-gazer." However, his teachers were impressed enough to arrange for the Duke of Brunswick to provide a scholarship for Gauss at the local secondary school. As a teenager there, he made original discoveries in number theory and began to speculate about non-Euclidean geometry. His scientific publications include important contributions in number theory, mathematical astronomy, mathematical geography, statistics, differential geometry, and magnetism. His diaries and private notes contain many other discoveries that he never published.

An austere, conservative man who had few friends and whose private life was generally unhappy, he was very concerned that proper credit be given for scientific discoveries. When he relied on the results of others, he was careful to acknowledge them; and when others independently discovered results in his private notes, he was quick to claim priority.

In his research Gauss used a method of calculation that later generations generalized to row reduction of matrices and named in his honor, although the method was used in China almost 2000 years earlier.

$^{+}$Wilhelm Jordan (1842–1899) was born in southern Germany. He attended college in Stuttgart and in 1868 became full professor of geodesy at the technical college in Karlsruhe, Germany. He participated in surveying several regions of Germany. Jordan was a prolific writer whose major work, *Handbuch der Vermessungskunde* (*Handbook of Geodesy*), was translated into French, Italian, and Russian. He was considered a superb writer and an excellent teacher. Unfortunately, the Gauss–Jordan reduction method has been widely attributed to Camille Jordan (1838–1922), a well-known French mathematician. Moreover, it seems that the method was also discovered independently at the same time by B. I. Clasen, a priest who lived in Luxembourg. This biographical sketch is based on an excellent article: S. C. Althoen and R. McLaughlin, "Gauss–Jordan reduction: A brief history," *MAA Monthly*, 94 (1987), 130–142.

$$\begin{bmatrix} 1 & c_{12} & c_{13} & \cdots & & c_{1n} & \vdots & d_1 \\ 0 & 1 & c_{23} & \cdots & & c_{2n} & \vdots & d_2 \\ \vdots & \vdots & \vdots & & & \vdots & \vdots & \vdots \\ 0 & 0 & 0 & \cdots & 1 & c_{n-1\,n} & \vdots & d_{n-1} \\ 0 & 0 & 0 & \cdots & 0 & 1 & \vdots & d_n \end{bmatrix}.$$

(The remaining cases are treated after Example 1.) This augmented matrix represents the linear system

$$\begin{aligned} x_1 + c_{12}x_2 + c_{13}x_3 + \ldots + c_{1n}x_n &= d_1 \\ x_2 + c_{23}x_3 + \ldots + c_{2n}x_n &= d_2 \\ \vdots \qquad\qquad \vdots \quad\ \vdots \\ x_{n-1} + c_{n-1\,n}x_n &= d_{n-1} \\ x_n &= d_n. \end{aligned}$$

Back substitution proceeds from the nth equation upward, solving for one variable from each equation:

$$\begin{aligned} x_n &= d_n \\ x_{n-1} &= d_{n-1} - c_{n-1\,n}x_n \\ &\ \ \vdots \\ x_2 &= d_2 - c_{23}x_3 - c_{24}x_4 - \cdots - c_{2n}x_n \\ x_1 &= d_1 - c_{12}x_2 - c_{13}x_3 - \cdots - c_{1n}x_n. \end{aligned}$$

EXAMPLE 1   The linear system

$$\begin{aligned} x + 2y + 3z &= 9 \\ 2x - y + z &= 8 \\ 3x \qquad - z &= 3 \end{aligned}$$

has the augmented matrix

$$[A \mid \mathbf{b}] = \begin{bmatrix} 1 & 2 & 3 & \vdots & 9 \\ 2 & -1 & 1 & \vdots & 8 \\ 3 & 0 & -1 & \vdots & 3 \end{bmatrix}.$$

Transforming this matrix to row echelon form, we obtain (verify)

$$[C \mid \mathbf{d}] = \begin{bmatrix} 1 & 2 & 3 & \vdots & 9 \\ 0 & 1 & 1 & \vdots & 2 \\ 0 & 0 & 1 & \vdots & 3 \end{bmatrix}.$$

Using back substitution, we now have

$$\begin{aligned} z &= 3 \\ y &= 2 - z = 2 - 3 = -1 \\ x &= 9 - 2y - 3z = 9 + 2 - 9 = 2; \end{aligned}$$

thus the solution is $x = 2$, $y = -1$, $z = 3$, which is unique.   ∎

The general case in which A is $m \times n$ is handled in a similar fashion, but we need to elaborate upon several situations that can occur. We thus consider $Cx = d$, where C is $m \times n$, and $\begin{bmatrix} C & | & d \end{bmatrix}$ is in row echelon form. Then, for example, $\begin{bmatrix} C & | & d \end{bmatrix}$ might be of the following form:

$$\begin{bmatrix} 1 & c_{12} & c_{13} & \cdots & & & c_{1n} & | & d_1 \\ 0 & 0 & 1 & c_{24} & \cdots & & c_{2n} & | & d_2 \\ \vdots & \vdots & \vdots & \vdots & & & \vdots & | & \vdots \\ 0 & 0 & \cdots & & 0 & 1 & c_{k-1\,n} & | & d_{k-1} \\ 0 & \cdots & & & \vdots & 0 & 1 & | & d_k \\ 0 & \cdots & & & & \vdots & 0 & | & d_{k+1} \\ \vdots & & & & & & \vdots & | & \vdots \\ 0 & \cdots & & & & & 0 & | & d_m \end{bmatrix}.$$

This augmented matrix represents the linear system

$$\begin{aligned} x_1 + c_{12}x_2 + c_{13}x_3 + \cdots \qquad + \quad c_{1n}x_n &= d_1 \\ x_3 + c_{24}x_4 + \cdots + \quad c_{2n}x_n &= d_2 \\ \vdots \qquad\qquad \\ x_{n-1} + c_{k-1\,n}x_n &= d_{k-1} \\ x_n &= d_k \\ 0x_1 + \quad + \quad \cdots \quad + \quad 0x_n &= d_{k+1} \\ \vdots \qquad\qquad \vdots \qquad\qquad \vdots \quad \\ 0x_1 + \quad + \quad \cdots \quad + \quad 0x_n &= d_m. \end{aligned}$$

First, if $d_{k+1} = 1$, then $Cx = d$ has no solution, since at least one equation is not satisfied. If $d_{k+1} = 0$, which implies that $d_{k+2} = \cdots = d_m = 0$ (since $\begin{bmatrix} C & | & d \end{bmatrix}$ was assumed to be in row echelon form), we then obtain $x_n = d_k$, $x_{n-1} = d_{k-1} - c_{k-1\,n}x_n = d_{k-1} - c_{k-1\,n}d_k$ and continue using back substitution to find the remaining unknowns corresponding to the leading entry in each row. Of course, in the solution some of the unknowns may be expressed in terms of others that can take on any values whatsoever. This merely indicates that $Cx = d$ has infinitely many solutions. On the other hand, every unknown may have a determined value, indicating that the solution is unique.

EXAMPLE 3 Let

$$\begin{bmatrix} C & | & d \end{bmatrix} = \begin{bmatrix} 1 & 2 & 3 & 4 & 5 & | & 6 \\ 0 & 1 & 2 & 3 & -1 & | & 7 \\ 0 & 0 & 1 & 2 & 3 & | & 7 \\ 0 & 0 & 0 & 1 & 2 & | & 9 \end{bmatrix}.$$

Then

$$x_4 = 9 - 2x_5$$
$$x_3 = 7 - 2x_4 - 3x_5 = 7 - 2(9 - 2x_5) - 3x_5 = -11 + x_5$$
$$x_2 = 7 - 2x_3 - 3x_4 + x_5 = 2 + 5x_5$$
$$x_1 = 6 - 2x_2 - 3x_3 - 4x_4 - 5x_5 = -1 - 10x_5$$
$$x_5 = \text{any real number.}$$

The system is consistent, and all solutions are of the form

$$x_1 = -1 - 10r$$
$$x_2 = 2 + 5r$$
$$x_3 = -11 + r$$
$$x_4 = 9 - 2r$$
$$x_5 = r, \text{ any real number.}$$

Since r can be assigned any real number, the given linear system has infinitely many solutions. ∎

EXAMPLE 3   If

$$[C \mid \mathbf{d}] = \begin{bmatrix} 1 & 2 & 3 & 4 & \vdots & 5 \\ 0 & 1 & 2 & 3 & \vdots & 6 \\ 0 & 0 & 0 & 0 & \vdots & 1 \end{bmatrix},$$

then $C\mathbf{x} = \mathbf{d}$ has no solution, since the last equation is

$$0x_1 + 0x_2 + 0x_3 + 0x_4 = 1,$$

which can never be satisfied. ∎

When using the Gauss–Jordan reduction procedure, we transform the augmented matrix $[A \mid \mathbf{b}]$ to $[C \mid \mathbf{d}]$, which is in reduced row echelon form. This means that we can solve the linear system $C\mathbf{x} = \mathbf{d}$ without back substitution, as the examples that follow show; but of course, it takes more effort to put a matrix in reduced row echelon form than to put it in row echelon form. It turns out that the techniques of Gaussian elimination and Gauss–Jordan reduction, as described in this book, require the same number of operations.

EXAMPLE 4   If

$$[C \mid \mathbf{d}] = \begin{bmatrix} 1 & 0 & 0 & 0 & \vdots & 5 \\ 0 & 1 & 0 & 0 & \vdots & 6 \\ 0 & 0 & 1 & 0 & \vdots & 7 \\ 0 & 0 & 0 & 1 & \vdots & 8 \end{bmatrix},$$

then the unique solution is

$$x_1 = 5$$
$$x_2 = 6$$
$$x_3 = 7$$
$$x_4 = 8.$$

∎

EXAMPLE 5

If

$$[C \mid \mathbf{d}] = \begin{bmatrix} 1 & 1 & 2 & 0 & -\frac{5}{2} & \mid & \frac{2}{3} \\ 0 & 0 & 0 & 1 & \frac{1}{2} & \mid & \frac{1}{2} \\ 0 & 0 & 0 & 0 & 0 & \mid & 0 \end{bmatrix},$$

then

$$x_4 = \tfrac{1}{2} - \tfrac{1}{2}x_5$$

$$x_1 = \tfrac{2}{3} - x_2 - 2x_3 + \tfrac{5}{2}x_5,$$

where x_2, x_3, and x_5 can take on any real numbers, so the system has infinitely many solutions. Thus a solution is of the form

$$x_1 = \tfrac{2}{3} - r - 2s + \tfrac{5}{2}t$$

$$x_2 = r$$

$$x_3 = s$$

$$x_4 = \tfrac{1}{2} - \tfrac{1}{2}t$$

$$x_5 = t,$$

where r, s, and t are any real numbers. ∎

We now solve a linear system both by Gaussian elimination and by Gauss–Jordan reduction.

EXAMPLE 6

Consider the linear system

$$x + 2y + 3z = 6$$
$$2x - 3y + 2z = 14$$
$$3x + y - z = -2.$$

We form the augmented matrix

$$[A \mid \mathbf{b}] = \begin{bmatrix} 1 & 2 & 3 & \mid & 6 \\ 2 & -3 & 2 & \mid & 14 \\ 3 & 1 & -1 & \mid & -2 \end{bmatrix}.$$

Add (-2) times the first row to the second row:

$$[A \mid \mathbf{b}]_{-2r_1 + r_2 \to r_2} = \begin{bmatrix} 1 & 2 & 3 & \mid & 6 \\ 0 & -7 & -4 & \mid & 2 \\ 3 & 1 & -1 & \mid & -2 \end{bmatrix}.$$

Add (-3) times the first row to the third row:

$$[A \mid \mathbf{b}]_{\substack{-2r_1 + r_2 \to r_2 \\ -3r_1 + r_3 \to r_3}} = \begin{bmatrix} 1 & 2 & 3 & \mid & 6 \\ 0 & -7 & -4 & \mid & 2 \\ 0 & -5 & -10 & \mid & -20 \end{bmatrix}.$$

Multiply the third row by $\left(-\frac{1}{5}\right)$ and interchange the second and third rows:

$$\left[A \mid \mathbf{b}\right]_{\substack{-2r_1+r_2 \to r_2 \\ -3r_1+r_3 \to r_3 \\ -\frac{1}{5}r_3 \to r_3 \\ r_2 \leftrightarrow r_3}} = \begin{bmatrix} 1 & 2 & 3 & \vdots & 6 \\ 0 & 1 & 2 & \vdots & 4 \\ 0 & -7 & -4 & \vdots & 2 \end{bmatrix}.$$

Add 7 times the second row to the third row:

$$\left[A \mid \mathbf{b}\right]_{\substack{-2r_1+r_2 \to r_2 \\ -3r_1+r_3 \to r_3 \\ -\frac{1}{5}r_3 \to r_3 \\ r_2 \leftrightarrow r_3 \\ 7r_2+r_3 \to r_3}} = \begin{bmatrix} 1 & 2 & 3 & \vdots & 6 \\ 0 & 1 & 2 & \vdots & 4 \\ 0 & 0 & 10 & \vdots & 30 \end{bmatrix}.$$

Multiply the third row by $\frac{1}{10}$:

$$\left[A \mid \mathbf{b}\right]_{\substack{-2r_1+r_2 \to r_2 \\ -3r_1+r_3 \to r_3 \\ -\frac{1}{5}r_3 \to r_3 \\ r_2 \leftrightarrow r_3 \\ 7r_2+r_3 \to r_3 \\ \frac{1}{10}r_3 \to r_3}} \begin{bmatrix} 1 & 2 & 3 & \vdots & 6 \\ 0 & 1 & 2 & \vdots & 4 \\ 0 & 0 & 1 & \vdots & 3 \end{bmatrix}.$$

This matrix is in row echelon form. This means that $z = 3$, and from the second row,

$$y + 2z = 4$$

so that

$$y = 4 - 2(3) = -2.$$

From the first row,

$$x + 2y + 3z = 6,$$

which implies that

$$x = 6 - 2y - 3z = 6 - 2(-2) - 3(3) = 1.$$

Thus $x = 1$, $y = -2$, and $z = 3$ is the solution. This gives the solution by Gaussian elimination.

To solve the given linear system by Gauss–Jordan reduction, we transform the last matrix to $\left[C \mid \mathbf{d}\right]$, which is in reduced row echelon form, by the following steps:

Add (-2) times the third row to the second row:

$$\left[C \mid \mathbf{d}\right]_{-2r_3+r_2 \to r_2} = \begin{bmatrix} 1 & 2 & 3 & \vdots & 6 \\ 0 & 1 & 0 & \vdots & -2 \\ 0 & 0 & 1 & \vdots & 3 \end{bmatrix}.$$

Now add (-3) times the third row to the first row:

$$\left[C \mid \mathbf{d}\right]_{\substack{-2r_3+r_2 \to r_2 \\ -3r_3+r_1 \to r_1}} = \begin{bmatrix} 1 & 2 & 0 & \vdots & -3 \\ 0 & 1 & 0 & \vdots & -2 \\ 0 & 0 & 1 & \vdots & 3 \end{bmatrix}.$$

Finally, add (-2) times the second row to the first row:

$$[C \mid \mathbf{d}]_{\substack{-2\mathbf{r}_3 + \mathbf{r}_2 \to \mathbf{r}_2 \\ -3\mathbf{r}_3 + \mathbf{r}_1 \to \mathbf{r}_1 \\ -2\mathbf{r}_2 + \mathbf{r}_1 \to \mathbf{r}_1}} = \begin{bmatrix} 1 & 0 & 0 & \vdots & 1 \\ 0 & 1 & 0 & \vdots & -2 \\ 0 & 0 & 1 & \vdots & 3 \end{bmatrix}.$$

The solution is $x = 1$, $y = -2$, and $z = 3$, as before.   ∎

Remarks

1. As we perform elementary row operations, we may encounter a row of the augmented matrix being transformed to reduced row echelon form whose first n entries are zero and whose $n + 1$ entry is not zero. In this case, we can stop our computations and conclude that the given linear system is inconsistent.

2. In both Gaussian elimination and Gauss–Jordan reduction, we can use only row operations. Do not try to use any column operations.

■ Applications

Linear systems arise in a great many applications. In this section we look at several of these.

Quadratic Interpolation

Various approximation techniques in science and engineering use a parabola that passes through three given data points $\{(x_1, y_1), (x_2, y_2), (x_3, y_3)\}$, where $x_i \neq x_j$ for $i \neq j$. We call these **distinct points**, since the x-coordinates are all different. The graph of a quadratic polynomial $p(x) = ax^2 + bx + c$ is a parabola, and we use the given data points to determine the coefficients a, b, and c as follows. Requiring that $p(x_i) = y_i$, $i = 1, 2, 3$, gives us three linear equations with unknowns a, b, and c:

$$\begin{aligned} p(x_1) = y_1 \quad &\text{or} \quad ax_1^2 + bx_1 + c = y_1 \\ p(x_2) = y_2 \quad &\text{or} \quad ax_2^2 + bx_2 + c = y_2 \\ p(x_3) = y_3 \quad &\text{or} \quad ax_3^2 + bx_3 + c = y_3. \end{aligned} \tag{3}$$

Let

$$A = \begin{bmatrix} x_1^2 & x_1 & 1 \\ x_2^2 & x_2 & 1 \\ x_3^2 & x_3 & 1 \end{bmatrix}$$

be the coefficient matrix, $\mathbf{v} = \begin{bmatrix} a \\ b \\ c \end{bmatrix}$ and $\mathbf{y} = \begin{bmatrix} y_1 \\ y_2 \\ y_3 \end{bmatrix}$. Then (3) can be written in

matrix equation form as $A\mathbf{v} = \mathbf{y}$ whose augmented matrix

$$[A \mid \mathbf{y}] = \begin{bmatrix} x_1^2 & x_1 & 1 & \vdots & y_1 \\ x_2^2 & x_2 & 1 & \vdots & y_2 \\ x_3^2 & x_3 & 1 & \vdots & y_3 \end{bmatrix}.$$

We solve this linear system by Gaussian elimination or Gauss–Jordan reduction, obtaining values for a, b, and c. It can be shown that there is a unique solution to this linear system if and only if the points are distinct. The construction of the parabola that matches the points of the given data set is called **quadratic interpolation**, and the parabola is called the **quadratic interpolant**. This process can be generalized to distinct data sets of $n + 1$ points and polynomials of degree n. We illustrate the construction of the quadratic in the following example:

EXAMPLE 7   Find the quadratic interpolant for the three distinct points $\{(1, -5), (-1, 1), (2, 7)\}$.

Solution

Setting up linear system (3), we find that its augmented matrix is (verify)

$$\left[\, A \mid \mathbf{y} \,\right] = \begin{bmatrix} 1 & 1 & 1 & \vdots & -5 \\ 1 & -1 & 1 & \vdots & 1 \\ 4 & 2 & 1 & \vdots & 7 \end{bmatrix}.$$

Solving this linear system, we obtain (verify)

$$a = 5, \quad b = -3, \quad c = -7.$$

Thus the quadratic interpolant is $p(x) = 5x^2 - 3x - 7$, and its graph is given in Figure 2.1. The asterisks represent the three data points. ∎

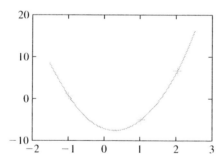

FIGURE 2.1

Temperature Distribution

A simple model for estimating the temperature distribution on a square plate gives rise to a linear system of equations. To construct the appropriate linear system, we use the following information: The square plate is perfectly insulated on its top and bottom so that the only heat flow is through the plate itself. The four edges are held at various temperatures. To estimate the temperature at an interior point on the plate, we use the rule that it is the average of the temperatures at its four compass-point neighbors, to the west, north, east, and south.

EXAMPLE 8   Estimate the temperatures T_i, $i = 1, 2, 3, 4$, at the four equispaced interior points on the plate shown in Figure 2.2.

Solution

We now construct the linear system to estimate the temperatures. The points at which we need the temperatures of the plate for this model are indicated in Figure 2.2 by dots. Using our averaging rule, we obtain the equations

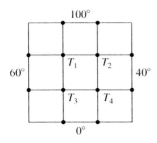

FIGURE 2.2

$$T_1 = \frac{60 + 100 + T_2 + T_3}{4} \quad \text{or} \quad 4T_1 - T_2 - T_3 \qquad = 160$$

$$T_2 = \frac{T_1 + 100 + 40 + T_4}{4} \quad \text{or} \quad -T_1 + 4T_2 \qquad - T_4 = 140$$

$$T_3 = \frac{60 + T_1 + T_4 + 0}{4} \quad \text{or} \quad -T_1 \qquad + 4T_3 - T_4 = 60$$

$$T_4 = \frac{T_3 + T_2 + 40 + 0}{4} \quad \text{or} \qquad - T_2 - T_3 + 4T_4 = 40.$$

The augmented matrix for this linear system is (verify)

$$\left[A \mid \mathbf{b} \right] = \begin{bmatrix} 4 & -1 & -1 & 0 & \vdots & 160 \\ -1 & 4 & 0 & -1 & \vdots & 140 \\ -1 & 0 & 4 & -1 & \vdots & 60 \\ 0 & -1 & -1 & 4 & \vdots & 40 \end{bmatrix}.$$

Using Gaussian elimination or Gauss–Jordan reduction, we obtain the unique solution (verify)

$$T_1 = 65°, \quad T_2 = 60°, \quad T_3 = 40°, \quad \text{and} \quad T_4 = 35°. \qquad \blacksquare$$

Global Positioning System

A Global Positioning System (GPS) is a satellite-based global navigation system enabling the user to determine his or her position in 3-dimensional coordinates without the need for further knowledge of navigational calculations. It was developed by the military as a locating utility, and the GPS system operated by the U.S. Department of Defense became operational in 1995. GPS technology has proven to be a useful tool for a wide variety of civilian applications as well and is now available in low-cost units. These units have been incorporated into boats, automobiles, airplanes, and handheld units available for general use such as hiking.

GPS is based on satellite ranging, that is, calculating the distances between a receiver and the position of three or more satellites (four or more if elevation is desired) and then applying some mathematics. Assuming that the positions of the satellites are known, the location of the receiver can be calculated by determining the distance from each of the satellites to the receiver. GPS takes these three or more known references and measured distances and "trilaterates" the position of the receiver. Trilateration is a method of determining the relative position of an object, in this case, orbiting satellites. For GPS calculations, there are three position variables, x, y, and z, together with a fourth variable, t, time. Time must be considered, since the GPS receiver processes signals from the satellites to determine the distances involved. Even though the signals move at the speed of light, there are small time delays for transmission, together with other factors like atmospheric conditions, that must be accounted for to ensure that accurate data are gathered. In this brief discussion of GPS we will use a simplified model to show how linear systems of equations enter into the mathematics that is part of the clever model involved in GPS.

For "real" GPS, we need to think in terms of three dimensions. In this context each satellite is represented by a sphere, and we need four spheres so that the location of the receiver can be determined by computing an intercept of the spheres; that is, a single point of intersection of the spheres. For our discussion, we will think in two dimensions and consider three satellites, each represented by a circle for which the coordinates of the center are known. We will assume that our GPS receiver can determine the distance between its location and the position of the satellite; thus, the radius of each circle is also known. Then, algebraically, we have the equations of three circles as shown in (4), where circle j has center (a_j, b_j) and radius r_j for $j = 1, 2, 3$.

$$\begin{aligned}
(x - a_1)^2 + (y - b_1)^2 &= r_1^2 \\
(x - a_2)^2 + (y - b_2)^2 &= r_2^2 \\
(x - a_3)^2 + (y - b_3)^2 &= r_3^2
\end{aligned} \tag{4}$$

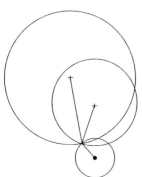

FIGURE 2.3

By construction, the location of the GPS receiver is on the circumference of each circle, so we are guaranteed that there is point (x, y) that satisfies each equation in (4). It is this point that will provide the coordinates of the GPS receiver. In Figure 2.3 we illustrate the system of the (nonlinear) equations in (4). [Why is (4) not a system of linear equations?]

A question that arises is, How do we solve the system of equations in (4), since they are not linear equations? The answer is, We first expand each equation and then eliminate the terms that contain x^2 and y^2 by using algebra. In (5) we show the expansion of each of the equations in (4); note that x^2 and y^2 appear in each equation.

$$\begin{aligned}
x^2 - 2a_1 x + a_1^2 + y^2 - 2b_1 y + b_1^2 &= r_1^2 \\
x^2 - 2a_2 x + a_2^2 + y^2 - 2b_2 y + b_2^2 &= r_2^2 \\
x^2 - 2a_3 x + a_3^2 + y^2 - 2b_3 y + b_3^2 &= r_3^2
\end{aligned} \tag{5}$$

Now we rearrange each equation in (5) to obtain the expressions shown in (6).

$$\begin{aligned}
x^2 - 2a_1 x + a_1^2 + y^2 - 2b_1 y + b_1^2 - r_1^2 &= 0 \\
x^2 - 2a_2 x + a_2^2 + y^2 - 2b_2 y + b_2^2 - r_2^2 &= 0 \\
x^2 - 2a_3 x + a_3^2 + y^2 - 2b_3 y + b_3^2 - r_3^2 &= 0
\end{aligned} \tag{6}$$

Next, set the left side of the first equation in (6) equal to the left side of the second equation in (6) and simplify. Do likewise for the second and third equations in (6). This gives the linear system in x and y in (7).

$$\begin{aligned}
-2a_1 x + a_1^2 - 2b_1 y + b_1^2 - r_1^2 &= -2a_2 x + a_2^2 - 2b_2 y + b_2^2 - r_2^2 \\
-2a_3 x + a_3^2 - 2b_3 y + b_3^2 - r_3^2 &= -2a_2 x + a_2^2 - 2b_2 y + b_2^2 - r_2^2
\end{aligned} \tag{7}$$

Finally, collect like terms in x and y to get the equations in (8).

$$\begin{aligned}
-2(a_1 - a_2)x - 2(b_1 - b_2)y &= (r_1^2 - r_2^2) + (a_2^2 - a_1^2) + (b_2^2 - b_1^2) \\
-2(a_3 - a_2)x - 2(b_3 - b_2)y &= (r_3^2 - r_2^2) + (a_2^2 - a_3^2) + (b_2^2 - b_3^2)
\end{aligned} \tag{8}$$

To simplify a bit further, we multiply each equation in (8) by -1 and show the matrix formulation for the resulting 2×2 system in (9).

$$\begin{bmatrix} 2(a_1 - a_2) & 2(b_1 - b_2) \\ 2(a_3 - a_2) & 2(b_3 - b_2) \end{bmatrix} \begin{bmatrix} x \\ y \end{bmatrix} = \begin{bmatrix} (r_2^2 - r_1^2) + (a_1^2 - a_2^2) + (b_1^2 - b_2^2) \\ (r_2^2 - r_3^2) + (a_3^2 - a_2^2) + (b_3^2 - b_2^2) \end{bmatrix} \quad (9)$$

So, given the coordinates of the centers and the radii of the three circles, we can determine the location of the GPS receiver in the two-dimensional model.

EXAMPLE 9   The coordinates of the centers and the radii of three circles are shown in Table 2.1. The corresponding system of equations is given in (10) (verify), and its solution is $x = 6$ and $y = 10$ (verify). Thus, the coordinates of the GPS receiver in the two-dimensional system for these three circles is $(6, 10)$.

TABLE 2.1

Circle	Center	Radius
1	$(-3, 50)$	41
2	$(11, -2)$	13
3	$(13, 34)$	25

$$\begin{bmatrix} -28 & 104 \\ 4 & 72 \end{bmatrix} \begin{bmatrix} x \\ y \end{bmatrix} = \begin{bmatrix} 872 \\ 744 \end{bmatrix}. \quad (10)$$

∎

Next we present an approach for GPS in three dimensions. In this case each of the equations in the system that is analogous to those in (4) has the form

$$(x - a_j)^2 + (y - b_j)^2 + (z - c_j)^2 = (\text{distance from receiver to satellite } j)^2 \quad (11)$$

for $j = 1, 2, 3, 4$, where (a_j, b_j, c_j) is the position of the satellite j. The distance from the receiver to satellite j is computed by measuring the time it takes the signal from satellite j to reach the receiver. The satellite contains a clock mechanism that sends the time the signal was sent to the receiver, and we let t be the time the signal was received. Since the signal travels at the speed of light, we can get a good approximation to the distance by using the basic formula distance = speed $\times$ elapsed time. Thus there are now four unknowns: x, y, z, and t. We proceed algebraically as we did to get expressions that are analogous to those in (7) and (8). This will yield a system of three equations in four unknowns analogous to the system in (9). We solve this system for x, y, and z in terms of time t. To determine the unknown t, we substitute these expressions for x, y, and z into any of the equations in (11) and then solve the resulting quadratic polynomial for t. Finally, we use the resulting value of t in the expressions for x, y, and z to determine the location of the receiver in three dimensions. This approach uses a system that has infinitely many solutions and then cleverly uses the underlying physical situation to determine the "free" variable t.

The real-life situation is even more complicated than our approach outlined for the three-dimensional case. The satellites are continually moving, so their locations vary with time, inherent errors in time calculations creep in, and a number of other factors introduce more inaccuracies. Highly accurate estimation of the receiver's position is beyond the scope of this course, but there are many books and discussions on the Internet that provide more detailed information. We have presented a basic component of GPS calculations, namely, that linear systems of equations are involved.

■ Homogeneous Systems

Now we study a homogeneous system $A\mathbf{x} = \mathbf{0}$ of m linear equations in n unknowns.

EXAMPLE 10

Consider the homogeneous system whose augmented matrix is

$$\begin{bmatrix} 1 & 0 & 0 & 0 & 2 & \vdots & 0 \\ 0 & 0 & 1 & 0 & 3 & \vdots & 0 \\ 0 & 0 & 0 & 1 & 4 & \vdots & 0 \\ 0 & 0 & 0 & 0 & 0 & \vdots & 0 \end{bmatrix}.$$

Since the augmented matrix is in reduced row echelon form, the solution is seen to be

$$\begin{aligned} x_1 &= -2r \\ x_2 &= s \\ x_3 &= -3r \\ x_4 &= -4r \\ x_5 &= r, \end{aligned}$$

where r and s are any real numbers.   ■

In Example 10 we solved a homogeneous system of m $(= 4)$ linear equations in n $(= 5)$ unknowns, where $m < n$ and the augmented matrix A was in reduced row echelon form. We can ignore any row of the augmented matrix that consists entirely of zeros. Thus let rows $1, 2, \ldots, r$ of A be the nonzero rows, and let the 1 in row i occur in column c_i. We are then solving a homogeneous system of r equations in n unknowns, $r < n$, and in this special case (A is in reduced row echelon form) we can solve for $x_{c_1}, x_{c_2}, \ldots, x_{c_r}$ in terms of the remaining $n - r$ unknowns. Since the latter can take on any real values, there are infinitely many solutions to the system $A\mathbf{x} = \mathbf{0}$; in particular, there is a nontrivial solution. We now show that this situation holds whenever we have $m < n$; A does not have to be in reduced row echelon form.

Theorem 2.4   A homogeneous system of m linear equations in n unknowns always has a nontrivial solution if $m < n$, that is, if the number of unknowns exceeds the number of equations.

Proof

Let B be a matrix in reduced row echelon form that is row equivalent to A. Then the homogeneous systems $A\mathbf{x} = \mathbf{0}$ and $B\mathbf{x} = \mathbf{0}$ are equivalent. As we have just shown, the system $B\mathbf{x} = \mathbf{0}$ has a nontrivial solution, and therefore the same is true for the system $A\mathbf{x} = \mathbf{0}$.   ▨

We shall use this result in the following equivalent form: If A is $m \times n$ and $A\mathbf{x} = \mathbf{0}$ has only the trivial solution, then $m \geq n$.

EXAMPLE 11

Consider the homogeneous system

$$\begin{aligned} x + \quad y + z + w &= 0 \\ x \quad\quad\quad\quad + w &= 0 \\ x + 2y + z \quad\quad &= 0. \end{aligned}$$

The augmented matrix

$$A = \left[\begin{array}{cccc|c} 1 & 1 & 1 & 1 & 0 \\ 1 & 0 & 0 & 1 & 0 \\ 1 & 2 & 1 & 0 & 0 \end{array} \right]$$

is row equivalent to (verify)

$$\left[\begin{array}{cccc|c} 1 & 0 & 0 & 1 & 0 \\ 0 & 1 & 0 & -1 & 0 \\ 0 & 0 & 1 & 1 & 0 \end{array} \right].$$

Hence the solution is

$$\begin{aligned} x &= -r \\ y &= \quad r \\ z &= -r \\ w &= \quad r, \text{ any real number.} \end{aligned}$$ ■

■ Application: Chemical Balance Equations

Chemical reactions can be described by equations. The expressions on the left side are called the reactants, and those on the right side are the products, which are produced from the reaction of chemicals on the left. Unlike mathematical equations, the two sides are separated by an arrow, either $\rightarrow$, which indicates that the reactants form the products, or $\leftrightarrow$, which indicates a reversible equation; that is, once the products are formed, they begin to form reactants. A chemical equation is balanced, provided that the number of atoms of each type on the left is the same as the number of atoms of the corresponding type on the right. In Example 12 we illustrate how to construct a homogeneous system of equations whose solution provides appropriate values to balance the atoms in the reactants with those in the products.

EXAMPLE 12

Sodium hydroxide (NaOH) reacts with sulfuric acid (H_2SO_4) to form sodium sulfate (Na_2SO_4) and water (H_2O). The chemical equation is

$$NaOH + H_2SO_4 \rightarrow Na_2SO_4 + H_2O.$$

To balance this equation, we insert unknowns, multiplying the chemicals on the left and right to get an equation of the form

$$x\text{NaOH} + y\text{H}_2\text{SO}_4 \rightarrow z\text{Na}_2\text{SO}_4 + w\text{H}_2\text{O}.$$

Next, we compare the number of sodium (Na), oxygen (O), hydrogen (H), and sulfur (S) atoms on the left side with the numbers on the right. We obtain four linear equations:

$$\text{Na: } x = 2z$$
$$\text{O: } x + 4y = 4z + w$$
$$\text{H: } x + 2y = 2w$$
$$\text{S: } y = z$$

Observe that we made use of the subscripts because they count the number of atoms of a particular element. Rewriting these equations in standard form, we see that we have a homogeneous linear system in four unknowns:

$$
\begin{aligned}
x \quad\quad - 2z \quad\quad &= 0 \\
x + 4y - 4z - \quad w &= 0 \\
x + 2y \quad\quad - 2w &= 0 \\
y - \quad z \quad\quad &= 0.
\end{aligned}
$$

Writing this system in matrix form, we have the augmented matrix

$$
\left[\begin{array}{cccc|c}
1 & 0 & -2 & 0 & 0 \\
1 & 4 & -4 & -1 & 0 \\
1 & 2 & 0 & -2 & 0 \\
0 & 1 & -1 & 0 & 0
\end{array}\right].
$$

The reduced row echelon form is

$$
\left[\begin{array}{cccc|c}
1 & 0 & 0 & -1 & 0 \\
0 & 1 & 0 & -\frac{1}{2} & 0 \\
0 & 0 & 1 & -\frac{1}{2} & 0 \\
0 & 0 & 0 & 0 & 0
\end{array}\right],
$$

and the solution is $x = w$, $y = \frac{1}{2}w$, and $z = \frac{1}{2}w$. Since w can be chosen arbitrarily and we are dealing with atoms, it is convenient to choose values so that all the unknowns are positive integers. One such choice is $w = 2$, which gives $x = 2$, $y = 1$, and $z = 1$. In this case our balanced equation is

$$2\text{NaOH} + \text{H}_2\text{SO}_4 \rightarrow \text{Na}_2\text{SO}_4 + 2\text{H}_2\text{O}. \qquad \blacksquare$$

■ Relationship between Nonhomogeneous Linear Systems and Homogeneous Systems

Let $A\mathbf{x} = \mathbf{b}$, $\mathbf{b} \neq \mathbf{0}$, be a consistent linear system. If $\mathbf{x}_p$ is a particular solution to the given nonhomogeneous system and $\mathbf{x}_h$ is a solution to the associated homogeneous system $A\mathbf{x} = \mathbf{0}$, then $\mathbf{x}_p + \mathbf{x}_h$ is a solution to the given system $A\mathbf{x} = \mathbf{b}$. Moreover, every solution $\mathbf{x}$ to the nonhomogeneous linear system $A\mathbf{x} = \mathbf{b}$ can be written as $\mathbf{x}_p + \mathbf{x}_h$, where $\mathbf{x}_p$ is a particular solution to the given nonhomogeneous system and $\mathbf{x}_h$ is a solution to the associated homogeneous system $A\mathbf{x} = \mathbf{0}$. For a proof, see Exercise 29.

■ Solving Linear Systems with Complex Entries

Gaussian elimination and Gauss–Jordan reduction can both be used to solve linear systems that have complex entries. The examples that follow show how to solve a linear system with complex entries by using these solution techniques. (For simplicity, we do not show the notation for row operations.) Further illustrations and exercises are given in Appendix B.2.

EXAMPLE 13   Solve the linear system

$$(1 - i)x + (2 + i)y = 2 + 2i$$
$$2x + (1 - 2i)y = 1 + 3i$$

by Gaussian elimination.

Solution

The augmented matrix of the given linear system is

$$\left[\begin{array}{cc|c} 1 - i & 2 + i & 2 + 2i \\ 2 & 1 - 2i & 1 + 3i \end{array} \right].$$

To transform this matrix to row echelon form, we first interchange the two rows (to avoid complicated fractions), obtaining

$$\left[\begin{array}{cc|c} 2 & 1 - 2i & 1 + 3i \\ 1 - i & 2 + i & 2 + 2i \end{array} \right].$$

Multiply the first row by $\frac{1}{2}$:

$$\left[\begin{array}{cc|c} 1 & \dfrac{1 - 2i}{2} & \dfrac{1 + 3i}{2} \\ 1 - i & 2 + i & 2 + 2i \end{array} \right].$$

Add $-(1 - i)$ times the first row to the second row:

$$\left[\begin{array}{cc|c} 1 & \dfrac{1 - 2i}{2} & \dfrac{1 + 3i}{2} \\ 0 & \dfrac{5 + 5i}{2} & i \end{array} \right].$$

Multiply the second row by $\dfrac{2}{5+5i}$:

$$\begin{bmatrix} 1 & \dfrac{1-2i}{2} & \vdots & \dfrac{1+3i}{2} \\[2mm] 0 & 1 & \vdots & \dfrac{2i}{5+5i} \end{bmatrix}.$$

Then

$$y = \frac{2i}{5+5i} = \frac{1}{5} + \frac{1}{5}i.$$

Using back substitution, we have

$$x = \frac{1+3i}{2} - \frac{1-2i}{2}y = \frac{1}{5} + \frac{8}{5}i \quad \text{(verify)}. \qquad \blacksquare$$

EXAMPLE 14   Solve the linear system whose augmented matrix is

$$\begin{bmatrix} i & 2 & 1-i & \vdots & 1-2i \\ 0 & 2i & 2+i & \vdots & -2+i \\ 0 & -i & 1 & \vdots & -1-i \end{bmatrix}$$

by Gauss–Jordan reduction.

Solution

Multiply the first row by $\dfrac{1}{i}$:

$$\begin{bmatrix} 1 & \dfrac{2}{i} & \dfrac{1-i}{i} & \vdots & \dfrac{1-2i}{i} \\[2mm] 0 & 2i & 2+i & \vdots & -2+i \\[2mm] 0 & -i & 1 & \vdots & -1-i \end{bmatrix}.$$

Multiply the second row by $\dfrac{1}{2i}$:

$$\begin{bmatrix} 1 & \dfrac{2}{i} & \dfrac{1-i}{i} & \vdots & \dfrac{1-2i}{i} \\[2mm] 0 & 1 & \dfrac{2+i}{2i} & \vdots & \dfrac{-2+i}{2i} \\[2mm] 0 & -i & 1 & \vdots & -1-i \end{bmatrix}.$$

Add i times the second row to the third row:

$$\begin{bmatrix} 1 & \dfrac{2}{i} & \dfrac{1-i}{i} & \vdots & \dfrac{1-2i}{i} \\[2mm] 0 & 1 & \dfrac{2+i}{2i} & \vdots & \dfrac{-2+i}{2i} \\[2mm] 0 & 0 & \dfrac{4+i}{2} & \vdots & \dfrac{-4-i}{2} \end{bmatrix}.$$

Multiply the third row by $\left(\dfrac{2}{4+i}\right)$:

$$\begin{bmatrix} 1 & \dfrac{2}{i} & \dfrac{1-i}{i} & \vdots & \dfrac{1-2i}{i} \\[2ex] 0 & 1 & \dfrac{2+i}{2i} & \vdots & \dfrac{-2+i}{2i} \\[2ex] 0 & 0 & 1 & \vdots & -1 \end{bmatrix}.$$

Add $\left(-\dfrac{2+i}{2i}\right)$ times the third row to the second row and $\left(-\dfrac{1-i}{i}\right)$ times the third row to the first row:

$$\begin{bmatrix} 1 & \dfrac{2}{i} & 0 & \vdots & \dfrac{2-3i}{i} \\[2ex] 0 & 1 & 0 & \vdots & 1 \\[2ex] 0 & 0 & 1 & \vdots & -1 \end{bmatrix}.$$

Add $\left(-\dfrac{2}{i}\right)$ times the second row to the first row:

$$\begin{bmatrix} 1 & 0 & 0 & \vdots & -3 \\ 0 & 1 & 0 & \vdots & 1 \\ 0 & 0 & 1 & \vdots & -1 \end{bmatrix}.$$

Hence the solution is $x = -3$, $y = 1$, $z = -1$.   ■

Key Terms

Gaussian elimination	Back substitution	Global positioning system
Gauss–Jordan reduction	Quadratic interpolation	Chemical balance equations
Homogeneous system	Quadratic interpolant	

Exercises

1. Each of the given linear systems is in row echelon form. Solve the system.

  (a) $\begin{aligned} x + 2y - z &= 6 \\ y + z &= 5 \\ z &= 4 \end{aligned}$ **(b)** $\begin{aligned} x - 3y + 4z + w &= 0 \\ z - w &= 4 \\ w &= 1 \end{aligned}$

2. Each of the given linear systems is in row echelon form. Solve the system.

  (a) $\begin{aligned} x + y - z + 2w &= 4 \\ w &= 5 \end{aligned}$ **(b)** $\begin{aligned} x - y + z &= 0 \\ y + 2z &= 0 \\ z &= 1 \end{aligned}$

3. Each of the given linear systems is in reduced row echelon form. Solve the system.

  (a) $\begin{aligned} x + y \quad\quad &= 2 \\ z + w &= -3 \end{aligned}$ **(b)** $\begin{aligned} x \quad\quad &= 3 \\ y \quad\quad &= 0 \\ z &= 1 \end{aligned}$

4. Each of the given linear systems is in reduced row echelon form. Solve the system.

  (a) $\begin{aligned} x \quad - 2z &= 5 \\ y + z &= 2 \end{aligned}$ **(b)** $\begin{aligned} x \quad\quad &= 1 \\ y \quad\quad &= 2 \\ z - w &= 4 \end{aligned}$

5. Consider the linear system

$$\begin{aligned} x + y + 2z &= -1 \\ x - 2y + z &= -5 \\ 3x + y + z &= 3. \end{aligned}$$

(a) Find all solutions, if any exist, by using the Gaussian elimination method.

(b) Find all solutions, if any exist, by using the Gauss–Jordan reduction method.

6. Repeat Exercise 5 for each of the following linear systems:

(a) $\begin{aligned} x + y + 2z + 3w &= 13 \\ x - 2y + z + w &= 8 \\ 3x + y + z - w &= 1 \end{aligned}$

(b) $\begin{aligned} x + y + z &= 1 \\ x + y - 2z &= 3 \\ 2x + y + z &= 2 \end{aligned}$

(c) $\begin{aligned} 2x + y + z - 2w &= 1 \\ 3x - 2y + z - 6w &= -2 \\ x + y - z - w &= -1 \\ 6x + z - 9w &= -2 \\ 5x - y + 2z - 8w &= 3 \end{aligned}$

In Exercises 7 through 9, solve the linear system, with the given augmented matrix, if it is consistent.

7. (a) $\left[\begin{array}{ccc|c} 1 & 1 & 1 & 0 \\ 1 & 1 & 0 & 3 \\ 0 & 1 & 1 & 1 \end{array}\right]$ (b) $\left[\begin{array}{ccc|c} 1 & 2 & 3 & 0 \\ 1 & 1 & 1 & 0 \\ 1 & 1 & 2 & 0 \end{array}\right]$

(c) $\left[\begin{array}{ccc|c} 1 & 2 & 3 & 0 \\ 1 & 1 & 1 & 0 \\ 5 & 7 & 9 & 0 \end{array}\right]$ (d) $\left[\begin{array}{ccc|c} 1 & 2 & 3 & 0 \\ 1 & 2 & 1 & 0 \end{array}\right]$

8. (a) $\left[\begin{array}{cccc|c} 1 & 2 & 3 & 1 & 8 \\ 1 & 3 & 0 & 1 & 7 \\ 1 & 0 & 2 & 1 & 3 \end{array}\right]$

(b) $\left[\begin{array}{cccc|c} 1 & 1 & 3 & -3 & 0 \\ 0 & 2 & 1 & -3 & 3 \\ 1 & 0 & 2 & -1 & -1 \end{array}\right]$

9. (a) $\left[\begin{array}{ccc|c} 1 & 2 & 1 & 7 \\ 2 & 0 & 1 & 4 \\ 1 & 0 & 2 & 5 \\ 1 & 2 & 3 & 11 \\ 2 & 1 & 4 & 12 \end{array}\right]$ (b) $\left[\begin{array}{ccc|c} 1 & 2 & 1 & 0 \\ 2 & 3 & 0 & 0 \\ 0 & 1 & 2 & 0 \\ 2 & 1 & 4 & 0 \end{array}\right]$

10. Find a 2×1 matrix $\mathbf{x}$ with entries not all zero such that

$$A\mathbf{x} = 4\mathbf{x}, \quad \text{where } A = \begin{bmatrix} 4 & 1 \\ 0 & 2 \end{bmatrix}.$$

[*Hint*: Rewrite the matrix equation $A\mathbf{x} = 4\mathbf{x}$ as $4\mathbf{x} - A\mathbf{x} = (4I_2 - A)\mathbf{x} = \mathbf{0}$, and solve the homogeneous linear system.]

11. Find a 2×1 matrix $\mathbf{x}$ with entries not all zero such that

$$A\mathbf{x} = 3\mathbf{x}, \quad \text{where } A = \begin{bmatrix} 2 & 1 \\ 1 & 2 \end{bmatrix}.$$

12. Find a 3×1 matrix $\mathbf{x}$ with entries not all zero such that

$$A\mathbf{x} = 3\mathbf{x}, \quad \text{where } A = \begin{bmatrix} 1 & 2 & -1 \\ 1 & 0 & 1 \\ 4 & -4 & 5 \end{bmatrix}.$$

13. Find a 3×1 matrix $\mathbf{x}$ with entries not all zero such that

$$A\mathbf{x} = 1\mathbf{x}, \quad \text{where } A = \begin{bmatrix} 1 & 2 & -1 \\ 1 & 0 & 1 \\ 4 & -4 & 5 \end{bmatrix}.$$

14. In the following linear system, determine all values of a for which the resulting linear system has

(a) no solution;

(b) a unique solution;

(c) infinitely many solutions:

$$\begin{aligned} x + y - z &= 2 \\ x + 2y + z &= 3 \\ x + y + (a^2 - 5)z &= a \end{aligned}$$

15. Repeat Exercise 14 for the linear system

$$\begin{aligned} x + y + z &= 2 \\ 2x + 3y + 2z &= 5 \\ 2x + 3y + (a^2 - 1)z &= a + 1. \end{aligned}$$

16. Repeat Exercise 14 for the linear system

$$\begin{aligned} x + y + z &= 2 \\ x + 2y + z &= 3 \\ x + y + (a^2 - 5)z &= a. \end{aligned}$$

17. Repeat Exercise 14 for the linear system

$$\begin{aligned} x + y &= 3 \\ x + (a^2 - 8)y &= a. \end{aligned}$$

18. Let

$$A = \begin{bmatrix} a & b \\ c & d \end{bmatrix} \quad \text{and} \quad \mathbf{x} = \begin{bmatrix} x_1 \\ x_2 \end{bmatrix}.$$

Show that the linear system $A\mathbf{x} = \mathbf{0}$ has only the trivial solution if and only if $ad - bc \neq 0$.

19. Show that $A = \begin{bmatrix} a & b \\ c & d \end{bmatrix}$ is row equivalent to I_2 if and only if $ad - bc \neq 0$.

20. Let $f: R^3 \rightarrow R^3$ be the matrix transformation defined by

$$f\left(\begin{bmatrix} x \\ y \\ z \end{bmatrix}\right) = \begin{bmatrix} 4 & 1 & 3 \\ 2 & -1 & 3 \\ 2 & 2 & 0 \end{bmatrix} \begin{bmatrix} x \\ y \\ z \end{bmatrix}.$$

Find x, y, z so that $f\left(\begin{bmatrix} x \\ y \\ z \end{bmatrix}\right) = \begin{bmatrix} 4 \\ 5 \\ -1 \end{bmatrix}$.

21. Let $f: R^3 \rightarrow R^3$ be the matrix transformation defined by

$$f\left(\begin{bmatrix} x \\ y \\ z \end{bmatrix}\right) = \begin{bmatrix} 1 & 2 & 3 \\ -3 & -2 & -1 \\ -2 & 0 & 2 \end{bmatrix} \begin{bmatrix} x \\ y \\ z \end{bmatrix}.$$

Find x, y, z so that $f\left(\begin{bmatrix} x \\ y \\ z \end{bmatrix}\right) = \begin{bmatrix} 2 \\ 2 \\ 4 \end{bmatrix}$.

22. Let $f: R^3 \rightarrow R^3$ be the matrix transformation defined by

$$f\left(\begin{bmatrix} x \\ y \\ z \end{bmatrix}\right) = \begin{bmatrix} 4 & 1 & 3 \\ 2 & -1 & 3 \\ 2 & 2 & 0 \end{bmatrix} \begin{bmatrix} x \\ y \\ z \end{bmatrix}.$$

Find an equation relating a, b, and c so that we can always compute values of x, y, and z for which

$$f\left(\begin{bmatrix} x \\ y \\ z \end{bmatrix}\right) = \begin{bmatrix} a \\ b \\ c \end{bmatrix}.$$

23. Let $f: R^3 \rightarrow R^3$ be the matrix transformation defined by

$$f\left(\begin{bmatrix} x \\ y \\ z \end{bmatrix}\right) = \begin{bmatrix} 1 & 2 & 3 \\ -3 & -2 & -1 \\ -2 & 0 & 2 \end{bmatrix} \begin{bmatrix} x \\ y \\ z \end{bmatrix}.$$

Find an equation relating a, b, and c so that we can always compute values of x, y, and z for which

$$f\left(\begin{bmatrix} x \\ y \\ z \end{bmatrix}\right) = \begin{bmatrix} a \\ b \\ c \end{bmatrix}.$$

Exercises 24 and 25 are optional.

24. **(a)** Formulate the definitions of column echelon form and reduced column echelon form of a matrix.

(b) Prove that every $m \times n$ matrix is column equivalent to a matrix in column echelon form.

25. Prove that every $m \times n$ matrix is column equivalent to a unique matrix in reduced column echelon form.

26. Find an equation relating a, b, and c so that the linear system

$$\begin{aligned} x + 2y - 3z &= a \\ 2x + 3y + 3z &= b \\ 5x + 9y - 6z &= c \end{aligned}$$

is consistent for any values of a, b, and c that satisfy that equation.

27. Find an equation relating a, b, and c so that the linear system

$$\begin{aligned} 2x + 2y + 3z &= a \\ 3x - y + 5z &= b \\ x - 3y + 2z &= c \end{aligned}$$

is consistent for any values of a, b, and c that satisfy that equation.

28. Show that the homogeneous system

$$\begin{aligned} (a - r)x + \quad dy &= 0 \\ cx + (b - r)y &= 0 \end{aligned}$$

has a nontrivial solution if and only if r satisfies the equation $(a - r)(b - r) - cd = 0$.

29. Let $Ax = b$, $b \neq 0$, be a consistent linear system.

(a) Show that if x_p is a particular solution to the given nonhomogeneous system and x_h is a solution to the associated homogeneous system $Ax = 0$, then $x_p + x_h$ is a solution to the given system $Ax = b$.

(b) Show that every solution x to the nonhomogeneous linear system $Ax = b$ can be written as $x_p + x_h$, where x_p is a particular solution to the given nonhomogeneous system and x_h is a solution to the associated homogeneous system $Ax = 0$. [*Hint*: Let $x = x_p + (x - x_p)$.]

30. Determine the quadratic interpolant to each of the given data sets. Follow the procedure in Example 7.

(a) $\{(0, 2), (1, 5), (2, 14)\}$

(b) $\{(-1, 2), (3, 14), (0, -1)\}$

31. (*Calculus Required*) Construct a linear system of equations to determine a quadratic polynomial $p(x) = ax^2 + bx + c$ that satisfies the conditions $p(0) = f(0)$, $p'(0) = f'(0)$, and $p''(0) = f''(0)$, where $f(x) = e^{2x}$.

32. (*Calculus Required*) Construct a linear system of equations to determine a quadratic polynomial $p(x) = ax^2 + bx + c$ that satisfies the conditions $p(1) = f(1)$, $p'(1) = f'(1)$, and $p''(1) = f''(1)$, where $f(x) = xe^{x-1}$.

33. Determine the temperatures at the interior points T_i, $i = 1, 2, 3, 4$ for the plate shown in the figure. (See Example 8.)

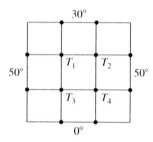

34. Determine the planar location (x, y) of a GPS receiver, using coordinates of the centers and radii for the three circles given in the following tables:

(a)

Circle	Center	Radius
1	$(-15, 20)$	25
2	$(5, -12)$	13
3	$(9, 40)$	41

(b)

Circle	Center	Radius
1	$(-10, 13)$	25
2	$(10, -19)$	13
3	$(14, 33)$	41

35. The location of a GPS receiver in a two-dimensional system is $(-4, 3)$. The data used in the calculation are given in the table, except that the radius of the first circle is missing. Determine the value of the missing piece of data.

Circle	Center	Radius
1	$(-16, 38)$	?
2	$(7, -57)$	61
3	$(32, 80)$	85

36. The location of a GPS receiver in a two-dimensional system is $(6, 8)$. The data used in the calculation are given in the table, except that the radii of circles 1 and 2 are missing. Determine the values of missing pieces of data.

Circle	Center	Radius
1	$(3, 4)$	?
2	$(10, 5)$	?
3	$(18, 3)$	13

37. Suppose you have a "special edition" GPS receiver for two-dimensional systems that contains three special buttons, labeled C1, C2, and C3. Each button when depressed draws a circle that corresponds to data received from one of three closest satellites. You depress button C1 and then C2. The image on your handheld unit shows a pair of circles that are tangent to each other. What is the location of the GPS receiver? Explain.

38. Rust is formed when there is a chemical reaction between iron and oxygen. The compound that is formed is the reddish brown scales that cover the iron object. Rust is iron oxide whose chemical formula is Fe_2O_3. So a chemical equation for rust is

$$Fe + O_2 \rightarrow Fe_2O_3.$$

Balance this equation.

39. Ethane is a gas similar to methane that burns in oxygen to give carbon dioxide gas and steam. The steam condenses to form water droplets. The chemical equation for this reaction is

$$C_2H_6 + O_2 \rightarrow CO_2 + H_2O.$$

Balance this equation.

In Exercises 40 and 41, solve each given linear system.

40.
$$(1 - i)x + (2 + 2i)y = 1$$
$$(1 + 2i)x + (-2 + 2i)y = i$$

41.
$$x + y = 3 - i$$
$$ix + y + z = 3$$
$$y + iz = 3$$

In Exercises 42 and 43, solve each linear system whose augmented matrix is given.

42. $\begin{bmatrix} 1 - i & 2 + 2i & | & i \\ 1 + i & -2 + 2i & | & -2 \end{bmatrix}$

43. $\begin{bmatrix} 1 & i & -i & | & -2 + 2i \\ 2i & -i & 2 & | & -2 \\ 1 & 2 & 3i & | & 2i \end{bmatrix}$

44. Determine whether the software you are using has a command for computing the reduced row echelon form of a matrix. If it does, experiment with that command on some of the previous exercises.

45. Determine whether the software you are using has a command for computing interpolation polynomials, given a set of ordered pairs. If it does, use the command to determine the quadratic interpolant for the data sets in Exercise 30.

46. Determine whether the software you are using has a graphing option as part of a command for computing interpolation polynomials, or if there is an easy way available to graph the interpolant. If it does, use it as follows:

   (a) Generate the graphs for the quadratic interpolants for the data sets in Exercise 30. Print out the graphs, and then mark the data points on the graph.

   (b) For the data set $\{(0, 0), (1, 1), (4, 2)\}$, generate the quadratic interpolant and graph it over the interval $[0, 4]$. Print out the graph and then mark the data points on the graph. This data set is a sample of the function $y = f(x) = \sqrt{x}$. Carefully sketch the graph of f on the printout, making sure it goes through the data points. Briefly discuss the error that would be incurred if you were to evaluate the interpolant at $x = 2$ and $x = 3$ to estimate $\sqrt{2}$ and $\sqrt{3}$, respectively.

Eigenvalues and Eigenvectors

7.1   Eigenvalues and Eigenvectors

■ Definitions and Examples

Let $L: V \to V$ be a linear transformation of an n-dimensional vector space V into itself (a linear operator on V). Then L maps a vector $\mathbf{v}$ in V to another vector $L(\mathbf{v})$ in V. A question that arises in a wide variety of applications is that of determining whether $L(\mathbf{v})$ can be a multiple of $\mathbf{v}$. If V is R^n or C^n, then this question becomes one of determining whether $L(\mathbf{v})$ can be parallel to $\mathbf{v}$. Note that if $\mathbf{v} = \mathbf{0}$, then $L(\mathbf{0}) = \mathbf{0}$, so $L(\mathbf{0})$ is a multiple of $\mathbf{0}$ and is then parallel to $\mathbf{0}$. Thus we need consider only nonzero vectors in V.

EXAMPLE 1

Let $L: R^2 \to R^2$ be a reflection with respect to the x-axis, defined by

$$L(\mathbf{v}) = L\left(\begin{bmatrix} x_1 \\ x_2 \end{bmatrix}\right) = \begin{bmatrix} x_1 \\ -x_2 \end{bmatrix},$$

which we considered in Example 4 of Section 1.6. See Figure 7.1. If we want

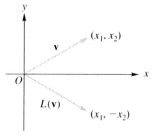

FIGURE 7.1

$L(\mathbf{v})$ to be parallel to a nonzero vector $\mathbf{v}$, we must have

$$L\left(\begin{bmatrix} x_1 \\ x_2 \end{bmatrix}\right) = \lambda \begin{bmatrix} x_1 \\ x_2 \end{bmatrix},$$

where λ is a scalar. Thus

$$\lambda \begin{bmatrix} x_1 \\ x_2 \end{bmatrix} = \begin{bmatrix} x_1 \\ -x_2 \end{bmatrix}$$

or

$$\lambda x_1 = x_1$$
$$\lambda x_2 = -x_2.$$

Since $\mathbf{v}$ is not the zero vector, both x_1 and x_2 cannot be zero. If $x_1 \neq 0$, then from the first equation it follows that $\lambda = 1$, and from the second equation we conclude that $x_2 = 0$. Thus $\mathbf{v} = \begin{bmatrix} r \\ 0 \end{bmatrix}$, $r \neq 0$, which represents any vector along the x-axis. If $x_2 \neq 0$, then from the second equation it follows that $\lambda = -1$, and from the first equation we have $x_1 = 0$. Thus $\mathbf{v} = \begin{bmatrix} 0 \\ s \end{bmatrix}$, $s \neq 0$, which represents any vector along the y-axis. Hence, for any vector $\mathbf{v}$ along the x-axis or along the y-axis, $L(\mathbf{v})$ will be parallel to $\mathbf{v}$. ■

EXAMPLE 2 Let $L: R^2 \to R^2$ be the linear operator defined by

$$L\left(\begin{bmatrix} x \\ y \end{bmatrix}\right) = \begin{bmatrix} \cos\phi & -\sin\phi \\ \sin\phi & \cos\phi \end{bmatrix} \begin{bmatrix} x \\ y \end{bmatrix},$$

a counterclockwise rotation through the angle ϕ, $0 \leq \phi < 2\pi$, as defined in Example 8 of Section 1.6. See Figure 7.2. It follows that if $\phi \neq 0$ and $\phi \neq \pi$, then for every vector $\mathbf{v} = \begin{bmatrix} x \\ y \end{bmatrix}$, $L(\mathbf{v})$ is oriented in a direction different from that of $\mathbf{v}$, so $L(\mathbf{v})$ and $\mathbf{v}$ are never parallel. If $\phi = 0$, then $L(\mathbf{v}) = \mathbf{v}$ (verify), which means that $L(\mathbf{v})$ and $\mathbf{v}$ are in the same direction and are thus parallel. If $\phi = \pi$, then $L(\mathbf{v}) = -\mathbf{v}$ (verify), so $L(\mathbf{v})$ and $\mathbf{v}$ are in opposite directions and are thus parallel. ■

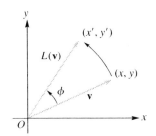

FIGURE 7.2

As we can see from Examples 1 and 2, the problem of determining all vectors $\mathbf{v}$ in an n-dimensional vector space V that are mapped by a given linear operator $L: V \to V$ to a multiple of $\mathbf{v}$ does not seem simple. We now formulate some terminology to study this important problem.

DEFINITION 7.1 Let $L: V \to V$ be a linear transformation of an n-dimensional vector space V into itself (a linear operator on V). The number λ is called an **eigenvalue** of L if there exists a *nonzero* vector $\mathbf{x}$ in V such that

$$L(\mathbf{x}) = \lambda\mathbf{x}. \tag{1}$$

Every nonzero vector $\mathbf{x}$ satisfying this equation is then called an **eigenvector** of L **associated with the eigenvalue** λ. The word *eigenvalue* is a hybrid (*eigen* in German means *proper*). Eigenvalues are also called **proper values**, **characteristic**

values, and **latent values**; and eigenvectors are also called **proper vectors**, and so on, accordingly.

Remark   In Definition 7.1, the number λ can be real or complex and the vector $\mathbf{x}$ can have real or complex components.

Note that if we do not require that $\mathbf{x}$ be nonzero in Definition 7.1, then *every* number λ would be an eigenvalue, since $L(\mathbf{0}) = \mathbf{0} = \lambda\mathbf{0}$. Such a definition would be of no interest. This is why we insist that $\mathbf{x}$ be nonzero.

EXAMPLE 3   Let $L: V \to V$ be the linear operator defined by $L(\mathbf{x}) = 2\mathbf{x}$. We can see that the only eigenvalue of L is $\lambda = 2$ and that every nonzero vector in V is an eigenvector of L associated with the eigenvalue $\lambda = 2$.   ∎

Example 3 shows that an eigenvalue λ can have associated with it many different eigenvectors. In fact, if $\mathbf{x}$ is an eigenvector of L associated with the eigenvalue λ [i.e., $L(\mathbf{x}) = \lambda\mathbf{x}$], then

$$L(r\mathbf{x}) = rL(\mathbf{x}) = r(\lambda\mathbf{x}) = \lambda(r\mathbf{x}),$$

for any real number r. Thus, if $r \neq 0$, then $r\mathbf{x}$ is also an eigenvector of L associated with λ so that eigenvectors are never unique.

EXAMPLE 4   Let $L: R^2 \to R^2$ be the linear operator defined by

$$L\left(\begin{bmatrix} a_1 \\ a_2 \end{bmatrix}\right) = \begin{bmatrix} -a_2 \\ a_1 \end{bmatrix}.$$

To find eigenvalues of L and associated eigenvectors, we proceed as follows: We need to find a number λ such that

$$L\left(\begin{bmatrix} a_1 \\ a_2 \end{bmatrix}\right) = \lambda\begin{bmatrix} a_1 \\ a_2 \end{bmatrix}.$$

Then

$$\begin{bmatrix} -a_2 \\ a_1 \end{bmatrix} = \lambda\begin{bmatrix} a_1 \\ a_2 \end{bmatrix},$$

so

$$-a_2 = \lambda a_1$$
$$a_1 = \lambda a_2,$$

so

$$-a_2 = \lambda^2 a_2.$$

If $a_2 \neq 0$, then $\lambda^2 = -1$. Hence

$$\lambda = i \quad \text{and} \quad \lambda = -i.$$

This means that there is no vector $\begin{bmatrix} a_1 \\ a_2 \end{bmatrix}$ in R^2 such that $L\left(\begin{bmatrix} a_1 \\ a_2 \end{bmatrix}\right)$ is parallel to $\begin{bmatrix} a_1 \\ a_2 \end{bmatrix}$. If we now consider L as defined previously to map C^2 into C^2, then L has the eigenvalue $\lambda = i$ with associated eigenvector $\begin{bmatrix} i \\ 1 \end{bmatrix}$ (verify), and the eigenvalue $\lambda = -i$ with associated eigenvector $\begin{bmatrix} -i \\ 1 \end{bmatrix}$ (verify). ■

EXAMPLE 5

Let $L: R^2 \rightarrow R^2$ be the linear operator defined by

$$L\left(\begin{bmatrix} a_1 \\ a_2 \end{bmatrix}\right) = \begin{bmatrix} a_2 \\ a_1 \end{bmatrix}.$$

It follows that

$$L\left(\begin{bmatrix} r \\ r \end{bmatrix}\right) = 1\begin{bmatrix} r \\ r \end{bmatrix} \quad \text{and} \quad L\left(\begin{bmatrix} r \\ -r \end{bmatrix}\right) = -1\begin{bmatrix} r \\ -r \end{bmatrix}.$$

Thus any vector of the form $\begin{bmatrix} r \\ r \end{bmatrix}$, where r is any nonzero real number—such as $\mathbf{x}_1 = \begin{bmatrix} 1 \\ 1 \end{bmatrix}$—is an eigenvector of L associated with the eigenvalue $\lambda = 1$; any vector of the form $\begin{bmatrix} r \\ -r \end{bmatrix}$, where r is any nonzero real number, such as $\mathbf{x}_2 = \begin{bmatrix} 1 \\ -1 \end{bmatrix}$, is an eigenvector of L associated with the eigenvalue $\lambda = -1$ (see Figure 7.3). ■

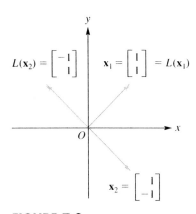

FIGURE 7.3

EXAMPLE 6

Let $L: R^2 \rightarrow R^2$ be counterclockwise rotation through the angle ϕ, $0 \leq \phi < 2\pi$, as defined in Example 2. It follows from our discussion in Example 2 that $\phi = 0$ and $\phi = \pi$ are the only angles for which L has eigenvalues. Thus, if $\phi = 0$, then $\lambda = 1$ is the only eigenvalue of L and every nonzero vector in R^2 is an eigenvector of L associated with the eigenvalue $\lambda = 1$. The geometric approach used in Example 2 shows that the linear operator L has no real eigenvalues and associated eigenvectors when $\phi = \pi/4$. Let us now proceed algebraically and consider the linear operator as defined in Example 2, but now mapping C^2 into C^2. In this case, we find that

$$\lambda = \frac{\sqrt{2}}{2} + \frac{\sqrt{2}}{2}i$$

is an eigenvalue of L with associated eigenvector $\begin{bmatrix} i \\ 1 \end{bmatrix}$ (verify) and

$$\lambda = \frac{\sqrt{2}}{2} - \frac{\sqrt{2}}{2}i$$

is an eigenvalue of L with associated eigenvector $\begin{bmatrix} i \\ -1 \end{bmatrix}$ (verify). ∎

EXAMPLE 7 Let $L: R_2 \to R_2$ be defined by $L\left(\begin{bmatrix} x_1 & x_2 \end{bmatrix}\right) = \begin{bmatrix} 0 & x_2 \end{bmatrix}$. We can then see that

$$L\left(\begin{bmatrix} r & 0 \end{bmatrix}\right) = \begin{bmatrix} 0 & 0 \end{bmatrix} = 0\begin{bmatrix} r & 0 \end{bmatrix},$$

so a vector of the form $\begin{bmatrix} r & 0 \end{bmatrix}$, where r is any nonzero real number (such as $\begin{bmatrix} 2 & 0 \end{bmatrix}$), is an eigenvector of L associated with the eigenvalue $\lambda = 0$. Also,

$$L\left(\begin{bmatrix} 0 & r \end{bmatrix}\right) = \begin{bmatrix} 0 & r \end{bmatrix} = 1\begin{bmatrix} 0 & r \end{bmatrix},$$

so a vector of the form $\begin{bmatrix} 0 & r \end{bmatrix}$, where r is any nonzero real number such as $\begin{bmatrix} 0 & 1 \end{bmatrix}$, is an eigenvector of L associated with the eigenvalue $\lambda = 1$. ∎

By definition, the zero vector cannot be an eigenvector. However, Example 7 shows that the scalar zero can be an eigenvalue.

EXAMPLE 8 (*Calculus Required*) Although we introduced this chapter with the requirement that V be an n-dimensional vector space, the notions of eigenvalues and eigenvectors can be considered for infinite-dimensional vector spaces. In this example we look at such a situation.

Let V be the vector space of all real-valued functions of a single variable that have derivatives of all orders. Let $L: V \to V$ be the linear operator defined by

$$L(f) = f'.$$

Then the problem presented in Definition 7.1 can be stated as follows: Can we find a number λ and a function $f \neq 0$ in V so that

$$L(f) = \lambda f? \tag{2}$$

If $y = f(x)$, then (2) can be written as

$$\frac{dy}{dx} = \lambda y. \tag{3}$$

Equation (3) states that the quantity y is one whose rate of change, with respect to x, is proportional to y itself. Examples of physical phenomena in which a quantity satisfies (3) include growth of human population, growth of bacteria and other organisms, investment problems, radioactive decay, carbon dating, and concentration of a drug in the body.

For each number λ (an eigenvalue of L) we obtain, by using calculus, an associated eigenvector given by

$$f(x) = Ke^{\lambda x},$$

where K is an arbitrary nonzero constant. ∎

Equation (3) is a simple example of a differential equation. The subject of differential equations is a major area in mathematics. In Section 8.4 we provide a brief introduction to homogeneous linear systems of differential equations.

Let L be a linear transformation of an n-dimensional vector space V into itself. If $S = \{\mathbf{x}_1, \mathbf{x}_2, \dots, \mathbf{x}_n\}$ is a basis for V, then there is an $n \times n$ matrix A that represents L with respect to S (see Section 6.3). To determine an eigenvalue λ of L and an eigenvector $\mathbf{x}$ of L associated with the eigenvalue λ, we solve the equation

$$L(\mathbf{x}) = \lambda \mathbf{x}.$$

Using Theorem 6.9, we see that an equivalent matrix equation is

$$A\left[\mathbf{x}\right]_S = \lambda \left[\mathbf{x}\right]_S.$$

This formulation allows us to use techniques for solving linear systems in R^n to determine eigenvalue–eigenvector pairs of L.

EXAMPLE 9

Let $L \colon P_2 \to P_2$ be a linear operator defined by

$$L(at^2 + bt + c) = -bt - 2c.$$

The eigen-problem for L can be formulated in terms of a matrix representing L with respect to a specific basis for P_2. Find the corresponding matrix eigen-problem for each of the bases $S = \{1 - t, 1 + t, t^2\}$ and $T = \{t - 1, 1, t^2\}$ for P_2.

Solution

To find the matrix A that represents L with respect to the basis S, we compute (verify)

$$L(1 - t) = t - 2 = -\tfrac{3}{2}(1 - t) - \tfrac{1}{2}(1 + t) + 0t^2, \qquad \text{so } \left[L(1 - t)\right]_S = \begin{bmatrix} -\tfrac{3}{2} \\ -\tfrac{1}{2} \\ 0 \end{bmatrix},$$

$$L(1 + t) = -t - 2 = -\tfrac{1}{2}(1 - t) - \tfrac{3}{2}(1 + t) + 0t^2, \quad \text{so } \left[L(1 + t)\right]_S = \begin{bmatrix} -\tfrac{1}{2} \\ -\tfrac{3}{2} \\ 0 \end{bmatrix},$$

$$L(t^2) = 0 = 0(1 - t) + 0(1 + t) + 0t^2, \qquad\qquad \text{so } \left[L(t^2)\right]_S = \begin{bmatrix} 0 \\ 0 \\ 0 \end{bmatrix}.$$

Then

$$A = \begin{bmatrix} -\frac{3}{2} & -\frac{1}{2} & 0 \\ -\frac{1}{2} & -\frac{3}{2} & 0 \\ 0 & 0 & 0 \end{bmatrix},$$

and the matrix eigen-problem for L with respect to S is that of finding a number λ and a nonzero vector $\mathbf{x}$ in R^3 or C^3 so that

$$A\mathbf{x} = \lambda\mathbf{x}.$$

In a similar fashion we can show that the matrix B which represents L with respect to the basis T is

$$B = \begin{bmatrix} -1 & 0 & 0 \\ 1 & -2 & 0 \\ 0 & 0 & 0 \end{bmatrix}$$

(verify), and the corresponding matrix eigen-problem for L with respect to T is

$$B\mathbf{x} = \lambda\mathbf{x}.$$

Thus the matrix eigen-problem for L depends on the basis selected for V. We show in Section 7.2 that the eigenvalues of L will not depend on the matrix representing L. ■

As we have seen in Example 9, the eigen-problem for a linear transformation can be expressed in terms of a matrix representing L. We now formulate the notions of eigenvalue and eigenvector for *any* square matrix. If A is an $n \times n$ matrix, we can consider, as in Section 6.1, the linear operator $L: R^n \to R^n$ ($C^n \to C^n$) defined by $L(\mathbf{x}) = A\mathbf{x}$ for $\mathbf{x}$ in R^n (C^n). If λ is a scalar (real or complex), and $\mathbf{x} \neq \mathbf{0}$ a vector in R^n (C^n) such that

$$A\mathbf{x} = \lambda\mathbf{x}, \tag{4}$$

then we say that λ is an **eigenvalue** of A and $\mathbf{x}$ is an **eigenvector** of A **associated with λ**. That is, λ is an eigenvalue of L and $\mathbf{x}$ is an eigenvector of L associated with λ.

Remark Although we began this chapter with the problem of finding the eigenvalues and associated eigenvectors of a linear operator, from now on we emphasize the problem of finding the eigenvalues and associated eigenvectors of an $n \times n$ matrix.

■ Computing Eigenvalues and Eigenvectors

Thus far we have found the eigenvalues and associated eigenvectors of a given linear transformation by inspection, geometric arguments, or very simple algebraic approaches. In the following example, we compute the eigenvalues and associated eigenvectors of a matrix by a somewhat more systematic method.

EXAMPLE 10

Let $A = \begin{bmatrix} 1 & 1 \\ -2 & 4 \end{bmatrix}$. We wish to find the eigenvalues of A and their associated eigenvectors. Thus we wish to find all numbers λ and all nonzero vectors $\mathbf{x} = \begin{bmatrix} x_1 \\ x_2 \end{bmatrix}$ that satisfy Equation (4):

$$\begin{bmatrix} 1 & 1 \\ -2 & 4 \end{bmatrix} \begin{bmatrix} x_1 \\ x_2 \end{bmatrix} = \lambda \begin{bmatrix} x_1 \\ x_2 \end{bmatrix}, \tag{5a}$$

which yields

$$\begin{array}{ccc} x_1 + x_2 = \lambda x_1 & & (\lambda - 1)x_1 - x_2 = 0 \\ -2x_1 + 4x_2 = \lambda x_2 & \text{or} & 2x_1 + (\lambda - 4)x_2 = 0. \end{array} \tag{5b}$$

This homogeneous system of two equations in two unknowns has a nontrivial solution if and only if the determinant of the coefficient matrix is zero. Thus

$$\begin{vmatrix} \lambda - 1 & -1 \\ 2 & \lambda - 4 \end{vmatrix} = 0.$$

This means that

$$\lambda^2 - 5\lambda + 6 = 0 = (\lambda - 3)(\lambda - 2),$$

and so $\lambda_1 = 2$ and $\lambda_2 = 3$ are the eigenvalues of A. That is, Equation (5b) will have a nontrivial solution only when $\lambda_1 = 2$ or $\lambda_2 = 3$. To find all eigenvectors of A associated with $\lambda_1 = 2$, we substitute $\lambda_1 = 2$ in Equation (5a):

$$\begin{bmatrix} 1 & 1 \\ -2 & 4 \end{bmatrix} \begin{bmatrix} x_1 \\ x_2 \end{bmatrix} = 2 \begin{bmatrix} x_1 \\ x_2 \end{bmatrix},$$

which yields

$$\begin{array}{ccc} x_1 + x_2 = 2x_1 & & (2 - 1)x_1 - x_2 = 0 \\ -2x_1 + 4x_2 = 2x_2 & \text{or} & 2x_1 + (2 - 4)x_2 = 0 \end{array}$$

$$\text{or} \quad \begin{array}{c} x_1 - x_2 = 0 \\ 2x_1 - 2x_2 = 0. \end{array}$$

Note that we could have obtained this last homogeneous system by merely substituting $\lambda_1 = 2$ in (5b). All solutions to this last system are given by

$$x_1 = x_2$$
$$x_2 = \text{any number } r.$$

Hence all eigenvectors associated with the eigenvalue $\lambda_1 = 2$ are given by $\begin{bmatrix} r \\ r \end{bmatrix}$, where r is any nonzero number. In particular, for $r = 1$, $\mathbf{x}_1 = \begin{bmatrix} 1 \\ 1 \end{bmatrix}$ is an eigenvector associated with $\lambda_1 = 2$. Similarly, substituting $\lambda_2 = 3$ in Equation (5b), we obtain

$$\begin{array}{ccc} (3 - 1)x_1 - x_2 = 0 & & 2x_1 - x_2 = 0 \\ 2x_1 + (3 - 4)x_2 = 0 & \text{or} & 2x_1 - x_2 = 0. \end{array}$$

All solutions to this last homogeneous system are given by

$$x_1 = \tfrac{1}{2}x_2$$
$$x_2 = \text{any number } s.$$

Hence all eigenvectors associated with the eigenvalue $\lambda_2 = 3$ are given by $\begin{bmatrix} \frac{s}{2} \\ s \end{bmatrix}$, where s is any nonzero number. In particular, for $s = 2$, $\mathbf{x}_2 = \begin{bmatrix} 1 \\ 2 \end{bmatrix}$ is an eigenvector associated with the eigenvalue $\lambda_2 = 3$. ∎

We now use the method followed in Example 10 as our standard for finding the eigenvalues and associated eigenvectors of a given matrix. We first state some terminology.

DEFINITION 7.2

Let $A = \begin{bmatrix} a_{11} & a_{12} & \cdots & a_{1n} \\ a_{21} & a_{22} & \cdots & a_{2n} \\ \vdots & \vdots & & \vdots \\ a_{n1} & a_{n2} & \cdots & a_{nn} \end{bmatrix}$ be an $n \times n$ matrix. Then the determinant of the matrix

$$\lambda I_n - A = \begin{bmatrix} \lambda - a_{11} & -a_{12} & \cdots & -a_{1n} \\ -a_{21} & \lambda - a_{22} & \cdots & -a_{2n} \\ \vdots & \vdots & & \vdots \\ -a_{n1} & -a_{n2} & \cdots & \lambda - a_{nn} \end{bmatrix}$$

is called the **characteristic polynomial** of A. The equation

$$p(\lambda) = \det(\lambda I_n - A) = 0$$

is called the **characteristic equation** of A.

Recall from Chapter 3 that each term in the expansion of the determinant of an $n \times n$ matrix is a product of n entries of the matrix, containing exactly one entry from each row and exactly one entry from each column. Thus, if we expand $\det(\lambda I_n - A)$, we obtain a polynomial of degree n. The expression involving λ^n in the characteristic polynomial of A comes from the product

$$(\lambda - a_{11})(\lambda - a_{22}) \cdots (\lambda - a_{nn}),$$

and so the coefficient of λ^n is 1. We can then write

$$\det(\lambda I_n - A) = p(\lambda) = \lambda^n + a_1 \lambda^{n-1} + a_2 \lambda^{n-2} + \cdots + a_{n-1}\lambda + a_n.$$

Note that if we let $\lambda = 0$ in $\det(\lambda I_n - A)$, as well as in the expression on the right, then we get $\det(-A) = a_n$, and thus the constant term of the characteristic polynomial of A is $a_n = (-1)^n \det(A)$.

EXAMPLE 11

Let $A = \begin{bmatrix} 1 & 2 & -1 \\ 1 & 0 & 1 \\ 4 & -4 & 5 \end{bmatrix}$. The characteristic polynomial of A is

$$p(\lambda) = \det(\lambda I_3 - A) = \begin{vmatrix} \lambda - 1 & -2 & 1 \\ -1 & \lambda & -1 \\ -4 & 4 & \lambda - 5 \end{vmatrix} = \lambda^3 - 6\lambda^2 + 11\lambda - 6$$

(verify). ∎

We now connect the characteristic polynomial of a matrix with its eigenvalues in the following theorem:

Theorem 7.1

Let A be an $n \times n$ matrix. The eigenvalues of A are the roots of the characteristic polynomial of A.

Proof

Let $\mathbf{x}$ in R^n be an eigenvector of A associated with the eigenvalue λ. Then

$$A\mathbf{x} = \lambda\mathbf{x} \quad \text{or} \quad A\mathbf{x} = (\lambda I_n)\mathbf{x} \quad \text{or} \quad (\lambda I_n - A)\mathbf{x} = \mathbf{0}.$$

This is a homogeneous system of n equations in n unknowns; a nontrivial solution exists if and only if $\det(\lambda I_n - A) = 0$. Hence λ is a root of the characteristic polynomial of A.

Conversely, if λ is a root of the characteristic polynomial of A, then $\det(\lambda I_n - A) = 0$, so the homogeneous system $(\lambda I_n - A)\mathbf{x} = \mathbf{0}$ has a nontrivial solution. Hence λ is an eigenvalue of A.

Thus, to find the eigenvalues of a given matrix A, we must find the roots of its characteristic polynomial $p(\lambda)$. There are many methods for finding approximations to the roots of a polynomial, some of them more effective than others. Two results that are sometimes useful in this connection are as follows: (1) The product of all the roots of the polynomial

$$p(\lambda) = \lambda^n + a_1\lambda^{n-1} + \cdots + a_{n-1}\lambda + a_n$$

is $(-1)^n a_n$; and (2) If $a_1, a_2, \ldots, a_n$ are integers, then $p(\lambda)$ cannot have a rational root that is not already an integer. Thus we need to try only the integer factors of a_n as possible rational roots of $p(\lambda)$. Of course, $p(\lambda)$ might well have irrational roots or complex roots.

To minimize the computational effort, and as a convenience to the reader, *most of the characteristic polynomials to be solved in the rest of this chapter have only integer roots*, and each of these roots is a factor of the constant term of the characteristic polynomial of A. The corresponding eigenvectors are obtained by substituting for λ in the matrix equation

$$(\lambda I_n - A)\mathbf{x} = \mathbf{0} \tag{6}$$

and solving the resulting homogeneous system. The solution to these types of problems has been studied in Section 4.7.

EXAMPLE 12 Compute the eigenvalues and associated eigenvectors of the matrix A defined in Example 11.

Solution

In Example 11 we found the characteristic polynomial of A to be

$$p(\lambda) = \lambda^3 - 6\lambda^2 + 11\lambda - 6.$$

The possible integer roots of $p(\lambda)$ are $\pm 1, \pm 2, \pm 3$, and ± 6. By substituting these values in $p(\lambda)$, we find that $p(1) = 0$, so $\lambda = 1$ is a root of $p(\lambda)$. Hence $(\lambda - 1)$ is a factor of $p(\lambda)$. Dividing $p(\lambda)$ by $(\lambda - 1)$, we obtain

$$p(\lambda) = (\lambda - 1)(\lambda^2 - 5\lambda + 6) \quad \text{(verify)}.$$

Factoring $\lambda^2 - 5\lambda + 6$, we have

$$p(\lambda) = (\lambda - 1)(\lambda - 2)(\lambda - 3).$$

The eigenvalues of A are then $\lambda_1 = 1$, $\lambda_2 = 2$, and $\lambda_3 = 3$. To find an eigenvector $\mathbf{x}_1$ associated with $\lambda_1 = 1$, we substitute $\lambda = 1$ in (6) to get

$$\begin{bmatrix} 1-1 & -2 & 1 \\ -1 & 1 & -1 \\ -4 & 4 & 1-5 \end{bmatrix} \begin{bmatrix} x_1 \\ x_2 \\ x_3 \end{bmatrix} = \begin{bmatrix} 0 \\ 0 \\ 0 \end{bmatrix}$$

or

$$\begin{bmatrix} 0 & -2 & 1 \\ -1 & 1 & -1 \\ -4 & 4 & -4 \end{bmatrix} \begin{bmatrix} x_1 \\ x_2 \\ x_3 \end{bmatrix} = \begin{bmatrix} 0 \\ 0 \\ 0 \end{bmatrix}.$$

The vector $\begin{bmatrix} -\frac{r}{2} \\ \frac{r}{2} \\ r \end{bmatrix}$ is a solution for any number r. Thus

$$\mathbf{x}_1 = \begin{bmatrix} -1 \\ 1 \\ 2 \end{bmatrix}$$

is an eigenvector of A associated with $\lambda_1 = 1$ (r was taken as 2).

To find an eigenvector $\mathbf{x}_2$ associated with $\lambda_2 = 2$, we substitute $\lambda = 2$ in (6), obtaining

$$\begin{bmatrix} 2-1 & -2 & 1 \\ -1 & 2 & -1 \\ -4 & 4 & 2-5 \end{bmatrix} \begin{bmatrix} x_1 \\ x_2 \\ x_3 \end{bmatrix} = \begin{bmatrix} 0 \\ 0 \\ 0 \end{bmatrix}$$

or

$$\begin{bmatrix} 1 & -2 & 1 \\ -1 & 2 & -1 \\ -4 & 4 & -3 \end{bmatrix} \begin{bmatrix} x_1 \\ x_2 \\ x_3 \end{bmatrix} = \begin{bmatrix} 0 \\ 0 \\ 0 \end{bmatrix}.$$

The vector $\begin{bmatrix} -\frac{r}{2} \\ \frac{r}{4} \\ r \end{bmatrix}$ is a solution for any number r. Thus $\mathbf{x}_2 = \begin{bmatrix} -2 \\ 1 \\ 4 \end{bmatrix}$ is an

eigenvector of A associated with $\lambda_2 = 2$ (r was taken as 4).

To find an eigenvector $\mathbf{x}_3$ associated with $\lambda_3 = 3$, we substitute $\lambda = 3$ in (6), obtaining

$$\begin{bmatrix} 3-1 & -2 & 1 \\ -1 & 3 & -1 \\ -4 & 4 & 3-5 \end{bmatrix} \begin{bmatrix} x_1 \\ x_2 \\ x_3 \end{bmatrix} = \begin{bmatrix} 0 \\ 0 \\ 0 \end{bmatrix}$$

or

$$\begin{bmatrix} 2 & -2 & 1 \\ -1 & 3 & -1 \\ -4 & 4 & -2 \end{bmatrix} \begin{bmatrix} x_1 \\ x_2 \\ x_3 \end{bmatrix} = \begin{bmatrix} 0 \\ 0 \\ 0 \end{bmatrix}.$$

The vector $\begin{bmatrix} -\frac{r}{4} \\ \frac{r}{4} \\ r \end{bmatrix}$ is a solution for any number r. Thus

$$\mathbf{x}_3 = \begin{bmatrix} -1 \\ 1 \\ 4 \end{bmatrix}$$

is an eigenvector of A associated with $\lambda_3 = 3$ (r was taken as 4).   ■

EXAMPLE 13

Compute the eigenvalues and associated eigenvectors of

$$A = \begin{bmatrix} 0 & 0 & 3 \\ 1 & 0 & -1 \\ 0 & 1 & 3 \end{bmatrix}.$$

Solution

The characteristic polynomial of A is

$$p(\lambda) = \det(\lambda I_3 - A) = \begin{vmatrix} \lambda - 0 & 0 & -3 \\ -1 & \lambda - 0 & 1 \\ 0 & -1 & \lambda - 3 \end{vmatrix} = \lambda^3 - 3\lambda^2 + \lambda - 3$$

(verify). We find that $\lambda = 3$ is a root of $p(\lambda)$. Dividing $p(\lambda)$ by $(\lambda - 3)$, we get $p(\lambda) = (\lambda - 3)(\lambda^2 + 1)$. The eigenvalues of A are then

$$\lambda_1 = 3, \quad \lambda_2 = i, \quad \lambda_3 = -i.$$

To compute an eigenvector $\mathbf{x}_1$ associated with $\lambda_1 = 3$, we substitute $\lambda = 3$ in (6), obtaining

$$\begin{bmatrix} 3-0 & 0 & -3 \\ -1 & 3-0 & 1 \\ 0 & -1 & 3-3 \end{bmatrix} \begin{bmatrix} x_1 \\ x_2 \\ x_3 \end{bmatrix} = \begin{bmatrix} 0 \\ 0 \\ 0 \end{bmatrix}.$$

We find that the vector $\begin{bmatrix} r \\ 0 \\ r \end{bmatrix}$ is a solution for any number r (verify). Letting $r = 1$, we conclude that

$$\mathbf{x}_1 = \begin{bmatrix} 1 \\ 0 \\ 1 \end{bmatrix}$$

is an eigenvector of A associated with $\lambda_1 = 3$. To obtain an eigenvector $\mathbf{x}_2$ associated with $\lambda_2 = i$, we substitute $\lambda = i$ in (6), which yields

$$\begin{bmatrix} i - 0 & 0 & -3 \\ -1 & i - 0 & 1 \\ 0 & -1 & i - 3 \end{bmatrix} \begin{bmatrix} x_1 \\ x_2 \\ x_3 \end{bmatrix} = \begin{bmatrix} 0 \\ 0 \\ 0 \end{bmatrix}.$$

We find that the vector $\begin{bmatrix} (-3i)r \\ (-3 + i)r \\ r \end{bmatrix}$ is a solution for any number r (verify). Letting $r = 1$, we conclude that

$$\mathbf{x}_2 = \begin{bmatrix} -3i \\ -3 + i \\ 1 \end{bmatrix}$$

is an eigenvector of A associated with $\lambda_2 = i$. Similarly, we find that

$$\mathbf{x}_3 = \begin{bmatrix} 3i \\ -3 - i \\ 1 \end{bmatrix}$$

is an eigenvector of A associated with $\lambda_3 = -i$. ∎

EXAMPLE 14 Let L be the linear operator on P_2 defined in Example 9. Using the matrix B obtained there representing L with respect to the basis $\{t - 1, 1, t^2\}$ for P_2, find the eigenvalues and associated eigenvectors of L.

Solution

The characteristic polynomial of

$$B = \begin{bmatrix} -1 & 0 & 0 \\ 1 & -2 & 0 \\ 0 & 0 & 0 \end{bmatrix}$$

is $p(\lambda) = \lambda(\lambda + 2)(\lambda + 1)$ (verify), so the eigenvalues of L are $\lambda_1 = 0$, $\lambda_2 = -2$, and $\lambda_3 = -1$. Associated eigenvectors are (verify)

$$\mathbf{x}_1 = \begin{bmatrix} 0 \\ 0 \\ 1 \end{bmatrix}, \quad \mathbf{x}_2 = \begin{bmatrix} 1 \\ 1 \\ 0 \end{bmatrix}, \quad \mathbf{x}_3 = \begin{bmatrix} 0 \\ 1 \\ 0 \end{bmatrix}.$$

These are the coordinate vectors of the eigenvectors of L, so the corresponding eigenvectors of L are

$$0(t - 1) + 0(1) + 1(t^2) = t^2$$
$$1(t - 1) + 1(1) + 0(t^2) = t$$

and

$$0(t - 1) + 1(1) + 0(t^2) = 1,$$

respectively. ∎

The procedure for finding the eigenvalues and associated eigenvectors of a matrix is as follows:

Step 1. Determine the roots of the characteristic polynomial

$$p(\lambda) = \det(\lambda I_n - A).$$

These are the eigenvalues of A.

Step 2. For each eigenvalue λ, find all the nontrivial solutions to the homogeneous system $(\lambda I_n - A)\mathbf{x} = \mathbf{0}$. These are the eigenvectors of A associated with the eigenvalue λ.

The characteristic polynomial of a matrix may have some complex roots, and it may, as seen in Example 13, even have no real roots. However, in the important case of symmetric matrices, all the roots of the characteristic polynomial are real. We prove this in Section 7.3 (Theorem 7.6).

Eigenvalues and eigenvectors satisfy many important and interesting properties. For example, if A is an upper (lower) triangular matrix, then the eigenvalues of A are the elements on the main diagonal of A (Exercise 11). Other properties are developed in the exercises for this section.

It must be pointed out that the method for finding the eigenvalues of a linear transformation or matrix by obtaining the real roots of the characteristic polynomial is not practical for $n > 4$, since it involves evaluating a determinant. Efficient numerical methods for finding eigenvalues and associated eigenvectors are studied in numerical analysis courses.

Warning When finding the eigenvalues and associated eigenvectors of a matrix A, do not make the common mistake of first transforming A to reduced row echelon form B and then finding the eigenvalues and eigenvectors of B. To see quickly how this approach fails, consider the matrix A defined in Example 10. Its eigenvalues are $\lambda_1 = 2$ and $\lambda_2 = 3$. Since A is a nonsingular matrix, when we transform it to reduced row echelon form B, we have $B = I_2$. The eigenvalues of I_2 are $\lambda_1 = 1$ and $\lambda_2 = 1$.

Key Terms

Eigenvalue	Characteristic value	Characteristic equation
Eigenvector	Latent value	Roots of the characteristic polynomial
Proper value	Characteristic polynomial	

Exercises

1. Let $L: R^2 \to R^2$ be counterclockwise rotation through an angle π. Find the eigenvalues and associated eigenvectors of L.

2. Let $L: P_1 \to P_1$ be the linear operator defined by $L(at + b) = bt + a$. Using the matrix representing L with respect to the basis $\{1, t\}$ for P_1, find the eigenvalues and associated eigenvectors of L.

3. Let $L: P_2 \to P_2$ be the linear operator defined by

$$L(at^2 + bt + c) = c - at^2.$$

Using the matrix representing L with respect to the basis $\{t^2 + 1, t, 1\}$ for P_2, find the eigenvalues and associated eigenvectors of L.

4. Let $L: R_3 \to R_3$ be defined by

$$L\left(\begin{bmatrix} a_1 & a_2 & a_3 \end{bmatrix}\right) = \begin{bmatrix} 2a_1 + 3a_2 & -a_2 + 4a_3 & 3a_3 \end{bmatrix}.$$

Using the natural basis for R_3, find the eigenvalues and associated eigenvectors of L.

5. Find the characteristic polynomial of each of the following matrices:

(a) $\begin{bmatrix} 2 & 1 \\ -1 & 3 \end{bmatrix}$ (b) $\begin{bmatrix} 1 & 2 & 1 \\ 0 & 1 & 2 \\ -1 & 3 & 2 \end{bmatrix}$

(c) $\begin{bmatrix} 4 & -1 & 3 \\ 0 & 2 & 1 \\ 0 & 0 & 3 \end{bmatrix}$ (d) $\begin{bmatrix} 4 & 2 \\ 3 & 3 \end{bmatrix}$

6. Find the characteristic polynomial, the eigenvalues, and associated eigenvectors of each of the following matrices:

(a) $\begin{bmatrix} 1 & 1 \\ 1 & 1 \end{bmatrix}$ (b) $\begin{bmatrix} 1 & 0 & 0 \\ -1 & 3 & 0 \\ 3 & 2 & -2 \end{bmatrix}$

(c) $\begin{bmatrix} 0 & 1 & 2 \\ 0 & 0 & 3 \\ 0 & 0 & 0 \end{bmatrix}$ (d) $\begin{bmatrix} 2 & 1 & 2 \\ 2 & 2 & -2 \\ 3 & 1 & 1 \end{bmatrix}$

7. Find the characteristic polynomial, the eigenvalues, and associated eigenvectors of each of the following matrices:

(a) $\begin{bmatrix} 1 & -1 \\ 2 & 4 \end{bmatrix}$ (b) $\begin{bmatrix} 2 & -2 & 3 \\ 0 & 3 & -2 \\ 0 & -1 & 2 \end{bmatrix}$

(c) $\begin{bmatrix} 2 & 2 & 3 \\ 1 & 2 & 1 \\ 2 & -2 & 1 \end{bmatrix}$ (d) $\begin{bmatrix} -2 & -2 & 3 \\ 0 & 3 & -2 \\ 0 & -1 & 2 \end{bmatrix}$

8. Find all the eigenvalues and associated eigenvectors of each of the following matrices:

(a) $\begin{bmatrix} 1 & 4 \\ 1 & -2 \end{bmatrix}$ (b) $\begin{bmatrix} 0 & -9 \\ 1 & 0 \end{bmatrix}$

(c) $\begin{bmatrix} 4 & 2 & -4 \\ 1 & 5 & -4 \\ 0 & 0 & 6 \end{bmatrix}$ (d) $\begin{bmatrix} 0 & -1 & 0 \\ 1 & 0 & 0 \\ 0 & 1 & 0 \end{bmatrix}$

9. Find the characteristic polynomial, the eigenvalues, and associated eigenvectors of each of the following matrices:

(a) $\begin{bmatrix} 0 & 1 \\ -1 & 0 \end{bmatrix}$ (b) $\begin{bmatrix} -2 & -4 & -8 \\ 1 & 0 & 0 \\ 0 & 1 & 0 \end{bmatrix}$

(c) $\begin{bmatrix} 2-i & 2i & 0 \\ 1 & 0 & 0 \\ 0 & 1 & 0 \end{bmatrix}$ (d) $\begin{bmatrix} 5 & 2 \\ -1 & 3 \end{bmatrix}$

10. Find all the eigenvalues and associated eigenvectors of each of the following matrices:

(a) $\begin{bmatrix} -1 & -1+i \\ 1 & 0 \end{bmatrix}$ (b) $\begin{bmatrix} i & 1 & 0 \\ 1 & i & 0 \\ 0 & 0 & 1 \end{bmatrix}$

(c) $\begin{bmatrix} 0 & -1 & 0 \\ 1 & 0 & 0 \\ 0 & 1 & 0 \end{bmatrix}$ (d) $\begin{bmatrix} 0 & 0 & -9 \\ 0 & 1 & 0 \\ 1 & 0 & 0 \end{bmatrix}$

11. Prove that if A is an upper (lower) triangular matrix, then the eigenvalues of A are the elements on the main diagonal of A.

12. Prove that A and A^T have the same eigenvalues. What, if anything, can we say about the associated eigenvectors of A and A^T?

13. Let

$$A = \begin{bmatrix} 1 & 2 & 3 & 4 \\ 0 & -1 & 3 & 2 \\ 0 & 0 & 3 & 3 \\ 0 & 0 & 0 & 2 \end{bmatrix}$$

represent the linear transformation $L: M_{22} \to M_{22}$ with respect to the basis

$$S = \left\{ \begin{bmatrix} 1 & 0 \\ 0 & 0 \end{bmatrix}, \begin{bmatrix} 0 & 1 \\ 0 & 0 \end{bmatrix}, \begin{bmatrix} 0 & 0 \\ 1 & 0 \end{bmatrix}, \begin{bmatrix} 0 & 0 \\ 0 & 1 \end{bmatrix} \right\}.$$

Find the eigenvalues and associated eigenvectors of L.

14. Let $L: V \to V$ be a linear operator, where V is an n-dimensional vector space. Let λ be an eigenvalue of L.

Prove that the subset of V consisting of $\mathbf{0}_V$ and all eigenvectors of L associated with λ is a subspace of V. This subspace is called the **eigenspace** associated with λ.

15. Let λ be an eigenvalue of the $n \times n$ matrix A. Prove that the subset of R^n (C^n) consisting of the zero vector and all eigenvectors of A associated with λ is a subspace of R^n (C^n). This subspace is called the **eigenspace** associated with λ. (This result is a corollary to the result in Exercise 14.)

16. In Exercises 14 and 15, why do we have to include $\mathbf{0}_V$ in the set of all eigenvectors associated with λ?

In Exercises 17 and 18, find a basis for the eigenspace (see Exercise 15) associated with λ for each given matrix.

17. (a) $\begin{bmatrix} 0 & 0 & 1 \\ 0 & 1 & 0 \\ 1 & 0 & 0 \end{bmatrix}, \lambda = 1$

(b) $\begin{bmatrix} 2 & 1 & 0 \\ 1 & 2 & 1 \\ 0 & 1 & 2 \end{bmatrix}, \lambda = 2$

18. (a) $\begin{bmatrix} 3 & 0 & 0 \\ -2 & 3 & -2 \\ 2 & 0 & 5 \end{bmatrix}, \lambda = 3$

(b) $\begin{bmatrix} 4 & 2 & 0 & 0 \\ 3 & 3 & 0 & 0 \\ 0 & 0 & 2 & 5 \\ 0 & 0 & 0 & 2 \end{bmatrix}, \lambda = 2$

19. Let $A = \begin{bmatrix} 0 & -4 & 0 \\ 1 & 0 & 0 \\ 0 & 1 & 0 \end{bmatrix}$.

(a) Find a basis for the eigenspace associated with the eigenvalue $\lambda_1 = 2i$.

(b) Find a basis for the eigenspace associated with the eigenvalue $\lambda_2 = -2i$.

20. Let $A = \begin{bmatrix} 2 & 2 & 3 & 4 \\ 0 & 2 & 3 & 2 \\ 0 & 0 & 1 & 1 \\ 0 & 0 & 0 & 1 \end{bmatrix}$.

(a) Find a basis for the eigenspace associated with the eigenvalue $\lambda_1 = 1$.

(b) Find a basis for the eigenspace associated with the eigenvalue $\lambda_2 = 2$.

21. Prove that if λ is an eigenvalue of a matrix A with associated eigenvector $\mathbf{x}$, and k is a positive integer, then λ^k

is an eigenvalue of the matrix

$$A^k = A \cdot A \cdot \cdots \cdot A \quad (k \text{ factors})$$

with associated eigenvector $\mathbf{x}$.

22. Let

$$A = \begin{bmatrix} 1 & 4 \\ 1 & -2 \end{bmatrix}$$

be the matrix of Exercise 8(a). Find the eigenvalues and eigenvectors of A^2 and verify Exercise 21.

23. Prove that if $A^k = O$ for some positive integer k [i.e., if A is a nilpotent matrix (see Supplementary Exercise 22 in Chapter 1)], then 0 is the only eigenvalue of A. (*Hint:* Use Exercise 21.)

24. Let A be an $n \times n$ matrix.

(a) Show that $\det(A)$ is the product of all the roots of the characteristic polynomial of A.

(b) Show that A is singular if and only if 0 is an eigenvalue of A.

(c) Also prove the analogous statement for a linear transformation: If $L: V \to V$ is a linear transformation, show that L is not one-to-one if and only if 0 is an eigenvalue of L.

(d) Show that if A is nilpotent (see Supplementary Exercise 22 in Chapter 1), then A is singular.

25. Let $L: V \to V$ be an invertible linear operator and let λ be an eigenvalue of L with associated eigenvector $\mathbf{x}$.

(a) Show that $1/\lambda$ is an eigenvalue of L^{-1} with associated eigenvector $\mathbf{x}$.

(b) State and prove the analogous statement for matrices.

26. Let A be an $n \times n$ matrix with eigenvalues λ_1 and λ_2, where $\lambda_1 \neq \lambda_2$. Let S_1 and S_2 be the eigenspaces associated with λ_1 and λ_2, respectively. Explain why the zero vector is the only vector that is in both S_1 and S_2.

27. Let λ be an eigenvalue of A with associated eigenvector $\mathbf{x}$. Show that $\lambda + r$ is an eigenvalue of $A + rI_n$ with associated eigenvector $\mathbf{x}$. Thus, adding a scalar multiple of the identity matrix to A merely shifts the eigenvalues by the scalar multiple.

28. Let A be an $n \times n$ matrix and consider the linear operator on R^n defined by $L(\mathbf{u}) = A\mathbf{u}$, for $\mathbf{u}$ in R^n. A subspace W of R^n is called **invariant** under L if for any $\mathbf{w}$ in W, $L(\mathbf{w})$ is also in W. Show that an eigenspace of A is invariant under L.

29. Let A and B be $n \times n$ matrices such that $A\mathbf{x} = \lambda\mathbf{x}$ and $B\mathbf{x} = \mu\mathbf{x}$. Show that

(a) $(A + B)\mathbf{x} = (\lambda + \mu)\mathbf{x}$;

(b) $(AB)\mathbf{x} = (\lambda\mu)\mathbf{x}$.

30. The **Cayley*–Hamilton†** **theorem** states that a matrix satisfies its characteristic equation; that is, if A is an $n \times n$ matrix with characteristic polynomial

$$p(\lambda) = \lambda^n + a_1\lambda^{n-1} + \cdots + a_{n-1}\lambda + a_n,$$

then

$$A^n + a_1 A^{n-1} + \cdots + a_{n-1}A + a_n I_n = O.$$

The proof and applications of this result, unfortunately, lie beyond the scope of this book. Verify the Cayley–Hamilton theorem for the following matrices:

(a) $\begin{bmatrix} 1 & 2 & 3 \\ 2 & -1 & 5 \\ 3 & 2 & 1 \end{bmatrix}$ **(b)** $\begin{bmatrix} 1 & 2 & 3 \\ 0 & 2 & 2 \\ 0 & 0 & -3 \end{bmatrix}$

(c) $\begin{bmatrix} 3 & 3 \\ 2 & 4 \end{bmatrix}$

31. Let A be an $n \times n$ matrix whose characteristic polynomial is

$$p(\lambda) = \lambda^n + a_1\lambda^{n-1} + \cdots + a_{n-1}\lambda + a_n.$$

If A is nonsingular, show that

$$A^{-1} = -\frac{1}{a_n}(A^{n-1} + a_1 A^{n-2} + \cdots + a_{n-2}A + a_{n-1}I_n).$$

[*Hint*: Use the Cayley–Hamilton theorem (Exercise 30).]

32. Let

$$A = \begin{bmatrix} a & b \\ c & d \end{bmatrix}.$$

Prove that the characteristic polynomial $p(\lambda)$ of A is given by

$$p(\lambda) = \lambda^2 - \text{Tr}(A)\lambda + \det(A),$$

where $\text{Tr}(A)$ denotes the trace of A (see Exercise 43 in Section 1.3).

33. Show that if A is a matrix all of whose columns add up to 1, then $\lambda = 1$ is an eigenvalue of A. (*Hint*: Consider the product $A^T\mathbf{x}$, where $\mathbf{x}$ is a vector all of whose entries are 1, and use Exercise 12.)

ARTHUR CAYLEY

WILLIAM ROWAN HAMILTON

---

*Arthur Cayley (1821–1895) was born in Richmond, Surrey, England, into an established and talented family, and died in Cambridge. As a youngster he showed considerable talent in mathematics, and his teachers persuaded his father to let him go to Cambridge instead of entering the family business as a merchant. At Cambridge he distinguished himself in his studies and published a number of papers as an undergraduate. After graduation, he accepted a Fellowship at Trinity College in Cambridge, but left to study law. Although he spent 14 years working as a successful lawyer, he was still able to spend considerable time working on mathematics and published nearly 200 papers during this period. In 1863, he was appointed to a Professorship at Cambridge University. His prolific work in matrix theory and other areas of linear algebra was of fundamental importance to the development of the subject. He also made many important contributions to abstract algebra, geometry, and other areas of modern mathematics.

† William Rowan Hamilton (1805–1865) was born and died in Dublin, Ireland. He was a child prodigy who had learned Greek, Latin, and Hebrew by the age of 5. His extraordinary mathematical talent became apparent by the age of 12. He studied at Trinity College in Dublin, where he was an outstanding student. As an undergraduate he was appointed Royal Astronomer of Ireland, Director of the Dunsink Observatory, and Professor of Astronomy. In his early papers he made significant contributions to the field of optics. At the age of 30 he was knighted after having his mathematical theory of conical refraction in optics confirmed experimentally. Hamilton is also known for his discovery of the algebra of quaternions, a set consisting of quadruples satisfying certain algebraic properties. He spent the last 20 years of his life working on quaternions and their applications.

34. Show that if A is an $n \times n$ matrix whose kth row is the same as the kth row of I_n, then 1 is an eigenvalue of A.

35. Let A be a square matrix.

(a) Suppose that the homogeneous system $A\mathbf{x} = \mathbf{0}$ has a nontrivial solution $\mathbf{x} = \mathbf{u}$. Show that $\mathbf{u}$ is an eigenvector of A.

(b) Suppose that 0 is an eigenvalue of A and $\mathbf{v}$ is an associated eigenvector. Show that the homogeneous system $A\mathbf{x} = \mathbf{0}$ has a nontrivial solution.

36. Determine whether your software has a command for finding the characteristic polynomial of a matrix A. If it does, compare the output from your software with the results in Examples 10 and 13. Software output for a characteristic polynomial often is just the set of coefficients of the polynomial with the powers of λ omitted. Carefully determine the order in which the coefficients are listed. Experiment further with the matrices in Exercises 5 and 6.

37. If your software has a command for finding the characteristic polynomial of a matrix A (see Exercise 36), it probably has another command for finding the roots of polynomials. Investigate the use of these commands in your software. The roots of the characteristic polynomial of A are the eigenvalues of A.

38. Assuming that your software has the commands discussed in Exercises 36 and 37, apply them to find the eigenvalues of $A = \begin{bmatrix} 0 & 1 \\ -1 & 0 \end{bmatrix}$. If your software is successful, the results should be $\lambda = i, -i$, where $i = \sqrt{-1}$. (See Appendix B.) (**Caution:** Some software does not handle complex roots and may not permit complex elements in a matrix. Determine the situation for the software you use.)

39. Most linear algebra software has a command for automatically finding the eigenvalues of a matrix. Determine the command available in your software. Test its behavior on Examples 12 and 13. Often, such a command uses techniques that are different than finding the roots of the characteristic polynomial. Use the documentation accompanying your software to find the method used. (**Warning:** It may involve ideas from Section 7.3 or more sophisticated procedures.)

40. Following the ideas in Exercise 39, determine the command in your software for obtaining the eigenvectors of a matrix. Often, it is a variation of the eigenvalue command. Test it on the matrices in Examples 10 and 12. These examples cover the types of cases for eigenvectors that you will encounter frequently in this course.

7.2 Diagonalization and Similar Matrices

If $L: V \to V$ is a linear operator on an n-dimensional vector space V, as we have already seen in Section 7.1 then we can find the eigenvalues of L and associated eigenvectors by using a matrix representing L with respect to a basis for V. The computational steps involved depend upon the matrix selected to represent L. An ideal situation would be the following one: Suppose that L is represented by a matrix A with respect to a certain basis for V. Find a basis for V with respect to which L is represented by a diagonal matrix D whose eigenvalues are the same as the eigenvalues of A. Of course, this is a very desirable situation, since the eigenvalues of D are merely its entries on the main diagonal. Now recall from Theorem 6.14 in Section 6.5 that A and D represent the same linear operator $L: V \to V$ with respect to two bases for V if and only if they are similar—that is, if and only if there exists a nonsingular matrix P such that $D = P^{-1}AP$. In this section we examine the type of linear transformations and matrices for which this situation is possible. For convenience, we work only with matrices all of whose entries and eigenvalues are real numbers.

Remark The need to compute powers of a matrix A (see Section 1.5) arises frequently in applications. (See the discussion of Fibonacci numbers in Section 1.5, and recursion relations in the exercises of Section 1.5 and Section 8.1.) If the matrix A is similar to a diagonal matrix D, then $D = P^{-1}AP$, for an appropriate matrix P. It follows that $A = PDP^{-1}$ (verify) and that $A^k = PD^kP^{-1}$ (verify).

Since D is diagonal, so is D^k, and its diagonal entries are d_{jj}^k. Hence A^k is easy to compute. In Section 8.4 we see another instance in which problems involving matrices that are similar to diagonal matrices can be solved quite efficiently.

DEFINITION 7.3   Let $L: V \to V$ be a linear operator on an n-dimensional vector space V. We say that L is **diagonalizable**, or can be **diagonalized**, if there exists a basis S for V such that L is represented with respect to S by a diagonal matrix D.

 In Example 2 of Section 6.5 we considered the linear transformation $L: R_3 \to R_3$ defined by

$$L\left(\begin{bmatrix} u_1 & u_2 & u_3 \end{bmatrix}\right) = \begin{bmatrix} 2u_1 - u_3 & u_1 + u_2 - u_3 & u_3 \end{bmatrix}.$$

In that example we used the basis

$$S' = \left\{\begin{bmatrix} 1 & 0 & 1 \end{bmatrix}, \begin{bmatrix} 0 & 1 & 0 \end{bmatrix}, \begin{bmatrix} 1 & 1 & 0 \end{bmatrix}\right\}$$

for R_3 and showed that the representation of L with respect to S' is

$$B = \begin{bmatrix} 1 & 0 & 0 \\ 0 & 1 & 0 \\ 0 & 0 & 2 \end{bmatrix}.$$

Hence L is a diagonalizable linear transformation.   ∎

We next show that similar matrices have the same eigenvalues.

Theorem 7.2   Similar matrices have the same eigenvalues.

Proof

Let A and B be similar. Then $B = P^{-1}AP$, for some nonsingular matrix P. We prove that A and B have the same characteristic polynomials, $p_A(\lambda)$ and $p_B(\lambda)$, respectively. We have

$$\begin{aligned} p_B(\lambda) &= \det(\lambda I_n - B) = \det(\lambda I_n - P^{-1}AP) \\ &= \det(P^{-1}\lambda I_n P - P^{-1}AP) = \det(P^{-1}(\lambda I_n - A)P) \\ &= \det(P^{-1})\det(\lambda I_n - A)\det(P) \\ &= \det(P^{-1})\det(P)\det(\lambda I_n - A) \\ &= \det(\lambda I_n - A) = p_A(\lambda). \end{aligned} \tag{1}$$

Since $p_A(\lambda) = p_B(\lambda)$, it follows that A and B have the same eigenvalues.   ▨

Note that in the proof of Theorem 7.2 we have used the facts that the product of $\det(P^{-1})$ and $\det(P)$ is 1 and that determinants are numbers, so their order as factors in multiplication does not matter.

Let $L: V \to V$ be a diagonalizable linear operator on an n-dimensional vector space V and let $S = \{\mathbf{x}_1, \mathbf{x}_2, \ldots, \mathbf{x}_n\}$ be a basis for V such that L is represented with respect to S by a diagonal matrix

$$D = \begin{bmatrix} \lambda_1 & 0 & \cdots & & 0 \\ 0 & \lambda_2 & \cdots & & 0 \\ \vdots & \vdots & \ddots & & \vdots \\ & & & & 0 \\ 0 & 0 & \cdots & 0 & \lambda_n \end{bmatrix},$$

where $\lambda_1, \lambda_2, \ldots, \lambda_n$ are real scalars. Now recall that if D represents L with respect to S, then the jth column of D is the coordinate vector $\big[L(\mathbf{x}_j) \big]_S$ of $L(\mathbf{x}_j)$ with respect to S. Thus we have

$$\big[L(\mathbf{x}_j) \big]_S = \begin{bmatrix} 0 \\ 0 \\ \vdots \\ 0 \\ \lambda_j \\ 0 \\ \vdots \\ 0 \end{bmatrix} \quad \leftarrow j\text{th row,}$$

which means that

$$L(\mathbf{x}_j) = 0\mathbf{x}_1 + 0\mathbf{x}_2 + \cdots + 0\mathbf{x}_{j-1} + \lambda_j\mathbf{x}_j + 0\mathbf{x}_{j+1} + \cdots + 0\mathbf{x}_n = \lambda_j\mathbf{x}_j.$$

Conversely, let $S = \{\mathbf{x}_1, \mathbf{x}_2, \ldots, \mathbf{x}_n\}$ be a basis for V such that

$$L(\mathbf{x}_j) = \lambda_j\mathbf{x}_j = 0\mathbf{x}_1 + 0\mathbf{x}_2 + \cdots + 0\mathbf{x}_{j-1}$$
$$+ \lambda_j\mathbf{x}_j + 0\mathbf{x}_{j+1} + \cdots + 0\mathbf{x}_n \quad \text{for } j = 1, 2, \ldots, n.$$

We now find the matrix representing L with respect to S. The jth column of this matrix is

$$\big[L(\mathbf{x}_j) \big]_S = \begin{bmatrix} 0 \\ 0 \\ \vdots \\ 0 \\ \lambda_j \\ 0 \\ \vdots \\ 0 \end{bmatrix}.$$

Hence

$$D = \begin{bmatrix} \lambda_1 & 0 & \cdots & & 0 \\ 0 & \lambda_2 & \cdots & & 0 \\ \vdots & \vdots & \ddots & & \vdots \\ & & & & 0 \\ 0 & 0 & \cdots & 0 & \lambda_n \end{bmatrix},$$

a diagonal matrix, represents L with respect to S, so L is diagonalizable.

We can now state the following theorem, whose proof has just been given:

Theorem 7.3 Let $L: V \to V$ be a linear operator on an n-dimensional vector space V. Then L is diagonalizable if and only if V has a basis S of eigenvectors of L. Moreover, if D is the diagonal matrix representing L with respect to S, then the entries on the main diagonal of D are the eigenvalues of L.

In terms of matrices, Theorem 7.3 can be stated as follows:

Theorem 7.4 An $n \times n$ matrix A is similar to a diagonal matrix D if and only if A has n linearly independent eigenvectors. Moreover, the elements on the main diagonal of D are the eigenvalues of A.

Remark If a matrix A is similar to a diagonal matrix, we say that A is **diagonalizable** or can be diagonalized.

To use Theorem 7.4, we need show only that there is a set of n eigenvectors of A that are linearly independent.

EXAMPLE 2 Let $A = \begin{bmatrix} 1 & 1 \\ -2 & 4 \end{bmatrix}$. In Example 10 of Section 7.1 we found that the eigenvalues of A are $\lambda_1 = 2$ and $\lambda_2 = 3$, with associated eigenvectors

$$\mathbf{x}_1 = \begin{bmatrix} 1 \\ 1 \end{bmatrix} \quad \text{and} \quad \mathbf{x}_2 = \begin{bmatrix} 1 \\ 2 \end{bmatrix},$$

respectively. Since

$$S = \left\{ \begin{bmatrix} 1 \\ 1 \end{bmatrix}, \begin{bmatrix} 1 \\ 2 \end{bmatrix} \right\}$$

is linearly independent (verify), A can be diagonalized. From Theorem 7.4, we conclude that A is similar to $D = \begin{bmatrix} 2 & 0 \\ 0 & 3 \end{bmatrix}$. ■

EXAMPLE 3 Let $A = \begin{bmatrix} 1 & 1 \\ 0 & 1 \end{bmatrix}$. Can A be diagonalized?

Solution

Since A is upper triangular, its eigenvalues are the entries on its main diagonal (Exercise 11 in Section 7.1). Thus, the eigenvalues of A are $\lambda_1 = 1$ and $\lambda_2 = 1$.

We now find eigenvectors of A associated with $\lambda_1 = 1$. Equation (6) of Section 7.1, $(\lambda I_n - A)\mathbf{x} = \mathbf{0}$, becomes, with $\lambda = 1$, the homogeneous system

$$(1 - 1)x_1 - \qquad x_2 = 0$$
$$(1 - 1)x_2 = 0.$$

The vector $\begin{bmatrix} r \\ 0 \end{bmatrix}$, for any number r, is a solution. Thus all eigenvectors of A are multiples of the vector $\begin{bmatrix} 1 \\ 0 \end{bmatrix}$. Since A does not have two linearly independent eigenvectors, it cannot be diagonalized. ■

If an $n \times n$ matrix A is similar to a diagonal matrix D, then $P^{-1}AP = D$ for some nonsingular matrix P. We now discuss how to construct such a matrix P. We have $AP = PD$. Let

$$D = \begin{bmatrix} \lambda_1 & 0 & \cdots & & 0 \\ 0 & \lambda_2 & \cdots & & 0 \\ \vdots & 0 & & & \vdots \\ & \vdots & & \ddots & 0 \\ 0 & 0 & \cdots & 0 & \lambda_n \end{bmatrix},$$

and let $\mathbf{x}_j$, $j = 1, 2, \ldots, n$, be the jth column of P. Note that the jth column of AP is $A\mathbf{x}_j$, and the jth column of PD is $\lambda_j \mathbf{x}_j$. (See Exercise 46 in Section 1.3.) Thus we have

$$A\mathbf{x}_j = \lambda_j \mathbf{x}_j,$$

which means that λ_j is an eigenvalue of A and $\mathbf{x}_j$ is an associated eigenvector.

Conversely, if $\lambda_1, \lambda_2, \ldots, \lambda_n$ are n eigenvalues of an $n \times n$ matrix A and $\mathbf{x}_1, \mathbf{x}_2, \ldots, \mathbf{x}_n$ are associated eigenvectors forming a linearly independent set, we let P be the matrix whose jth column is $\mathbf{x}_j$. Then rank $P = n$, so by Corollary 4.7, P is nonsingular. Since $A\mathbf{x}_j = \lambda_j \mathbf{x}_j$, $j = 1, 2, \ldots, n$, we have $AP = PD$, or $P^{-1}AP = D$, which means that A is diagonalizable. Thus, if n eigenvectors $\mathbf{x}_1, \mathbf{x}_2, \ldots, \mathbf{x}_n$ of the $n \times n$ matrix A form a linearly independent set, we can diagonalize A by letting P be the matrix whose jth column is $\mathbf{x}_j$, and we find that $P^{-1}AP = D$, a diagonal matrix whose entries on the main diagonal are the associated eigenvalues of A. Of course, the order of columns of P determines the order of the diagonal entries of D.

EXAMPLE 4   Let A be as in Example 2. The eigenvalues of A are $\lambda_1 = 2$ and $\lambda_2 = 3$, and associated eigenvectors are

$$\mathbf{x}_1 = \begin{bmatrix} 1 \\ 1 \end{bmatrix} \quad \text{and} \quad \mathbf{x}_2 = \begin{bmatrix} 1 \\ 2 \end{bmatrix},$$

respectively. Thus

$$P = \begin{bmatrix} 1 & 1 \\ 1 & 2 \end{bmatrix} \quad \text{and} \quad P^{-1} = \begin{bmatrix} 2 & -1 \\ -1 & 1 \end{bmatrix} \quad \text{(verify)}.$$

Hence

$$P^{-1}AP = \begin{bmatrix} 2 & -1 \\ -1 & 1 \end{bmatrix} \begin{bmatrix} 1 & 1 \\ -2 & 4 \end{bmatrix} \begin{bmatrix} 1 & 1 \\ 1 & 2 \end{bmatrix} = \begin{bmatrix} 2 & 0 \\ 0 & 3 \end{bmatrix}.$$

On the other hand, if we let $\lambda_1 = 3$ and $\lambda_2 = 2$, then

$$\mathbf{x}_1 = \begin{bmatrix} 1 \\ 2 \end{bmatrix} \quad \text{and} \quad \mathbf{x}_2 = \begin{bmatrix} 1 \\ 1 \end{bmatrix};$$

$$P = \begin{bmatrix} 1 & 1 \\ 2 & 1 \end{bmatrix} \quad \text{and} \quad P^{-1} = \begin{bmatrix} -1 & 1 \\ 2 & -1 \end{bmatrix},$$

and

$$P^{-1}AP = \begin{bmatrix} -1 & 1 \\ 2 & -1 \end{bmatrix} \begin{bmatrix} 1 & 1 \\ -2 & 4 \end{bmatrix} \begin{bmatrix} 1 & 1 \\ 2 & 1 \end{bmatrix} = \begin{bmatrix} 3 & 0 \\ 0 & 2 \end{bmatrix}.$$ ∎

The following useful theorem identifies a large class of matrices that can be diagonalized:

Theorem 7.5 If the roots of the characteristic polynomial of an $n \times n$ matrix A are all different from each other (i.e., distinct), then A is diagonalizable.

Proof

Let $\{\lambda_1, \lambda_2, \dots, \lambda_n\}$ be the set of distinct eigenvalues of A, and let $S = \{\mathbf{x}_1, \mathbf{x}_2, \dots, \mathbf{x}_n\}$ be a set of associated eigenvectors. We wish to prove that S is linearly independent.

Suppose that S is linearly dependent. Then Theorem 4.7 implies that some vector $\mathbf{x}_j$ is a linear combination of the preceding vectors in S. We can assume that $S_1 = \{\mathbf{x}_1, \mathbf{x}_2, \dots, \mathbf{x}_{j-1}\}$ is linearly independent, for otherwise, one of the vectors in S_1 is a linear combination of the preceding ones, and we can choose a new set S_2, and so on. We thus have that S_1 is linearly independent and that

$$\mathbf{x}_j = a_1 \mathbf{x}_1 + a_2 \mathbf{x}_2 + \cdots + a_{j-1} \mathbf{x}_{j-1}, \tag{2}$$

where $a_1, a_2, \dots, a_{j-1}$ are scalars. This means that

$$\begin{aligned} A\mathbf{x}_j &= A(a_1\mathbf{x}_1 + a_2\mathbf{x}_2 + \cdots + a_{j-1}\mathbf{x}_{j-1}) \\ &= a_1 A\mathbf{x}_1 + a_2 A\mathbf{x}_2 + \cdots + a_{j-1} A\mathbf{x}_{j-1}. \end{aligned} \tag{3}$$

Since $\lambda_1, \lambda_2, \dots, \lambda_j$ are eigenvalues and $\mathbf{x}_1, \mathbf{x}_2, \dots, \mathbf{x}_j$ are associated eigenvectors, we know that $A\mathbf{x}_i = \lambda_i \mathbf{x}_i$ for $i = 1, 2, \dots, n$. Substituting in (3), we have

$$\lambda_j \mathbf{x}_j = a_1 \lambda_1 \mathbf{x}_1 + a_2 \lambda_2 \mathbf{x}_2 + \cdots + a_{j-1} \lambda_{j-1} \mathbf{x}_{j-1}. \tag{4}$$

Multiplying (2) by λ_j, we get

$$\lambda_j \mathbf{x}_j = \lambda_j a_1 \mathbf{x}_1 + \lambda_j a_2 \mathbf{x}_2 + \cdots + \lambda_j a_{j-1} \mathbf{x}_{j-1}. \tag{5}$$

Subtracting (4) from (3), we have

$$\begin{aligned} \mathbf{0} &= \lambda_j \mathbf{x}_j - \lambda_j \mathbf{x}_j \\ &= a_1(\lambda_1 - \lambda_j)\mathbf{x}_1 + a_2(\lambda_2 - \lambda_j)\mathbf{x}_2 + \cdots + a_{j-1}(\lambda_{j-1} - \lambda_j)\mathbf{x}_{j-1}. \end{aligned}$$

Since S_1 is linearly independent, we must have

$$a_1(\lambda_1 - \lambda_j) = 0, \quad a_2(\lambda_2 - \lambda_j) = 0, \quad \dots, \quad a_{j-1}(\lambda_{j-1} - \lambda_j) = 0.$$

Now $(\lambda_1 - \lambda_j) \neq 0$, $(\lambda_2 - \lambda_j) \neq 0, \dots, (\lambda_{j-1} - \lambda_j) \neq 0$, since the λ's are distinct, which implies that

$$a_1 = a_2 = \cdots = a_{j-1} = 0.$$

This means that $\mathbf{x}_j = \mathbf{0}$, which is impossible if $\mathbf{x}_j$ is an eigenvector. Hence S is linearly independent, so A is diagonalizable. ▨

Remark   In the proof of Theorem 7.5 we have actually established the following somewhat stronger result: Let A be an $n \times n$ matrix and let $\lambda_1, \lambda_2, \ldots, \lambda_k$ be k distinct eigenvalues of A with associated eigenvectors $\mathbf{x}_1, \mathbf{x}_2, \ldots, \mathbf{x}_k$. Then $\mathbf{x}_1, \mathbf{x}_2, \ldots, \mathbf{x}_k$ are linearly independent (Exercise 25).

If all the roots of the characteristic polynomial of A are not all distinct, then A may or may not be diagonalizable. The characteristic polynomial of A can be written as the product of n factors, each of the form $\lambda - \lambda_0$, where λ_0 is a root of the characteristic polynomial. Now the eigenvalues of A are the roots of the characteristic polynomial of A. Thus the characteristic polynomial can be written as

$$(\lambda - \lambda_1)^{k_1} (\lambda - \lambda_2)^{k_2} \cdots (\lambda - \lambda_r)^{k_r},$$

where $\lambda_1, \lambda_2, \ldots, \lambda_r$ are the distinct eigenvalues of A, and $k_1, k_2, \ldots, k_r$ are integers whose sum is n. The integer k_i is called the **multiplicity** of λ_i. Thus in Example 3, $\lambda = 1$ is an eigenvalue of

$$A = \begin{bmatrix} 1 & 1 \\ 0 & 1 \end{bmatrix}$$

of multiplicity 2. It can be shown that A can be diagonalized if and only if, for each eigenvalue λ of multiplicity k, we can find k linearly independent eigenvectors. This means that the solution space of the homogeneous system $(\lambda I_n - A)\mathbf{x} = \mathbf{0}$ has dimension k. It can also be shown that if λ is an eigenvalue of A of multiplicity k, then we can never find more than k linearly independent eigenvectors associated with λ.

EXAMPLE 5

Let

$$A = \begin{bmatrix} 0 & 0 & 1 \\ 0 & 1 & 2 \\ 0 & 0 & 1 \end{bmatrix}.$$

Then the characteristic polynomial of A is $p(\lambda) = \lambda(\lambda - 1)^2$ (verify), so the eigenvalues of A are $\lambda_1 = 0$, $\lambda_2 = 1$, and $\lambda_3 = 1$; thus $\lambda_2 = 1$ is an eigenvalue of multiplicity 2. We now consider the eigenvectors associated with the eigenvalues $\lambda_2 = \lambda_3 = 1$. They are computed by solving the homogeneous system $(1I_3 - A)\mathbf{x} = \mathbf{0}$ [Equation (6) in Section 7.1]:

$$\begin{bmatrix} 1 & 0 & -1 \\ 0 & 0 & -2 \\ 0 & 0 & 0 \end{bmatrix} \begin{bmatrix} x_1 \\ x_2 \\ x_3 \end{bmatrix} = \begin{bmatrix} 0 \\ 0 \\ 0 \end{bmatrix}.$$

The solutions are the vectors of the form

$$\begin{bmatrix} 0 \\ r \\ 0 \end{bmatrix},$$

where r is any number, so the dimension of the solution space of $(1I_3 - A)\mathbf{x} = \mathbf{0}$ is 1 (Why?), and we cannot find two linearly independent eigenvectors. Thus A cannot be diagonalized.   ∎

EXAMPLE 6   Let $A = \begin{bmatrix} 0 & 0 & 0 \\ 0 & 1 & 0 \\ 1 & 0 & 1 \end{bmatrix}$. The characteristic polynomial of A is $p(\lambda) = \lambda(\lambda - 1)^2$ (verify), so the eigenvalues of A are $\lambda_1 = 0$, $\lambda_2 = 1$, and $\lambda_3 = 1$; thus $\lambda_2 = 1$ is again an eigenvalue of multiplicity 2. Now we consider the eigenvectors associated with the eigenvalues $\lambda_2 = \lambda_3 = 1$. They are computed by solving the homogeneous system $(1I_3 - A)\mathbf{x} = \mathbf{0}$ [Equation (6) in Section 7.1]:

$$\begin{bmatrix} 1 & 0 & 0 \\ 0 & 0 & 0 \\ -1 & 0 & 0 \end{bmatrix} \begin{bmatrix} x_1 \\ x_2 \\ x_3 \end{bmatrix} = \begin{bmatrix} 0 \\ 0 \\ 0 \end{bmatrix}.$$

The solutions are the vectors of the form $\begin{bmatrix} 0 \\ r \\ s \end{bmatrix}$ for any numbers r and s. Thus

$\mathbf{x}_2 = \begin{bmatrix} 0 \\ 1 \\ 0 \end{bmatrix}$ and $\mathbf{x}_3 = \begin{bmatrix} 0 \\ 0 \\ 1 \end{bmatrix}$ are eigenvectors.

Next, we look for an eigenvector associated with $\lambda_1 = 0$. We have to solve the homogeneous system

$$\begin{bmatrix} 0 & 0 & 0 \\ 0 & -1 & 0 \\ -1 & 0 & -1 \end{bmatrix} \begin{bmatrix} x_1 \\ x_2 \\ x_3 \end{bmatrix} = \begin{bmatrix} 0 \\ 0 \\ 0 \end{bmatrix}.$$

The solutions are the vectors of the form $\begin{bmatrix} r \\ 0 \\ -r \end{bmatrix}$ for any number r. Thus $\mathbf{x}_1 = \begin{bmatrix} 1 \\ 0 \\ -1 \end{bmatrix}$ is an eigenvector associated with $\lambda_1 = 0$. Now $S = \{\mathbf{x}_1, \mathbf{x}_2, \mathbf{x}_3\}$ is linearly independent, so A can be diagonalized.   ■

Thus an $n \times n$ matrix will fail to be diagonalizable only if it does not have n linearly independent eigenvectors.

Now define the **characteristic polynomial** of a linear operator $L: V \to V$ as the characteristic polynomial of any matrix representing L; by Theorem 7.2 all representations of L will give the same characteristic polynomial. It follows that a scalar λ is an eigenvalue of L if and only if λ is a root of the characteristic polynomial of L.

EXAMPLE 7   In Example 14 of Section 7.1, we derived the matrix eigen-problem for the linear operator $L: P_2 \to P_2$, defined in Example 9 of that section, by $L(at^2 + bt + c) = -bt - 2c$ by using the matrix

$$B = \begin{bmatrix} -1 & 0 & 0 \\ 1 & -2 & 0 \\ 0 & 0 & 0 \end{bmatrix},$$

which represents L with respect to the basis $\{t - 1, 1, t^2\}$ for P_2. We computed the characteristic polynomial of B to be $p(\lambda) = \lambda(\lambda + 2)(\lambda + 1)$, so this is also the characteristic polynomial of L. Since the eigenvalues are distinct, it follows that B and L are diagonalizable. Of course, any other matrix representing L could be used in place of B.   ■

Key Terms

Diagonalizable
Diagonalized
Similar matrices

Characteristic polynomial
Eigenvalues/eigenvectors
Distinct eigenvalues

Multiplicity of an eigenvalue

7.2   Exercises

1. Let $L: P_2 \rightarrow P_2$ be the linear operator defined by $L(p(t)) = p'(t)$ for $p(t)$ in P_2. Is L diagonalizable? If it is, find a basis S for P_2 with respect to which L is represented by a diagonal matrix.

2. Let $L: P_1 \rightarrow P_1$ be the linear operator defined by

$$L(at + b) = -bt - a.$$

   Find, if possible, a basis for P_1 with respect to which L is represented by a diagonal matrix.

3. Let $L: P_2 \rightarrow P_2$ be the linear operator defined by

$$L(at^2 + bt + c) = at^2 - c.$$

   Find, if possible, a basis for P_2 with respect to which L is represented by a diagonal matrix.

4. **(Calculus Required)** Let V be the vector space of continuous functions with basis $\{\sin t, \cos t\}$, and let $L: V \rightarrow V$ be defined as $L(g(t)) = g'(t)$. Is L diagonalizable?

5. Let $L: P_2 \rightarrow P_2$ be the linear operator defined by

$$L(at^2 + bt + c) = (2a + b + c)t^2$$
$$+ (2c - 3b)t + 4c.$$

   Find the eigenvalues and eigenvectors of L. Is L diagonalizable?

6. Which of the following matrices are diagonalizable?

   (a) $\begin{bmatrix} 1 & 4 \\ 1 & -2 \end{bmatrix}$ (b) $\begin{bmatrix} 1 & 0 \\ -2 & 1 \end{bmatrix}$

   (c) $\begin{bmatrix} 1 & 1 & -2 \\ 4 & 0 & 4 \\ 1 & -1 & 4 \end{bmatrix}$ (d) $\begin{bmatrix} 1 & 2 & 3 \\ 0 & -1 & 2 \\ 0 & 0 & 2 \end{bmatrix}$

7. Which of the following matrices are diagonalizable?

   (a) $\begin{bmatrix} 3 & 1 & 0 \\ 0 & 3 & 1 \\ 0 & 0 & 3 \end{bmatrix}$ (b) $\begin{bmatrix} -2 & 2 \\ 5 & 1 \end{bmatrix}$

   (c) $\begin{bmatrix} 2 & 0 & 3 \\ 0 & 1 & 0 \\ 0 & 1 & 2 \end{bmatrix}$ (d) $\begin{bmatrix} 2 & 3 & 3 & 5 \\ 3 & 2 & 2 & 3 \\ 0 & 0 & 2 & 2 \\ 0 & 0 & 0 & 2 \end{bmatrix}$

8. Find a 2×2 nondiagonal matrix whose eigenvalues are 2 and -3, and associated eigenvectors are $\begin{bmatrix} -1 \\ 2 \end{bmatrix}$ and $\begin{bmatrix} 1 \\ 1 \end{bmatrix}$, respectively.

9. Find a 3×3 nondiagonal matrix whose eigenvalues are -2, -2, and 3, and associated eigenvectors are $\begin{bmatrix} 1 \\ 0 \\ 1 \end{bmatrix}$, $\begin{bmatrix} 0 \\ 1 \\ 1 \end{bmatrix}$, and $\begin{bmatrix} 1 \\ 1 \\ 1 \end{bmatrix}$, respectively.

10. For each of the following matrices find, if possible, a nonsingular matrix P such that $P^{-1}AP$ is diagonal:

   (a) $\begin{bmatrix} 4 & 2 & 3 \\ 2 & 1 & 2 \\ -1 & -2 & 0 \end{bmatrix}$ (b) $\begin{bmatrix} 1 & 1 & 2 \\ 0 & 1 & 0 \\ 0 & 1 & 3 \end{bmatrix}$

   (c) $\begin{bmatrix} 1 & 2 & 3 \\ 0 & 1 & 0 \\ 2 & 1 & 2 \end{bmatrix}$ (d) $\begin{bmatrix} 0 & -1 \\ 2 & 3 \end{bmatrix}$

11. For each of the following matrices find, if possible, a nonsingular matrix P such that $P^{-1}AP$ is diagonal:

   (a) $\begin{bmatrix} 3 & -2 & 1 \\ 0 & 2 & 0 \\ 0 & 0 & 0 \end{bmatrix}$ (b) $\begin{bmatrix} 2 & 2 & 2 \\ 2 & 2 & 2 \\ 2 & 2 & 2 \end{bmatrix}$

   (c) $\begin{bmatrix} 3 & 0 & 0 \\ 2 & 3 & 0 \\ 0 & 0 & 3 \end{bmatrix}$ (d) $\begin{bmatrix} 1 & 0 & 1 \\ 0 & 1 & 0 \\ 0 & 1 & 2 \end{bmatrix}$

12. Let A be a 2×2 matrix whose eigenvalues are 3 and 4, and associated eigenvectors are $\begin{bmatrix} -1 \\ 1 \end{bmatrix}$ and $\begin{bmatrix} 2 \\ 1 \end{bmatrix}$, respectively. Without computation, find a diagonal matrix D that is similar to A, and a nonsingular matrix P such that $P^{-1}AP = D$.

13. Let A be a 3×3 matrix whose eigenvalues are -3, 4, and 4, and associated eigenvectors are

$$\begin{bmatrix} -1 \\ 0 \\ 1 \end{bmatrix}, \quad \begin{bmatrix} 0 \\ 0 \\ 1 \end{bmatrix}, \quad \text{and} \quad \begin{bmatrix} 0 \\ 1 \\ 1 \end{bmatrix},$$

respectively. Without computation, find a diagonal matrix D that is similar to A, and a nonsingular matrix P such that $P^{-1}AP = D$.

14. Which of the following matrices are similar to a diagonal matrix?

(a) $\begin{bmatrix} 2 & 3 & 0 \\ 0 & 1 & 0 \\ 0 & 0 & 2 \end{bmatrix}$ **(b)** $\begin{bmatrix} 2 & 3 & 1 \\ 0 & 1 & 0 \\ 0 & 0 & 2 \end{bmatrix}$

(c) $\begin{bmatrix} -3 & 0 \\ 1 & 2 \end{bmatrix}$ **(d)** $\begin{bmatrix} 1 & 1 & 0 \\ 2 & 2 & 0 \\ 3 & 3 & 3 \end{bmatrix}$

15. Show that each of the following matrices is diagonalizable and find a diagonal matrix similar to each given matrix:

(a) $\begin{bmatrix} 4 & 2 \\ 3 & 3 \end{bmatrix}$ **(b)** $\begin{bmatrix} 3 & 2 \\ 6 & 4 \end{bmatrix}$

(c) $\begin{bmatrix} 2 & -2 & 3 \\ 0 & 3 & -2 \\ 0 & -1 & 2 \end{bmatrix}$ **(d)** $\begin{bmatrix} 0 & -2 & 1 \\ 1 & 3 & -1 \\ 0 & 0 & 1 \end{bmatrix}$

16. Show that none of the following matrices is diagonalizable:

(a) $\begin{bmatrix} 1 & 1 \\ 0 & 1 \end{bmatrix}$ **(b)** $\begin{bmatrix} 2 & 0 & 0 \\ 3 & 2 & 0 \\ 0 & 0 & 5 \end{bmatrix}$

(c) $\begin{bmatrix} 10 & 11 & 3 \\ -3 & -4 & -3 \\ -8 & -8 & -1 \end{bmatrix}$ **(d)** $\begin{bmatrix} 2 & 3 & 3 & 5 \\ 3 & 2 & 2 & 3 \\ 0 & 0 & 1 & 1 \\ 0 & 0 & 0 & 1 \end{bmatrix}$

17. A matrix A is called **defective** if A has an eigenvalue λ of multiplicity $m > 1$ for which the associated eigenspace has a basis of fewer than m vectors; that is, the dimension of the eigenspace associated with λ is less than m. Use the eigenvalues of the following matrices to determine which matrices are defective:

(a) $\begin{bmatrix} 8 & 7 \\ 0 & 8 \end{bmatrix}$, $\lambda = 8, 8$

(b) $\begin{bmatrix} 3 & 0 & 0 \\ -2 & 3 & -2 \\ 2 & 0 & 5 \end{bmatrix}$, $\lambda = 3, 3, 5$

(c) $\begin{bmatrix} 3 & 3 & 3 \\ 3 & 3 & 3 \\ -3 & -3 & -3 \end{bmatrix}$, $\lambda = 0, 0, 3$

(d) $\begin{bmatrix} 0 & 0 & 1 & 0 \\ 0 & 0 & 0 & -1 \\ 1 & 0 & 0 & 0 \\ 0 & -1 & 0 & 0 \end{bmatrix}$, $\lambda = 1, 1, -1, -1$

18. Let $D = \begin{bmatrix} 2 & 0 \\ 0 & -2 \end{bmatrix}$. Compute D^9.

19. Let $A = \begin{bmatrix} 3 & -5 \\ 1 & -3 \end{bmatrix}$. Compute A^9. (*Hint*: Find a matrix P such that $P^{-1}AP$ is a diagonal matrix D and show that $A^9 = PD^9P^{-1}$.)

20. Let $A = \begin{bmatrix} a & b \\ c & d \end{bmatrix}$. Find necessary and sufficient conditions for A to be diagonalizable.

21. Let A and B be nonsingular $n \times n$ matrices. Prove that AB and BA have the same eigenvalues.

22. (*Calculus Required*) Let V be the vector space of continuous functions with basis $\{e^t, e^{-t}\}$. Let $L: V \to V$ be defined by $L(g(t)) = g'(t)$ for $g(t)$ in V. Show that L is diagonalizable.

23. Prove that if A is diagonalizable, then **(a)** A^T is diagonalizable, and **(b)** A^k is diagonalizable, where k is a positive integer.

24. Show that if A is nonsingular and diagonalizable, then A^{-1} is diagonalizable.

25. Let $\lambda_1, \lambda_2, \ldots, \lambda_k$ be distinct eigenvalues of an $n \times n$ matrix A with associated eigenvectors $x_1, x_2, \ldots, x_k$. Prove that $x_1, x_2, \ldots, x_k$ are linearly independent. (*Hint*: See the proof of Theorem 7.5.)

26. Let A and B be nonsingular $n \times n$ matrices. Prove that AB^{-1} and $B^{-1}A$ have the same eigenvalues.

27. Show that if a matrix A is similar to a diagonal matrix D, then $\text{Tr}(A) = \text{Tr}(D)$, where $\text{Tr}(A)$ is the trace of A. [*Hint*: See Exercise 43, Section 1.3, where part (c) establishes $\text{Tr}(AB) = \text{Tr}(BA)$.]

28. Let A be an $n \times n$ matrix and let $B = P^{-1}AP$ be similar to A. Show that if x is an eigenvector of A associated with the eigenvalue λ of A, then $P^{-1}x$ is an eigenvector of B associated with the eigenvalue λ of the matrix B.

Answers to Odd-Numbered Exercises

CHAPTER 2

Section 2.1, p. 94

1. **(a)** Possible answer:

$$\mathbf{r}_1 \to -\mathbf{r}_1$$
$$\mathbf{r}_2 \to \mathbf{r}_2 - 2\mathbf{r}_1$$
$$\mathbf{r}_3 \to \mathbf{r}_3 - 2\mathbf{r}_1$$
$$\mathbf{r}_2 \to \tfrac{1}{3}\mathbf{r}_2$$
$$\mathbf{r}_3 \to \mathbf{r}_3 - 2\mathbf{r}_2$$
$$\mathbf{r}_3 \to -3\mathbf{r}_3$$

$$\begin{bmatrix} 1 & -2 & 5 \\ 0 & 1 & -\tfrac{4}{3} \\ 0 & 0 & 1 \end{bmatrix}$$

(b) Possible answer:

$$\mathbf{r}_2 \to \mathbf{r}_2 - 3\mathbf{r}_1$$
$$\mathbf{r}_3 \to \mathbf{r}_3 - 5\mathbf{r}_1$$
$$\mathbf{r}_4 \to \mathbf{r}_4 + 2\mathbf{r}_1$$

$$\begin{bmatrix} 1 & 1 & -1 \\ 0 & 1 & 2 \\ 0 & 0 & 0 \\ 0 & 0 & 0 \end{bmatrix}$$

3. (a) $\begin{matrix} \mathbf{r}_2 \to \mathbf{r}_2 + 2\mathbf{r}_3 \\ \mathbf{r}_1 \to \mathbf{r}_1 - 4\mathbf{r}_3 \\ \mathbf{r}_1 \to \mathbf{r}_1 - 2\mathbf{r}_2 \end{matrix}$ $\begin{bmatrix} 1 & 0 & 0 \\ 0 & 1 & 0 \\ 0 & 0 & 1 \end{bmatrix}$

(b) $\begin{matrix} \mathbf{r}_2 \to \mathbf{r}_2 + 4\mathbf{r}_3 \\ \mathbf{r}_1 \to \mathbf{r}_1 - 5\mathbf{r}_3 \\ \mathbf{r}_1 \to \mathbf{r}_1 - 3\mathbf{r}_3 \end{matrix}$ $\begin{bmatrix} 1 & 4 & 0 & 0 \\ 0 & 0 & 1 & 0 \\ 0 & 0 & 0 & 1 \\ 0 & 0 & 0 & 0 \end{bmatrix}$

5. (a) $\begin{matrix} \mathbf{r}_2 \to \mathbf{r}_2 + 2\mathbf{r}_1 \\ \mathbf{r}_3 \to \mathbf{r}_3 - 3\mathbf{r}_1 \\ \mathbf{r}_3 \to \mathbf{r}_3 - 2\mathbf{r}_2 \end{matrix}$ $\begin{bmatrix} 1 & 0 & -2 \\ 0 & 1 & 5 \\ 0 & 0 & 0 \end{bmatrix}$

(b) $\begin{matrix} \mathbf{r}_2 \to \mathbf{r}_2 + \mathbf{r}_1 \\ \mathbf{r}_4 \to \mathbf{r}_4 + 2\mathbf{r}_1 \\ \mathbf{r}_2 \to \frac{1}{2}\mathbf{r}_2 \\ \mathbf{r}_3 \to \mathbf{r}_3 - \mathbf{r}_2 \\ \mathbf{r}_4 \to \mathbf{r}_4 - 7\mathbf{r}_2 \\ \mathbf{r}_3 \to 2\mathbf{r}_3 \\ \mathbf{r}_4 \to \mathbf{r}_4 - \frac{1}{2}\mathbf{r}_3 \\ \mathbf{r}_2 \to \mathbf{r}_2 + \frac{1}{2}\mathbf{r}_3 \\ \mathbf{r}_1 \to \mathbf{r}_1 - \mathbf{r}_3 \end{matrix}$ $\begin{bmatrix} 1 & 0 & 0 \\ 0 & 1 & 0 \\ 0 & 0 & 1 \\ 0 & 0 & 0 \end{bmatrix}$

7. (a) N **(b)** REF **(c)** RREF.

11. (a) Possible answer: $\begin{bmatrix} 1 & 0 & 0 & 0 \\ -1 & 1 & 0 & 0 \\ 0 & \frac{1}{2} & 1 & 0 \\ 2 & -\frac{1}{2} & 3 & 1 \end{bmatrix}$

(b) $I_4 = \begin{bmatrix} 1 & 0 & 0 & 0 \\ 0 & 1 & 0 & 0 \\ 0 & 0 & 1 & 0 \\ 0 & 0 & 0 & 1 \end{bmatrix}$

13. $\begin{bmatrix} 1 & 0 \\ 0 & 1 \end{bmatrix}$.

Section 2.2, p. 113

1. (a) $x = 8, y = 1, z = 4$.

(b) $x = -21 + 3t, y = t, z = 5, w = 1$.

3. (a) $x = 2 - s, y = s, z = -3 - t, w = t$.

(b) $x = 3, y = 0, z = 1$.

5. (a) $x = 1, y = 2, z = -2$.

(b) $x = 1, y = 2, z = -2$.

7. (a) $x = -1, y = 4, z = -3$.

(b) $x = y = z = 0$.

(c) $x = r, y = -2r, z = r$, where r = any real number.

(d) $x = -2r, y = r, z = 0$, where r = any real number.

9. (a) $x = 1, y = 2, z = 2$.

(b) $x = y = z = 0$.

11. $\mathbf{x} = \begin{bmatrix} r \\ r \end{bmatrix}, r \neq 0$. **13.** $\mathbf{x} = \begin{bmatrix} -\frac{1}{2}r \\ \frac{1}{2}r \\ r \end{bmatrix}, r \neq 0$.

15. (a) $a = \pm\sqrt{3}$. **(b)** $a \neq \pm\sqrt{3}$.

(c) There is no value of a such that this system has infinitely many solutions.

17. (a) $a = -3$. **(b)** $a \neq \pm 3$. **(c)** $a = 3$.

21. $x = -2 + r, y = 2 - 2r, z = r$, where r is any real number.

23. $c - b - a = 0$.

27. $-a + b - c = 0$.

31. $2x^2 + 2x + 1$.

33. $T_1 = 36.25°, T_2 = 36.25°, T_3 = 28.75°, T_4 = 28.75°$.

35. Radius $= 37$.

39. One solution is $2C_2H_6 + 7O_2 \to 4CO_2 + 6H_2O$.

41. $\begin{bmatrix} 1 - i \\ 2 \\ -i \end{bmatrix}$. **43.** $\begin{bmatrix} i \\ 2i \\ -1 \end{bmatrix}$.

CHAPTER 7

Section 7.1, p. 450

1. The only eigenvalue of L is $\lambda = -1$. Every nonzero vector in R^2 is an eigenvector of L associated with λ.

3. The eigenvalues are $\lambda_1 = 1$, $\lambda_2 = -1$, $\lambda_3 = 0$. Associated eigenvectors are 1, t^2, and t, respectively.

5. (a) $p(\lambda) = \lambda^2 - 5\lambda + 7$.

   (b) $p(\lambda) = \lambda^3 - 4\lambda^2 + 7$.

   (c) $p(\lambda) = (\lambda - 4)(\lambda - 2)(\lambda - 3) = \lambda^3 - 9\lambda^2 + 26\lambda - 24$.

   (d) $p(\lambda) = \lambda^2 - 7\lambda + 6$.

7. (a) $p(\lambda) = \lambda^2 - 5\lambda + 6$. The eigenvalues are $\lambda_1 = 2$ and $\lambda_2 = 3$. Associated eigenvectors are

$$\mathbf{x}_1 = \begin{bmatrix} 1 \\ -1 \end{bmatrix} \quad \text{and} \quad \mathbf{x}_2 = \begin{bmatrix} 1 \\ -2 \end{bmatrix}.$$

   (b) $p(\lambda) = \lambda^3 - 7\lambda^2 + 14\lambda - 8$. The eigenvalues are $\lambda_1 = 1$, $\lambda_2 = 2$, and $\lambda_3 = 4$. Associated eigenvectors are

$$\mathbf{x}_1 = \begin{bmatrix} -1 \\ 1 \\ 1 \end{bmatrix}, \quad \mathbf{x}_2 = \begin{bmatrix} 1 \\ 0 \\ 0 \end{bmatrix}, \quad \text{and}$$

$$\mathbf{x}_3 = \begin{bmatrix} 7 \\ -4 \\ 2 \end{bmatrix}.$$

(c) $p(\lambda) = \lambda^3 - 5\lambda^2 + 2\lambda + 8$. The eigenvalues are $\lambda_1 = -1$, $\lambda_2 = 2$, and $\lambda_3 = 4$. Associated eigenvectors are

$$\mathbf{x}_1 = \begin{bmatrix} 1 \\ 0 \\ -1 \end{bmatrix}, \quad \mathbf{x}_2 = \begin{bmatrix} -2 \\ -3 \\ 2 \end{bmatrix}, \quad \text{and}$$

$$\mathbf{x}_3 = \begin{bmatrix} 8 \\ 5 \\ 2 \end{bmatrix}.$$

(d) $p(\lambda) = \lambda^3 - 3\lambda^2 - 6\lambda + 8$. The eigenvalues are $\lambda_1 = -2$, $\lambda_2 = 4$, and $\lambda_3 = 1$. Associated eigenvectors are

$$\mathbf{x}_1 = \begin{bmatrix} 1 \\ 0 \\ 0 \end{bmatrix}, \quad \mathbf{x}_2 = \begin{bmatrix} 7 \\ -12 \\ 6 \end{bmatrix}, \quad \text{and}$$

$$\mathbf{x}_3 = \begin{bmatrix} 1 \\ 3 \\ 3 \end{bmatrix}.$$

9. (a) $p(\lambda) = \lambda^2 + 1$. The eigenvalues are $\lambda_1 = i$ and $\lambda_2 = -i$. Associated eigenvectors are

$$\mathbf{x}_1 = \begin{bmatrix} 1 \\ i \end{bmatrix} \quad \text{and} \quad \mathbf{x}_2 = \begin{bmatrix} 1 \\ -i \end{bmatrix}.$$

(b) $p(\lambda) = \lambda^3 + 2\lambda^2 + 4\lambda + 8$. The eigenvalues are $\lambda_1 = -2$, $\lambda_2 = 2i$, and $\lambda_3 = -2i$. Associated eigenvectors are

$$\mathbf{x}_1 = \begin{bmatrix} 4 \\ -2 \\ 1 \end{bmatrix}, \quad \mathbf{x}_2 = \begin{bmatrix} -4 \\ 2i \\ 1 \end{bmatrix}, \quad \text{and}$$

$$\mathbf{x}_3 = \begin{bmatrix} -4 \\ -2i \\ 1 \end{bmatrix}.$$

(c) $p(\lambda) = \lambda^3 + (-2 + i)\lambda^2 - 2i\lambda$. The eigenvalues are $\lambda_1 = 0$, $\lambda_2 = -i$, and $\lambda_3 = 2$. Associated eigenvectors are

$$\mathbf{x}_1 = \begin{bmatrix} 0 \\ 0 \\ 1 \end{bmatrix}, \quad \mathbf{x}_2 = \begin{bmatrix} -1 \\ -i \\ 1 \end{bmatrix}, \quad \text{and} \quad \mathbf{x}_3 = \begin{bmatrix} 4 \\ 2 \\ 1 \end{bmatrix}.$$

(d) $p(\lambda) = \lambda^2 - 8\lambda + 17$. The eigenvalues are $\lambda_1 = 4 + i$ and $\lambda_2 = 4 - i$. Associated eigenvectors are

$$\mathbf{x}_1 = \begin{bmatrix} 2 \\ -1 + i \end{bmatrix} \quad \text{and} \quad \mathbf{x}_2 = \begin{bmatrix} 2 \\ -1 - i \end{bmatrix}.$$

13. The characteristic polynomial of A is

$$p(\lambda) = (\lambda - 1)(\lambda + 1)(\lambda - 3)(\lambda - 2).$$

The eigenvalues of L are $\lambda_1 = 1$, $\lambda_2 = -1$, $\lambda_3 = 3$, and $\lambda_4 = 2$. Associated eigenvectors are

$$\begin{bmatrix} 1 & 0 \\ 0 & 0 \end{bmatrix}, \quad \begin{bmatrix} 1 & -1 \\ 0 & 0 \end{bmatrix},$$

$$\begin{bmatrix} 9 & 3 \\ 4 & 0 \end{bmatrix}, \quad \text{and} \quad \begin{bmatrix} -29 & -7 \\ -9 & 3 \end{bmatrix}.$$

17. (a) $\left\{ \begin{bmatrix} 1 \\ 0 \\ 1 \end{bmatrix}, \begin{bmatrix} 0 \\ 1 \\ 0 \end{bmatrix} \right\}$. **(b)** $\left\{ \begin{bmatrix} -1 \\ 0 \\ 1 \end{bmatrix} \right\}$.

19. (a) $\left\{ \begin{bmatrix} -4 \\ 2i \\ 1 \end{bmatrix} \right\}$. **(b)** $\left\{ \begin{bmatrix} -4 \\ -2i \\ 1 \end{bmatrix} \right\}$.

Section 7.2, p. 461

1. L is not diagonalizable. The eigenvalues of L are $\lambda_1 = \lambda_2 = \lambda_3 = 0$. The set of associated eigenvectors does not form a basis for P_2.

3. $\{t^2, t, 1\}$.

5. The eigenvalues of L are $\lambda_1 = 2$, $\lambda_2 = -3$, and $\lambda_3 = 4$. Associated eigenvectors are t^2, $t^2 - 5t$, and $9t^2 + 4t + 14$. L is diagonalizable.

7. (a) Not diagonalizable. **(b)** Diagonalizable.

(c) Not diagonalizable.

(d) Not diagonalizable.

9. $\begin{bmatrix} 3 & 5 & -5 \\ 5 & 3 & -5 \\ 5 & 5 & -7 \end{bmatrix}$.

11. (a) $P = \begin{bmatrix} 1 & 2 & 1 \\ 0 & 1 & 0 \\ 0 & 0 & -3 \end{bmatrix}$.

(b) $P = \begin{bmatrix} -1 & -1 & 1 \\ 1 & 0 & 1 \\ 0 & 1 & 1 \end{bmatrix}$.

(c) Not possible.

(d) Not possible.

13. $D = \begin{bmatrix} -3 & 0 & 0 \\ 0 & 4 & 0 \\ 0 & 0 & 4 \end{bmatrix}$, $P = \begin{bmatrix} -1 & 0 & 0 \\ 0 & 0 & 1 \\ 1 & 1 & 1 \end{bmatrix}$.

15. (a) $D = \begin{bmatrix} 6 & 0 \\ 0 & 1 \end{bmatrix}.$ **(b)** $D = \begin{bmatrix} 0 & 0 \\ 0 & 7 \end{bmatrix}.$

(c) $D = \begin{bmatrix} 2 & 0 & 0 \\ 0 & 4 & 0 \\ 0 & 0 & 1 \end{bmatrix}.$

(d) $D = \begin{bmatrix} 1 & 0 & 0 \\ 0 & 2 & 0 \\ 0 & 0 & 1 \end{bmatrix}.$

17. (a) Defective.

(b) Not defective.

(c) Not defective.

(d) Not defective.

19. $\begin{bmatrix} 768 & -1280 \\ 256 & -768 \end{bmatrix}.$

Appendix

Applications

Next to each listed application is the page on which it appears.

List of Frequently Used Symbols

$A = \begin{bmatrix} a_{ij} \end{bmatrix}$	an $m \times n$ matrix, p. 11
$\displaystyle\sum_{i=1}^{n} a_i$	summation notation, p. 17
A^T	the transpose of A, p. 18
$\mathbf{a} \cdot \mathbf{b}$	the dot product of the n-vectors $\mathbf{a}$ and $\mathbf{b}$ in R^n, p. 21
$\begin{bmatrix} A \vdots B \end{bmatrix}$	an augmented matrix, pp. 27, 44
O	the zero $m \times n$ matrix, p. 34
I_n	the $n \times n$ identity matrix, p. 42
A^{-1}	the inverse of the matrix A, pp. 46–47
$Cor(\mathbf{x}, \mathbf{y})$	the correlation coefficient, p. 77
XY^T	outer product, p. 82
E, F	elementary matrices, pp. 117–118, 124
P, Q	nonsingular matrices, pp. 126, 129
L, U	lower and upper triangular matrices, respectively, such that $A = LU$, p. 133
$j_1 j_2 \cdots j_n$	a permutation of $S = \{1, 2, \ldots, n\}$, p. 144
$\det(A), |A|$	the determinant of the matrix A, p. 142
$\det(M_{ij})$	the minor of a_{ij}, p. 157
A_{ij}	the cofactor of a_{ij}, p. 157
adj A	the adjoint of the matrix A, p. 166
$\mathbf{u}, \mathbf{v}, \mathbf{w}, \mathbf{x}, \mathbf{y}$	vectors, pp. 177, 183, 186
$\mathbf{0}$	the zero vector, pp. 182, 185, 189
$\mathbf{0}_V$	the zero vector in the vector space V, p. 260
V, W	vector spaces, pp. 189, 197
R^n	the vector space of all $n \times 1$ matrices, p. 190
M_{mn}	the vector space of all $m \times n$ matrices, p. 190
R_n	the vector space of all $1 \times n$ matrices, p. 191
$p(t)$	a polynomial in t, p. 192
P_n	the vector space of all polynomials of degree $\leq n$ and the zero polynomial, p. 192
P	the vector space of all polynomials, p. 193
$C(-\infty, \infty)$	the vector space of all real-valued continuous functions, p. 193
span $\{\mathbf{v}_1, \mathbf{v}_2, \ldots, \mathbf{v}_k\}$	the set of all vectors of the form $a_1\mathbf{v}_1 + a_2\mathbf{v}_2 + \cdots + a_k\mathbf{v}_k$, p. 209
$\mathbf{e}_i$	an $n \times 1$ matrix with a 1 in the ith row, zeros in all other rows, p. 229
$\{\mathbf{e}_1, \mathbf{e}_2, \ldots, \mathbf{e}_n\}$	the natural basis for R^n, p. 229
$\mathbf{i}, \mathbf{j}, \mathbf{k}$	the natural basis for R^3, p. 229
S, T, S', T'	bases for a vector space, pp. 231, 237
dim V	the dimension of the vector space V, p. 238
$\{\mathbf{e}'_1, \mathbf{e}'_2, \ldots, \mathbf{e}'_n\}$	the natural basis for R_n, p. 239

$[\mathbf{v}]_S$	the coordinate vector of the vector $\mathbf{v}$ with respect to the ordered basis S for the vector space V, p. 253
$P_{S \leftarrow T}, Q_{T \leftarrow S}$	transition matrices, pp. 261, 264
$\mathrm{NS}(A)$	the null space of the matrix A, p. 287
$\|\mathbf{v}\|$	the length of the vector $\mathbf{v}$, pp. 290, 312
$\|\mathbf{u} - \mathbf{v}\|$	the distance between vectors $\mathbf{u}$ and $\mathbf{v}$, pp. 292, 315
$\cos \theta$	the cosine of the angle between two nonzero vectors $\mathbf{u}$ and $\mathbf{v}$, pp. 294, 315
$\mathbf{u} \cdot \mathbf{v}$	the standard inner product on R^2 or R^3, p. 294
$(\mathbf{u}, \mathbf{v})$	an inner product, p. 307
$\mathbf{u} \times \mathbf{v}$	the cross product operation, p. 299
$W^\perp$	the orthogonal complement of a subspace W, p. 332
$\mathrm{proj}_W \mathbf{v}$	the orthogonal projection of $\mathbf{v}$ on W, p. 341
$\|\ \ \|_1$	the 1-norm, p. 360
L, L_1, L_2	linear transformations, pp. 363, 399
$p'(t)$	the derivative of $p(t)$ with respect to t, p. 373
$\ker L$	the kernel of the linear transformation L, p. 376
$\mathrm{range}\ L$	the range of the linear transformation L, p. 378
λ_j	an eigenvalue, pp. 437, 442
$\mathbf{x}_j$	an eigenvector, pp. 437, 442
$\det(|\lambda I_n - A|) = p(\lambda)$	the characteristic polynomial of A, p. 444
$\det(|\lambda I_n - A|) = p(\lambda) = 0$	the characteristic equation of A, p. 444
D	a diagonal matrix, p. 455
$\mathbf{x}^{(k)}$	age distribution at time k, p. 481
$\mathbf{x}(t) = \begin{bmatrix} x_1(t) \\ x_2(t) \\ \vdots \\ x_n(t) \end{bmatrix}$	an $n \times 1$ matrix whose entries are functions of t, p. 515
$\mathbf{x}'(t) = \begin{bmatrix} x_1'(t) \\ x_2'(t) \\ \vdots \\ x_n'(t) \end{bmatrix}$	p. 516
$g(\mathbf{x}) = \mathbf{x}^T A \mathbf{x}$	a real quadratic form in n variables, p. 535
$c = a + bi$	a complex number, p. A-5
$\bar{c} = a - bi$	the conjugate of $c = a + bi$, p. A-6
$|c| = |a + bi| = \sqrt{a^2 + b^2}$	the absolute value or modulus of $c = a + bi$, p. A-8
$\overline{A} = \left[\bar{a}_{ij} \right]$	the conjugate of the matrix $A = \left[a_{ij} \right]$, p. A-8
p, q	statements or propositions, pp. A-22, A-23
$\sim p$	the negation of p, p. A-22
$p \wedge q$	p and q, p. A-23
$p \vee q$	p or q, p. A-23
$p \Longrightarrow q$	if p then q, p. A-24
$p \Longleftrightarrow q$	p if and only if q, p. A-25